DATA PROCESSING SECTION
DEPARTMENT OF LABORATORY MEDICINE
THE JOHNS HOPKINS HOSPITAL

STATISTICAL METHOD
IN
BIOLOGICAL ASSAY

Books of Cognate Interest

Design of Experiments

Experimental design: selected papers   F. YATES
*The mathematics of experimental design   S. VAJDA
*Statistical models and their experimental application

P. OTTESTAD

Statistics and Mathematics—Chemical Analysis

Biomathematics (2 vol.)   CEDRIC A. B. SMITH
The mathematical theory of epidemics   N. T. J. BAILEY
*The analysis of variance   A. HUITSON
The advanced theory of statistics (3 vol.)

M. G. KENDALL & A. STUART

Statistical papers of George Udny Yule

ed. by A. STUART & M. G. KENDALL

An introduction to the theory of statistics

G. U. YULE & M. G. KENDALL

A course in theoretical statistics   N. A. RAHMAN
*Fundamentals of statistical reasoning   M. H. QUENOUILLE
Rapid statistical calculations   M. H. QUENOUILLE
Clinical chemistry and automation: a study in
    laboratory proficiency   R. ROBINSON
The analysis of drugs and chemicals   N. EVERS & W. SMITH

*In the series, "Griffin's Statistical Monographs and Courses"

———————————

Descriptive catalogue available from the Publishers

STATISTICAL METHOD
IN
BIOLOGICAL ASSAY

D. J. FINNEY, M.A., Sc.D., F.R.S., F.R.S.E.

*Professor of Statistics, University of Edinburgh, and
Director, A.R.C. Unit of Statistics, Edinburgh
Chairman of the Computer Board for Universities and
Research Councils*

SECOND EDITION
Second Impression

HAFNER PRESS
A Division of Macmillan Publishing Co., Inc.
866 Third Avenue, New York, N.Y. 10022

CHARLES GRIFFIN & COMPANY LIMITED
42 DRURY LANE, LONDON, WC2B 5RX

Copyright © 1971

First published	.. ..	1952
Second edition	.. ..	1964
Second impression	..	1971

xix + 668 pages, 22 illustrations, 189 tables
ISBN 0 85264 014 5

PRINTED IN GREAT BRITAIN BY COMPTON PRINTING LIMITED
LONDON AND AYLESBURY

PREFACE TO FIRST EDITION

In this book, I have attempted to provide a comprehensive account of designs and statistical analyses for biological assays, both as a textbook for the student of statistics and as a work of reference for the practitioner of bioassay. Simple introductions to the subject are to be found in C. W. Emmens's *Principles of Biological Assay*, and in special chapters of P. György's *Vitamin Methods* and J. H. Burn's *Biological Standardization*. My aim, however, has been to develop the theory and methods as far as seems practicable at this time, and to show the unity of the various aspects of the subject. Although considerations of length have compelled me to assume in my readers a reasonable familiarity with the basic statistical techniques used in scientific research (§ 1.5), I have given detailed explanation and illustration of all matters peculiar to the statistics of assays.

Many experimenters who are not themselves statisticians can, usefully and without undue difficulty, attain sufficient knowledge of statistical techniques to aid their own work. Nevertheless, I make no apology for emphasizing in this book the rôle of the professional statistician rather than that of a particular group of experimental scientists. The proper function of the statistician in scientific research and technology is no longer merely that of analysing and summarizing large bodies of numerical data : he must also be prepared to advise on the plan and economy of each investigation, in the light of its operational efficiency for a particular purpose. The efficiency attainable will depend upon the nature and reliability of existing information. The statistician must therefore be a major contributor to the answering of the question : " In the present state of knowledge about the nature and behaviour of certain materials and subjects of experimentation (or of non-experimental observation), how should the next investigation be planned in order to obtain the most trustworthy information on specified points from limited resources of materials, subjects, or time ? " He must later analyse the data from the investigation, report on the information they give for the immediate purpose, and be prepared to integrate this information with that previously existing, as a prelude to the

v

planning of further investigations on the same or related topics. The cycle of design, analysis, report, and integration recurs frequently in the work of the statistician, and the intimate relationship between its parts is particularly well exemplified in biological assay. A familiarity with the details of assay design and analysis is to-day necessary to many statisticians working as consultants in scientific research; in addition, a study of the manner in which the parts of this cycle interlock may be enlightening even to those whose chief interests have no connexion with bioassay.

I cannot adequately express my gratitude to Dr Eric C. Wood, who has for seven years stimulated my interest in biological assay. His persistent refusal to be satisfied by any incomplete answer to a question has compelled me to examine carefully the statistical techniques needed for assays, an inquiry which naturally disclosed gaps in the theory and practice of a branch of statistics that had scarcely been regarded as a unified whole. I have tried to make my own contribution to the filling of these gaps, but my part has mostly been to develop and express more fully the ideas of the pioneers of the subject—Bliss, Burn, Fieller, Gaddum, Hartley, Irwin, Trevan, to name only a few. Many of my own ideas, especially in connexion with slope ratio assays, originated in discussion with Dr Wood; he has given much thought to the logical basis, validity, and interpretation of assays; he has advised me on details of biological, chemical, and experimental theory and practice with which I am unfamiliar; finally, he has given most generously of his time in reading and criticizing the typescript of this book, and has suggested many improvements in matter and presentation.

In 1947, Professor J. H. Burn asked me to write a chapter on statistical methods for his *Biological Standardization*; in 1949, Professor Gertrude M. Cox invited me to lecture on biological assay in the Summer Session in Statistics at the University of North Carolina. I am grateful to Professor Burn and to Professor Cox for having caused me to put my thoughts on bioassay into logical order, for out of the work then done this book has grown.

My understanding of bioassay has gained immeasurably from conversations and correspondence with many other friends. I want to thank especially Dr Joseph Berkson, whose ideas on quantal responses have greatly influenced the argument of this book (though possibly not always in the way he would wish), and Dr. N. K. Jerne, who, with Dr Wood, first formulated the ideas in Chapter 15. I am also glad to acknowledge my gratitude to Professor P. A. P. Moran, to my father, and to my wife, for reading the typescript of this book and commenting on style and content; to Miss M. Callow, for a final checking of almost all the calculations and for drawing the diagrams; to Mr A. L. Bacharach, for the many occasions on which he has drawn my attention to interesting problems in analysis and for permission to publish the data in Tables 12.1 and 14.2; to Dr W. F. J. Cuthbertson, for permission to publish the data in Table 16.1; to Professor R. A. Fisher, Dr F. Yates, and Messrs Oliver and Boyd, Ltd, for permission to publish full or abridged versions of Tables III, V, V_1, IV, and XII from their *Statistical Tables for Biological, Agricultural and Medical Research* as Appendix Tables I, II, III, IV, and XI; and to the Cambridge University Press for permission to publish Tables III and IV from my *Probit Analysis* as Appendix Tables VI and VII.

D. J. FINNEY

Oxford,

April, 1951

PREFACE TO SECOND EDITION

The plan of this book remains unchanged, but I have attempted to bring it up to date by insertion of comments on recent important contributions to the theory of bioassay and to papers on some of the more interesting applications. The section on single subject assays has been completely rewritten, and several additions have been made to Chapter 13. New tests for heterogeneity of results of dilution series have been described; for permission to include Table XVIII, which aids the application of a particularly simple test due to Stevens, I am indebted to the editors of the *Journal of the Royal Statistical Society*, Series B.

The opportunity has been taken to correct many small errors and to rewrite several passages that were obscure in the first edition. I am grateful to a number of friends, among them Dr. F. B. Leech, Mr. S. C. Pearce, Dr. M. R. Sampford, and Dr. E. C. Wood, for drawing my attention to some of these. Dr. C. I. Bliss has told me that, in one of the last conversations they had, Sir Ronald Fisher expressed to him the wish that Professor W.-U. Behrens be ascribed priority as the discoverer of the distribution so frequently termed the " Behrens–Fisher "; despite Fisher's great contributions to the understanding of this distribution and its place in statistical theory, I have therefore thought it proper to correct my terminology. Dr. A. S. Outschoorn has kindly helped me with information on international biological standards.

I wish particularly to thank Professors David D. Rutstein and William G. Cochran for the hospitality I have enjoyed in the Departments of Preventive Medicine and Statistics of Harvard University, during the time of preparation of this edition. I also thank Miss Ann Blanchard for her patient typing of successive drafts.

D. J. FINNEY

Boston, Mass.
April, 1963

CONTENTS

CONTENTS

CONTENTS

CONTENTS

SCHEMES OF STUDY

The arrangement of this book has been planned to give a comprehensive account of the subject for a student of statistical science who is already fairly familiar with less specialized techniques of analysis and with the principles of experimental design. The reader well grounded in the methods of statistical science should encounter little difficulty in a systematic study of the whole book, except, perhaps, in a few sections (such as §§ 2.7, 3.13, 14.3, 17.5, 19.3). Nevertheless, at his first trial he would be wise not to read each chapter fully, but rather should select the more important sections.

Many regular practitioners of biological assay, however, would be reluctant to regard themselves as statisticians, primarily because they lack formal mathematical training. Some understanding of the statistical principles and techniques on which bioassay depends is necessary to them; I am convinced that they can attain a good working knowledge without burdening themselves unduly with mathematical theory. Although this book has not been written for them, judicious choice of sections for study may enable them to gain something useful from it.

In order to guide those who do not propose to read the whole book consecutively, I have prepared suggestions for a first reading by four different categories of readers. These are :—

(A) *The professional statistician desiring a short course in biological assay.* Unless he is already experienced in applications of statistical methods to biological experimentation, he ought first to read one or two of the general accounts of bioassay mentioned in § 1.2, in order to appreciate better the background. This course of study might form part of the programme of instruction for a graduate in mathematics who is beginning to specialize in statistical science.

(B) *The non-mathematical user of biological assays.* He will find much of this book beyond him unless he knows something of the normal, t, χ^2, and variance ratio distributions,

xvii

significance tests, the analysis of variance, and the elements of experimental design. He ought first to study these in one of the textbooks mentioned in § 1.5; he may find his understanding of the present book further helped by reading either Emmens (1948) or Chapter III of Burn *et al.* (1950).

(C) *The reader, whether statistician, biologist, or chemist, who requires a general survey of the function of statistical science in biological assay.* The sections suggested for him are those which outline the main features of methods and give simple numerical examples, without much emphasis on details of argument or calculation.

(D) *The reader whose interest lies almost entirely in assays based on quantal responses.* Though he will wish to give most of his attention to the theory and practice of probit analysis and related techniques, he ought at least to read enough of sections from chapters other than 17–21 to enable him to relate these topics to the general theory of bioassay.

The table that follows lists the sections recommended to readers in each of these classes. In general, I would advise that they be read in the order of the book, but in some respects alterations could reasonably be made; for example, all or part of Chapter 15 could be read immediately after Chapter 8, or Chapters 7 and 8 could be deferred until any later stage that seemed convenient. The reader in class B may find that §§ 4.13–4.18 are more easily understood after §§ 5.1 and 5.3. Of course, the sections listed are not necessarily completely self-contained : when the reader encounters references to other sections, he should pursue such of these as seem important to his interest.

Chapter	Sections to be read			
	A	**B**	**C**	**D**
1	All	All	1–5, 9	All
2	1–5, 9–11, **14,** 15	1–5, 9–11, 14, 15	1–3, 9, 11, **14,** 15	1–5, 9–11, 14, 15
3	1–6, 9–12, 14–16	1–5, 9, 11, 14–16	1–5, 14–16	All
4	1–18, 21, 22	1–13, 15–18, 21, 22	1–12, 21, 22	1–12, 21, 22
5	1–5	1, 3–10	1, 9, 10	—
6	All	1–8, 10, 11	1–8, 11	1–8, 11
7	1–10	1–6, 9, 10, 13	1–6	—
8	1–4, **6**	1, 2, 4, **6**	1, 4, **6**	—
9	1–6, 8, **9**	1–4, 8	1–4, 8	—
10	1–4	1–3, 7	1, 2, 4, 7	—
11	1, 2	1, 2	1, 6	—
12	1–4, 6	1, 6	1, 6	—
13	1	1, 4	1, 4	—
14	1, 4	4	—	—
15	All	1–5	All	1–5
16	—	—	—	—
17	1–8, 10, 11, 14–16	1–4	1–4	All
18	1–3, 6	1, 2, 6	1, 2	All
19	1–3, 5, 8	1, 2, 5, 7	1, 2, 5, 7, 8	All
20	1–3, 5, 6, 12	1, 2, 12	1, 2, 12	All
21	5	5, 6	5	All
22	All	1–3	1, 2, 4	All

INTRODUCTION

1.1 The purpose of biological assay

Biological assays are methods for the estimation of the nature, constitution, or potency of a material (or of a process) by means of the reaction that follows its application to living matter. For example, a substance might be identified by means of a characteristic reaction produced in a particular species of organism. Qualitative assays of this type, however, do not present any statistical problems. Quantitative assays, with which this book is concerned, are similar to methods of physical measurement or of quantitative chemical analysis in that their function is to provide numerical assessment of some property of the material to be assayed ; an essential part in this assessment is played by measurement of growth or other changes in animals, plants, animal tissue, micro-organisms, or some other form of living matter. An assay is thus a form of biological experiment, but the interest lies in comparing the potencies of treatments on an agreed scale instead of in comparing the magnitudes of effects of different treatments. The experimental technique may be the same as is used in a purely comparative experiment, but the difference in purpose will affect the optimal experimental design and the statistical analysis. An investigation into the effects of different samples of insulin on the blood sugar of rabbits is not necessarily a biological assay ; it becomes one if the experimenter's interest lies not simply in the changes in blood sugar but in their use for the estimation of the potencies of the samples on a scale of standard units of insulin. Again, a field trial of the responses of potatoes to various phosphatic fertilizers would not generally be regarded as an assay ; nevertheless, if the yields of potatoes are to be used in assessing the potency of a natural rock phosphate relative to a standard superphosphate, and perhaps even in estimating the availability of phosphorus in the rock phosphate, the experiment is an assay within the terms of the description here given.

From a slightly more general point of view, Wood (1946) wrote
' If one attempts to classify analytical procedures with reference
not to the substances analysed nor to the ingredients determined,
but to the fundamental principles involved—the strategy underlying the attack, as it were—one soon finds that many methods,
which vary widely from the former view-point, can be broadly
described in the same terms. First, some physical quantity must
be found—it may be the weight of an animal, the volume of a
reagent, the reading on the dial of an instrument—the magnitude
of which depends on, and varies regularly with, the amount of
the substance it is desired to estimate, and which I shall refer to
as " Factor X ". Second, the quantitative relation between the
amount of " factor X " and the magnitude of the effect it causes
is determined by performing parallel sets of operations with various
known amounts or " doses " of the factor and measuring the result,
which we may call the " response ". The relation between the dose
and the response may be concisely expressed either diagrammatically
in the form of a graph, or algebraically in the form of an equation.
Finally, a known amount of the material to be analysed is put through
an identical series of operations, the response is measured, and the
amount of factor X present is deduced from the graph or the
equation '. Wood pointed out that his description included purely
physical procedures, such as the absorptiometric determination of
trace-elements in alloys, as well as true biological assays, The
distinguishing feature of the latter is that the dependence upon
living matter almost inevitably introduces considerable variability
between measurements obtained by apparently identical operations ;
within an experiment of practicable size, the estimation of the dose-
response relationship, and consequently of the potency of the
material to be analysed, is far from perfect, and the methods of
statistical science are necessary if best use is to be made of the
available data.

Bacharach (1945) has discussed the relationship of biological
assay to chemical analysis. He has emphasized that, when both
biological and chemical methods are available for the same purpose,
the greater precision of the chemical does not invariably make it
preferable. If the result required is an estimate of the biological

potency of a complex material, the greater specificity of a biological
method may give it an advantage over the alternative of a chemical
analysis followed by numerical synthesis of the potency of the
original material from knowledge of the potency of its constituents,

1.2 The history of biological assay

Biological assay is often regarded as a recent development in
scientific method.   In reality, though it could not become an
instrument for precise measurement until knowledge of statistical
science was adequate, the basic principle has been in use for a long
time.   Indeed, one of the best known passages in ancient literature
contains an excellent account of an assay that, although only
qualitative in character, has the essence of the modern quantal
response techniques :

' And it came to pass at the end of forty days, that Noah opened
the windows of the ark which he had made :

And he sent forth a raven, which went to and fro, until the
waters were dried up from off the earth.

Also he sent forth a dove from him, to see if the waters were
abated from off the face of the ground ;

But the dove found no rest for the sole of her foot, and she
returned unto him into the ark, for the waters were on the
face of the whole earth : then he put forth his hand, and
took her, and pulled her in unto him into the ark.

And he stayed yet other seven days ; and again he sent forth
the dove out of the ark ;

And the dove came in to him in the evening : and lo, in her
mouth was an olive leaf pluckt off ; so Noah knew that the
waters were abated from off the earth.' (*Genesis*, 8, vi-xi)

The three essential constituents of an assay, stimulus (the depth
of water), subject (the dove), and response (the plucking of an
olive leaf), are present in this description.   Knowledge of the
response enabled Noah to estimate, or rather, in this instance, to
place an upper limit to the size of the stimulus.   The limitations
of his animal house made his replication less than would to-day
be thought adequate, but in other respects his experiment was
admirable for its purpose.

The serious scientific history of biological assay began at the
close of the nineteenth century with Ehrlich's investigations into

the standardization of diphtheria antitoxin. Since then, the standardization of materials by means of the reactions of living matter has become a common practice, not only in pharmacology but in other branches of science such as plant pathology. The development of pharmacological standardization in the past fifty years has been described in a number of papers, notably by Dale (1939), Gautier (1945), and Hartley (1935, 1945b) ; a paper by Miles (1948) should be consulted for its excellent account of the function of biological assay and standardization in pharmacology to-day. Not until the early attempts at standardizing insulin, about 1920–1925, was any assessment of the trustworthiness of assay results attempted. The potency of materials assayed was at first measured in animal units, the unit being the amount required to produce a certain response in an animal of a particular species. This was unsatisfactory, because animals are as variable in their responses to, and in their tolerances of drugs as they are in more easily measurable bodily characteristics. A cat unit of digitalis, or a mouse unit of insulin, was soon discovered not to be a constant. The introduction of standard preparations of various drugs, against which others could be assayed, was a great advance which made possible the measurement of potency on a fixed scale, independently of the particular animals used : the difference is analogous to that between a spring balance and a balance using a standardized set of weights. A valuable paper by Burn (1930) emphasized the importance of making this the general practice, and so of ' transforming this whole subject from the plane of an insidious means of self-deception to that of a well-ordered and progressive science '.

No detailed history will be given here. Papers by Irwin (1937) and Bliss and Cattell (1943) described many of the methods and ideas introduced in recent years. Bliss and Cattell also gave a lengthy bibliography of work on the theory and practice of assays, and their list could be greatly extended by subsequent publications. Contributions to the statistical methodology were scattered through a large number of papers in journals of biological subjects, and until 1948 no comprehensive account was available. Finney (1947a) gave a systematic account of the statistical principles on which the analysis of biological assays is based. Jerne and Wood (1949) and Miles (1949) have published valuable detailed discussions of the assumptions common to most assay techniques. In 1948, Emmens published the first book devoted purely to the statistical aspects of biological assay; Burn, Finney and Goodwin (1950) included a chapter on statistical technique, of content similar to Emmens's book, in their *Biological Standardization*. Bliss (1952a) has published separately a revised text of a long chapter first written for a book by György (1951); he includes much that complements the present book and many valuable numerical examples, but he has less to say on the choice of an assay design. Coward (1947) and Gaddum (1948) are primarily concerned with the biological problems of assay, though naturally both give some attention to methods for the statistical analysis of results.

1.3   The structure of a biological assay

The typical bioassay involves a *stimulus* (for example, a vitamin, a drug, a fungicide) applied to a *subject* (for example, an animal, a piece of animal tissue, a plant, a bacterial culture). The intensity of the stimulus may be varied, generally in accordance with the wish of the investigator, so as to vary the dose given to the subject, and this dose can be measured (perhaps as a weight, a volume, or a concentration). Application of the stimulus is followed by a change in some measurable characteristic of the subject, the magnitude of the change being dependent upon the dose. A measurement of this characteristic (for example, a weight of the whole subject or of some particular organ, an analytical value such as blood sugar content or bone ash percentage, or even a simple record of occurrence or non-occurrence of a certain muscular contraction, recovery from symptoms of a dietary deficiency, or death) is the *response* of the subject. The relationship between dose and response will not be exact, but will be obscured by random variations between replicate subjects, or, if the response is one that can be produced more than once in the same subject, in the responsiveness of one subject on different occasions. Nevertheless, the relationship can be used to indicate the potency of a dose from knowledge of the responses it produces.

As will be apparent from subsequent chapters, biological assays are usually comparative, the estimate of potency being obtained relative to a *standard preparation* of the stimulus. This standard preparation may be merely a convenient working standard adopted in a particular laboratory as a scale of reference or it may have a wider currency. The Permanent Commission on Biological Standardization, established by the Health Organization of the League of Nations, has performed great services in the definition, preparation, and supply of standard preparations of many important therapeutic substances, For most assays of these substances, the standard preparation is likely to be a sample of either the international standard or a more readily available working standard whose potency relative to the international standard has previously been carefully evaluated.

The potency of the standard is expressed either in ordinary units of weight or volume or in arbitrary units, such as the international units adopted for insulin and penicillin. Any *test preparation* of the stimulus, having an unknown potency, is assayed by finding the mean response to a selected dose, and equating this dose to that of the standard preparation shown by experiment to produce the same mean response ; experimentation with several different doses of one or both preparations is almost always needed in order to accomplish this satisfactorily. The ratio of the two equally effective doses is an estimate of the potency of the test preparation relative to that of the standard.

The methods of this book are presented largely as applicable to an ideal situation in which the test and standard preparations are identical in their biologically active principle and differ only in the extents to which they are diluted by inactive materials (solvents and the like). This situation is discussed in detail in §§ 2.9, 3.3, 3.4 and Chapter 15. An assertion that all assays should be of this kind would be unrealistic. Indeed, certainty under this head may often imply so complete an understanding of the preparations that quantitative chemical analysis can replace biological assay for potency estimation: such a change is not necessarily desirable even when possible, but its advantages, both economic and in precision, need consideration. Unfortunately for the peace of mind of the statistician, many assays that are important in practice will not conform to the ideal conditions. It then becomes necessary to discuss the nature of the departure from the ideal and the manner in which this should affect the interpretation of any statistical analysis. The primary considerations are not really statistical; they pertain to the use that is to be made of assay results and the question of whether a relative potency estimated from one response or one species of subject can be assumed to have even approximate validity for another response or species.

The *British Pharmacopoeia* (1958) and the *United States Pharmacopeia* (1960) now contain sections describing, in condensed form, the computations required for the more important biological assays. The latter follows Bliss's style and notation, and has been supplemented by separate publication of a series of numerical examples (Bliss, 1956). Rather surprisingly, the *Pharmacopoea Internationalis* (1951–59) gives nothing more than rather vague comments on the precision that ought to be achieved in good assays conducted according to instructions. Perhaps even more surprising in all these publications is the absence of any serious discussion of the validity of the basic assumptions mentioned in the previous paragraph and treated more thoroughly in Chapter 15. The *U.S. Pharmacopeia* commends statistical tests for the identification and rejection of markedly aberrant responses. Most statisticians are reluctant to reject a datum solely because it appears not to conform to the remaining data: if the model postulated for a frequency distribution is somewhat wrong, biases resulting from such rejection may easily be more serious than would follow retention of the datum. When other evidence that an experimental or observational mistake occurred supports a purely statistical test, rejection may be more justifiable.

1.4 International standards

The precise nature of internationally accepted standard preparations is perhaps not of especial importance to the matters under discussion in this book, though it may be vitally important to the proper interpretation of an assay. Even the statistician, however, ought to be aware of the general character of the precautions taken in selecting a standard, in preparing and preserving it, and in distributing it for world-wide use. ' The biological standard chosen for international adoption must fulfil certain conditions. In nearly every case the standard is a dry preparation of an arbitrarily chosen but representative sample of the substance for which it is to serve as a standard, or, when a pure substance is available, the sample must comply with accurately defined physical constants. It is obvious that, since the standard must satisfy world requirements for many years, the quantity set aside as a standard must be large. Secondly, the standard must be stable, a condition which is fulfilled by preparing it in the absolutely dry condition and preserving it constantly at temperatures at, or below, the freezing point, in sealed containers, and protected from the action of light, moisture and oxygen. Thirdly, the standard must be dispensed in such a form as to be readily accessible and capable of being brought into use by the laboratory worker with a minimum of trouble, additional manipulation or delay.' (Hartley, 1935.) Gautier (1945) and Hartley (1945a) have described the methods necessary to careful control over all stages of the preparation and distribution.

Up to the time of publication of the first edition of this book, forty-one international standards had been prepared through the efforts of the Permanent Commission, and its successor, the World Health Organization Expert Committee on Biological Standardization. Since then the growth has been rapid. In 1963, international standards and reference preparations for forty-seven antibiotics, hormones, and other pharmacological substances were held by the National Institute for Medical Research in London, and those for fifty-eight antigens and antibodies were held by the Statens Seruminstitut, Copenhagen (Anon., 1963). Jerne and Perry (1956) have reported on the stability of some international standards. Not all standards need the techniques discussed in this book, but to many of them and also to research on new standards the methods are relevant. The establishment and use of standards have been described by Dale (1939) and Hartley (1945b). The purpose of a biological assay is analogous to that of a balance, and the standard preparation plays the part of a standard set of weights: without a standard that has at least some permanence in one laboratory and preferably a wider acceptability, biological assay becomes merely a scheme of comparisons between unknowns and is of little absolute value.

1.5   Statistical science and biological assay

The statistician has three contributions to make to the practice of biological assay. He must advise on the general statistical principles that underlie the assay method; he must construct experimental designs that, in the light of existing information, seem likely to give the most useful and reliable results; and he must analyse, or instruct the investigator how to analyse, the experimental data so as to make the best use of all the evidence on potency. The word 'design' is here used in the sense adopted by Fisher for his book *The Design of Experiments* (1960). It comprises a statement of the number and magnitudes of doses of each preparation to be tested, the number of subjects to be used at each dose, the system of allocating subjects to doses, the order in which subjects shall be treated and measured, and related characteristics of the experiment. Advice on experimental design is recognized to be often the most important function of the statistician : no ingenuity of statistical analysis can force a badly designed experiment to yield evidence on points to which insufficient thought was given in the designing, whereas even an imperfect or inefficient analysis of a well-designed experiment may give conclusions that are enlightening and substantially correct. The close connexion that subsists between the design of an experiment and the analysis of the results, however, ensures that questions of optimal design cannot be separated from those of statistical analysis. In this book, I have endeavoured to show the interrelationship of logical principles, design, and analysis ; naturally, there is most to be said on the last, but, unless the principles and the design of an assay are sound, statistical analysis is at best a tentative numerical evaluation of the data, at worst a groping in the dark that may prove disastrously misleading.

The special problems of biological assay form an important branch of statistical science, and their study should take its proper place in any programme of training for statisticians. Apart from the intrinsic value of this study, I believe that increased attention to bioassay would benefit the outlook of statisticians on other fields of science. The impetus to developments in the design and analysis of scientific experiments, so evident in the period 1920–1940, came largely from agricultural research, and this has left its mark upon the standard text-books of statistical science. One consequence has been a tendency to place too much emphasis on tests of significance, and not enough on the theoretical and practical problems of estimation. The analysis of biological assays is a valuable corrective to this attitude, because the part that each must play is there clearly distinguishable. The validity of an assay needs to be checked by means of various significance tests, without which the assay is worthless save in so far as the experimenter is prepared to guarantee validity from information external to the experiment : nevertheless, the main object of every assay is to estimate certain parameters, and especially to estimate and assign fiducial limits to the parameter representing the potency of a test preparation relative to a standard.

To a great extent, the basic experimental designs and methods of statistical analysis required in biological assay are those now familiar in many branches of scientific research, and in this book a considerable knowledge of them will be assumed. Thus, if he is to understand fully the chapters that follow, the reader will find that he needs facility in the analysis of variance and covariance, and in regression analysis. He should therefore be familiar with standard methods such as are described by Cochran and Cox (1957), Fisher (1960, 1958), Mather (1946), Quenouille (1950), Snedecor (1956), and Yates (1937), or at least should know where to find elementary accounts to supplement what is said here. If discussion of the design and analysis of assays is to be relevant to biometric problems, however, and not merely a series of exercises in statistical manipulation, the logical basis of the assay argument, especially as it is developed in Chapters 2 and 3, must be kept in mind and related to particular circumstances. In some respects, therefore, the statistical methods needed for potency estimation differ from those needed for experiments in which the interest lies in the comparison of effects : these aspects of statistical science will be emphasized and discussed in detail.

1.6 The scope of this book

This book is intended to present a connected account of statistical science for biological assays, or, more strictly, for that class of assays known as dilution assays (§ 2.9). The amount of formal theory to be studied is small, the number of important variations on the main theme large. Many numerical examples are used to illustrate the discussion ; most of these are taken from published work, although occasionally the data have been modified in order to emphasize an important point or to avoid an irrelevant complication. In one or two instances, completely artificial data have been used, because no records of experiments satisfactorily illustrating certain topics could be found.

In almost all fields of application of statistical methods to the analysis of experiments, the technique known as the analysis of variance occupies a central position. This is true of biological assay, but perhaps the fundamental importance of regression and related concepts is here more apparent than in most types of experimentation. Complex experimental designs, such as have been found valuable in other fields of research, must sometimes be adopted if available materials are to be used to best advantage ; in this book, I have laid great stress on general problems of experimental planning, in relation to the choice of doses and the degree of replication, and also on the relative merits of particular designs. The great interest shown in recent years in ' probits ', and in other methods of analysis for quantal response data, must influence any discussion of the design and analysis of assays based upon quantal responses. Techniques such as covariance analysis and discriminant analysis have obvious relevance to bioassay, but have not yet been fully exploited ; I have given some illustrations of their use, and have tried to indicate how their value to the economy of assay practice may be assessed. Almost any proposal for the statistical analysis of biological data involves, explicitly or implicitly, assumptions about the interrelationships of the data that can best be expressed in terms of a mathematico-probabilistic model : the need for this model, and the importance of considering its effect upon the conclusions reached is especially evident in bioassay. Much further work on this topic has still to be done, but I have endeavoured to keep the problem before my readers.

Chapter 2 is concerned with direct assays, in which potency is assessed from direct measurement of the dose necessary to produce a specified response. Chapter 3 introduces the idea of an indirect assay based upon the relationship between dose and a quantitative response. Problems of experimental design and statistical analysis for these assays are considered in Chapters 3 to 16 : Chapters 7 and 8 deal with slope ratio assays, the others primarily with parallel line assays, though many of their ideas are common to the two types. After the general discussion of methods of analysis in Chapters 3, 4, 5, 7, and of efficiency of design in Chapters 6 and 8, the structure and analysis of special designs are considered in Chapters 9, 10, 11. Chapters 12 and 13 relate to the combination of measurements of different qualities of the subjects, Chapter 14 to the combination of potency estimates from different assays. In Chapter 15 the logic and validity of the arguments on which the assay method rests are re-examined in greater detail than was attempted in Chapter 3 ; special attention is given to the validity of the statistical models adopted, and to the objectivity of the conclusions drawn. Chapter 16 provides illustration of certain transformation procedures suggested in the general theory of Chapter 3. Assays based upon quantal responses are considered in Chapters 17 to 21 : they are not discussed in such variety and detail as are those for quantitative responses, in part because many of the quantitative methods can easily be adapted to the quantal, in part because the more complex designs are not usually needed in quantal assays. Although these chapters to some extent repeat methods and ideas presented in my *Probit Analysis* (1952), the amount of overlap of the two books, is not great ; the emphasis in one is on the study of the relationship between quantal response and dose, and in the other is on the use of that relationship in potency estimation. In particular, questions of experimental design (Chapter 19), and rapid methods of analysis commonly associated with the names of Kärber, Reed and Muench, and others (Chapter 20) are discussed much more thoroughly than in the earlier book. In Chapter 21, a method for estimating densities of bacterial suspensions from a dilution series is presented, Chapter 22 contains an account of special problems encountered when the response is a time measurement.

1.7 Computation

I have included many fully-worked numerical examples, and have tried to exhibit systematic patterns of computing suitable for desk calculating machines, although the ideal pattern will depend upon the particular machine available. Early examples include considerable arithmetic detail; thereafter the reader is assumed able to adapt himself to the variations necessitated by each new problem. Electronic calculating machines make possible much more rapid calculations, and doubtless programmes are being written for standard assay designs.

Whether desk or electronic computers are used, careful checks for arithmetic accuracy and internal consistency of analysis should be considered mandatory. Preferably a check should be an independent set of calculations that passes from one stage to another of an analysis by an alternative route; ideally, when a desk calculator is used, a different operator should make check calculations. I have not described the checking routines; often nothing more complicated is needed than confirming that the sum of column totals agrees with the sum of row totals or verifying that independently computed squares with single degrees of freedom add to the right component of an analysis of variance. The imposition of checks should always be regarded as a guarantee that no mistakes occurred in the first working, and not as an excuse for carelessness at that stage.

I have tried also to adhere to reasonable standards in the number of decimal places carried in computation. Assays are scarcely ever sufficiently precise to warrant quotation of results to more than four significant digits : a statement that a test preparation is estimated to have a potency of 35·71685 units per g. is both stupid and confusing. In intermediate stages of an analysis, more digits may be retained in order to maintain internal consistency and to avoid troubles consequent upon the occurrence of differences between two large and nearly equal quantities. Even so, six significant digits are enough for almost any set of calculations. To waste effort by having too many digits is better than to err by having too few, especially when a calculating machine is used, but retention of an excessive number may increase both the labour and the danger of mistakes. For routine work, the accuracy should never need to be greater than this book illustrates for assays analysed in detail : for exposition of method, or discussion of statistical theory, additional digits may sometimes be desirable.

1.8 Statistical tables

The practice of statistical analysis of scientific data requires frequent reference to tables of the numerical values of special functions, such as values in the t, χ^2, and variance ratio distributions corresponding to selected probability levels. In addition, the better known mathematical tables of square roots, logarithms, and trigonometric functions are often used. A good volume of statistical tables is essential to any research worker who analyses his own data, and inclusion in this book of tables of all functions employed is therefore unnecessary. In order to aid the reader who is studying statistical method, rather than using the text for reference in practical assay work, a series of appendices contains simplified versions of the more important tables. The values required for numerical examples, however, have usually been obtained, directly or by interpolation, from Fisher and Yates's *Statistical Tables for Agricultural, Biological and Medical Research*; in that collection will be found detailed tables relating to the normal, t, χ^2, variance ratio and Behrens distributions, which are frequently used in the methods of subsequent chapters, as well as tables of elementary mathematical functions. Certain tables relating to assays based on quantal responses are not so readily available elsewhere, and these are therefore included as Appendices V–XVIII.

1.9 Terminology and notation

In the literature of biological assay, the great variety of notation used is a source of confusion to the reader. Many recent papers have been concerned with short-cut computational schemes for routine assays of a standard pattern. Admirable as they may be for their particular purposes, these schemes often become complicated or obscure when applied to assays of slightly different type ; their highly specialized notations may then be inconvenient or confusing. Though some of them will be mentioned, this book is primarily intended to treat of the general approach to assay problems, and to show how it is based upon the theory of regression, a theory well known to all users of statistical science. When a new statistical problem in bioassay is encountered, whether it be a minor modification in design or a method of analysing data of a totally unfamiliar type, the only sure way of avoiding gross blunders is to begin from the nature of the dose-response relationship. If the general form of the appropriate statistical analysis is understood, anyone with a moderate facility in elementary algebra can ' stream-line ' the details of computation so that superfluous steps are avoided.

For the account of biological assay now to be presented, an attempt has been made to devise a reasonably consistent notation. Inevitably some of the conventions adopted conflict with past usages by other writers. No claim of perfect consistency is made, for the price of that would be the use of unfamiliar type-founts and the adornment of symbols with many suffices. Only the pedant would insist that ' r ' or ' S ' should be used always with the same meaning, when in fact these symbols can conveniently play two or more roles without ambiguity. The following are the more important conventions used throughout the book :

    (i) The words ' stimulus ', ' subject ', ' dose ', and ' response ' are used as described in § 1.3 to indicate the entities of an assay in general form. A particular example may relate to a dose of vitamin D given to rats, but the same statistical technique may be appropriate to a completely different stimulus and subject, such as penicillin applied to agar plates inoculated with *Staphylococcus aureus.*

    (ii) The letters S and T refer to the standard and test preparations respectively. With numerical suffices, they indicate doses, or groups of subjects at a dose of either preparation ; when themselves used as suffices, they indicate totals, means, or other quantities relating to all the data on either preparation.

    (iii) So far as is reasonably convenient, Greek letters are used for the parameters of a population, Roman for values determined from observational or experimental data.

    (iv) The true value of a relative potency is denoted by ρ, its estimate from an assay by R. The symbol M is used for the logarithm of R (to any convenient base), or for this logarithm reduced by a constant dependent upon the scales of measurement of the doses.

    (v) The symbol x is used for a measure of dose, y for a measure of response. These need not be the actual quantities measured by the experimenter, and may instead be obtained after metametric transformations.

    (vi) Summations over observations relating to one preparation are indicated by S, summations over different preparations or over several assays by Σ. (Since S as referring to the standard preparation rarely occurs *in formulæ* except as a suffix, no ambiguity arises). A condensed symbolism is used to represent sums of squares and products of deviations. For example, S_{xy} represents the sum of products of the deviations of corresponding values of the variates x, y from their means for one preparation :

$$S_{xy} = S\{(x - \bar{x})(y - \bar{y})\} \; ;$$

a weighted sum of products is implied where differential weighting of the data occurs. Again, ΣS_{xx} represents the sum of squares of deviations of a variate x, summed for the two or more preparations in an assay or over several assays according to the context.

(vii) Except where the contrary is stated, all significance tests are made at the probability level $P = 0.05$, and all fiducial limits are determined for this probability. Opinions appear to differ on whether such limits are better called 95 per cent. or 5 per cent. fiducial limits : the former name is used. This convention must not be regarded as attaching any special sanctity to the probability of 0.05, or even as suggesting that an investigator ought always to use the same significance level. It is adopted in order to simplify descriptions of analyses, and is without prejudice to the choice of the ideal significance level in any particular circumstances (*cf.* § 4.10).

(viii) In the first edition, I used the word *sensitivity* as usually referring to the sensitivity of subjects to change in dose rather than to the level of dose at which a specified response appeared; I regarded as sensitive subjects those having a high value of β (see below) rather than those manifesting a stated response at a low dose. Later I discovered that the other usage is favoured by pharmacologists. This explanation, and later minor clarifications, should remove confusion as effectively as any more drastic rephrasing and will permit me to retain my own preference. I have used the word *responsiveness* to refer to the subjects' ability to respond to low doses.

Table 1.1 summarizes the standardized uses of symbols. When any letter is used with a meaning other than that stated in the Table, this will be clear from the text.

TABLE 1.1—Glossary of symbols

Symbol	Meaning
a	Constant term in linear regression equation, estimating α
b	Regression coefficient of y on x, estimating β. With distinguishing suffix, used for other regression coefficients in covariance analyses
c	In slope ratio assay, ratio of lowest to highest dose of either preparation
d	Sukhatme's d-statistic (§ 2.6); on the null hypothesis, distributed as shown in Appendix Table III or Interval between successive log doses
e	Base of natural logarithms, $2{\cdot}71828\ldots$
f	A number of degrees of freedom. Also used as a functional symbol
g	Statistic used in fiducial limit calculations, and equal to $t^2 V(b)/b^2$ (§ 2.5)
h	In parallel line assay, $(M - \bar{x}_S + \bar{x}_T)/X$; in slope ratio assay, RX_T/X_S
i	Indicator of particular dose, as x_i $(i = 1, 2, \ldots k)$
j, k	In Chapter 17, estimates of $\mathcal{J}$, K
k	Number of doses per preparation
m	Estimate of μ
n	Number of subjects per dose
p	r/n, unless complications of § 17.5 occur. (Also used with entirely different meanings, e.g. in Chapters 6, 13, 14)
q	$(1 - p)$
r	No. of subjects manifesting a quantal response in a batch of n at one dose. (Also used with entirely different meaning in Chapter 14)
s	Estimate of standard deviation for the distribution of log tolerances or of response metameters at a fixed dose, according to context; based upon a sum of squares of deviations. Most usually occurs as s^2, the estimated variance
t	Statistic which, on the null hypothesis, is distributed as shown in Appendix Table I
u	Response as measured
v_{ii}	The variance multiplier for the estimate of the ith parameter, whose variance is therefore $\sigma^2 v_{ii}$ or $s^2 v_{ii}$; a diagonal element of V
v_{ij}	The covariance multiplier for the estimates of the ith and jth parameters, whose covariance is therefore $\sigma^2 v_{ij}$ or $s^2 v_{ij}$; a non-diagonal element of V
w	A weighting coefficient, especially for quantal responses
x	Dose metameter, usually equal to z or $\log z$
y	Response metameter, usually equal to u; in quantal response assays, the working equivalent deviate at dose x
z	Dose as measured

Table 1.1 (*cont.*)

Symbol	Meaning
A	The range, used in calculating working responses, especially for quantal response assays where it is $1/Z$. (Also used with entirely different meaning in Chapters 6 and 8)
C	The blanks, or the sum of the responses for the blanks, in a slope ratio assay. (Also used with entirely different meaning in Chapters 17 and 18)
D	The ratio between successive doses in a symmetrical assay
$E(\ )$	Statistical expectation of quantity in brackets
F	A variance ratio which, on the null hypothesis, is distributed as shown in Appendix Table II
$F(\ )$	Regression function for u on z, or analogously with quantal responses
G	$\bar{x}_T - \bar{x}_S$
H	$\bar{y}_T - \bar{y}_S$
I	Square of semi-fiducial interval for M in parallel line assays, or for R in slope ratio assays
$\mathcal{J}, K$	Additional parameters for quantal response data (§ 17.5)
K	Also used with entirely different meanings in Chapters 6, 8, 9, and 10
L	Logarithm of likelihood (Chapters 3, 17) **or** A typical contrast between responses
$L_{\bullet}$	In parallel line assay, preparation contrast
L_1	In parallel line assay, regression contrast
L_2, L_2', L_3, L_3'	In parallel line assay, various curvature contrasts
L_B	In slope ratio assay, blanks contrast
L_I	In slope ratio assay, intersection contrast
$L_{2S}, L_{2T}, L_{3S}, L_{3T}$	In slope ratio assay, various curvature contrasts
M	Estimate of log potency, usually obtained from equation (4.11)
M_L, M_U ...	Lower and upper fiducial limits for M
N	Total number of subjects in an assay
N_S, N_T ...	Total number of subjects for standard and test preparation respectively
P	Probability of occurrence of a quantal response
Q	$(1 - P)$
R	Estimate of ρ, equal to antilog M in a parallel line assay, b_T/b_S in a slope ratio assay
R_L, R_U ...	Lower and upper fiducial limits for R
R_0	Guessed value of relative potency used in planning an assay
S	Indicator of the standard preparation
S_1, S_2, S_3 ...	Doses, or sums of responses to doses, of the standard preparation
$S(\ )$	Summation of quantity in brackets, over data for a particular preparation ; for a slope ratio assay it usually represents summation over all data

Table 1.1 (*cont.*)

Symbol			Meaning
S_{xx}	...	...	$S\{(x - \bar{x})^2\}$ or $S\{nw\,(x - \bar{x})^2\}$
S_{xy}	...	...	$S\{(x - \bar{x})(y - \bar{y})\}$ or $S\{nw\,(x - \bar{x})(y - \bar{y})\}$
S_{yy}	...	...	$S\{(y - \bar{y})^2\}$ or $S\{nw\,(y - \bar{y})^2\}$
T	...	...	Indicator of the test preparation
T_1, T_2, T_3	...	...	Doses, or sums of responses to doses, of the test preparation
U	...	...	$E(u)$
V	...	...	Matrix of variance and covariance multipliers, (v_{ij}), often calculated as an inverse matrix in the solution of linear equations
$V(\ )$	...	...	Variance of quantity in brackets
W	...	...	Total weight attached to response metameter at a dose, usually $= nw$
X	...	...	In parallel line assay, interval between highest and lowest log dose
X_S, X_T		...	In slope ratio assay, highest doses of standard and test preparations
Y	...	...	Response metameter corresponding to U, usually expressed as linear regression function of empirical or working metameter on x
Y_0, Y_1 ...		...	Minimum and maximum working equivalent deviates
Z	...	...	Standardized ordinate of tolerance distribution
Z_S, Z_T ...		...	Corresponding doses of standard and test preparations, either equipotent (§ 3.3) or guessed to be equipotent
α	...	...	Constant term in true regression equation, $Y = \alpha + \beta x$
β	...	...	True regression coefficient of y on x
γ	...	...	Coefficient of x^2 in quadratic regression equation
δ	...	...	Used only in combination with other symbols, to denote increment to estimates during iteration, as δa, δb, δj, etc.
ε	...	...	Used as a typical base of logarithms (§ 4.3), as a random error (§ 14.4), or as $\log_{10} e$ (§ 16.3)
η	...	...	Working loglog deviate
η_0, η_1 ...		...	Minimum and maximum working loglog deviates
θ	...	...	Angle used as ancillary statistic (§ 2.6) in association with Sukhatme's d. (Also used with several entirely different meanings)
λ	...	...	Index of z in definition of power dose metameter (§§ 3.7, 7.1) **or** Auxiliary variate in maximum likelihood estimation for quantal responses (§ 17.5) **and never** s/b or $1/b$, as often in the literature of bioassay
μ	...	...	Mean of log tolerance distribution **or** Density of bacterial suspension
μg.	...	...	Microgram
ν	...	...	In § 17.6, used for number of doses

Table 1.1 (*cont.*)

Symbol			*Meaning*
π	...	...	Ratio of circumference to diameter of a circle, 3·14159 . . .
ρ	...	...	True potency of test preparation relative to standard
σ	...	...	Standard deviation for the distribution of log tolerances or of response metameters at a fixed dose, according to context
$\varphi\,(U)$	...	...	Expression of σ^2 as a function of U (§ 3.10)
χ^2	...	...	Statistic which, on the null hypothesis, is distributed as shown in Appendix Table IV
ω	...	...	Weight used in combining data from different assays
ψ^2	...	...	Inter-litter variance of β (§ 14.4)
Σ	...	...	Summation over data for different preparations in one assay, or over several assays

Several symbols not listed above, and many of those that are listed, are occasionally used with different meanings where there is no fear of confusion.

A bar over the top of a symbol ($\bar{x}$, $\bar{s}^2$, ...) indicates a mean value, unweighted or weighted according to the context ; a suffix distinguishes values corresponding to different preparations (b_S, b_T, ...) or to different parts of an assay or different assays (s_1, s_2, b_1, b_2, ...) ; a 'dash' or 'prime' usually indicates values that have been adjusted for regression on a concomitant variate (y', s', ...) ; an asterisk usually denotes a transformed, compounded, or modified variate (u^*, y^*, ...).

Unfortunately Bliss's book (1952*a*), which in so many respects parallels and complements this, differs most completely in notation. Yet, because of the differences in content and purpose, neither Dr. Bliss nor I could bring our notations into conformity without radical changes of style of presentation. One important difference is that Bliss writes in terms of C instead of g, where

$$C = 1/(1 - g),$$

so that C ranges from slightly more than 1·0 for a good assay to a very large value for a poor one.

CHAPTER 2

DIRECT ASSAYS

2.1 Types of biological assay

In addition to purely qualitative assays, three main types of biological assay are at present in common use for the numerical estimation of potencies:

(i) Direct assays,

(ii) Indirect assays based upon quantitative responses,

(iii) Indirect assays based upon quantal ('all-or-nothing') responses.

The last two are very similar in the form of statistical analysis that they require. Both make use of dose-response regression relationships, though the full calculations are usually more laborious for quantal responses on account of the need for differential weighting of the observations. In logical structure, however, assays with quantal responses are more closely related to direct assays than to those with quantitative responses. An understanding of direct assays is essential to a proper appreciation of the other types. Moreover, the problems of design and analysis of direct assays are very similar to those familiar to biometricians for other investigations involving planned experimentation; their discussion, indeed, is not only a convenient introduction to more specialized assay problems, but also a good illustration of the application of standard methods of statistical science.

Rather surprisingly, recognition of this simplest type of assay seems to have been neglected. Its fundamental importance is sufficient justification for devoting a whole chapter to it, though the analysis will present few novelties to those who are accustomed to analysis of variance techniques.

2.2 The nature of direct assays

The principle of a direct assay is that doses of the standard and test preparations sufficient to produce a specified response are directly measured. The ratio between these doses estimates the potency of the test preparation relative to the standard : by definition, this potency is the amount of the standard equivalent in effect to one unit of the test. Such a technique is practicable only for certain stimuli and subjects, for it depends upon the possibility of measuring just the dose needed and not merely one that is at least large enough. The response must therefore be clear-cut and easily recognized, and the dose must be capable of administration in such a manner that the exact amount needed to produce the response can be given and measured. The critical dose will generally vary considerably from subject to subject, and even from one occasion to another with the same subject ; hence the results obtained are only estimates of potency, and calculation from averages over a number of trials is desirable. Ideally, trials of both preparations should be made on each subject used, as in this way the estimation is independent of differences between subjects and, in consequence, more precise. Often this is impossible, however, as once a subject has responded it may not be usable again, or may be so changed as to make a second trial far from comparable with the first ; often, indeed, the response used is death of the subject.

A typical example of a direct assay is the ' cat ' method for the assay of digitalis (Burn, Finney, and Goodwin, 1950 ; Hatcher and Brody, 1910). The standard or the test preparation is infused, at a fixed rate, into the blood-stream of a cat until the heart stops beating. The total period of the infusion is multiplied by the rate to give a measure of the dose. This is repeated on several cats for each preparation, and the mean doses are determined. The most obvious form of calculation is illustrated in § 2.3, and criticisms of the method and of this analysis are given in subsequent sections.

2.3 An assay of strophanthus

Table 2.1 shows the fatal doses or *tolerances* of three groups of cats for two tinctures of strophanthus and a preparation of ouabain (Burn *et al.*, 1950). The experimental procedure was of the same general character as that mentioned in § 2.2 for digitalis. The doses were recorded as quantities per kg. body weight of cat, and unfortunately the total doses are not available : the tolerance is thus assumed to vary in proportion to body weight, or at least to show an approximately proportional variation rather than independence of body weight. Provided that the cats have been assigned at random to the different preparations, either form of expression of dose gives a valid method of estimating potency, but neither necessarily makes the best possible use of information on body weight (§ 2.11).

TABLE 2.1—Tolerances of cats for tinctures of strophanthus and ouabain

Preparation	Strophanthus A (in 0·01 c.c. per kg.)	Strophanthus B (in 0·01 c.c. per kg.)	Ouabain (in 0·01 mg. per kg.)
Tolerances ...	1·55	2·42	5·23
	1·58	1·85	9·91
	1·71	2·00	4·76
	1·44	2·27	6·51
	1·24	1·70	6·68
	1·89	1·47	5·76
	2·34	2·20	4·93
	—	—	4·58
	—	—	6·69
Total ...	11·75	13·91	55·05
Mean ...	1·68	1·99	6·12

Suppose that tincture B is to be regarded as the standard preparation, and A is to be compared with it as a test preparation. From the means at the foot of Table 2.1, 0·0168 c.c. of A is estimated to produce the same results as 0·0199 c.c. of B, either being just sufficient, on an average, to kill a cat. Hence the relative potency is estimated to be

$$R = \frac{0 \cdot 0199}{0 \cdot 0168}$$
$$= 1 \cdot 18 ;$$

1 c.c. of tincture A is estimated to be equivalent to 1·18 c.c. of tincture B. As a statement of the findings in an experiment of this kind, the conclusion is satisfactory, except that, of course

allowance must be made for statistical errors of estimation (§ 2.4 *et seq*). The experimenter, however, often wishes to make a more general inference, namely, that 1 c.c. of tincture A contains the same amount of some effective constituent as does 1·18 c.c. of tincture B. This introduces complications into the logic of the argument, which will be discussed again in § 2.9, and, more fully, in Chapters 3 and 15.

The two tinctures of strophanthus may be regarded as containing the same effective constituent, so that the relative potency will estimate the ratio between the concentrations of this constituent in the tinctures. Ouabain, on the other hand, though closely related, is not an identical substance, and, however useful a relative potency figure may be in comparing it with strophanthus, that figure must not be interpreted as having the same analytical significance. The calculation is made in just the same manner :

$$R = \frac{0 \cdot 0199}{0 \cdot 0612}$$
$$= 0 \cdot 325,$$

and 1 mg. ouabain is estimated to be equivalent to 0·325 c.c. of tincture B.

2.4 Precision of estimates

Statement of an estimate of potency, based upon individual observations known to show considerable variation, is little use unless some indication of the limits of the error to which it is subject is also given. Standard errors of the mean tolerances can be calculated by familiar processes, and from these must be derived a measure of precision. A naive result commonly quoted enables the coefficients of variation* (C.V.) of two independent quantities a, b to be combined to give the coefficient of variation of the ratio of a to b ; it states that

$$\{ \text{C.V. of } a/b \}^2 = \{ \text{C.V. of } a \}^2 + \{ \text{C.V. of } b \}^2. \qquad (2.1)$$

This equation is based upon assumptions that are inconsistent with rigorous statistical theory, and, as numerical examples will show, its application should be limited to data for which the coefficient

---

* The coefficient of variation of a is defined to be the ratio of the standard error of a to a itself, and is usually expressed as a percentage.

of variation of b is small. The calculations now to be described for the data of Table 2.1 are therefore not recommended as a general procedure, but are shown here because of their common use in the literature of the subject.

Consider first the two strophanthus tinctures, and ignore the ouabain data. Sums of squares of deviations may be used to estimate the variances of $\bar{x}_A$, $\bar{x}_B$, the two mean doses, and then, since

$$R = \frac{\bar{x}_B}{\bar{x}_A}, \tag{2.2}$$

equation (2.1) gives the variance of R as

$$V(R) = \frac{1}{\bar{x}_A^2} [V(\bar{x}_B) + R^2 V(\bar{x}_A)]. \tag{2.3}$$

For tincture A,
$$S(x - \bar{x})^2 = (1\cdot55)^2 + (1\cdot58)^2 + \ldots + (2\cdot34)^2 - (11\cdot75)^2/7$$
$$= 20\cdot4819 - 19\cdot7232$$
$$= 0\cdot7587.$$
Similarly for tincture B,
$$S(x - \bar{x})^2 = 28\cdot3227 - 27\cdot6412$$
$$= 0\cdot6815.$$

Since both sums of squares have 6 degrees of freedom, A and B are seen to have about the same variability in their tolerances. Hence the usual practice of pooling the sums of squares, so as to obtain a single estimate of the variance per cat, seems reasonable : the logical flaw is discussed in § 2.9. This involves writing

$$s^2 = \frac{0\cdot7587 + 0\cdot6815}{6 + 6}$$
$$= 0\cdot1200.$$

Both $\bar{x}_A$ and $\bar{x}_B$ are means of seven observations, and therefore

$$V(\bar{x}_A) = V(\bar{x}_B) = \frac{s^2}{7}.$$

Hence, from equation (2.3),

$$V(R) = \frac{s^2}{\bar{x}_A^2} \left[\frac{1}{7} + \frac{R^2}{7} \right]$$
$$= \frac{0\cdot1200}{(1\cdot68)^2} \times \left[\frac{1}{7} + \frac{(1\cdot18)^2}{7} \right]$$
$$= 0\cdot0145,$$

and
$$R = 1\cdot18 \pm 0\cdot120.$$

A convenient method of summarizing the results of an assay, and one that is adopted throughout this book, is to quote limits within which the unknown true potency is almost certain to lie. Complete certainty in any one instance is impossible, but rules of calculation can ensure that the statement has a high probability of being correct. Two systems of inference, that of *confidence intervals* and that of *fiducial intervals* (Kendall & Stuart, 1961, Ch. 20, 21),. are in common use for problems of this nature in all branches of statistical science. The logical difference between them is important to the theorist, but this is not the place for discussing it. In practice, for many simple problems the two give identical intervals, but this is not invariably true. Indeed, Fieller's theorem (§ 2.5), which is of great importance to the methods of statistical analysis in this book and which unquestionably provides fiducial limits for estimates of relative potency, is believed by some not to give valid confidence limits. Throughout this book, fiducial inference will be used, though (as in the next paragraph) limits quoted are sometimes approximations to true fiducial limits based upon inadequate statistical theory.

In the present assay, s^2 is based on 12 degrees of freedom, and the corresponding t-deviate for a probability of 0·05 is 2·18 (Appendix Table I ; Fisher and Yates, 1963, Table III). The 95 per cent. fiducial range will therefore extend $2·18 \times 0·120$, or 0·26 on either side of R: the fiducial limits may be written (*cf.* Fisher, 1960, § 62)

$$R_L = 0·92,$$
$$R_U = 1·44.$$

With a degree of confidence expressed by the 95 per cent. probability level, 1 c.c. of A may be asserted to be not less potent than 0·92 c.c. of B, and not more potent than 1·44 c.c. of B.

This is simple enough, and in fact the result is very close to that from the preferred system of calculation described later (§ 2.10). A complication occurs if the potency of ouabain is to be considered. For the nine cats in this group

$$S (x - \bar{x})^2 = 358·4361 - 336·7225$$
$$= 21·7136.$$

In order to avoid additional problems arising in the simultaneous testing of the three preparations, the tincture A data will now be ignored. An assumption of equal variance per cat for tincture B and ouabain would be quite contrary to the evidence of much greater variability for ouabain. Separate variances for the two groups must therefore be taken as

$$s_B^2 = \frac{0 \cdot 6815}{6} = 0 \cdot 1136,$$

and

$$s_0^2 = \frac{21 \cdot 7136}{8} = 2 \cdot 714.$$

In § 2.3, a value of $0 \cdot 325$ was obtained for R, and equation (2.3) gives

$$V(R) = \frac{1}{(6 \cdot 12)^2} \times \left[\frac{0 \cdot 1136}{7} + \frac{2 \cdot 714 \times (0 \cdot 325)^2}{9} \right]$$
$$= 0 \cdot 001284,$$

whence

$$R = 0 \cdot 325 \pm 0 \cdot 036.$$

This standard error, however, cannot be used so simply for the assessment of fiducial limits to R, for, even on the assumption of normality for the distributions of tolerances of the two preparations, the t distribution is not applicable to a standard error compounded of two independent variance estimates. For safety, a t-deviate with 6 degrees of freedom might be used, but in reality some modification in theory is needed. Though the difficulty is best removed by a logarithmic transformation, as described in § 2.9, a less satisfactory alternative that is closely related to the method of this section will be given in § 2.8.

2.5 Fieller's theorem

A theorem on the fiducial limits of a ratio may conveniently be introduced at this point ; it is not essential here, but will be required in later chapters. This theorem was first given in its general form by Fieller (1940), though the particular case of zero covariance had been used earlier, for example by Bliss (1935b).

Suppose that α, β are two parameters, and write

$$\mu = \frac{\alpha}{\beta} \cdot \tag{2.4}$$

Suppose further that a, b are unbiased estimates of α, β, obtained as linear functions of a set of observations with normally distributed errors ; the typical situation is that in which a, b are means, differences between means, or regression coefficients calculated from experimental data. Freedom from bias means that

$$E\,(a) = \alpha,$$
$$E\,(b) = \beta,$$

where $E\,(a)$, the *expectation* of a is the limit of the mean value of a obtainable by infinite repetition of the experiment producing the observations. Moreover, if s^2 is an error mean square with f degrees of freedom from the analysis of variance of the data, the variances of a, b, and their covariance may be expressed as $s^2 v_{11}$, $s^2 v_{22}$, and $s^2 v_{12}$ respectively ; v_{11}, v_{22}, and v_{12} depend only on the design of the experiment and on the coefficients of the observations in the definitions of a, b. For example, if a is the arithmetic mean of certain observations, v_{11} is the reciprocal of the number of observations used in a, or if a is a regression coefficient of y on x, v_{11} is the reciprocal of the sum of squares of deviations of the values of x about their mean. Now

$$m = \frac{a}{b} \tag{2.5}$$

will naturally be taken as an estimate of μ ; Fieller's theorem states that upper and lower fiducial limits to μ are*

$$m_L, m_U = \left[m - \frac{g v_{12}}{v_{22}} \pm \frac{ts}{b} \left\{ v_{11} - 2m v_{12} + m^2 v_{22} \right. \right.$$
$$\left. \left. - g \left(v_{11} - \frac{v^2_{12}}{v_{22}} \right) \right\}^{\frac{1}{2}} \right] \div (1 - g). \tag{2.6}$$

In this formula, t is the ordinary t-deviate (Appendix Table I), with f degrees of freedom and at the chosen probability level, and

$$g = \frac{t^2 s^2 v_{22}}{b^2}. \tag{2.7}$$

The proof follows immediately from consideration of the expression $(a - \mu b)$. For any μ, this also is a linear function of the observations ;

---

* The symbol ' $\pm$ ' is generally used to introduce a standard error. In the calculation of fiducial limits, however, by Fieller's theorem or one of its analogues, the symbol is used to indicate the two alternative operations of subtraction and addition that must be used in order to form the lower and upper limits.

it is therefore normally distributed with
$$E(a - \mu b) = \alpha - \mu \beta = 0,$$
and has an estimated variance
$$V(a - \mu b) = s^2 (v_{11} - 2\mu v_{12} + \mu^2 v_{22}),$$
with f degrees of freedom. Hence, with a probability appropriate to the value of t used,
$$(a - \mu b)^2 \leqslant t^2 s^2 (v_{11} - 2\mu v_{12} + \mu^2 v_{22}), \qquad (2.8)$$
and the equality sign gives a quadratic equation in μ, whose solution is (2.6).

This theorem is required frequently in biological assay, as a method of assigning fiducial limits to a ratio of two means, a ratio of two regression coefficients, or a horizontal distance between two regression lines (for the latter is expressed algebraically in terms of the ratio of a difference of two means to a regression coefficient). When b is large compared with its standard error, g will be small. If g is neglected, (2.6) becomes

$$m_L, m_U = m \pm \frac{ts}{b} (v_{11} - 2mv_{12} + m^2 v_{22})^{\frac{1}{2}}, \qquad (2.9)$$

a result the same as would be derived from use of the approximate 'naive' formula for the variance of m

$$V(m) = \frac{s^2}{b^2} (v_{11} - 2mv_{12} + m^2 v_{22}). \qquad (2.10)$$

If $v_{12} = 0$, as must be true when a and b are formed from different observations, equation (2.10) reduces to (2.3).

When g is less than 0·05, which requires that (for the 0·95 probability level) b is at least nine times its standard error, equations (2.3) and (2.9) are good enough for most practical purposes. When g exceeds 0·2, the width of the fiducial interval will be much understated by use of variance formulae. Since calculation of (2.6) is easily adopted as a routine, it is made the standard practice throughout this book. Difficulties arise if g exceeds 1·0, as b is then not significantly different from zero. The fiducial interval is then infinite in extent (perhaps with a central finite section excluded; Fieller, 1954), and, taken alone, the data must be regarded as valueless for estimating μ.

2.6 The Behrens distribution

In the form just quoted, Fieller's theorem is not applicable to all the situations in which fiducial limits to a ratio are needed in biological assay. Complications arise when more than one error mean square occurs. Similar formulae based on the Behrens distribution instead of the t distribution can be used for data involving two independent mean squares; these are needed in the problem of ouabain potency discussed in §§ 2.4, 2.8, and, for example, in assays using complex designs such as those of Chapter 9. The main properties of this distribution will be summarized before the fiducial limit formulae are discussed.

Suppose that a, b are unbiased estimates of α, β, again defined as linear functions of observations with normally distributed errors, but now with variances

$$V(a) = s_1^2 v_{11},$$
$$V(b) = s_2^2 v_{22},$$

and zero covariance, where s_1^2, s_2^2 are independent mean squares with f_1, f_2 degrees of freedom respectively. Then the variance of $(a - b)$ is estimated as

$$V(a - b) = s_1^2 v_{11} + s_2^2 v_{22}.$$

If s_1^2, s_2^2 were the same mean square, the deviation of $(a - b)$ from its expectation divided by the estimated standard error,

$$\frac{(a - b) - (\alpha - \beta)}{(s_1^2 v_{11} + s_2^2 v_{22})^{\frac{1}{2}}}, \tag{2.11}$$

would follow the t distribution with f degrees of freedom, a result which is the basis of § 2.5. When s_1^2, s_2^2 are independent mean squares, however, this is no longer true, and the distribution of the ratio (2.11) is the Behrens distribution (Appendix Table III; Fisher and Yates, 1963, Table V_1). The ratio is known as the Sukhatme d-statistic. Its distribution is defined in terms of the degrees of freedom f_1, f_2, and the angle θ such that

$$\tan \theta = \sqrt{\left(\frac{s_1^2 v_{11}}{s_2^2 v_{22}} \right)}. \tag{2.12}$$

When θ is $0°$, the distribution of d is the same as that of t with f_2 degrees of freedom ; when θ is $90°$, the distribution is that of t with f_1 degrees of freedom. For other angles, the value of d for any probability level is generally (but not always) intermediate between $t_{[f_1]}$ and $t_{[f_2]}$. When $f_1 = f_2$, the value of d for any probability level is about equal to, but a little less than, the corresponding t, irrespective of the size of θ. The d-test provides a test of significance for the difference between two means, or two regression coefficients, whose variances are based on independent mean squares; it avoids the assumption, essential to the t-test, that the two mean squares are estimates of the same population value and may be pooled. (The assumption that the ratio (2.11) can be referred to the t distribution is often made, but is theoretically wrong and may be seriously misleading if f_1 and f_2 are small.)

Suppose now that a and b are as before, but are known to be estimates of the same quantity (so that $\alpha = \beta$). They may, for example, be two estimates of the same mean from different sets of observations with different variances, or two estimates of a regression coefficient. Then the most precise estimate that can be compounded of a and b is a weighted mean having the reciprocals of the variances as weights; this mean is $\bar{a}$, where

$$\bar{a} \left(\frac{1}{s_1^2 v_{11}} + \frac{1}{s_2^2 v_{22}} \right) = \frac{a}{s_1^2 v_{11}} + \frac{b}{s_2^2 v_{22}}, \tag{2.13}$$

and

$$V(\bar{a}) = \left(\frac{1}{s_1^2 v_{11}} + \frac{1}{s_2^2 v_{22}} \right)^{-1} \tag{2.14}$$

Yates (1939) and Finney (1951b) have pointed out that the deviation of $\bar{a}$ from α, divided by its standard error,

$$(\bar{a} - \alpha) \left(\frac{1}{s_1^2 v_{11}} + \frac{1}{s_2^2 v_{22}} \right)^{\frac{1}{2}} \tag{2.15}$$

follows the Behrens distribution with degrees of freedom f_1, f_2, and an angle θ defined by

$$\tan \theta = \sqrt{\left(\frac{s_2^2 v_{22}}{s_1^2 v_{11}} \right)}. \tag{2.16}$$

Hence the same distribution may be used in testing the significance of the deviation of a weighted mean, $\bar{a}$, from a theoretical value; alternatively, it may be used to assign fiducial limits to α, which are placed at

$$d \left(\frac{1}{s^2 v_{11}} + \frac{1}{s^2 v_{22}} \right)^{-\frac{1}{2}}$$

on either side of $\bar{a}$, d being taken as the tabular value for the chosen probability level. This neglects information on the distribution of $\bar{a}$ provided by the magnitude of $(a - b)$; Fisher (1961a, b) has shown how to take account of the information, which may be important, but no tables exist.

2.7 Two analogues of Fieller's theorem

The Behrens distribution may be used to give two results analogous to Fieller's theorem (Finney, 1951b). Suppose that a and b are exactly as specified in § 2.6, and that again the ratio

$$\mu = \frac{\alpha}{\beta}$$

is to be estimated. The ratio of $(a - \mu b)$ to its standard error estimated from

$$V(a - \mu b) = s_1^2 v_{11} + u^2 s_2^2 v_{22}$$

follows the Behrens distribution, with f_1, f_2 degrees of freedom and an angle θ given by

$$\tan \theta = \frac{1}{\mu} \sqrt{\left(\frac{s_1^2 v_{11}}{s_2^2 v_{22}} \right)}. \tag{2.17}$$

By an argument like that in § 2.5, the fiducial limits are shown to be the roots of the quadratic equation

$$(a - \mu b)^2 = d^2 (s_1^2 v_{11} + \mu^2 s_2^2 v_{22}). \tag{2.18}$$

Since d is dependent upon θ, which is in turn a function of μ, no explicit solution of equation (2.18) can be given. The solution may be written as

$$m_L, m_U = \left[m \pm \frac{d}{b} \left\{ s_1^2 v_{11} (1 - g) + m^2 s_2^2 v_{22} \right\}^{\frac{1}{2}} \right] \div (1 - g), \tag{2.19}$$

where

$$g = \frac{d^2 s_2^2 v_{22}}{b^2}; \tag{2.20}$$

numerical evaluation of m_L, m_U, however, requires interpolation or iteration, since each must have its value of d corresponding to the θ given by equation (2.17) when the fiducial limit itself is substituted for μ. The procedure will be made clear by an example in § 2.8.

The second analogue of Fieller's theorem is computationally simpler than the first, since it requires no iterative calculations; its statement, however, is more complicated and its usefulness will not be apparent until Chapter 9 is reached. Suppose that a_1, b_1

are defined as were a, b in § 2.5, having variances $s_1^2 v_{11}$, $s_1^2 v_{22}$ and covariance $s_1^2 v_{12}$ based upon a single mean square, s_1^2, with f_1 degrees of freedom. Suppose also that a second pair of estimates, a_2, b_2, of α, β, have the property that their variances and covariance, based upon a second mean square, s_2^2, with f_2 degrees of freedom, have the same ratios to one another as before : thus the variances and covariance for a_2, b_2, may be written $s_2^2 k v_{11}$, $s_2^2 k v_{22}$, $s_2^2 k v_{12}$, where k is known. The second result in § 2.6 may then be adapted to finding fiducial limits to a ratio of weighted means of a_1, a_2 and b_1, b_2.

The theorem in § 2.5 would apply directly to the determination of fiducial limits for a_1/b_1 or a_2/b_2 as estimates of μ. It is reasonable to suppose that, if mean values $\bar{a}$, $\bar{b}$ are determined by weighting inversely as the variances, so that

$$\bar{a} \left(\frac{1}{s_1^2 v_{11}} + \frac{1}{s_2^2 k v_{11}} \right) = \frac{a_1}{s_1^2 v_{11}} + \frac{a_2}{s_2^2 k v_{11}} \tag{2.21}$$

and

$$\bar{b} \left(\frac{1}{s_1^2 v_{22}} + \frac{1}{s_2^2 k v_{22}} \right) = \frac{b_1}{s_1^2 v_{22}} + \frac{b_2}{s_2^2 k v_{22}}, \tag{2.22}$$

the ratio

$$\bar{m} = \frac{\bar{a}}{\bar{b}} \tag{2.23}$$

will be a more precise estimate of μ than either m_1 or m_2. Now

$$V(\bar{a}) = v_{11} \left(\frac{1}{s_1^2} + \frac{1}{k s_2^2} \right)^{-1}$$

$$V(\bar{b}) = v_{22} \left(\frac{1}{s_1^2} + \frac{1}{k s_2^2} \right)^{-1},$$

and the covariance of $\bar{a}$, $\bar{b}$ is

$$C(\bar{a}, \bar{b}) = v_{12} \left(\frac{1}{s_1^2} + \frac{1}{k s_2^2} \right)^{-1}.$$

The important point is that the weights used in the formation of $\bar{a}$, $\bar{b}$ are proportional, and the variances and covariance of the weighted means therefore preserve the same ratios as those of a_1, b_1 and a_2, b_2. Consideration of $(\bar{a} - \mu \bar{b})$ then shows that the fiducial limits of $\bar{m}$ are the roots of the quadratic

$$(\bar{a} - \mu b)^2 = \frac{d^2 \left(v_{11} - 2\mu v_{12} + \mu^2 v_{22}\right)}{\dfrac{1}{s_1^2} + \dfrac{1}{ks_2^2}}, \tag{2.24}$$

where d is a tabular value for f_1, f_2 degrees of freedom and

$$\tan \theta = \frac{s_2 \sqrt{k}}{s_1}. \tag{2.25}$$

If s^2 be defined by

$$s^2 = \left(\frac{1}{s_1^2} + \frac{1}{ks_2^2}\right)^{-1}, \tag{2.26}$$

equation (2.24) becomes identical with the equality in (2.8), except that d replaces t. Hence the solution of equation (2.24) may be written in the same form as equation (2.6):

$$\bar{m}_L, \bar{m}_U = \left[\bar{m} - \frac{g v_{12}}{v_{22}} \pm \frac{ds}{b} \left\{ v_{11} - 2\bar{m}v_{12} + \bar{m}^2 v_{22} \right. \right.$$
$$\left. \left. - g \left(v_{11} - \frac{v_{12}^2}{v_{22}}\right) \right\}^{\frac{1}{2}} \right] \div (1 - g) \tag{2.27}$$

where

$$g = \frac{d^2 s^2 v_{22}}{b^2}. \tag{2.28}$$

At first sight, the condition that the variances and covariances of a_2, b_2 should be in the same ratio as those of a_1, b_1 might seem to be so restrictive as to make the theorem useless. The condition will automatically be fulfilled, however, by two experiments of the same basic design but possibly different replication—for example, two randomized block experiments for the same treatments, but with different numbers of blocks. The result is therefore useful in the combination of evidence from two assays. Fieller's theorem may be regarded as a particular case of equation (2.27), obtained as a limit when ks_2^2 becomes large: the information on μ provided by a_2, b_2 then becomes negligible, $\bar{m}$ is identical with m_1, and d becomes t for f_1 degrees of freedom.

By generalization of the Behrens distribution so as to include more than two component variances, a result analogous to that in the second part of § 2.6 could be obtained for a weighted mean of several estimates, and this could form the basis of a further generalization of equation (2.27). The principle is obvious, the labour of tabulating the distribution great. Enough has been said of the general theory for the present, though the problem will be raised again in Chapter 14.

2.8 Fiducial limits in the strophanthus assay

If the tolerances of individual cats are assumed to be normally distributed with constant variance, Fieller's theorem is directly applicable to the calculation of fiducial limits for the potency of tincture A relative to tincture B. From § 2.4,

$$s^2 v_{11} = s^2 v_{22} = \frac{0 \cdot 1200}{7},$$

and

$$v_{12} = 0.$$

Hence

$$g = \frac{(2 \cdot 18)^2 \times 0 \cdot 1200}{(1 \cdot 68)^2 \times 7}$$

$$= 0 \cdot 0289,$$

a value small enough to be practically negligible. Consequently, the theorem will give limits almost the same as the approximate values based on equation (2.3). The limits are

$$R_L, R_U = \left[1 \cdot 18 \pm \frac{2 \cdot 18}{1 \cdot 68} \left\{ \frac{0 \cdot 1200}{7} \times (0 \cdot 9711 + 1 \cdot 18^2) \right\}^{\frac{1}{2}} \right] \div 0 \cdot 9711$$

$$= 0 \cdot 95, \ 1 \cdot 48,$$

and, as a more exact statement than that in § 2.4, 1 c.c. of A may be asserted to have a potency lying between 0·95 c.c. and 1·48 c.c. of B.

For the ouabain assay, the evident inequality of variances makes necessary an application of the first analogue of Fieller's theorem (§ 2.7). Again from § 2.4,

$$s_1^2 v_{11} = \frac{0 \cdot 1136}{7} = 0 \cdot 01623,$$

$$s_2^2 v_{22} = \frac{2 \cdot 714}{9} = 0 \cdot 3016,$$

and

$$v_{12} = 0.$$

Hence

$$\sqrt{\left(\frac{s_1^2 v_{11}}{s_2^2 v_{22}} \right)} = 0 \cdot 2320.$$

The Sukhatme d for $f_1 = 6$, $f_2 = 8$, at the 5 per cent. probability level, may for a start be taken roughly as 2·36 (Appendix Table III ; Fisher and Yates, 1963, Table V_1). Using the standard error of R quoted in § 2.4, the limits are found to be approximately 0·085 on either side of R, or 0·240, 0·410 ; these must be used in an iterative evaluation of R_L, R_U by equation (2.19). From the approximate lower limit, by equation (2.17)

$$\tan \theta = \frac{0.2320}{0.240} = 0.97,$$

whence

$$\theta = 44°.$$

For this angle, the table of the Behrens distribution states that

$$d = 2.362,$$

and therefore, by equation (2.20),

$$g = \frac{(2.362)^2 \times 0.3016}{(6.12)^2}$$
$$= 0.0449.$$

The lower limit may be recalculated by equation (2.19) as

$$R_L = \left[0.325 - \frac{2.362}{6.12} \{0.9551 \times 0.01623 \right.$$
$$\left. + (0.325)^2 \times 0.3016\}^{\frac{1}{2}} \right] \div 0.9551$$
$$= [0.325 - 0.084] \div 0.9551$$
$$= 0.252.$$

This must be substituted in equation (2.17) to give a new angle, $\theta = 43°$. The calculations should be repeated with the new θ, but the change from 44° to 43° scarcely alters R_L and the iteration can stop at the value found. For the upper limit, the first approximation gives

$$\tan \theta = \frac{0.2320}{0.410} = 0.566,$$

whence

$$\theta = 30°.$$

Therefore

$$d = 2.331,$$

giving

$$g = \frac{(2{\cdot}331)^2 \times 0{\cdot}3016}{(6{\cdot}12)^2}$$
$$= 0{\cdot}0438$$

and, by equation (2.19),

$$R_U = \left[0{\cdot}325 + \frac{2{\cdot}331}{6{\cdot}12} \{0{\cdot}9562 \times 0{\cdot}01623 \right.$$
$$\left. + (0{\cdot}325)^2 \times 0{\cdot}3016\}^{\frac{1}{2}} \right] \div 0{\cdot}9562$$

$$= [0{\cdot}325 + 0{\cdot}083] \div 0{\cdot}9562$$
$$= 0{\cdot}427.$$

The slight change in θ now required, from 30° to 29°, has little effect on the calculations. Thus the estimated potency, 0·325 c.c. of tincture B per mg. ouabain, is assigned fiducial limits of 0·252 c.c. per mg. and 0·427 c.c. per mg.

2.9 Dilution assays

The process of estimating potency and assessing fiducial limits must take some account of the nature of the frequency distribution of tolerances. This distribution will be discussed in Chapter 17, but some thought needs to be given to it here. The analyses made in §§ 2.4, 2.8 have assumed that the tolerances of individuals for a particular preparation, in respect of the stimulus and response used, are normally distributed. Moreover, as the two examples in § 2.8 illustrate, the calculations are much easier if the variance per response is the same for all preparations involving one type of stimulus. In statistical analyses of experimental data, the assumption of normality is often made without any consideration of the possible consequences of its failure to correspond to reality. Fortunately, by virtue of the central limit theorem (Cramér, 1946, § 17.4; Kendall & Stuart, 1963), unless the basic distribution of tolerances is very different from the normal form, the distribution of means of a number of measurements is likely to be satisfactorily approximated by the normal, and application of techniques developed for the normal distribution is not likely to be seriously misleading on this score. Nevertheless, further examination of the principles involved in the analyses of earlier sections is desirable and helpful.

In many assays, the test preparation behaves as though it were simply a dilution (or a concentration) of the standard preparation in a diluent that is completely inert in respect of the response used. Thompson (1948) has pointed out that not all valid assays need be of this character ; assays in current use, however, are almost all either strictly or approximately *dilution assays*, to which category the theory and methods of this book are restricted. In some assays, there may be strong reasons for believing that all constituents of the test preparation other than one are without effect on the response of the subjects. An assay of the preparation against a standard preparation of the effective constituent is then equivalent to an analysis for determining its content of the constituent : this may be described as an *analytical dilution assay*. In other circumstances, the two preparations may for assay purposes behave as though qualitatively the same in effective constituent, though in fact they are known not to be the same ; the statistical methods appropriate to analytical assays may still be useful for arriving at convenient summaries of results, but such a *comparative dilution assay* is of more limited value as a basis for inference. For example, two insecticides, of related but different chemical composition, in their effects on one species of insect may behave as though one was a dilution of the other, though the apparent ' dilution ' may depend upon the species or upon the conditions of experiment. Nevertheless, a relative potency figure may still be useful as a concise expression of the results of a particular experiment.

For two preparations, A and B, suppose that any pair of equivalent doses is represented by x_A, x_B, and that B behaves exactly as a dilution of A by a factor ρ, the relative potency. This implies that

$$\rho x_A = x_B, \qquad (2.29)$$

for all possible pairs of doses, x_A, x_B. Consequently, whatever the form of the distributions of tolerances, the variance of the B distribution must be ρ^2 times that of the A distribution. When ρ is near to unity, as for the two strophanthus tinctures in Table 2.1, little harm will result from an assumption of equality of variance. When ρ is very different from unity, however, as in the comparison of the ouabain preparation with strophanthus, the inconsistency of this assumption may have more serious consequences and lead to wrong conclusions.

Equation (2.29) may be written

$$\log x_{\mathrm{A}} + \log \rho = \log x_{\mathrm{B}}, \qquad (2.30)$$

which shows that the distributions of the logarithms of equivalent doses of A and B must be identical, except for a shift of log ρ in the mean. In particular, the variances of the log tolerances of the two distributions are necessarily the same. This suggests that an analysis in terms of log doses may be more satisfactory than one in absolute units. Moreover, a little consideration shows that normality of distribution is more likely to be found in logarithmic units. A tolerance distribution must be curtailed at zero, since all doses must be positive, yet it need not have any sharply defined upper limit ; the distribution is therefore likely to be positively skewed. Logarithmic doses are measured on a scale which can extend from large negative to large positive values, and, *a priori*, the distribution seems more likely to be symmetrical. Investigations such as those of Bliss and Hanson (1939) and Bliss (1944*a*) have shown that a normal distribution of log tolerances is often a good approximation to the truth.

In direct assays, the assumption of a normal distribution of log tolerances, if admissible, has many advantages. All variance estimates may be pooled in order to give the best possible estimate of the population variance, so allowing a more precise estimation than if each preparation must provide its own. Also, since the estimate of relative potency is obtained as the antilogarithm of the difference of two means, instead of as a ratio of two means, fiducial limits are calculated from simple standard error formulæ without the use of Fieller's theorem. Of course, these would be specious arguments for the logarithmic transformation of doses without some reason for accepting its assumptions. There can scarcely be any demonstration that normality represents absolute truth, but use of the normal distribution is as reasonable here as in the many other branches of statistical science in which it is regularly applied. Experimental evidence indicates that normality is at least not violently in conflict with the facts, and the central limit theorem is a fair insurance that the approach to normality of distributions of mean values will improve as the number of observations is increased. Undoubtedly there are philosophical objections to the assumption, but in general the alternatives are less attractive :

(i) No alternative parametric formulation of the distribution has even as strong a theoretical justification as the normal. Except where experimental evidence strongly indicates a specific alternative as desirable, to adopt one is likely to be analytically more complicated, and to remove the comfort of the central limit theorem, without any compensating advantage.

(ii) Non-parametric methods have been developed in recent years for a number of statistical problems. Satisfactory non-parametric methods for biological assay have not yet been reported, and, even if they are found, they are likely to involve considerable sacrifice of information contained in the data. When the form of the tolerance distribution is unknown, to assess exactly the worth of numerical observations is difficult ; nevertheless, to deny all knowledge of even an approximation to the distribution of tolerances or to deny all value in the data save as indicators of rank order seems deplorably wasteful.

(iii) The third alternative is to deny the possibility of making any quantitative assessment of relative potency from experimental data of the kind here described. Those who adopt this point of view will be spared any need of reading further in a book which accepts the opposite as axiomatic. They must not imagine, however, that they are at liberty to reject the more sophisticated statistical techniques, but to retain the more primitive ones to which they may have been longer accustomed. To reject the methods of analysis illustrated in § 2.10 or later in this book, on the grounds that the conditions of the statistical theory are not exactly fulfilled, and then to adopt the methods of §§ 2.3, 2.4 or the standard curve method of § 3.14 because they appear simple common sense, would be as irrational as to refute Newton's cosmology by appeal to Einstein and then to accept Ptolemaic views because ' obviously the sun goes round the earth '. Old and new statistical methods rest upon similar foundations, but the new at least have a self-consistency that the old often lack.

2.10 Revised computations for the strophanthus assay

The computational advantages of the assumption of normality of the log tolerance distribution are readily seen by application to the data of Table 2.1. The logarithms of the tolerances in that table are shown in Table 2.2, together with calculations leading to the sums of squares of deviations ; the symbol x is now used for log dose, instead of for absolute dose, in accordance with the convention of § 3.8. As shown by equation (2.30), homogeneity of variance is a necessary condition for fundamental validity, the basic hypothesis of a dilution assay (§ 15.1). Inspection of the

TABLE 2.2—Logarithms of the tolerances shown in Table 2.1

Preparation	Strophanthus A	Strophanthus B	Ouabain
Tolerances ...	0·190 0·199 0·233 0·158 0·093 0·276 0·369 —	0·384 0·267 0·301 0·356 0·230 0·167 0·342 —	0·718 0·996 0·678 0·814 0·825 0·760 0·693 0·661 0·825
Total ...	1·518	2·047	6·970
Mean ...	0·217	0·292	0·774
Sum of squares ...	0·3759 0·3292	0·6338 0·5986	5·4858 5·3979
S_{xx}	0·0467	0·0352	0·0879

sums of squares is sufficient to show that the mean squares for the three preparations do not differ significantly. If a proper test of this were needed, Bartlett's test for the homogeneity of a set of variances might be used (§ 3.11), but here it is sufficient to note that the ratio of the largest mean square to the smallest,

$$F = \frac{0 \cdot 0879}{8} \div \frac{0 \cdot 0352}{6}$$

$$= 1 \cdot 87,$$

is far from being judged significant even by a variance ratio test that makes no allowance for the selection of extremes.

The variance per cat is therefore estimated with 20 degrees of freedom as

$$s^2 = \frac{0 \cdot 0467 + 0 \cdot 0352 + 0 \cdot 0879}{6 + 6 + 8}$$

$$= 0 \cdot 00849.$$

The symbol M is generally used to represent the estimate of log potency, as an abbreviation for log R ; equation (2.30) shows that, in the notation now adopted, its value for these data is given by

$$M = \bar{x}_B - \bar{x}_A \qquad (2.31)$$
$$= 0 \cdot 075.$$

Moreover, the variance of M is given quite simply by

$$V(M) = s^2 \left(\frac{1}{N_B} + \frac{1}{N_A} \right) \qquad (2.32)$$

$$= 0 \cdot 00849 \left(\frac{1}{7} + \frac{1}{7} \right)$$

$$= (0 \cdot 0493)^2.$$

On the assumption of normal distribution of the log tolerances, fiducial limits to M are found exactly by direct application of the t distribution. For 20 degrees of freedom, the 5 per cent. t-deviate is $2 \cdot 086$, and therefore

$$M_L = 0 \cdot 075 - 2 \cdot 086 \times 0 \cdot 0493 = \bar{1} \cdot 972$$
$$M_U = 0 \cdot 075 + 2 \cdot 086 \times 0 \cdot 0493 = 0 \cdot 178.$$

The antilogarithms of M and its limits give the relative potency and its limits : these are $1 \cdot 19$ c.c. per c.c. with limits at $0 \cdot 94$ c.c. per c.c. and $1 \cdot 51$ c.c. per c.c., almost identical with the results in § 2.8. Similarly, for the potency of the ouabain preparation relative to B,

$$M = 0 \cdot 292 - 0 \cdot 774$$
$$= \bar{1} \cdot 518 ;$$

also

$$V(M) = s^2 \left(\frac{1}{7} + \frac{1}{9} \right)$$

$$= (0 \cdot 0464)^2,$$

and therefore

$$M_L, \ M_U = \bar{1} \cdot 421, \ \bar{1} \cdot 615.$$

Hence the potency of ouabain is estimated as 0·330 c.c. per mg., with limits at 0·264 c.c. per mg., 0·412 c.c. per mg. The fiducial range is appreciably narrower than that calculated in § 2.8, primarily because of the greater number of degrees of freedom available for calculation of the variance.

2.11 Adjustment for body weight

The tolerances shown in Table 2.1 were expressed as amounts per kg. body weight of cat.   This is a common practice in pharmacological assays, at least when there is some evidence that large subjects tend to have greater tolerances than small.   In vitamin assays, on the other hand, the practice seems to be to disregard the possibility that the dose which produces a specified response is correlated with the size of the subject.   Provided that subjects are assigned to preparations entirely at random, or in accordance with some restricted form of experimental design for which the appropriate statistical analysis is made, either method is legitimate in the sense that it should lead to a valid estimate of potency.   The choice between them may be made on the basis of precision of estimation.

When information on body weight is available, to ignore its possible correlation with tolerance is wasteful.   Equally undesirable, however, is a too ready assumption that, because some relationship between weight and tolerance may exist, the adjustment of doses by proportionality is ideal (Braun and Siegfried, 1947).   Administration of therapeutic doses to human beings according to such a rule, for example, would almost certainly require extremes of dose greater than physicians would sanction.   Where the range of body weights is not great, the proportional adjustment may prove fairly satisfactory, though perhaps not a great improvement on the use of unadjusted doses.   For a wider range, however, proportional adjustment may sometimes represent so serious an over-simplication of the weight-tolerance relationship as to do more harm than good.

A better procedure is to make the data determine their own adjustment, by means of an analysis of covariance.   This involves finding a regression coefficient of log dose on log weight, and using the coefficient to adjust mean log doses to a standard weight.   A zero regression coefficient corresponds to absence of any need for adjustment, and a coefficient of unity corresponds to the proportional adjustment. Intermediate values will sometimes occur, however, as also may values that exceed unity or are negative ; for such data, neglect of any adjustment, or a dogmatic assumption that doses should be expressed per unit of body weight, will lead to estimates of potency less precise than the best that can be formed. Moreover, the covariance technique may be easily extended so as to make adjustment for two or more concomitant observations, so resolving the dilemma of the experimenter who is unsure whether to express his doses as per unit of body weight or per unit weight of some particular organ.

The calculation of adjustments by a covariance analysis is undoubtedly a greater computational labour than adjustment by proportionality, but it does permit the adjustment to be evaluated in relation to the economy of the assay. If the labour of making the concomitant measurements for each subject (body weights, heart weights, or any others) together with the labour of statistical calculation does not increase the precision by at least as much as would an equally costly use of additional subjects, the practice of adjustment should be abandoned for that class of assays. This aspect of the problem is discussed in § 2.13.

2.12 A direct assay with covariance

The only data published for the strophanthus assay in § 2.3 are doses per unit weight. A more extensive experiment will therefore be used to illustrate the covariance technique in direct assays. The data are those of Chen *et al.* (1942), and relate to the assay of digitalis-like principles in ouabain and other cardiac substances. The method was the Hatcher and Brody (1910) technique of slow infusion of a suitable dilution of a drug into an anæsthetized cat until death occurred, at which point the dose was measured and recorded.

Three observers collaborated in tests of the following twelve drugs :

        A : α-Antiarin
        B : β-Antiarin
        C : Bufotalin
        D : Calotoxin
        E : Calotropin
        F : Convallotoxin

G :   Coumingine HCl
H :   Cymarin
I :   Emicymarin
J :   Ouabain (to be taken as the standard)
K :   Periplocymarin
L :   Uscharin.

Each drug was to be tested on twelve cats. In view of the impracticability of an observer's testing more than four cats per day, and the possibility that the general level of tolerance might change from day to day, some scheme for balancing observer differences and day differences had to be found. This was achieved by the use of a 12 × 12 Latin square (Table 2.3). The columns of this square represent the twelve cats tested on any one day ; the rows represent the first and second cat (a, b) tested by each of the observers (I, II, III) in the morning and afternoon of each day. The square was derived from the 12 × 12 Latin square given by Fisher and Yates (1963) by randomization of the order of rows (scarcely as complete a randomization as most statisticians would think desirable).

For each cat, the body weight in kg. and the heart weight in g. were measured, as well as the fatal dose of drug in μg. (The data as published showed the fatal doses expressed as proportions of body weight or heart weight, but the actual doses have been reconstructed from these). The three weights for each cat have been expressed as logarithms : in fact, for convenience of arithmetic, the data in Table 2.3 are shown as

$$x_1 = 1{,}000 \times \log \text{body weight in kg.,}$$
$$x_2 = \phantom{1{,}0}100 \times \log \text{heart weight in g.,}$$
$$x = 1{,}000 \times \log \text{dose in } \mu\text{g.,}$$

the three figures for each cat being x_1, x_2, x in that order.

The heart weight may be expected to be more valuable than the body weight in the adjustment of tolerances, but both might be useful. In the first instance, therefore, the multiple covariance analysis of x_1, x_2, x needs to be computed ; it is shown as Table 2.4. The method of computing this analysis will not be described here. The calculation of the analysis of variance for each of the three variates should be a familiar process, and those to whom the covariance calculations are new should need no more

TABLE 2.3—Tolerances of cats for various cardiac substances

(Table shows values of x_1, x_2, x, in that order, for 144 cats : for explanation, see text)

Date	6/3	7/3	8/3	9/3	13/3	14/3	16/3	21/3	24/3	27/3	30/3	3/4	Total
a.m. I a	I 359 95 525	J 410 104 273	B 323 89 315	L 363 91 557	H 208 85 189	G 290 92 228	F 375 88 54	K 323 87 473	D 273 83 165	E 270 86 254	A 336 88 193	C 271 90 358	3801 1078 3584
a.m. I b	K 424 108 737	G 304 97 345	J 262 83 195	H 425 100 425	I 346 100 444	B 439 112 350	L 344 99 557	C 312 86 209	E 280 97 335	F 247 76 22	D 300 98 605	A 371 93 237	4054 1149 4461
a.m. II a	B 314 89 293	L 336 92 427	G 329 92 371	C 384 103 413	D 359 103 515	J 450 104 307	K 355 99 446	E 261 79 301	H 352 93 266	A 286 93 368	F 274 86 198	I 357 96 515	4057 1129 4420
a.m. II b	E 309 94 299	D 424 102 437	F 363 100 411	G 359 92 400	J 225 85 173	K 353 100 661	A 324 91 250	L 410 100 449	C 402 91 573	I 327 89 316	B 395 97 347	H 253 81 228	4144 1122 4544
a.m. III a	C 289 91 601	K 306 93 398	A 381 98 400	B 422 113 502	F 426 106 385	L 294 89 443	I 337 95 329	D 260 86 394	G 435 92 444	H 361 87 377	J 336 85 307	E 353 95 247	4200 1130 4827
a.m. III b	F 231 73 35	H 313 94 355	K 263 87 384	E 375 95 451	G 247 82 378	C 230 85 444	D 372 98 394	B 291 83 211	A 288 87 218	L 336 81 442	I 258 81 473	J 257 89 239	3461 1035 4024
p.m. I a	J 323 92 376	C 341 87 540	E 406 97 350	K 364 86 512	A 356 98 501	I 383 107 674	H 316 89 256	F 239 81 126	B 284 96 253	G 401 98 336	L 366 95 373	D 260 88 132	4039 1114 4429

	1	2	3	4	5	6	7	8	9	10	11	12	Total
p.m. I b	329 / D 93 / 313	440 / F 93 / 284	358 / I 91 / 348	287 / A 90 / 326	280 / L 90 / 537	415 / E 105 / 501	330 / C 86 / 523	446 / G 108 / 402	387 / J 98 / 199	277 / B 90 / 270	388 / H 88 / 387	347 / K 96 / 473	4285 / 1128 / 4563
p.m. II a	294 / A 81 / 309	320 / B 85 / 294	357 / C 94 / 446	391 / D 94 / 336	393 / E 100 / 349	399 / F 102 / 283	356 / G 99 / 322	308 / H 88 / 377	312 / I 91 / 477	365 / J 96 / 305	249 / K 86 / 650	256 / L 85 / 580	4000 / 1101 / 4728
p.m. II b	342 / H 97 / 261	384 / E 96 / 419	357 / L 94 / 625	342 / J 97 / 368	407 / C 100 / 426	450 / A 100 / 460	281 / B 86 / 211	294 / I 91 / 348	417 / K 98 / 716	291 / D 82 / 289	248 / G 83 / 402	340 / F 100 / 181	4153 / 1124 / 4706
p.m. III a	297 / G 89 / 363	367 / I 101 / 606	372 / D 94 / 651	405 / F 106 / 360	257 / K 93 / 453	376 / H 93 / 336	321 / J 95 / 185	287 / A 91 / 205	347 / L 93 / 437	381 / C 99 / 632	253 / E 85 / 337	248 / B 76 / 167	3911 / 1115 / 4732
p.m. III b	340 / L 94 / 521	408 / A 104 / 387	386 / H 96 / 326	384 / I 103 / 692	423 / B 100 / 461	406 / D 100 / 369	350 / E 98 / 348	311 / J 93 / 313	279 / F 87 / 139	391 / K 98 / 439	301 / C 88 / 447	265 / G 85 / 398	4244 / 1146 / 4840
Total ...	3851 / 1096 / 4633	4353 / 1148 / 4765	4157 / 1115 / 4822	4501 / 1170 / 5342	3927 / 1142 / 4811	4486 / 1189 / 5056	4061 / 1123 / 3875	3742 / 1073 / 3808	4056 / 1106 / 4222	3933 / 1075 / 4050	3704 / 1060 / 4719	3578 / 1074 / 3755	48,349 / 13,371 / 53,858

Drug totals :—

	A	B	C	D	E	F	G	H	I	J	K	L
	4068	4017	4005	4037	4050	4018	3977	4028	4082	3989	4049	4029
	1114	1116	1100	1121	1127	1098	1109	1091	1140	1121	1131	1103
	3854	3674	5612	4600	4191	2478	4389	3783	5747	3240	6342	5948

instruction than that they must use products of corresponding pairs of observations or of totals in exactly the same manner as they used squares for the analyses of variance. Some of the books mentioned in § 1.5 give accounts of the method. The 11 degrees of freedom for ' rows ' in the analysis could be subdivided into the main effects of time of day (1 d.f.), observers (2 d.f.), first versus second cat (1 d.f.), and the interactions of these. In a comparative experiment these would be interesting, but they are not relevant to the problem of assay : the experimental design has deliberately been balanced in such a way as to eliminate their effects. Of course, large effects might disturb the validity of the assay, by making the error variance different for different observers, days, or times of day, but inspection of the data and of Table 2.4 makes clear that no such worries arise here. Mean squares for the analyses of variance of x_1 and x_2 are not shown in Table 2.4, but inspection of the table shows the absence of any significant differences between drugs in respect of body or heart weight ; had differences occurred, they would presumably have indicated a non-random allocation of drugs to cats, and the data then might have had to be entirely rejected.

The error line of Table 2.4 shows x to be correlated with both x_1 and x_2 taken separately, and the partial regression coefficients $b_{1.2}$ and $b_{2.1}$ therefore require to be investigated. These are the solutions of

$$341,700\, b_{1.2} + 30,995\, b_{2.1} = 250,743, \\ 30,995\, b_{1.2} + 5,185\, b_{2.1} = 35,056. $$

Hence

$$b_{1.2} = 0{\cdot}2632\,9875, \\ b_{2.1} = 5{\cdot}1870\,8874 ; $$

the large number of decimal places is desirable for the calculation of the sum of squares, with 2 degrees of freedom, accounted for by the regression, namely

$$250,743\, b_{1.2} + 35,056\, b_{2.1} = 247,859.$$

Of this amount, a regression on x_1 alone would account for

$$\frac{(250,743)^2}{341,700} = 183,998,$$

and a similar calculation may be made for x_2 alone. The analysis in Table 2.5 then follows.

TABLE 2.4—Analysis of variance and covariance for the data of Table 2.3

Adjustments for means		16,233,513	4,489,406	1,241,553	18,083,198	5,000,940	20,143,640
Nature of variation	d.f.	$S_{x_1 x_1}$	$S_{x_1 x_2}$	$S_{x_2 x_2}$	$S_{x_1 x}$	$S_{x_2 x}$	S_{xx}
Rows	11	46,707	5,833	900	51,422	7,060	121,133
Days (columns) ...	11	83,120	10,281	1,574	100,193	13,752	254,750
Drugs	11	865	212	197	11,201	5,657	1,307,259
Error	110	341,700	30,995	5,185	250,743	35,056	1,113,282
Total	143	472,392	47,321	7,856	413,559	61,525	2,796,424

Table 2.5 shows that, whereas inclusion of x_2 in a regression equation after x_1 has been used gives a significant reduction in the residual mean square, inclusion of x_1 in an equation that already contains x_2 gives scarcely any advantage. Since x_1 and x_2 are themselves fairly closely correlated, it is scarcely surprising that a regression on either accounts for much the same variation as a regression on the other. Allowance for the regression on x_2 appears

TABLE 2.5—Error regression analysis for Table 2.4

Nature of variation	d.f.	Sum of squares	Mean square
Regression on x_1 alone ...	1	183,998	
Additional for x_2	1	63,861	63,861
Regression on x_1, x_2 ...	2	247,859	
Regression on x_2 alone ...	1	237,015	
Additional for x_1	1	10,844	10,844
Regression on x_1, x_2 ...	2	247,859	
Residual	108	865,423	8,013
Total	110	1,113,282	

to be sufficient here. (The significance tests given by Table 2.5 are in fact tests of the partial regression coefficients of x on x_1, x_2). The regression coefficient on x_2 alone is

$$b_2 = \frac{35,056}{5,185}$$

$$= 6 \cdot 761.$$

Moreover, the residual variance is now

$$s^2 = \frac{1,113,282 - 237,015}{109}$$

$$= 8,039$$

with 109 degrees of freedom.   Hence, by the usual regression formula

$$V(b_2) = \frac{s^2}{S_{x_2 x_2}} \qquad (2.33)$$

$$= \frac{8,039}{5,185}$$

$$= (1 \cdot 245)^2,$$

where $S_{x_2 x_2}$ is written for the error sum of squares of x_2.   If in fact the variation in tolerance were proportional to variation in heart weight, the regression coefficient ought to be 10 in the logarithmic units used here.   Chen *et al.* suggested that the tolerance was proportional to (heart weight)$^{\frac{2}{3}}$, to which rule would correspond a regression coefficient of 6·67.   Clearly b_2 is significantly less than 10, but differs very little from 6·67.

The second column in Table 2.6 contains the mean value of x for each of the twelve drugs, unadjusted for any variation in x_2. The standard error of these means is obtained from

$$V(\bar{x}) = \frac{1,113,282}{110 \times 12}$$

$$= (29 \cdot 0)^2.$$

In order to adjust for x_2, a column of means for this variate must be added.   From the regression calculations, each observation on x is estimated to be increased by (6·761 $\times$ deviation of the corresponding x_2 from its general mean), on account of the correlation of x with x_2.   Hence each $\bar{x}$ may be adjusted to an $\bar{x}'$, the value that it would be expected to take if all cats had had the same heart weight :

$$\bar{x}' = \bar{x} - b_2(\bar{x}_2 - \bar{\bar{x}}_2), \qquad (2.34)$$

where $\bar{\bar{x}}_2$ represents the general mean.   The variance of $\bar{x}'$ is given by

$$V(\bar{x}') = s^2 \left[\frac{1}{n} + \frac{(\bar{x}_2 - \bar{\bar{x}}_2)^2}{S_{x_2 x_2}} \right], \qquad (2.35)$$

where n is the number of subjects tested for a particular dose.   Thus the variance depends upon which drug is in question, and the variance of a difference between two values of $\bar{x}'$ cannot be found simply by addition of variances.   Finney (1946a) has pointed out that, unless the concomitant variate (here x_2) varies widely in its means for different treatments (drugs), a variance averaged over all comparisons may reasonably be used ; this merely requires that the usual formulæ involving s^2 and reciprocals of numbers of replicates should be multiplied by

$$1 + \frac{\text{Mean square of } x_2 \text{ for treatments}}{\text{Error sum of squares for } x_2} \qquad (2.36)$$

in every comparison made. Here the mean square for drugs in the x_2 analysis has already been observed to be small compared with the error, and the factor (2.36) is

$$1 + \frac{197}{5,185 \times 11} = 1\cdot0035.$$

Hence

$$V(\bar{x}') = \frac{8,039}{12} \times 1\cdot0035$$
$$= (25\cdot9)^2.$$

TABLE 2.6—Unadjusted and adjusted mean log tolerances, from the data of Table 2.3

Drug	$\bar{x}$	$\bar{x}_2$	$b_2(\bar{x}_2 - \bar{\bar{x}}_2)$	$\bar{x}'$
A	321·2	92·83	− 0·1	321·3
B	306·2	93·00	1·0	305·2
C	467·7	91·67	− 8·0	475·7
D	383·3	93·42	3·9	379·4
E	349·2	93·92	7·2	342·0
F	206·5	91·50	− 9·1	215·6
G	365·8	92·42	− 2·9	368·7
H	315·2	90·92	− 13·0	328·2
I	478·9	95·00	14·5	464·4
J	270·0	93·42	3·9	266·1
K	528·5	94·25	9·5	519·0
L	495·7	91·92	− 6·3	502·0
Mean ...	374·0	92·85	0·0	374·0
Standard error	± 29·0	—	—	± 25·9

Now J, ouabain, was to be taken as the standard. The remaining steps are just as in the previous example. For drug A

$$M = \bar{x}_J - \bar{x}_A$$
$$= - 51\cdot2,$$

with a standard error obtained in the obvious manner as
$$\text{S.E. } (M) = 29{\cdot}0\sqrt{2}$$
$$= 41{\cdot}0.$$
Since x was $1{,}000 \times$ log dose,
$$\log R = \frac{M}{1{,}000}$$
$$= \bar{1}{\cdot}9488$$
and therefore
$$R = 0{\cdot}889.$$
The standard error is based upon 109 degrees of freedom, for which $t = 1{\cdot}982$; hence
$$\log R_L = \frac{(-51{\cdot}2 - 1{\cdot}982 \times 41{\cdot}0)}{1{,}000} = \bar{1}{\cdot}8675,$$
$$\log R_U = \frac{(-51{\cdot}2 + 1{\cdot}982 \times 41{\cdot}0)}{1{,}000} = 0{\cdot}0301,$$
and the fiducial limits to the estimate of relative potency are
$$R_L = 0{\cdot}737,$$
$$R_U = 1{\cdot}072.$$
These have been calculated for the unadjusted means. Exactly the same process may be applied to the $\bar{x}'$ column in Table 2·6 to give for A
$$M' = \bar{x}'_J - \bar{x}'_A$$
$$= -55{\cdot}2 \pm 36{\cdot}6,$$
whence
$$\log R' = \bar{1}{\cdot}9448,$$
$$\log R'_L = \bar{1}{\cdot}8723,$$
$$\log R'_U = 0{\cdot}0173,$$
and therefore
$$R' = 0{\cdot}881,$$
$$R'_L = 0{\cdot}745,$$
$$R'_U = 1{\cdot}041.$$
In Table 2.7 all these results are put together, and are compared with the values of R given by Chen *et al.* after calculations based upon dose per unit (heart weight)$^{\frac{2}{3}}$ in absolute, not logarithmic, units. In every case the three potency figures agree well, but the

fiducial range is narrowed a little by reason of the adjustment for heart weight.

TABLE 2.7—Estimates of relative potency and their fiducial limits,
for the data of Table 2.3

Drug	Unadjusted		Adjusted for heart weight		Chen *et al.*
	R	Limits	R	Limits	R
A	0·889	0·737–1·072	0·881	0·745–1·041	0·873
B	0·920	0·763–1·109	0·914	0·773–1·080	0·903
C	0·634	0·526–0·765	0·617	0·522–0·729	0·611
D	0·770	0·639–0·929	0·770	0·652–0·910	0·763
E	0·833	0·691–1·005	0·840	0·711–0·992	0·830
F	1·157	0·960–1·396	1·123	0·951–1·327	1·115
G	0·802	0·665–0·967	0·790	0·668–0·933	0·781
H	0·901	0·747–1·086	0·867	0·734–1·024	0·858
I	0·618	0·513–0·745	0·633	0·536–0·749	0·628
J	1·000	—	1·000	—	1·000
K	0·551	0·457–0·665	0·559	0·473–0·660	0·553
L	0·595	0·493–0·717	0·581	0·492–0·686	0·575

In practice, only the adjusted potencies would be reported, and detailed calculation of the unadjusted would not be required after a significant regression of x on x_2 had been demonstrated. A simplification in calculation would be effected by forming Table 2.6 in terms of totals of the groups of twelve subjects instead of means. Exactly the same procedure would lead to adjusted totals of x', and a number of divisions would thereby be saved. The method used here was chosen because it illustrates better the structure of the calculations, and might be required in a less symmetrical experiment.

2.13 Efficiency and utility of concomitant measurements

The gain in precision, as shown by the narrowing of the fiducial range, perhaps appears to be surprisingly small after the discovery of a highly significant regression. The gain may be best expressed in terms of the ratio of the variances of unadjusted and adjusted dose means in Table 2.6 :

$$\frac{(29\cdot0)^2}{(25\cdot9)^2} = 1\cdot25.$$

This shows a 25 per cent. increase in precision : to obtain the same precision without the covariance adjustment, 25 per cent. more cats would be needed, a total of 180 instead of 144. An increase of 36 cats would almost certainly be more expensive of time and labour than the extra computations required for the covariance analysis. On the other hand, if 180 cats were used, the same precision would be obtainable without dissection and weighing of the hearts ; whether the larger number of subjects with less labour on each would make a more economical assay is for the experimenter to judge. An important practical consideration here is that a covariance adjustment on body weight would have been almost as good as that on heart weight. In this assay, both weights were recorded, and the analysis in Table 2.5 demonstrated that adjustment for heart weights gave the greater reduction of error variance. Had the body weights been used instead, however, in a regression adjustment of the same kind, the loss of precision would have been only 6 per cent. Since presumably the determination of heart weights was a more laborious and expensive part of the experiment than that of body weights, the most efficient procedure in future assays of the same kind might be to measure body weights and to use these as the concomitant variate. The decision is not just a matter of statistical theory, but depends upon relative costs, in time, labour, or money, of various experimental operations.

Undoubtedly in this example much the same precision would have been obtained if an assumption of direct proportionality of tolerance and heart weight (or body weight) had been made, either by direct analysis of their ratio and formation of R from ratios of means (as in § 2.3) or, theoretically preferable and computationally simpler in the fiducial limit calculations for reasons already described, by a logarithmic analysis of $(x - 10x_2)$. Better still would have been an assumption of proportionality of the tolerances to (heart weight)$^{\frac{2}{3}}$, preferably by analysis of $(x - 6\cdot67x_2)$. But these are all open to the objection that the relationship is either guessed or taken from other experiments. Unless strong evidence from past similar experiments indicates that a particular adjustment is suitable, estimation of the relationship from the data of the current assay is desirable. Results based on a guessed relationship between tolerance and a concomitant variate such as heart or body weight could be even less precise than if the concomitant were ignored.

Exploration of the possibility that a simply determined concomitant measurement, such as a body weight, will improve the precision of assay results is often worth while. Complicated though the calculations may seem at first, they may take very much less time than an equivalent increase in the number of subjects. Of course, if several assays of similar character showed no increase in precision from covariance analysis, the calculations would be abandoned for further assays of that kind. A concomitant such as heart weight, which is much more trouble to measure, may give better results, but the improvement may not always compensate for the labour of measuring it. Each type of investigation needs to be considered on its own merits.

2.14   The design of direct assays

The primary object of a direct dilution assay is to obtain the most precise estimate of a difference between two mean log doses that is possible within the limits of the material available. If normality of the distribution of individual log tolerances is to be assumed, this aim is exactly of the same kind as that underlying most comparative experiments : measurements are to be made on two groups of differently treated subjects with a view to forming an estimate of the difference in means attributable to the contrast of treatments. Out of the need for planning experiments so as to give precise estimates of treatment differences has grown the subject of experimental design. The general principles of design, as described from various points of view by Cochran and Cox (1957), Cox (1958), Finney (1955, 1960), and Fisher (1960), are applicable to direct assays. An example of the use of a Latin square has been given in § 2.12, and the user of direct assay techniques needs also to be familiar with complete and incomplete randomized block designs and the simpler factorial designs. When only a single test preparation is to be assayed against a standard, little complexity will be needed. In multiple assays such as that of § 2.12, however, greater finesse is possible and often desirable.

Indirect assays, with which the remaining chapters of this book are concerned, have special problems of experimental design apart from those general to all experimentation, and these will be discussed in Chapters 6, 8, 9, 10, 11, and 19.

2.15 A criticism of direct assays

One important objection to the technique of direct assay seems to have received insufficient attention from experimenters (Bliss and Allmark, 1944), though Miles and Perry (1950) have noted a related point.   If two stimuli of unequal potency are applied at equal rates (*e.g.* two drugs infused at equal speeds), subjects receiving the less potent stimulus will have longer average times under treatment than those receiving the more potent.   If there is any time-lag in the production of effects on the subject, or any cumulative effect other than of a simply additive nature, the comparison of the two drugs will be biased.   This difficulty might be largely overcome by applying equipotent doses of each stimulus per unit of time, but that presupposes knowledge of the relative potency ; to say how much even quite small deviations from this ideal affect the validity of the potency estimate may be impossible. The question is one for the physiologist and pharmacologist to consider, in the light of their knowledge of the mode of action of the drugs or other stimuli studied, and the decision as to whether the method is valid may vary from one type of assay to another. The statistician has fulfilled his duty by giving warning of a danger which, in all the calculations of this chapter, is assumed to be unimportant.

CHAPTER 8

QUANTITATIVE DOSE-RESPONSE RELATIONSHIPS

3.1 Indirect assays

The purpose of a biological assay is to discover equally effective doses of the standard and test preparations, that is to say, doses whose inverse ratio will estimate the potency of the test preparation relative to the standard. One objection to the direct procedure described in Chapter 2, namely, bias produced by time-lag, has been mentioned in § 2.15. Even when this danger is absent, technical difficulties may prevent the experimenter from ensuring that subjects receive just the right dose to produce the characteristic response: to determine individual tolerances of cats for digitalis may require no more than reasonable skill and care, but to determine individual tolerances of aphids for an insecticide is impossible, and a different method of assay must be sought.

In an indirect assay, specified doses are given, each to several subjects, and the nature of their responses is recorded. The record for each test may state merely that a characteristic response, such as death, is or is not produced : this is a *quantal* or ' all-or-nothing ' response. Alternatively, the magnitude of some property of the subject, its weight, the weight of a particular organ, or its time of survival, may be measured ; this is a *quantitative* response. Logically, quantal response assays are closely related to direct assays, but mathematically and analytically they are more difficult, and their discussion is deferred until Chapters 17 and 18. With suitable restrictions on the choice of doses, quantitative response assays could be analysed by rejection of all observations except those which showed a specified response, and treatment of these observations as giving a direct assay. This procedure, indeed, is the basis of methods sometimes used when each subject can be tested many times ; successive adjustments of dose are tried until one which produces a certain size or character of response is found.

Unless the variance of response for a particular dose is very small, however, the method seems wasteful of effort and of information. Far more valuable is a method which takes account of the relationship between dose and the magnitude of a response. If the form of this relationship is known for the two preparations, equally effective doses may be estimated and, by appropriate statistical procedures, the precision of the corresponding estimate of potency may be assessed (Bliss, 1940b).

3.2 The dose–response regression

Consider the results obtained from subjects receiving a dose z of a particular stimulus, and suppose that the response for any subject is u. (The convention of using x for a dose, y for a response is temporarily abandoned ; z and u are intended to represent the dose and response as actually measured, x and y will be transformations of these to be used in the statistical analysis, as described later.) For a given population of subjects (or for repeated trials with the same subject, where these can be made without affecting the independence of successive responses), the average or expected response in random sampling may be written

$$E(u) = U. \tag{3.1}$$

Now a response which is to be of any use for assay purposes must clearly depend in some manner upon the dose, and, at least for assays at present in use*, this involves dependence of the expected response upon z :

$$U = F(z), \tag{3.2}$$

where $F(z)$ represents a function of z. Equation (3.2) is a regression function of u on z. At present, no restriction need be placed on the form of $F(z)$, except that it must be a single-valued real function of z for all doses in the range that interests the experimenter.

3.3 The condition of similarity

If regression functions for the standard and test preparations are

$$\left.\begin{aligned} U_S &= F_S(z), \\ U_T &= F_T(z), \end{aligned}\right\} \tag{3.3}$$

respectively, then, for a selected U, doses Z_S, Z_T of the two

---

* In theory, an assay might be based upon a system in which U was constant, but changes in z affected, say, the variance of u. This is unlikely to be of practical importance.

preparations can be defined such that the mean response to either is U. At this level of response, Z_S and Z_T are equally effective doses. Nothing that has yet been stated excludes the possibility of response curves, such as that shown in Fig. 3.2, for which the value of z corresponding to certain values of U is not uniquely determined, and a conventional rule for associating equivalent doses of the two preparations would be needed; other values of U might have no corresponding z (cf. Finney, 1952, § 41). For analytical dilution assays (see below), these difficulties disappear, because the two regression curves must then be similar in shape.

The potency of the test preparation relative to the standard, *at the level of response U*, is Z_S/Z_T, and a diagram might be constructed to represent this potency as a function of U. For two completely unrelated stimuli, the curve so obtained could be of any form, and a request that a single numerical value be assigned to the relative potency cannot be met.

Consider now the meaning of an analytical dilution assay (§ 2.9). Wood (1946a) states the basic assumptions as :

'(a) that the response supposed to be produced by the known amounts of " factor X " (*i.e.* the effective constituent of the standard preparation) is actually due to the factor itself and not to some other substance associated with it, *e.g.*, an impurity ; and (b) that the response produced by the material to be analysed is also due solely to the presence in it of " factor X ", without augmentation, diminution, or modification by any other substance also present. In other words, if we use the terms " Standard Preparation " and " Test Preparation " to denote respectively the solution of allegedly pure " factor X " and the solution prepared from the material to be analysed, we assume that the Std. Prep. contains no substance, other than factor X itself, contributing to the response we measure, and that the Test Prep. behaves for the purpose of the analysis so similarly to the Std. Prep. that it may be regarded simply as a dilution of the Std. Prep. in a completely inert diluent '.

With the convention that the term ' dilution ' includes ' concentration ', so as to cover assays in which the test preparation is more potent than the standard, this is a full description of analytical dilution assays.

If the two preparations contain the same effective constituent, (or the same effective constituents in fixed proportions to one another), and all other constituents are without effect on U, so that one behaves as a dilution of the other in an inert diluent, the potency ratio, Z_S/Z_T, must be independent of U, say

$$Z_S/Z_T = \rho. \tag{3.4}$$

Consequently, the two regression functions in equations (3.3) must be related by

$$F_T(z) = F_S(\rho z) \tag{3.5}$$

for all z, where ρ is a constant, the potency of the test preparation relative to the standard. This is the algebraic statement of the *condition of similarity*, a prerequisite of all dilution assays.

The fundamental assay problem is then as follows: A standard preparation, whose content of the effective constituent either is known or is defined in arbitrary units, has a dose-response regression function $U = F(z)$ under specified conditions of testing. A test preparation is known to have the same effective constituent, and the amount present in unit dose is to be estimated, making use of the fact that the dose-response regression function for this preparation must be $U = F(\rho z)$, where ρ is the relative potency, the number of units of effective constituent contained in or equivalent to unit dose of the test preparation. An estimate, R, of ρ must be formed from observations on dose-response tests, usually after simultaneous estimation of parameters of the regression function. An understanding of this argument is essential to the avoidance of such gross mistakes as that of Kolb *et al.* (1961), who used a ratio of mean responses as an estimate of ρ.

3.4 Assay validity

If the data from a series of tests cannot adequately be described by the same form of regression function for both preparations, either the conditions of testing have been allowed to differ for the two preparations or the basic assumption of similarity is false. Judged as a dilution assay, the assay is invalid, either because of insufficient care in the control of the experiment or because of the inherent incommensurability of the preparations. When the two regression functions are markedly different, no other conclusion can be drawn. It may sometimes happen that, over a wide range of responses, the two functions are nearly the same, so that the ratio of equally effective doses varies little in that range even though at extremes it is far from constant. Many experiments may then fail to show evidence against the condition of similarity, or may give a ratio of equally effective doses whose variations are too small to be of practical importance; in such circumstances, an average value of the ratio may still be a convenient expression of the relative potency of the preparations in the production of a particular type of response. The result of such a *comparative dilution assay* need not have any validity under conditions other than those of its estimation. In an analytical dilution assay, on the other hand, the estimate of potency should be independent of the assay technique employed, and should agree with an estimate from a process (perhaps chemical or physical) not using bioassay (Gaddum, 1950). The choice of subject, response, and experimental conditions should be irrelevant to the estimate that is formed, except in so far as they affect the precision of estimation.

This requirement that the estimate of potency be independent of the experimental method used in its determination is of great practical, as well as theoretical, importance. In an analytical dilution assay, the biological system plays a part analogous to that played by a balance in weighing an object: it is an instrument, and not a factor influencing the magnitude of the result. The practice of the W.H.O. Expert Committee on Biological Standardization is of interest in this connexion. The Committee has established standard preparations of various antitoxins, vitamins, hormones, and other drugs, the potency of each being defined in arbitrary international units (§ 1.4). The potency of a test preparation of any of these substances may be assayed by comparison with a sample of the international standard. Referring to the Commission that was the Committee's predecessor, Hartley (1935) wrote:

' As a rule a method of assay is described; while this method is one which has proved practicable and satisfactory, it is emphasized that its use is not in any way compulsory, individual workers being expected to use those methods which they have in regular use and in which they have confidence. The Commission takes the view that, while standards and units should be fixed and stable, and determinations of potency should always be carried out in strict comparison with the standard preparation (or its exact equivalent) and expressed in international units, no attempt should be made to fix or impose any particular method by which these comparative tests should be carried out. Improvement in existing methods of assay and the devising of new ones, and the progress of research, are more likely to be advanced by leaving to individual workers freedom of choice as to the method by which assays are carried out, rather than by insistence upon the details of a particular method which, on the one hand, may be difficult to describe adequately, and, on the other, may appear to give an air of finality in a field of biological standardisation in which every encouragement should be given for improvement and advance.'

The fact that two preparations give responses whose measurements agree with, or do not significantly deviate from, equation (3.5) is no demonstration that they have a common effective constituent : the condition is necessary, but not sufficient. No purely statistical process can distinguish between Wood's ' factor X ' and a chemically distinct substance that affects the measured response in the same manner. For example, Martin (1940, 1942) has found that several active principles isolated from derris root, of different (though related) chemical structure, show constant relative toxicities when used in insecticidal sprays. Under particular conditions of test, even preparations of widely different composition may act in conformity with equation (3.5). Bliss and Cattell (1943) quote instances of materials whose relative potencies in man have been found to be completely different from estimates obtained with laboratory mammals. Such assays are comparative, not analytical. The technique of statistical analysis may be the same, but the logical difference is very important, and, as Wood (1944b) has pointed out, this may affect the choice of an optimal experimental design.

3.5 Preliminary regression investigation

Before any relationship between dose and response can be made the basis of an assay, something must be known about the form of the regression function $F(z)$. Data from each single assay will not be sufficient for a study of this *ab initio*, though they may provide useful confirmation that an assumed form is not seriously wrong and may allow the estimation of one or more parameters of the function as well as of ρ. In order to establish the form of the regression function, a preliminary investigation is needed. In the past, formal study of this kind has probably seldom been made, and instead knowledge has slowly accumulated ; undoubtedly careful experimental study of $F(z)$ ought to precede any attempt to use a dose-response relationship for assay purposes. A study of this kind has been described by Bliss (1946c), and the analysis of another is illustrated in § 3.9. Wood (1946a) has emphasized the need for separating this study from regular assay work, especially because the requirements in respect of experimental design are different. In particular, for examination of the form of $F(z)$, many different values of z must be tested, but this is seldom the most economic procedure in an assay (cf. §§ 6.10, 8.4).

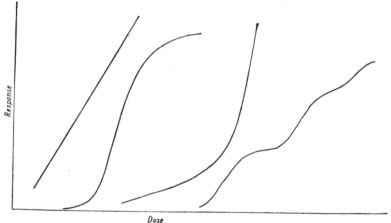

Fig. 3.1—Some examples of strictly monotonic (increasing) dose-response regression curves

3.6 The condition of monotony

For most, if not all, assays at present in use, $F(z)$ is a *strictly monotonic* function of z within the dose range of normal experimentation. Without loss of generality, attention may be restricted to increasing functions, since corresponding results for decreasing functions require only certain obvious sign changes. The general condition is that, for every pair of doses z_1, z_2, if

$$z_2 > z_1,$$

then

$$F(z_2) > F(z_1) \ ;$$

the reader should note that equality is explicitly excluded. Fig. 3.1 illustrates some strictly increasing regression functions.

Non-monotonic dose-response relationships can occur, and, provided that the condition of similarity is fulfilled, assay techniques could be based upon them. For a relationship having maxima and minima, such as is shown in Fig. 3.2, the dose of the standard preparation equipotent with certain doses of the test preparation is not uniquely determined, but equation (3.5) would still apply

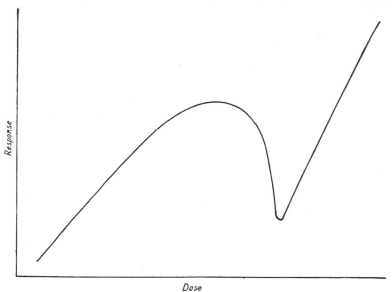

Fig. 3.2—**An example of a non-monotonic dose-response regression curve**
(*cf*. Finney, 1952, § 41)

and would show that the one curve must be a magnification of the other by a factor ρ. Obviously, any rigorous statistical technique for estimating ρ would be difficult, especially as the mathematical specification of the regression relationship must be very complicated. From the purely experimental point of view, a relationship of this kind may be valuable for the information it gives on the mode of action of the stimulus ; for assay purposes, it might be a strong argument against use of that combination of stimulus and response as a method of estimating potency. In practice, the difficulty would probably be overcome by confining assays to a monotonic section of the curve, perhaps even to a portion believed to be very nearly linear.

3.7 Linearizing transformations

For many dose-response relationships, the standard regression equation (3.2) can be adequately represented by

$$U_s = f(a + \beta z^\lambda) \tag{3.6}$$

(Finney, 1947a), in which a, β, λ are the only parameters, $f(\ )$ being a completely specified function which satisfies the condition of monotony. An important case is the limiting form as λ approaches zero, which (with a re-definition of β) may be proved to be equivalent to the use of

$$U_s = f(a + \beta \log z) ; \tag{3.7}$$

in all subsequent work, $\lambda = 0$ in equation (3.6) will be regarded as referring to equation (3.7).* These equations have the great merit of being easily transformed into straight lines, an advantage for computation and graphical representation, and an aid to the description of the statistical technique.

---

* This point appears to have mystified a number of non-mathematical bioassayists. The explanation is that the use to be made of the dose-response regression depends upon the rate of change of $(a + \beta z^\lambda)$ per unit change in z, the value of which for a particular z is the differential coefficient

$$\frac{d}{dz}(a + \beta z^\lambda) = \beta \lambda z^{\lambda-1}.$$

The ratio of this rate of increase to its value at $z = 1$ is $z^{\lambda-1}$, a quantity that, as λ increases, steadily increases if $z > 1$ and steadily decreases if $z < 1$. In this argument, λ can assume positive or negative values, but a discontinuity enters for $\lambda = 0$. Since

$$\frac{d}{dz}(a + \beta \log_e z) = \beta z^{-1},$$

the convention that $\lambda = 0$ refers to equation (3.7) removes the discontinuity. If a set of assay data were analysed (by methods to be described in subsequent chapters) first as though $\lambda = 0\cdot1$, then as though $\lambda = 0\cdot01$, then $\lambda = 0\cdot001$, and so on, the conclusions on validity and relative potency would be found to tend to those based on equation (3.7) (*cf.* the examples in § 15.5). For theoretical discussion, natural logarithms are convenient, but in practice logarithms to base 10 can equally well be used.

If a new scale of measurement of dose is defined by

$$x = z^\lambda \tag{3.8}$$

for equation (3.6), or by

$$x = \log z \tag{3.9}$$

for equation (3.7), both types of regression equation may be comprised in

$$U_S = f(a + \beta x). \tag{3.10}$$

Such a transformed measure of dose may be described as the *dose metameter*,* though it may be termed simply the dose where there is no fear of any confusion. If now a *response metameter* is defined by means of the inverse function $f^{-1}(\ )$, so that corresponding to an expected response U is the metametric value

$$Y = f^{-1}(U), \tag{3.11}$$

equation (3.10) may be rewritten as

$$Y_S = a + \beta x. \tag{3.12}$$

Since a linear relationship exists between Y and x, the statistical analysis may be put into the form of a process for estimating a linear regression of the metametric value of u on x. Equation (3.5) shows that, if equation (3.12) relates to the standard preparation, the corresponding equation for the test preparation must be

$$Y_T = a + \beta \rho^\lambda x \qquad (\lambda \neq 0) \tag{3.13}$$

or

$$Y_T = a + \beta \log \rho + \beta x \qquad (\lambda = 0). \tag{3.14}$$

Thus the standard and the test regression equations are transformed into straight lines simultaneously. If $\lambda \neq 0$, the lines intersect at $x = 0$, and R, the estimate of ρ, is taken as the ratio of the slopes raised to the power of $1/\lambda$; if $\lambda = 0$, the lines are parallel, and R is the antilogarithm of the distance between them measured parallel to the x-axis.

If λ is known, since $f(\ )$ is by definition a known function, the natural method of estimating potency from data on two preparations is to express doses and responses metametrically, and to fit two straight lines subject to the constraint either of intersection at $x = 0$ or of parallelism. The lines might be fitted by eye on a

---

* The convenient word 'metameter' was first used by Bacharach *et al.* (1942), who ascribe its invention to Professor Lancelot Hogben.

diagram and an estimate of ρ obtained by measurement, so giving a graphical procedure, or equations to the lines might be obtained by calculation.   Much of this book is concerned with methods of calculation for various types of data.   A more general problem is that which requires λ also to be estimated from the data of each assay.   The calculations then become more complicated : an example has been given elsewhere (Finney, 1952, § 45).   This does not seem of great practical importance, however, as data for a single assay are seldom extensive enough to discriminate satisfactorily between different values of λ (§ 15.5).   Usually a better policy is to regard the preliminary investigation (§ 3.5) as determining both the form of $f(\ )$ and the value of λ.   The most common values of λ are 0 and 1, and probably most data can be adequately represented by these or other simple ones such as $\frac{1}{2}$, $\frac{1}{3}$, -1, $-\frac{1}{2}$.   The response metameter also is usually taken as a simple function ;   examples are

$$Y = U,$$
$$Y = \log U,$$
$$Y = 1/U,$$
$$Y = U^{\frac{1}{2}}.$$

The work of Ipsen (1941) suggests a purely empirical method of constructing a linearizing transformation, although Ipsen does not explicitly describe it for this purpose (*cf.* Kapteyn, 1903 ; Kapteyn and Van Uven, 1916). His concern was with time-mortality studies, but his idea might be adapted for use with assays in which no obvious choice of dose and response metameters as known functions produces a linear regression, and might be helpful in the analysis of assays dependent upon otherwise intractable forms of response curve.   From tests at a large number of doses, in a preliminary investigation of the standard preparation, the relationship between U and a logarithmic dose metameter would be determined empirically.   This would involve plotting $\bar{u}$, the mean response, against x, and fitting a regression relationship by eye, by means of a polynomial equation, or by any other procedure that gave a reasonable fit to the observations.   The result, expressed graphically or as a table, may be written

$$U = F_0(x). \tag{3.15}$$

Provided that this relationship satisfies the condition of monotony

(§ 3.6), a dose metameter x and a response metameter

$$Y = F_0^{-1}(U) \qquad (3.16)$$

may be tried in subsequent simultaneous tests of the standard and a test preparation. If the standard regression relationship were unchanged, the metametric regressions would be

$$\left. \begin{array}{l} Y_S = x \\ Y_T = \log \rho + x \end{array} \right\} . \qquad (3.17)$$

Even if conditions have changed a little since the preliminary investigation, so that the standard regression is altered, equations (3.12), (3.14) may represent the new regression curves adequately for practical purposes. For graphical estimation, nothing more than plotting the response y against x and drawing parallel lines would be needed, but for a full analysis, the transformation (3.16) might have to be used in the manner described in § 3.13.

3.8 Non-linear regressions

Emmens (1940) has suggested that a logistic function might represent the regression of a quantitative response on dose when the range of responses is too great for a simple linear regression of u on $x = \log z$ to hold ; this function may be written

$$U = \tfrac{1}{2}H \{1 + \tanh (\alpha + \beta x)\}, \qquad (3.18)$$

where 'tanh' represents the hyperbolic tangent, defined by

$$\tanh \varphi = \frac{e^{2\varphi} - 1}{e^{2\varphi} + 1} . \qquad (3.19)$$

Emmens found equation (3.18) to be a good representation of a number of series of data. In view of the importance of the logistic function as a growth curve, its relevance to assays in which the responses are growth measurements is not surprising. If H were known, or could be reliably estimated from previous investigations, the metametric transformation

$$Y = \tanh^{-1} \left(\frac{2U - H}{H} \right) \qquad (3.20)$$

would reduce equation (3.18) to the form of equation (3.12), and the method of estimation in § 3.13 would apply. More commonly, however, H will be unknown and must itself be estimated. The equations for maximum likelihood estimation can be extended so as to estimate H also, at the expense of some increase in complexity ; the analogous problem in which the normal sigmoid

$$U = H \int_{-\infty}^{\alpha + \beta x} \frac{1}{\sqrt{2\pi}} e^{-\frac{1}{2}t^2} dt \qquad (3.21)$$

replaces the logistic has been described elsewhere (Finney, 1952, § 47). Neither this nor the alternative method proposed by Emmens seems likely to be adopted very often. For large negative values of x, the regression curve flattens and approaches a limiting value zero, for large positive x it again flattens and approaches a limit H. The flat portions of the curve will be of little use in assays (because small changes in response correspond with large dose differences), and no great loss will result from restriction of interest to a middle portion of the curve that is approximately linear. The variance of a response whose regression curve approaches limiting values at extremes of dose, however, is likely to depend upon the response, and to be reduced when the expected response is close to either limit (§ 3.10) ; allowance for this would further complicate the analysis.

If the dose response regression cannot be put into the form of equation (3.6), or of some simple modification involving perhaps an extra parameter in the manner of equation (3.18), the assay problem is much more complicated. Even for a quadratic regression

$$U_S = \alpha + \beta x + \gamma x^2 \qquad (3.22)$$

for the standard preparation, with therefore

$$U_T = \alpha + \beta \rho^\lambda x + \gamma \rho^{2\lambda} x^2 \qquad (\lambda \neq 0) \quad (3.23)$$

or

$$U_T = \alpha + \beta (\log \rho + x) + \gamma (\log \rho + x)^2 \qquad (\lambda = 0), \quad (3.24)$$

for the test preparation, the computations required for simultaneous estimation of ρ, α, β, γ would be very troublesome. No assay dependent upon such a specification seems to be in use at present (but see § 5.11).

3.9 The line test for vitamin D

An example of what is needed for a preliminary investigation of a regression function is provided by data on the response of rats to vitamin D (data from E. C. Wood ; Burn *et al.*, 1950, Chapter III), though the data were in fact obtained only after the assay technique had been in use for many years. Six doses of vitamin D were tested, each on a group of about ten rats, and the results were assessed by means of a line test on bones, a procedure which measures the antirachitic activity of the vitamin on an arbitrary scale running from 0 to 6 in half-units. Because personal bias may enter into the assignment of a score, each bone was read by two observers. The average of the two scores for each rat, multiplied by 4 in order to give integral values, is tabulated as the response in Table 3.1, and will be denoted by y since it will be used as the response metameter.

TABLE 3.1—Line test scores for rats dosed with vitamin D

The scores are multiplied by 4

	Dose (i.u. of vitamin D)					
	0·32	0·64	1·28	2·15	4·30	8·60
Responses	1	2	4	8	14	20
	4	0	9	17	14	21
	1	2	4	6	13	16
	0	4	13	14	19	21
	0	0	3	17	17	15
	1	5	7	16	17	14
	0	3	4	8	20	20
	2	4	4	—	18	20
	2	2	10	—	17	15
	2	6	12	—	—	20
	0	1	11	—	—	20
n	11	11	11	7	9	11
Sy	13	29	81	86	149	202
$\bar{y}$	1·18	2·64	7·36	12·29	16·56	18·36
x	−0·495	−0·194	0·107	0·332	0·633	0·934

At the foot of Table 3.1 is shown the mean response to each of the six doses. Clearly nothing as simple as a linear regression on dose will explain these. A natural alternative to try, since it has so frequently been found appropriate, might seem to be a linear regression on the logarithm of dose; the values of this dose metameter, x, are also shown at the foot of the table, and in Fig. 3.3 the mean responses, $\bar{y}$, are graphed against x. As is to be expected with a response constrained to lie between certain limits (necessarily, $0 \leqslant y \leqslant 24$), at extremes of dose some sigmoidal tendency in the regression is evident. Nevertheless, the middle four doses give

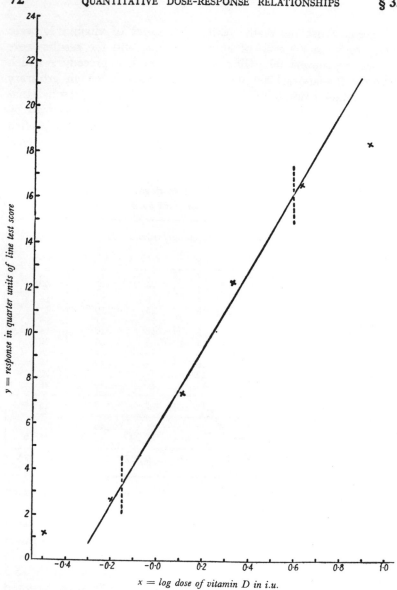

Fig. 3.3—Dose-response relationship for the data of Table 3.1

    ✕ : Mean responses
        The straight line has been fitted to the four middle doses, as
        described in § 3.9, and is expressed by equation (3.29)
        Broken lines indicate roughly the region of linearity

points lying fairly close to a straight line, and an analysis of this portion of the data alone seems desirable.

The 38 rats on these doses may be used in the estimation of a linear regression equation of y on x, by a well-known form of statistical calculation. For them,

$$\bar{x} = \frac{11 \times (-0\cdot194) + 11 \times 0\cdot107 + 7 \times 0\cdot332 + 9 \times 0\cdot633}{38}$$

$$= \frac{7\cdot064}{38}$$

$$= 0\cdot186,$$

$$\bar{y} = \frac{345}{38}$$

$$= 9\cdot079.$$

Also,

$$S_{xx} = 11 \times (-0\cdot194)^2 + 11 \times (0\cdot107)^2 + 7 \times (0\cdot332)^2$$
$$+ 9 \times (0\cdot633)^2 - \frac{(7\cdot064)^2}{38}$$

$$= 3\cdot6045,$$

$$S_{xy} = -0\cdot194 \times 29 + 0\cdot107 \times 81 + 0\cdot332 \times 86$$
$$+ 0\cdot633 \times 149 - \frac{7\cdot064 \times 345}{38}$$

$$= 61\cdot776,$$

and

$$S_{yy} = 2^2 + 0^2 + 2^2 + \ldots + 18^2 + 17^2 - \frac{(345)^2}{38}$$

$$= 1426\cdot76.$$

The sum of squares between doses is calculated as

$$\frac{29^2}{11} + \frac{81^2}{11} + \frac{86^2}{7} + \frac{149^2}{9} - \frac{345^2}{38} = 1{,}064\cdot01,$$

with 3 degrees of freedom, and the linear regression accounts for a portion of this of amount

$$\frac{S_{xy}^2}{S_{xx}} = \frac{(61\cdot776)^2}{3\cdot6045} \tag{3.25}$$
$$= 1{,}058\cdot75$$

with 1 degree of freedom. The analysis of variance in Table 3.2 may now be completed.

The significance of the regression is clear : no examination of the ratio of the regression mean square to the mean square within doses is needed in order to make apparent the association between increase in dose and increase in response. If this were not so, line test scores would be of no use for assay purposes. A more

TABLE 3.2—Analysis of variance for the data of Table 3.1

Adjustment for mean		3,132·24	Mean square
Nature of variation	d.f.	Sum of squares	
Regression	1	1,058·75	
Deviations from regression	2	5·26	2·63
Between doses	3	1,064·01	
Within doses	34	362·75	10·67
Total	37	1,426·76	

interesting test is that of deviations from linearity. If a linear regression is an adequate expression of the dose response relationship over the range of doses examined, the mean square for deviations from regression will differ from the mean square within doses only on account of sampling variation ; if the regression is not linear, the mean square for deviations from regression will be increased by a component of variation due to departures from the linear law while the mean square within doses is unaffected. A variance ratio test of the first mean square against the second is therefore a test of the evidence against linearity : significance would indicate a need to abandon the hypothesis of a linear response and log dose regression. In Table 3.2, no evidence of deviation from linearity is found, the mean square actually being less than that within doses. Over a dose range of, say, 0·7 i.u. to 4·0 i.u., the relationship appears to be effectively linear. No attempt should be made to use the linear regression outside the range for which it has been determined. For any type of response, a departure from linearity is almost sure to be found at extremes of dose. Indeed, for these data, a flattening of the curve has already been noted at doses of 0·32 i.u. and 8·60 i.u. ; this does not detract from the usefulness of the linear relation over the range of its validity, for no assumption that the true regression is perfectly linear is involved.

The regression coefficient is estimated as

$$b = \frac{S_{xy}}{S_{xx}} \tag{3.26}$$
$$= \frac{61\cdot776}{3\cdot6045}$$
$$= 17\cdot14,$$

with a variance

$$V(b) = \frac{s^2}{S_{xx}} \tag{3.27}$$
$$= \frac{10\cdot67}{3\cdot6045}$$
$$= 2\cdot960.$$

The equation of linear regression, over the range of doses indicated, is therefore

$$Y = \bar{y} + b\,(x - \bar{x}) \tag{3.28}$$
$$= 9\cdot079 + 17\cdot14\,(x - 0\cdot186)$$

or

$$Y = 5\cdot89 + 17\cdot14x. \tag{3.29}$$

The regression coefficient estimates the increase in response per unit increase in dose. For example, within the region of linearity, a doubling of the dose, which implies increasing x by 0·301, corresponds to an increase of 5·16 ($= 17\cdot14 \times 0\cdot301$) in response or, on the conventional line test scale, an increase of 1·29 in score.

3.10 Heterogeneity of variance

The responses of chief importance for assays are those which are direct measures of size or growth, and not conventional scores. For them, the variance of individual values of u (about their expectation for a specified dose) is often found to be practically independent of U, at least over such range of responses as is of interest to the experimenter. The regression of u on z is then said to be *homoscedastic*. In the method of estimating the regression equation to be described in § 3.13, homoscedasticity is assumed.

Even for responses of this type, however, and still more for scores and other arbitrary measures, the possibility of heteroscedasticity must be borne in mind. If the preliminary investigation shows that $\sigma^2(u)$, the variance of u for a specified z, is dependent upon U, a *scedasticity transformation* is required before the analysis can proceed. In practice, slight heterogeneity of variance will not affect the statistical analysis very much, and a transformation that is approximately correct will be adequate. Suppose that theoretical considerations lead to

$$\sigma^2(u) = \varphi(U), \tag{3.30}$$

where $\varphi(\ )$ is a known function, or that such a variance function is determined empirically by the preliminary investigation. Write

$$u^* = \int \frac{du}{\sqrt{\varphi(u)}}. \tag{3.31}$$

Then, to a first order approximation,

$$\sigma^2(u^*) \doteqdot \frac{\sigma^2(u)}{\varphi(u)} \tag{3.32}$$
$$= 1,$$

as may easily be proved (Bartlett, 1947). Hence the transformation of responses to u^* may be expected to give a homoscedastic regression.

Important cases that occur in bioassay (and in other branches of biometry) are

$$\sigma^2(u) \propto U, \tag{3.33}$$

which gives

$$u^* = u^{\frac{1}{2}}, \tag{3.34}$$

and

$$\sigma^2(u) \propto U^2, \tag{3.35}$$

which gives

$$u^* = \log u. \tag{3.36}$$

If responses must lie between two fixed limits, the variance is likely to be reduced in the neighbourhood of the limits. When the limits are known, the scale of measurement may be chosen to make them 0, H. As an approximation to the variance function,

$$\sigma^2(u) \propto U(H - U), \tag{3.37}$$

is sometimes satisfactory ; for it, the appropriate scedasticity transformation is

$$u^* = \sin^{-1}\left(\frac{u}{H}\right)^{\frac{1}{2}}. \tag{3.38}$$

Equation (3.38) represents the well-known angle transformation of the proportion u/H (Appendix Table XIII ; Fisher and Yates, 1963, Table XII).

3.11   Scedasticity transformation of line test scores

The analysis of variance in Table 3.2, and the interpretation of it that has been made, assume that the variance of a response is independent of the expected response. Inspection of Table 3.1 shows that, as might be expected for any response of this type with imposed lower and upper limits, the variance decreases at extreme doses. Table 3.3 summarizes the variances within each of the six dose groups, and makes apparent that there are considerable variations even within the range of doses used for the linear regression.

TABLE 3.3—Variance estimates for the data of Table 3.1

Dose (i.u.)	$\bar{y}$	d.f.	Variance per response (s_i^2)	$\log s_i^2$
0·32	1·18	10	1·56	0·193
0·64	2·64	10	3·86	0·587
1·28	7·36	10	14·06	1·148
2·15	12·29	6	22·90	1·360
4·30	16·56	8	5·78	0·762
8·60	18·36	10	7·45	0·872

Bartlett's test (Bartlett, 1937; Emmens, 1948, § 9.6; Snedecor, 1956, § 10.13) is often used to examine the significance of the heterogeneity of several independent variance estimates. If the estimate within dose group i is s_i^2 with f_i degrees of freedom, the test criterion is

$$\chi^2_{[k-1]} = 2 \cdot 3026 \times \{f \log s^2 - S(f_i \log s_i^2)\}/C; \tag{3.39}$$

here k is the number of variance estimates, s^2 and f relate to a pooled variance estimate given by

$$f = S(f_i), \tag{3.40}$$

$$fs^2 = S(f_i s_i^2), \tag{3.41}$$

the adjustment factor C is defined by

$$C = 1 + \frac{1}{3(k-1)}\{S(1/f_i) - 1/f\}, \tag{3.42}$$

and 2·3026 appears because logarithms to base 10 are being used.

From Table 3.3, for the four middle doses alone,

$$\chi^2_{[3]} = 2{\cdot}3026 \times (34 \log 10{\cdot}67 - 10 \times 0{\cdot}587 - 10 \times 1{\cdot}148$$
$$- 6 \times 1{\cdot}360 - 8 \times 0{\cdot}762) \div C$$
$$= 7{\cdot}70/C.$$

Since C is always greater than unity (here $C = 1{\cdot}051$), $\chi^2_{[3]}$ is necessarily less than the 5 per cent significance level, 7·82, obtained by reference to a standard table of the χ^2 distribution with $(k-1)$ degrees of freedom (Appendix Table IV; Fisher and Yates, 1963, Table IV).

Box (1953) has severely criticized the practice of relying upon Bartlett's test to indicate whether analysis of variance may be safely used. He found the test to be very sensitive to non-normality, whereas analysis of variance tests are 'robust' in the face of non-normality. Consequently, such a preliminary test on variances is, he says, ' like putting to sea in a rowing boat to find out whether conditions are sufficiently calm for an ocean liner to leave port!'. Experience shows that only very great variance heterogeneity will seriously affect conclusions drawn from a good assay (Chapters 15, 16). For the line test data, use of s^2 as found in Table 3.2 will certainly not mislead. Bartlett's test applied to all six dose groups gives

$$\chi^2_{[5]} = 16{\cdot}83,$$

a strong indication of heterogeneity: even if the regression were linear over the whole range of doses, the hypothesis of homoscedasticity would be untenable. In fact the trend shown by s_i^2 in Table 3.3 agrees roughly with what might be expected for a response that must lie between fixed limits (§ 3.10).

The present data are too few for an adequate investigation of the variance function, $\varphi(U)$, but equation (3.37) might be expected to be somewhere near the truth.   Table 3.4 shows results similar to those of Table 3.3 obtained when an angle transformation of the data of Table 3.1 is made, according to equation (3.38) with $H = 24$.   It is apparent that a large part of the heteroscedasticity has disappeared, though the variance at high doses is still relatively low.   Possibly a smaller value of H, say $H = 22$, should be used because observers never report the highest degrees of healing, so that the true maximum response is less than 24, but there is insufficient evidence to warrant this, and $H = 24$ is certainly good enough for practical purposes.

TABLE 3.4—Variance estimates for the transformed data of Table 3.1

The data transformed by $u^* = \sin^{-1}\left(\dfrac{u}{24}\right)^{\frac{1}{2}}$

Dose (i.u.)	$\bar{y}$	d.f.	Variance per response
0·32	10·09	10	75·5
0·64	17·18	10	98·6
1·28	33·00	10	98·2
2·15	45·57	6	139·3
4·30	56·33	8	40·0
8·60	61·56	10	56·9

In terms of the transformed response, the line test data still show approximate linearity of regression on log dose for the four middle doses, but the indications of a flattening of the relationship at low or high doses remain.   On the hypothesis now being used, the regression of the transformed response on log dose is homoscedastic.   The regression equation for the four middle doses is found to be just as satisfactorily linear as with the untransformed data.   If the symbol y is used for the response, instead of u^*, the equation is

$$Y = 27\cdot34 + 47\cdot95x, \tag{3.43}$$

with

$$V(b) = \frac{91\cdot86}{3\cdot6045} \hspace{2cm} (3.44)$$
$$= 25\cdot48.$$

The analysis of variance is given as Table 3.5.

TABLE 3.5—Analysis of variance for the transformed data of Table 3.1

The data are transformed by $u^* = \sin^{-1}\left(\dfrac{u}{24}\right)^{\frac{1}{2}}$

Adjustment for mean		49,970·63	
Nature of variation	d.f.	Sum of squares	Mean square
Regression	1	8,288·94	
Deviations from regression	2	65·08	32·54
Between doses	3	8,354·02	
Within doses	34	3,123·35	91·86
Total	37	11,477·37	

3.12 The method of maximum likelihood

One of the most important problems of statistical inference is that of how to estimate an unknown parameter, or set of parameters. Certain experimental or observational data are known or assumed to be related according to a mathematical law involving one or more parameters : what values should be estimated for these parameters, in the light of the evidence provided by the data ? For example, the data might be observations of responses, y, at various dose levels, x, believed to be related according to a homoscedastic linear regression ; that is to say

$$E(y) = Y = \alpha + \beta x, \hspace{2cm} (3.45)$$

and the variance of individual y values about Y is a constant, σ^2.

The parameters are then a, β, σ^2. In order to make this problem more definite and amenable to analysis, some assumption about the nature of the frequency distribution of y is necessary, such as the statement that for any x, the distribution of y is normal with mean Y and variance σ^2.

Many general principles of estimation have been proposed by theoretical statisticians, and a comprehensive discussion of them would need a book in itself. An excellent elementary account has been given by Solomon (1948a, b). The principle in most common use to-day is that of *maximum likelihood*, which owes its origin to R. A. Fisher (1912, 1922). The *likelihood* that a set of parameters should have any particular values is defined to be a quantity whose magnitude is proportional to the probability that the totality of observations should be the data recorded. Some writers (Fisher, 1925) fix the factor of proportionality by the condition that the maximum value of the likelihood is unity. The method of maximum likelihood then states that the estimated values of the parameters are to be chosen so as to make the likelihood take its maximum value. Maximum likelihood estimates have a number of important properties, chief amongst which are the following :

(i) The maximum likelihood estimate of a parameter is *consistent* ; that is to say, if the number of observations is increased without limit, the estimate is almost certain to be within any specified narrow interval that includes the true value. The distinction between consistency and freedom from bias needs to be borne in mind. An unbiased estimate is one whose expected mean value in repeated samples of data is equal to the true value of the parameter, even when all the samples are of fixed finite size. A consistent estimate need not be unbiased ; an unbiased estimate need not be, but usually is, consistent. An estimate obtained by the method of maximum likelihood is not necessarily unbiased.

(ii) The frequency distribution of the maximum likelihood estimate of a parameter is *asymptotically normal*. For a fixed number of observations, per sample, repeated samplings would give different sets of data, from each of which a maximum likelihood estimate could be formed, and thus would generate a frequency distribution of the estimate.

If the number of observations is increased without limit, this distribution approaches the normal form.

(iii) The maximum likelihood estimate of a parameter is *asymptotically efficient* ; that is to say, if the number of observations is increased without limit, the ratio of the sampling variance of the estimate to the sampling variance of any alternative estimate tends to a limit not greater than unity. Less exactly, this means that the estimate has the minimum possible variance in large samples, but the wording of the previous sentence is preferable.

(iv) The estimate will be *efficient* in finite samples, if an efficient estimate for the particular problem exists : if any estimate having a sampling variance as small as a certain theoretically calculable minimum exists, the method of maximum likelihood will give one.

(v) If a *sufficient* estimate of the parameter exists, the maximum likelihood estimate will either be equal to it or be a function of it. Sufficiency is the technical name for a remarkable property possessed by some estimates of utilizing all the information on the value of the parameter that is contained in a particular set of observations.

Some restrictions on the mathematical specification of data in terms of the parameters are necessary conditions for the truth of (i)–(v) above; these are not so severe as to be often important in general practice. The reader should not regard this section as having full logical and mathematical rigour, and should consult a text-book of statistical theory (Cramér, 1946; Kendall and Stuart, 1961) if he wishes for more precise statements about maximum likelihood and other principles of estimation. Verbal description of the theory of statistical estimation is unsatisfactory, but is adopted here for the benefit of the non-mathematical reader.

The method of maximum likelihood is certainly not the only general principle that can be proposed for the estimation of parameters. Moreover, it has certain obvious flaws, notably its possible bias and the uncertainty as to its efficiency in small samples when no fully efficient estimate exists. No alternative principle, however, has yet been proved to be free from these disadvantages, either in general or for problems of the type considered in this book. Maximum likelihood is not above criticism, and for any one type of problem may reasonably be abandoned as soon as some alternative is demonstrated to be superior. Nevertheless, it appears to be the most serviceable principle known to-day, and, in the absence of evidence to its discredit, in any particular situation may reasonably form a standard of comparison for alternatives. In biological assay, it is often identical with the older, and less adaptable, *principle of least squares*, and for quantal responses it is closely related to the *method of minimum* χ^2 (§ 20.3). As will be seen from subsequent sections and chapters, it leads to computational processes which can be easily arranged for routine work, and often reduces to the ' common-sense ' calculations that would be adopted by a reader who ignored §§ 3.12, 3.13.

3.13 Estimation of the parameters of regression equations

Fieller (1947) expressed the opinion that a transformation of response which produces homoscedasticity will often also suffice to give linearity of regression on log dose over a wide range of doses. Undoubtedly many instances of this could be adduced, but the rule is not universal ; indeed, for data such as those of Table 3.1, a transformation which equalizes the variances does not improve the linearity at extreme doses. Nevertheless, when $\sigma^2(u)$ is not independent of U, a transformation of observed responses, u, to a scale u^*, in order to equalize the variances, seems very desirable even if it is no more than a preliminary to a further transformation (Finney, 1947a).

If it be supposed that u now represents a response *after* this scedasticity transformation, the remaining problem is that of estimating a, β in the regression equation (3.10), where individual responses for various values of x have been determined by experiment and the variance of any such u about U is σ^2, a constant. An *assumption of normality* will be made, namely, that the frequency distribution of u in repeated sampling for a fixed x is a normal distribution with mean U and variance σ^2. Corresponding results might be derived for distributions other than normal, provided that they were exactly specified in terms of U and σ^2, but there seems no good reason for adopting any alternative here. In practice, most estimates of relative potency will use means of several observations, and conclusions based upon the assumption of normality are therefore likely to be protected from serious flaws by the *central limit theorem* : though the distribution of individual responses be non-normal, unless its form is very extreme the distribution of means will tend to normality as the number of observations is increased (see § 15.4).

Application of the linearizing transformation enables graphical estimation of potency to be made rapidly. Individual response metameters are plotted against the corresponding dose metameters for the two preparations. Two straight lines are drawn by eye, subject to the constraint either of intersection at $x = 0$ or of parallelism, and R is derived from the ratio of slopes or from the distance between the lines measured parallel to the x-axis. If no assessment of precision is wanted, this procedure may be sufficiently exact with good data ; indeed, with experience, lines drawn after a brief inspection of the diagram can yet be made to give a value of R very close to that later calculated much more laboriously. Nevertheless, the method lacks objectivity, and might give biased results in the hands of a user who, however honest in intention, had some interest in showing a particular conclusion. Moreover, in most assays, some idea of the reliability of a value of R as an indicator of ρ is needed, and to this end computation of R and of its precision is essential.

In the general practice of biological assay with quantitative responses, the calculations are usually adaptations of unweighted linear regression techniques. Numerical examples in Chapters 4–15 are all of this kind. This section, however, is concerned with the development of a general theory, and in consequence is mathematically more complicated than is necessary for most purposes. The elaborate iterative process described below includes the familiar methods of analysis as particular cases based upon certain simplifying assumptions. The reader anxious to come to the more practical aspects of assay analysis might well omit the remainder of this section, though he may be glad to return to it after reading Chapter 17.

Consider for the present only the standard preparation, for which a series of pairs of values of z, u have been observed (some or all of the doses may have several independent measures of response, as in Table 3.1). The likelihood of particular values α, β, σ^2 for the parameters is proportional to the product of the probabilities of all the observations on the assumption that the parameters have these values, and is therefore proportional to the product of expressions like

$$\frac{1}{\sigma} \exp \left\{ - \frac{(u - U)^2}{2\sigma^2} \right\} , \qquad (3.46)$$

where U is as defined in equation (3.10). Simultaneous estimation of the three parameters could be effected by maximizing this likelihood. Alternatively, two variance parameters might be used, one representing the variation of u within dose groups and the other the variation of the means of dose groups about the supposed regression equation ; this corresponds to an analysis of variance between and within doses, equality of the two variances being a requirement for validity of the regression equation. The two procedures are easily seen to give the same estimates of α and β, their difference being only whether a single estimate of σ^2 shall be obtained by pooling all available information, or whether two separate estimates shall be compared as a test of the significance of deviations from the regression (*cf.* Table 3.2). Both are maximum likelihood methods, but the second has a more useful specification of the mathematical model ; either could be used, provided that neither the statistician nor the experimenter biases his conclusions by deciding which he will have at the end of the analysis !

The second, and recommended, method may be regarded as using variation between dose groups only in the estimation of α and β, σ^2 being estimated from the pooled sums of squares of u within dose groups. The residual variation between dose groups, after taking account of predictions based upon the estimated α and β, may then be compared with σ^2 as a test of the adequacy of a regression equation of the prescribed form for representing the facts ; the analyses in §§ 3.9, 3.11 are instances of this. The logarithm of the likelihood of α, β is then written as

$$L = \text{constant} - \frac{S (u - U)^2}{2\sigma^2} , \qquad (3.47)$$

where S denotes summation over all observations and terms involving σ but not α or β have been included in the constant. The method of maximum likelihood requires that the estimates of a, β be so chosen as to maximize L. This is the same as choosing estimates to minimize $S(u - U)^2$, so that the method of least squares is here the same as the method of maximum likelihood.

The estimates are therefore solutions of the equations

$$\left.\begin{aligned} \frac{\partial L}{\partial a} &= 0, \\ \frac{\partial L}{\partial \beta} &= 0. \end{aligned}\right\} \tag{3.48}$$

Let the solutions be a, b. Suppose that a_1, b_1 are approximations to a, b obtained in any manner ; the easiest procedure is usually to read them from the diagram described earlier in this section, using eye estimates of the lines, but a rough calculation of an unweighted linear regression for the values of y corresponding to each u may be used if preferred. By the Taylor-Maclaurin expansion, to the first order of small quantities, improved values for the estimates will be $a_2 = a_1 + \delta a_1$, $b_2 = b_1 + \delta b_1$, where the increments δa_1, δb_1 are the solutions of

$$\left.\begin{aligned} \frac{\partial L}{\partial a_1} + \delta a_1 \frac{\partial^2 L}{\partial a_1{}^2} + \delta b_1 \frac{\partial^2 L}{\partial a_1 \partial \beta_1} &= 0, \\ \frac{\partial L}{\partial \beta_1} + \delta a_1 \frac{\partial^2 L}{\partial a_1 \partial \beta_1} + \delta b_1 \frac{\partial^2 L}{\partial \beta_1{}^2} &= 0. \end{aligned}\right\} \tag{3.49}$$

Addition of a suffix 1 to a, β indicates replacement by a_1, b_1 after differentiation. An iterative process may be based upon equations (3.49), replacing a_1, b_1 by a_2, b_2 and solving for increments δa_2, δb_2 and so on until a satisfactorily close approach to a, b is achieved.

The equations must next be put into a form more suitable for computation. Consider

$$\frac{\partial L}{\partial a} = \frac{1}{\sigma^2} S\left\{(u - U)\frac{\partial U}{\partial a}\right\}. \tag{3.50}$$

In iterative solutions of maximum likelihood equations, the second differential coefficients of L may be replaced by their expected values ; this is often convenient because expected values can be tabulated, whereas observed values need more calculation (*cf.* § 18.5). From equation (3.50), by substitution of $u = U$ after differentiation,

$$E\left(\frac{\partial^2 L}{\partial a^2}\right) = -\frac{1}{\sigma^2} S\left(\frac{\partial U}{\partial a}\right)^2 ;$$

similarly

$$E\left(\frac{\partial^2 L}{\partial a \partial \beta}\right) = -\frac{1}{\sigma^2} S\left(\frac{\partial U}{\partial a}\right)\left(\frac{\partial U}{\partial \beta}\right),$$

and

$$E\left(\frac{\partial^2 L}{\partial \beta^2}\right) = -\frac{1}{\sigma^2} S\left(\frac{\partial U}{\partial \beta}\right)^2 . \tag{3.51}$$

Write

$$\frac{\partial U}{\partial Y} = f'(Y), \tag{3.52}$$

and define the *weighting coefficient*, w, by

$$w = \{ f'(Y) \}^2. \tag{3.53}$$

Then equations (3.51) may be rewritten

$$E\left(\frac{\partial^2 L}{\partial \alpha^2}\right) = -\frac{1}{\sigma^2} Sw\left(\frac{\partial Y}{\partial \alpha}\right)^2$$

$$= -Sw/\sigma^2,$$

$$E\left(\frac{\partial^2 L}{\partial \alpha \partial \beta}\right) = -Swx/\sigma^2, \tag{3.54}$$

and

$$E\left(\frac{\partial^2 L}{\partial \beta^2}\right) = -Swx^2/\sigma^2.$$

Corresponding to the approximate estimates a_1, b_1, is an expected value of the response metameter, Y_1, given by

$$Y_1 = a_1 + b_1 x. \tag{3.55}$$

Substitution into equations (3.49) from equations (3.53)–(3.55) enables them to be written in the form

$$\delta a_1 Sw_1 + \delta b_1 Sw_1 x = S\left\{\frac{w_1(u - U_1)}{f'(Y_1)}\right\},$$

$$\delta a_1 Sw_1 x + \delta b_1 Sw_1 x^2 = S\left\{\frac{w_1 x(u - U_1)}{f'(Y_1)}\right\}. \tag{3.56}$$

The next step in the simplification is to add $Sw_1 Y_1$ to each side of the first of equations (3.56), and $Sw_1 x Y_1$ to each side of the second. If y, the *working response**, be defined by

$$y = Y + \frac{u - U}{f'(Y)}, \tag{3.57}$$

the resulting equations may be written

$$\left. \begin{array}{l} a_2 Sw_1 + b_2 Sw_1 x = Sw_1 y_1, \\ a_2 Sw_1 x + b_2 Sw_1 x^2 = Sw_1 xy_1. \end{array} \right\} \tag{3.58}$$

Equations (3.58) show that

$$Y = a_2 + b_2 x \tag{3.59}$$

is obtainable as the weighted linear regression equation of y_1 on x, and it is in this form that a_2, b_2 are most conveniently calculated. If the weighted means of x and y_1 are written

$$\bar{x}_1 = Sw_1 x / Sw_1, \tag{3.60}$$

and

$$\bar{y}_1 = Sw_1 y_1 / Sw_1, \tag{3.61}$$

and the notation previously used for sums of squares and products of deviations is extended to represent weighted sums, so that

$$S_{xx} = Swx^2 - (Swx)^2 / Sw, \tag{3.62}$$

and

$$S_{xy} = Swxy - (Swx)(Swy) / Sw, \tag{3.63}$$

then the revised estimates are

$$b_2 = S_{x_1 y_1} / S_{x_1 x_1} \tag{3.64}$$

and

$$a_2 = \bar{y}_1 - b_2 \bar{x}_1. \tag{3.65}$$

The process may now be repeated with a_2, b_2 replacing a_1, b_1, a new set of weighting coefficients and working responses being based upon these ; further cycles are computed in the same manner, until the smallness of the differences between successive approximations indicates close approach to a, b.

---

* Note that y as defined by equation (3.57) in general differs from the empirical response metameter obtainable from equation (3.11) as $f^{-1}(u)$. In the many assays for which the identical transformation, $Y = U$, is used, the two are the same, but for the general method a special symbol to represent the empirical response metameter is unnecessary. Expected values Y and U are always related by equation (3.11) ; u represents the original observation, or the value obtained after a scedasticity transformation, y is always used for the working response related to u by equation (3.57).

Thus the estimation of α, β from experimental data requires only the iteration of weighted linear regression calculations. Fisher (1935) first suggested this method for quantal responses, and Garwood (1940) developed the theory more fully. Further extensions to quantal responses (1949b, 1952) and to quantitative responses (1947a) were shown by Finney. Not only are the estimates obtained in this manner, but also their variances, for

$$V(\bar{y}) = \sigma^2/Sw \qquad (3.66)$$

and

$$V(b) = \sigma^2/S_{xx}, \qquad (3.67)$$

where all quantities now relate to the limit of the iteration. For practical purposes, Sw and S_{xx} taken from the last cycle of iteration computed will be close enough to the limiting values to be used in equation (3.66), (3.67). The true variance, σ^2, will be replaced by an estimate, s^2, based upon the sum of squares of deviations of the individual values of u about the estimated regression equation.

If a particular metametric transformation has to be used often, construction of a special set of tables will help greatly. First a table of the transformation (3.11) is required, from which may be read the empirical response metameters. Secondly, a table of the weighting coefficient, equation (3.53), the *minimum working response*,

$$Y_0 = Y - \frac{U}{f'(Y)}, \qquad (3.68)$$

and the *range*

$$A = \frac{1}{f'(Y)}, \qquad (3.69)$$

as functions of Y, is formed. The names are given on the analogy of quantal responses (*cf.* Chapter 17), though Y_0 is not a true minimum and A not a true range. The suffices used in the earlier part of this section may now be dropped, as the iteration will not be confused by their absence. The first step in the calculation is to read from the first table the empirical response corresponding to each observed u, and to plot these against x A straight line is drawn, by eye, through the points ; with experience some allowance for unequal weights can be made when judging the position of the line. *Expected responses*, Y, are read from the line to correspond with each x in the observations. From the second table, the weighting coefficient for each Y is read, and the corresponding working response is formed as

$$y = Y_0 + uA. \tag{3.70}$$

The weighted linear regression of y on x is calculated ; it gives a new set of values for expected responses, with which a second cycle of iteration may be performed. Further cycles may be computed until a_{r-1}, b_{r-1} are found to be almost the same as a_r, b_r ; the latter are then regarded as the maximum likelihood estimates of α, β.

In practice, this apparently lengthy process is quite rapid. Seldom are many cycles necessary. Indeed, often the first cycle and almost always the second will give results sufficiently good for whatever use is to be made of them. If the first approximations are determined objectively, and by a method that is not of zero efficiency (scarcely a serious restriction !), the first cycle gives estimates that are asymptotically fully efficient in large samples, though in general these will not coincide with the maximum likelihood estimates ; the efficiency in small samples is not known. Moreover, the method in its general form is seldom required for quantitative responses, but it is readily adapted for use with quantal responses and there forms the basis of a number of the more important computing techniques (Chapters 17, 18, 21).

For quantitative responses, if the original observations are homoscedastic or if a scedasticity transformation has been made, a simple choice of dose metameter is often the only further step required in order to linearize the regressions. The metametric transformation for responses is then

$$Y = U, \tag{3.71}$$

for which

$$f'(Y) = 1. \tag{3.72}$$

Hence

$$w = 1 \tag{3.73}$$

by equation (3.53), and

$$y = u \tag{3.74}$$

by equation (3.57). The elaborate iterative process then reduces to the calculation of an unweighted linear regression, and obviously one cycle completes the calculation. Subsequent discussion of assays based upon quantitative responses will be concerned mostly with this type ; no claim is made that σ^2 is absolutely constant or that the regression is perfectly linear, but the evidence accumulated from many experiments may fail to show any consistent or large departures from these conditions. An example illustrative of the full technique is discussed in Chapter 16.

3.14 Standard curve estimation

The equation (3.29),

$$Y = 5 \cdot 89 + 17 \cdot 14x,$$

was obtained as a regression relationship between log dose of standard vitamin D and a response based upon the line test. What use can be made of this equation? It might be used for assay purposes in one of three ways ; two of these must be discarded as general methods, though they are of interest as illustrating the argument.

The first method, that of *standard curve estimation*, need not be restricted to a straight line, though fiducial limits could not be determined so easily for a non-linear regression. It is easily illustrated for line test assays. Suppose that, in an assay of a cod-liver oil for its vitamin D content, ten rats each received a dose of 50 mg. and the average degree of healing was 2·10, or a score of 8·40 on the scale of quarter-units used in Table 3.1. From the regression equation, the log dose having an expected response of 8·40 is

$$x = (8 \cdot 40 - 5 \cdot 89)/17 \cdot 14$$
$$= 0 \cdot 146.$$

Hence the dose of vitamin D judged to have the same effect as 50 mg. cod-liver oil is antilog 0·146, or 1·40 i.u. ; 1 g. cod-liver oil is estimated to contain 28·0 i.u. vitamin D.

If the sample of rats used for the assay were drawn from the same population and tested under the same conditions as that used in the earlier calculation of the regression line, this method would give a valid estimate of potency. Unfortunately it is practically useless, as even slight and possibly random variations in experimental conditions within a laboratory are liable to alter the true dose response relationship from day to day in an unpredictable manner. In the line test, for example, the severity of the initial rickets will vary from batch to batch of rats, and this in turn will affect the level of healing observed at any dose. In general, the assumption that a response curve once determined can be used in future assays is inadmissible. Bliss and Packard (1941) have reported one of the few known exceptions to this rule: they found the curve relating percentage survival of eggs of *Drosophila melanogaster* to X-ray dosage to remain constant over a period of years, so that it might be used as a basis for the standardization of dosage.

Even less permissible is the use of a standard curve estimated in one laboratory as a standard of comparison for test preparations in another. The curve is then likely to be quite irrelevant because of differences in strains of animals and experimental technique. Except where the contrary has been demonstrated by careful experiment, it may be stated as axiomatic that tests of the standard preparation, *S*, must be run simultaneously with, and as an integral part of, the assay of any test preparation, *T*.

3.15 Standard slope estimation

Though the response regression is likely to shift from day to day, for some types of response the shift may represent a change in position only, the sensitivity of the subjects to variations in dose remaining unaltered ; in other words, the response to each dose may change, but the increase in response per unit increase in log dose (or the increase corresponding to multiplications of the dose by a stated factor) is constant. The standard curve method, if it were trustworthy, would be applicable whatever the form of the regression relationship for the standard preparation, but the standard slope method is limited to assays for which the regression of response on log dose is linear.

If experience has shown the assumption of constant slope for a linear regression on log dose to be justified for the standard preparation, *S*, a test preparation, *T*, can be assayed relative to *S* by simultaneous experimentation with one dose of *S* and one dose of *T* under comparable conditions. The two doses should be chosen well within the range of linearity and as nearly equivalent as existing information makes possible.

Suppose that a group of eight rats received 5 i.u. vitamin D each and showed a mean response of 12·25, at the same time as the group of ten rats mentioned in § 3.14 received their 50 mg. cod-liver oil. The difference in response, 3·85, corresponds to a difference of 3·85/17·14 in log dose, on the assumption that the regression coefficient previously determined is still applicable. More generally, if x_S, x_T are the log doses of S and T respectively, and $\bar{y}_S$, $\bar{y}_T$ the corresponding mean responses, the logarithm of the estimate of relative potency is

$$M = x_S - x_T - \frac{\bar{y}_S - \bar{y}_T}{b}, \tag{3.75}$$

and the estimate is

$$R = \text{antilog } M. \tag{3.76}$$

In this example

$$M = \log 5 - \log 50 - \frac{3\cdot85}{17\cdot14}$$

$$= -1 - 0\cdot225$$

$$= \bar{2}\cdot775.$$

The antilogarithm of this is $0\cdot0596$: the cod-liver oil is estimated to contain $59\cdot6$ i.u. vitamin D per g.

TABLE 3.6—Hypothetical assay of vitamin D by the standard slope method

	Response to		Equivalent angles	
	5 i.u. S	50 mg. T	5 i.u. S	50 mg. T
Responses	15	4	52	24
	10	10	40	40
	18	12	60	45
	6	7	30	33
	9	5	38	27
	14	5	50	27
	12	9	45	38
	14	14	50	50
	—	10	—	40
	—	8	—	35
n	8	10	8	10
Sy	98	84	365	359
$\bar{y}$	12·25	8·40	45·62	35·90

This result may be compared with that obtained by the angle transformation described in § 3.11 and used in Table 3.4. If the individual responses are as shown in the first two columns of Table 3.6, equation (3.38) gives the values shown in the last two columns as the corresponding angles. Equation (3.75), with the regression coefficient taken from equation (3.43), then gives

$$M = \log 5 - \log 50 - \frac{9 \cdot 72}{47 \cdot 95}$$
$$= \bar{2} \cdot 797.$$

The potency is now estimated as 62·7 i.u. per g., not a great change from the estimate based on untransformed scores.

Some expression of the precision of the estimate is desirable. Inspection of Table 3.6 indicates variances of the same order as those summarized in Tables 3.3, 3.4. Variance estimates might be pooled with those obtained in the calculations for the regression lines, giving an additional 16 degrees of freedom. In general, the regression line would be based on much more extensive data than any one assay, so that the additional degrees of freedom would be little gain. Alternatively, in assessing the fiducial limits of M, b might be assigned a variance based upon the earlier calculations and $(\bar{y}_S - \bar{y}_T)$ a variance based upon the current assay ; the first analogue of Fieller's theorem (§ 2.7) would then be required. An allowance for a variance per response in the assay different from that found in the original regression investigation, however, would be tantamount to an admission that experimental conditions had changed so much as to make the applicability of the regression coefficient doubtful. The method of assay is of limited usefulness, and here only the easiest method of assessing fiducial limits will be given, namely, that which ignores completely all information on variance from the current assay and assumes the s^2 from the regression calculations still to be applicable.

From equation (3.75)

$$M - (x_S - x_T) = -\frac{\bar{y}_S - \bar{y}_T}{b},$$

and, using

$$s^2 = 10 \cdot 67$$

from Table 3.2, the standard form of Fieller's theorem may be applied. Here

$$\left.\begin{array}{l} v_{11} = \dfrac{1}{N_S} + \dfrac{1}{N_T}, \\[2mm] v_{12} = 0, \\[2mm] v_{22} = \dfrac{1}{S_{xx}}, \end{array}\right\} \qquad (3.77)$$

where N_S, N_T are the numbers of subjects for the standard and test preparations respectively and S_{xx} is to be taken from the regression calculations. Hence equation (2.7) becomes

$$g = \frac{t^2 s^2}{b^2 S_{xx}} \tag{3.78}$$

$$= \frac{(2{\cdot}03)^2 \times 10{\cdot}67}{(17{\cdot}14)^2 \times 3{\cdot}6045}$$

$$= 0{\cdot}0415.$$

This value is so small (less than 0·05) that to ignore it would make little difference to the conclusions, but, once it has been evaluated, the full formula based upon Fieller's theorem is almost as quickly computed as that based upon an approximate variance for M. The limits for $M - (x_S - x_T)$ are in fact given by

$$\left[M - x_S + x_T \pm \frac{ts}{b} \left\{ (1 - g) \left(\frac{1}{N_S} + \frac{1}{N_T} \right) + \frac{(M - x_S + x_T)^2}{S_{xx}} \right\}^{\frac{1}{2}} \right]$$
$$\div (1 - g) ; \quad (3.79)$$

if g is put equal to zero in (3.79). the formula becomes that based upon the approximate $V(M)$. Using (3.79) as it stands, the limits are found as

$$M_L, M_U = (x_S - x_T) + \left[- 0{\cdot}225 \pm \frac{2{\cdot}03}{17{\cdot}14} \left\{ \left(0{\cdot}9585 \times 0{\cdot}225 \right. \right. \right.$$
$$\left. \left. \left. + \frac{(0{\cdot}225)^2}{3{\cdot}6045} \right) \times 10{\cdot}67 \right\}^{\frac{1}{2}} \right] \div 0{\cdot}9585$$

$$= - 1 + [- 0{\cdot}225 \pm 0{\cdot}185] \div 0{\cdot}9585$$

$$= - 1{\cdot}428, - 1{\cdot}042$$

$$= \bar{2}{\cdot}572, \bar{3}{\cdot}958.$$

Hence the estimated potency of 59·6 i.u. per g. has fiducial limits 37·3 i.u. per g. and 90·8 i.u. per g.

If the angle transformation were used, the same procedure would give

$$g = \frac{(2{\cdot}03)^2 \times 91{\cdot}86}{(47{\cdot}95)^2 \times 3{\cdot}6045}$$

$$= 0{\cdot}0457.$$

The limits are

$$M_L, M_U = -1 + \left[-0.203 \pm \frac{2.03}{47.95} \left\{ \left(0.9543 \times 0.225 \right. \right.\right.$$
$$\left.\left. + \frac{(0.203)^2}{3.6045} \right) \times 91.86 \left. \right\}^{\frac{1}{2}} \right] \div 0.9543$$
$$= -1 + [-0.203 \pm 0.193] \div 0.9543$$
$$= -1.415, \; -1.010.$$

The limits to the potency estimate of 62·7 i.u. per g. are therefore 38·5 i.u. per g. and 97·7 i.u. per g. Comparison with the results based upon the untransformed responses shows that the scedasticity transformation has not greatly altered the conclusions to be drawn from the assay.

When the only data available are responses to one dose of each preparation, as in Table 3.6, no statistical theory or test can demonstrate that the standard slope method is valid. Herein lies considerable danger, for the simplicity of the method is a temptation. The experimenter who is satisfied from experience that his regression coefficient does not change may use it, but must recognize the risk that unexpected changes can make his results entirely misleading. If $\bar{y}_S$ and $\bar{y}_T$ are nearly equal, the effect of b upon M may be practically negligible : choice of x_S, x_T as equivalent dosages is therefore desirable, although even this cannot ensure that the precision of the estimate will be correctly assessed. The regression coefficient measures the sensitivity of subjects to changes in dose ; it might vary with season, it might show steady increase over a period in which the stock of animals was being bred selectively for sensitivity and homogeneity, or it might vary erratically because of lack of control of experimental conditions.

3.16 Simultaneous trial estimation

The only way of overcoming the objections to the standard curve and standard slope methods of estimating potency is to perform simultaneous trials of both preparations, under strictly comparable conditions, using two or more doses of each. All quantities required in the computation of the results of the assay are then obtainable from responses measured in the current assay, and, if the design has been well chosen, any validity tests needed can be made on the same data. The statistical analysis and

estimation are entirely self-contained, in accordance with widely
accepted principles of good experimental design. The preliminary
investigation is used for giving the information that the regression
is nearly linear, and for locating a suitable range of doses, but the
position and slope of the line are estimated afresh for each assay.
The apparent precision of estimation of potency is likely to be less
than if the standard slope method were used, because the regression
coefficient is less precise. In a good assay, however, the variance of
the regression coefficient is not a major factor in the assessment of
the precision of the potency estimate ; a regression coefficient
determined for the assay itself, even though its variance be relatively
large, is usually to be preferred to one with a small variance that
may be inappropriate to the current assay.

The simultaneous trial method is the basis of the assay techniques
described in subsequent chapters. The general iterative procedure
introduced in § 3.13 requires little modification for use in assays.
Empirical responses for both the standard and test preparations
must be plotted against x, and two provisional regression lines
drawn, subject to the constraint either of intersection at $x = 0$
or of parallelism. The weighted regression calculations are applied
to improve the approximations to the estimates of all parameters
involved, the intersection or parallelism constraint being maintained.
Eventually the estimate of ρ is formed, as in the graphical method,
either from the ratio of slopes or from the horizontal distance
between parallel lines.

The relationship between the different forms of estimation may
be summarized as follows :

    (i) Standard curve :   Regression equation, not necessarily
                                            linear, assumed to remain fixed in
                                            position ;

    (ii) Standard slope :   Regression equation on log dose
                                            assumed linear, with constant re-
                                          gression coefficient ;

    (iii) Simultaneous trial,
          two doses of each
          preparation :   Regression on dose metameter assumed
                                            linear, but each assay provides its
                                            own estimate of all parameters ;

(iv) Simultaneous trial, three or more doses of each preparation :   As (iii), but each assay also gives a test of deviations from linearity.

The standard curve and standard slope methods for quantitative responses will not be discussed further.

CHAPTER 4

PARALLEL LINE ASSAYS

4.1 Unsymmetrical designs

The earliest type of simultaneous trial assay to be used, and probably still the type of widest application, is that for which the response (or some simple metametric transformation of the response) has a linear regression on log dose. The condition of similarity then requires that the lines for the standard and test preparations shall be parallel (§3.7).

Before discussing points of good design, a general unsymmetrical design will be illustrated and criticized. Such a design is rightly stigmatized by Emmens (1948, § 11.1) as a badly planned test, on the grounds that ' Not only is the amount of information which may be extracted from the material much reduced, but the arithmetic becomes tedious '. As will be apparent from study of Chapters 5 and 6, symmetry in the number and spacing of doses and in the allocation of subjects to doses has advantages both for ease of computation and for precision. Nevertheless, unsymmetrical assays cannot always be avoided : an accident may convert a symmetrical design into an unsymmetrical, or shortage of material may force the adoption of an unsymmetrical design.

4.2 Data for an unsymmetrical assay

The data in Table 4.1 relate to an assay of vitamin D_3 in cod-liver oil by means of its antirachitic activity in chickens. The response used was the percentage bone ash. The data have been taken from a publication (British Standards Institution, 1940) which describes the experimental technique and gives instructions for the statistical analysis. The notation and the pattern of the analysis will be modified here, in order to conform to the general practice of this book ; the conclusions, of course, are unaltered. When the measured responses for an assay are percentages, both non-linearity and heteroscedasticity of the regression are likely to be encountered, at least at extreme values (cf. § 3.9). In this assay, almost all the responses lay between 30 per cent. and 45 per cent., and no difficulties of statistical invalidity (§§ 4.5, 4.6) were encountered when an analysis based on a linear regression of response on log dose was applied.

Much arithmetical labour can often be saved by a preliminary *coding* of the data, this implying the use of a linear metametric transformation to reduce the absolute magnitudes of the responses

TABLE 4.1—Responses in an assay of cod-liver oil for vitamin D₃

(Units of response defined by equation (4.1))

	Dose of standard preparation, S (B.S.I. units per 100 g. food)			Dose of test preparation, T (mg. C.L.O. per 100 g. food)			
	5·76	9·6	16	32·4	54	90	150
	35	62	116	20	26	57	140
	30	67	105	39	60	89	133
	24	95	91	16	48	103	142
	37	62	94	27	−8	129	118
	28	54	130	−12	46	139	137
	73	56	79	2	77	128	84
	31	48	120	31		89	101
	21	70	124			86	
	−5	94					
		42					
n	9	10	8	7	6	8	7
Sy	274	650	859	123	249	820	855
$\bar{y}$	30·4	65·0	107·4	17·6	41·5	102·5	122·1
x	−2	0	2	−3	−1	1	3

and to remove decimal digits by a change in the scale of measurement ; the opportunity may also be taken to discard any excessive number of digits (§ 1.7). Here, the bone ash percentages, u, were transformed by

$$y = 10\,(u - 30), \qquad (4.1)$$

so that responses 33·5, 33·0, 29·5, etc., were coded as 35, 30, − 5, etc. Equation (4.1) was chosen so that almost all the values of y are positive. A linear metametric transformation has no effect on scedasticity or linearity of regression, and does not alter the potency estimate. When the original data are in fractions, multiplication by the least common multiple of the denominators similarly effects a simplification of arithmetic (*cf.* Table 3.1). The entries in

Table 4.1 show the coded data for the vitamin D_3 assay ; the original percentages may be found as

$$u = 30 + 0.1y.$$

One good feature of the assay is that the doses were at equal logarithmic spacing : for both preparations, the ratio of successive doses was 5/3. This is always desirable when a logarithmic dose metameter is to be used, as it both ensures that the dose range is adequately covered and simplifies the arithmetic. The calculations could be performed using $\log_{10} z$ as the metameter. By using instead

$$x = \log_\varepsilon z - \log_\varepsilon 9.6 \qquad (4.2)$$

for S, and

$$x = \log_\varepsilon z - \tfrac{1}{2}(\log_\varepsilon 54 + \log_\varepsilon 90) \qquad (4.3)$$

for T, where

$$\varepsilon = (5/3)^{\frac{1}{2}},$$

the doses are representable by the simple integers shown in the last line of Table 4.1. Alternatively, in order to avoid negative values, metameters might have been chosen so that the values of x were 0, 1, 2, for S and 0, 1, 2, 3 for T, but the set used here has the advantage of making $\bar{x}$ almost zero (not exactly, because of unequal numbers of subjects per dose) for each preparation. The essential feature of the metameter scale is that the same base of logarithms is used for both preparations. Provided that this is done, the actual choice of base, and the addition (or subtraction) of different quantities to the logarithms for each preparation affect only the intermediate arithmetic ; at the end of the analysis, a simple adjustment removes all effects of these simplifying steps.

4.3 The dose–response diagram

A diagram should be drawn to show mean response at each dose level plotted against x (Fig. 4.1). Not only is this useful as leading to a rapid estimation of potency, but it is also a protection against gross errors or misinterpretations of the statistical analysis. The experienced user of assay techniques may often dispense with the diagram, at least for symmetrical designs, because he can visualize its form without drawing it, but to others a sketch is practically essential. In Fig. 4.1, two parallel lines have been drawn by eye so as to fit the points approximately, and these may be used to give a rough idea of the potency. From the diagram,

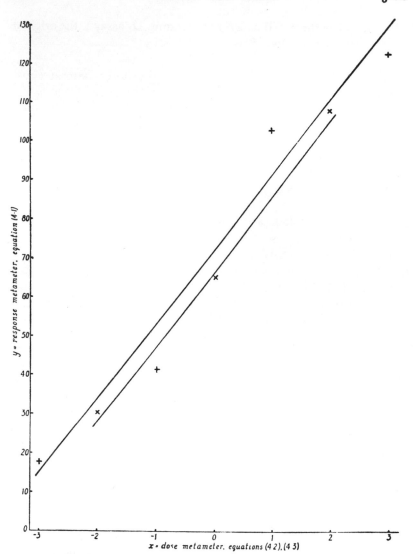

Fig. 4.1—Linear dose-response regressions for the assay of vitamin D₃, Table 4.1

× : Mean responses to standard preparation
+ : Mean responses to test preparation

The straight lines are those drawn by eye (§ 4.3), but the equations calculated in § 4.11 are almost identical with them.

the difference in x between doses giving equal responses, which is the horizontal distance between the lines, is

$$M = 0\cdot3.$$

Since

$$\log_{10} R = \log_e R \times \log_{10} \varepsilon, \tag{4.4}$$

for any ε, by the use of equations (4.2) and (4.3) an estimate of relative potency is obtained from

$$\log_{10} R = M \times \tfrac{1}{2}\log_{10}(\tfrac{5}{3}) + \log_{10} 9\cdot6 - \tfrac{1}{2}(\log_{10} 54 + \log_{10} 90)$$
$$= 0\cdot1109M + \bar{1}\cdot1390 \tag{4.5}$$
$$= \bar{1}\cdot1723,$$

whence

$$R = 0\cdot149. \tag{4.6}$$

Thus the potency of the cod-liver oil is estimated as 149 units per g.

One feature of the assay noticeable in the diagram must generally be regarded as bad (§ 6.8) : the dose range and the response range for the test preparation are wider than for the standard preparation. If the dose range for S was as wide as the experimenter dared risk in order to be sure of remaining within the region of linearity, his choice of a wider spread of doses for T was unwise as it was almost sure to take him outside the range of linearity. If the dose range for S was not as wide as he dared risk, he was at fault for not making it wider, at least up to the width used for T. This design, however, may not be quite as bad as strict application of the principles of § 6.8 suggests. If the experimenter had little idea of the potency of T before he made his assay, he might have chosen four doses, extending over a wide range, with the intention of discarding the data from that one of the extremes which proved to be outside the region of linearity ; when he found satisfactory linearity over the whole range, he naturally retained all the data. Even so, the data suggest that a wider range of doses of S could safely and advantageously have been used.

4.4 Analysis of variance

The next stage is to form the analysis of variance, using a procedure very similar to that for the data on a single regression discussed in § 3.9. For the standard preparation, the appropriate summations give :

$N_S = 27,$

$Sx = -9 \times 2 + 8 \times 2$

$\quad = -2,$

$\bar{x}_S = -2/27$

$\quad = -0.0741,$

$Sy = 1,783,$

$\bar{y}_S = 66.04,$

$S_{xx} = 9 \times 4 + 8 \times 4 - \dfrac{(-2)^2}{27}$

$\quad = 67.8519,$

$S_{xy} = -2 \times 274 + 2 \times 859 - \dfrac{(-2) \times 1,783}{27}$

$\quad = 1,302.07.$

Similarly, for the test preparation,

$N_T = 28,$

$Sx = 2,$

$\bar{x}_T = 0.0714,$

$Sy = 2,047,$

$\bar{y}_T = 73.11,$

$S_{xx} = 7 \times 9 + 6 \times 1 + 8 \times 1 + 7 \times 9 - \dfrac{2^2}{28}$

$\quad = 139.8571,$

$S_{xy} = -3 \times 123 - 1 \times 249 + 1 \times 820 + 3 \times 855 - \dfrac{2 \times 2,047}{28}$

$\quad = 2,620.79.$

The analysis of variance may then be completed, and is given in Table 4.2. Notes on each item of the sum of squares column are given below the table, in the order in which they are most conveniently computed. Mean squares are inserted for the items of chief interest.

TABLE 4.2—Analysis of variance for the data of Table 4.1

1	Adjustment for mean		266,707	
	Nature of variation	d.f.	Sum of squares*	Mean square
4	Preparations ...	1	687	687
5	Regression	1	74,088	74,088
6	Parallelism	1	10	10
7	Linearity	3	2,312	771
3	Between doses ...	6	77,097	
8	Error (within doses)	48	22,928	477·67
2	Total	54	100,025	

* Notes on formation of sums of squares :—

(1) $\dfrac{(1{,}783 + 2{,}047)^2}{55} = 266{,}707.$

(2) $35^2 + 30^2 + 24^2 + \ldots + 84^2 + 101^2 - 266{,}707 = 100{,}025.$

(3) $\dfrac{274^2}{9} + \dfrac{650^2}{10} + \dfrac{859^2}{8} + \dfrac{123^2}{7} + \dfrac{249^2}{6} + \dfrac{820^2}{8} + \dfrac{855^2}{7} - 266{,}707 = 77{,}097.$

(4) $\dfrac{1{,}783^2}{27} + \dfrac{2{,}047^2}{28} - 266{,}707 = 687.$

(5) Pooled regression component, given by

$$\frac{(\Sigma S_{xy})^2}{\Sigma S_{xx}} = \frac{(1{,}302 \cdot 07 + 2{,}620 \cdot 79)^2}{67 \cdot 8519 + 139 \cdot 8571}$$
$$= \frac{(3{,}922 \cdot 86)^2}{207 \cdot 7090}$$
$$= 74{,}088.$$

(6) Difference between fitting two independent regression coefficients and one pooled value

$$\Sigma \left\{ \frac{(S_{xy})^2}{S_{xx}} \right\} - \frac{(\Sigma S_{xy})^2}{\Sigma S_{xx}} = \frac{1{,}302 \cdot 07^2}{67 \cdot 8519} + \frac{2{,}620 \cdot 79^2}{139 \cdot 8571} - 74{,}088.$$
$$= 10.$$

(7) $77{,}097 - (687 + 74{,}088 + 10) = 2{,}312.$

(8) $100{,}025 - 77{,}097 = 22{,}928.$

The components of the analysis must next be examined in detail. The mean square from the error line of the analysis,

$$s^2 = 477 \cdot 67, \tag{4.7}$$

will be used as the basic variance estimate, unless any evidence of its unsuitability is found.

4.5 Scedasticity

The error sum of squares in Table 4.2 comprises contributions from each of the seven doses. These may be examined separately in order to discover whether there is any evidence of heteroscedasticity. The tests of significance for other validity tests (§§ 4.6–4.8), and the assessment of precision of the potency estimate (§ 4.12), in theory require that $\sigma^2(y)$ be independent of Y, the expected response to any dose, though experience shows that even quite large departures from homoscedasticity do not matter much. In more complex designs, to test the homogeneity of variance may be impracticable, but care in the preliminary investigation and in the choice of doses will generally remove the risk of a degree of heteroscedasticity that might seriously disturb the estimation.

TABLE 4.3—Test of variance heterogeneity for the data of Table 4.1

	f_i	Sum of squares	s_i^2	$\log s_i^2$
	8	3,268	408·5	2·611
S	9	2,808	312·0	2·494
	7	2,280	325·7	2·513
	6	1,854	309·0	2·490
	5	4,356	871·2	2·940
T	7	5,392	770·3	2·887
	6	2,971	495·2	2·695
	48	22,929	477·7	2·679

Table 4.3 shows the seven mean squares, s_i^2, with their degrees of freedom, f_i ; the last line of the table contains the total number

of degrees of freedom, f, the pooled sum of squares (in agreement with Table 4.2 except for a discrepancy in the last digit), and the pooled mean square, s^2. A final column shows the logarithms of the mean squares. Bartlett's test (§ 3.11) then gives, by equation (3.39),

$$\chi^2_{[6]} = 2\cdot3026 \times 1\cdot648$$
$$= 3\cdot79 \; ;$$

this χ^2 is well below the 5 per cent. significance level (12.6), so that it need not be adjusted by the factor C, equation (3.42). The data give no cause for worry about heteroscedasticity.

4.6 Linearity

The mean square for ' Linearity ', or, more fully, ' Deviations from linearity ' should next be examined. A preliminary investigation will be presumed to have established that, over a range of responses such as occurs here, the regression of bone ash percentage on log dose is practically linear. Before the potency of the cod-liver oil is estimated, a check is required that nothing has seriously disturbed this linearity. Unless accompanied by other danger signals, a mean square that is large relative to the error would most probably indicate *statistical invalidity*, that is to say, inappropriateness of the form of analysis adopted. For example, bad choice of doses for either preparation might take most of the observations off the linear portion of the response curve ; the conditions of similarity and monotony might be fulfilled, so that in theory the data would still be suitable for an assay, but the assumption of a linear regression would no longer be justified. This non-linearity would not in itself be regarded as evidence against the inherent comparability of the two preparations. The assay might be rejected, however, because a satisfactory linearizing transformation could not be found without more extensive data, it might be rejected because the low sensitivity to changes in dose for the level of response attained would make any estimate of ρ hopelessly imprecise, or it might still be usable (see also § 4.22).

The mean square for linearity in Table 4.2 is greater than that for error, but not significantly so, and indeed the difference is not great enough to occasion any alarm.

4.7 The difference in preparations

Unlike an ordinary experiment for the comparison of different treatments, no direct interest attaches to the mean difference in response between the two preparations. Nevertheless, a large mean square for this component is an indication that the assay is not very satisfactory. A large difference between means will seldom arise unless the responses to either the lowest or the highest doses of the test preparation lie far outside the range of responses to the standard, though the converse is not necessarily true. As already noted (§ 4.3), in a well-planned assay this should not happen : if it does, either the range of doses for the standard preparation ought to have been wider or that for the test preparation was too wide and extended beyond the region of linearity. Moreover, as will be apparent from § 4.12, a large difference in mean responses will decrease the precision of potency estimation (§ 6.8).

In this assay, at both extremes of dose the responses to the test preparation lie outside the range for the standard, and in the formation of the mean response these extremes compensate for one another. The mean square for preparations, therefore, is only a little greater than the error mean square, yet the assay is certainly open to criticism on account of the choice of doses of the test preparation. Though a large mean square for the difference in preparations is always to be interpreted as a danger signal, a small one is no assurance that all is well. Results of an assay like the present should be treated with some reserve, and the response diagram should be inspected for any serious indications of non-linearity at the extremes of the test preparation regression.

4.8 Parallelism

If other tests had disclosed no significantly large mean squares for linearity or preparations, a large mean square for the component based on deviations from parallelism would indicate *fundamental invalidity* of the assay. As shown in § 3.3, the condition of similarity, an essential condition for an analytical dilution assay, demands the parallelism of regression curves when log dose is used as a metameter. If these curves are linear (§ 3.7), a non-parallelism of the lines would be a violation of the condition of similarity : the initial assumption that the test preparation acted as a dilution of the standard either is inherently false or has been obscured by the presence of an impurity in one preparation. Data that behaved in this manner would be no use for a dilution assay, and would have to be discarded ; this, of course, is without prejudice to the possibility of deliberately using non-parallel regressions for other types of assay, as suggested by Thompson (1948).

If danger signals appeared simultaneously in several of these tests, assignment of the cause to any one of the explanations given might be impossible. The whole assay is then suspect, and should be discarded ; whether it is fundamentally invalid or statistically intractable matters little, except in so far as the planning and experimental technique for the next assay may be affected.

Table 4.2 shows no evidence of deviations from parallelism.

4.9 Regression

In any good assay, the mean square for regression ought to be relatively large. If there were no regression, the dose-response 'relationship' could be of no use for the estimation of potency. No assay should be undertaken without strong prior belief in the existence of a regression, and the variance ratio for the regression component will therefore generally be highly significant. Here, for example, it is

$$F = \frac{74,088}{477 \cdot 67}$$
$$= 155.$$

Moreover, unless this ratio is large, the value of g used in the assessment of fiducial limits will be large (§§ 2.5, 4.12).

4.10 Significance levels

In the validity tests described in §§ 4.5–4.8, though a significance test at a probability of 0·05 was implied, the decision was clear cut every time and any reasonable probability level would have given the same answer. What level is ideal for these tests in general ?

The experimenter need not feel bound to use the level that is to be used later for the fiducial limits. Some might think, that very stringent tests should be applied, especially for parallelism, because of the importance of rejecting invalid analyses : perhaps a probability of 0·10 should be used instead of 0·05. Others might think this extravagant, because many good sets of data would be rejected on account of the mischances of random sampling. Experience suggests that, at least as regards statistical validity, in a well planned assay even fairly large deviations from the strict theoretical requirements will have little effect on the estimate of ρ and not much on the assessment of its precision. If the design is symmetrical, with the same number of doses for both preparations and equal numbers of subjects at every dose (Chapter 5), and if the experimenter guesses his doses of T so successfully that they are almost exactly equivalent to those of S, a determination of R

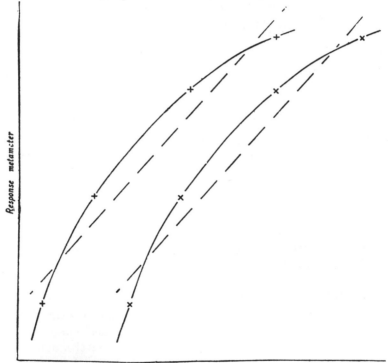

Dose metameter

Fig. 4.2—Illustration of the manner in which a successful choice of doses allows a valid estimation of potency to be formed from parallel linear regressions, even though the true regression is curved.

    × : Mean responses to standard preparation
    + : Mean responses to test preparation
        Full lines indicate true regression curves, broken lines are hypothetical estimated linear regressions.

from the horizontal distance between linear regressions will be valid even though the true regression is curved. This is illustrated by Fig. 4.2. The assessment of error in such a situation may be (not necessarily will be ; *cf.* § 5.11) seriously upset. On the other hand, with the same type of regression, a bad choice of doses may give apparent parallelism but a hopelessly biased estimate (Fig. 4.3), or complete non-parallelism (Fig. 4.4), in spite of the fundamental validity of the assay.

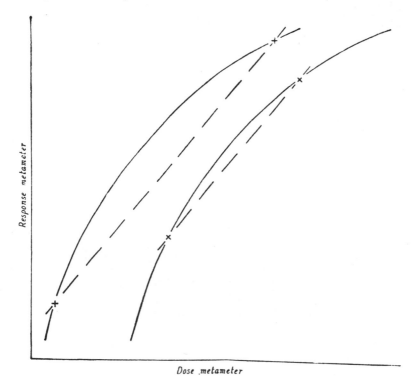

Dose metameter

Fig. 4.3—Illustration of a 4-point assay showing apparent parallelism of linear regressions but biased estimation of potency, with true regressions conforming to the condition of similarity

    × :   Mean responses to standard preparation

    + :   Mean responses to test preparation

        Full lines indicate true regression curves, broken lines are hypothetical estimated linear regressions.

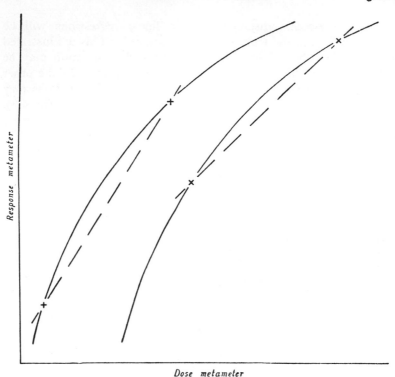

Fig. 4.4—Illustration of a 4-point assay showing non-parallelism of linear
regressions, even though the true regressions conform to the
condition of similarity

× : Mean responses to standard preparation
+ : Mean responses to test preparation
Full lines indicate true regression curves, broken lines are
hypothetical estimated linear regressions.

Perhaps the chief danger is that of unparallelism, for this is
a warning of fundamental invalidity, and a reasonably stringent
test therefore seems desirable.   A deviation from parallelism
significant at a probability level of 0·05 should be regarded as
sufficient cause for the rejection of an assay, unless there are
extenuating circumstances which not only explain the situation
but ensure a statistically valid analysis.   In the absence of a strong
presumption of parallelism from previous work, even a deviation
significant at a probability of 0·10 should be a little suspect.

Provided that experience of the assay technique (*i.e.* the method
for analysis of test preparations with respect to a particular effective

constituent, by a standard procedure, and on a known stock of subjects) has given grounds for belief in the condition of similarity and in the statistical validity of the method of evaluation of the data, and also that the current assay gives no evidence of unparallelism, less stringent tests for heteroscedasticity, deviations from linearity, and the difference between preparations might be allowed. The important features are the magnitude of the deviations from homoscedasticity, the magnitude of the deviations from linearity, and the magnitude of the difference between preparations ; to assign satisfactory numerical measures to the first two, or in any simple manner to express quantitatively how they affect the estimation, is difficult. In practice, acceptance of the analysis as statistically valid unless one or more of these criteria are significant at a probability of 0·01 seems reasonable. This is intended as a working rule, to be applied and interpreted intelligently, not uncritically. The question is not entirely one of statistics ; the knowledge of the chemist and biologist about the materials of the assay must also be taken into account. For routine assays, quality control techniques may with advantage be applied to the criteria of statistical validity (§ 5.10).

4.11 Potency estimation

The cod-liver oil assay of Table 4.1 has disclosed no evidence of invalidity. The regression coefficient is estimated as

$$b = \frac{\varSigma S_{xy}}{\varSigma S_{xx}} \tag{4.8}$$
$$= \frac{3{,}922 \cdot 86}{207 \cdot 7090}$$
$$= 18 \cdot 89.$$

The regression equations fitted to the data, obtained as

$$Y = \bar{y} + b\,(x - \bar{x}) \tag{4.9}$$

for each preparation, therefore become

$$Y_S = 67 \cdot 44 + 18 \cdot 89x$$
$$Y_T = 71 \cdot 76 + 18 \cdot 89x.$$

These equations are not needed explicitly ; if plotted in Fig. 4.1, they would give lines almost identical with those drawn earlier by eye. All that is wanted here is the difference between equipotent values of x, the horizontal distance between the two lines, to be reckoned as positive if the test preparation is more potent than the standard on the scales of x used. This difference is

$$M = \frac{Y_T - Y_S}{b},\qquad(4.10)$$

more usefully written as

$$M = \bar{x}_S - \bar{x}_T - \frac{\bar{y}_S - \bar{y}_T}{b};\qquad(4.11)$$

equation (4.11) differs from that used in the standard slope method, equation (3.75), by having $\bar{x}_S$, $\bar{x}_T$ for x_S, x_T. Here

$$M = -0.0741 - 0.0714 - \frac{66.04 - 73.11}{18.89}$$

$$= -0.1455 + \frac{7.07}{18.89}$$

$$= 0.2288.$$

This must be transformed by equation (4.5) to give

$$\log_{10} R = \bar{1}.1644,$$

whence

$$R = 0.1460,$$

as compared with the graphical estimate, 0.149, in equation (4.6).

4.12 Fiducial limits

Equation (4.11) might be written

$$M - (\bar{x}_S - \bar{x}_T) = \frac{\bar{y}_T - \bar{y}_S}{b}.$$

Since $(\bar{x}_S - \bar{x}_T)$ is a constant imposed by the choice of doses in the experiment, fiducial limits to M may be found by applying Fieller's theorem to the ratio $(\bar{y}_T - \bar{y}_S)/b$ and adding $(\bar{x}_S - \bar{x}_T)$ to the results. The general formula for the limits to $(M - \bar{x}_S + \bar{x}_T)$ is

$$\left[M - \bar{x}_S + \bar{x}_T \pm \frac{ts}{b}\left\{ (1-g)\left(\frac{1}{N_S} + \frac{1}{N_T}\right) + \frac{(M - \bar{x}_S + \bar{x}_T)^2}{\Sigma S_{xx}} \right\}^{\frac{1}{2}} \right]$$
$$\div (1-g),\qquad(4.12)$$

where

$$g = \frac{t^2 s^2}{b^2 \,\Sigma S_{xx}};\qquad(4.13)$$

the close similarity to (3.79) and (3.78) is apparent. Here, with s^2 taken from equation (4.7),

$$g = \frac{(2 \cdot 010)^2 \times 477 \cdot 67}{(18 \cdot 89)^2 \times 207 \cdot 7090}$$

$$= 0 \cdot 0260.$$

Alternatively, g may be calculated as the ratio of the tabulated significance point for the variance ratio for 'regression' to the value calculated from the analysis of variance. The variance ratio here has (1,48) degrees of freedom, whence (Appendix Table II)

$$g = \frac{4 \cdot 04 \times 477 \cdot 67}{74,088}$$

$$= 0 \cdot 0260 \; ;$$

this form of calculation is sometimes more convenient. The limits to $(M + 0 \cdot 1455)$ are now evaluated as

$$\left[0 \cdot 3743 \pm \frac{2 \cdot 010}{18 \cdot 89} \sqrt{\left\{ 0 \cdot 9740 \left(\frac{1}{27} + \frac{1}{28} \right) + \frac{(0 \cdot 3743)^2}{207 \cdot 7090} \right\} \times 477 \cdot 67} \right] \div 0 \cdot 9740$$

$$= [0 \cdot 3743 \pm 0 \cdot 6220] \div 0 \cdot 9740$$

$$= - 0 \cdot 2543, \; 1 \cdot 0229.$$

Therefore

$$M_L = - 0 \cdot 3998,$$
$$M_U = 0 \cdot 8774.$$

Once again equation (4.5) is used, and gives

$$\log_{10} R_L = \bar{1} \cdot 0947,$$
$$\log_{10} R_U = \bar{1} \cdot 2363,$$

whence

$$R_L = 0 \cdot 1244,$$
$$R_U = 0 \cdot 1723.$$

In this instance, g was so small that it could safely have been ignored. The equation

$$V(M) = \frac{s^2}{b^2} \left\{ \frac{1}{N_S} + \frac{1}{N_T} + \frac{(M - \bar{x}_S + \bar{x}_T)^2}{\Sigma S_{xx}} \right\} \tag{4.14}$$

is frequently quoted as the variance for M ; it is in fact an expression of equation (2.10) in the present notation. If used for these data, it gives $0 \cdot 3135$ as the standard error of M, and fiducial limits of M

are obtained by subtracting and adding 2·010 times this, as in equation (2.9). Table 4.4 summarizes the results by the various methods. Here the effect of ignoring g is of no importance. Nevertheless, once g has been calculated, to use Fieller's theorem is little more trouble than to use the formula for $V(M)$, and the former is the safer practice. The results of both are presented here for the interest of the comparison, but with no suggestion that this should always be done. The quotation of both ' exact ' and ' approximate ' fiducial limits, in reports and papers whose concern is with the results of assays and not with statistical methodology, is to be deprecated; it is a waste of space on irrelevant and misleading quantities. When g is large, Fieller's theorem should always be used, and values based on any formula for $V(M)$ are wrong.

TABLE 4.4—Estimated potency of cod-liver oil

(In units vitamin D_3 per g.)

	Graphical method	Calculated	
		Ignoring g	Fieller's theorem
Potency ...	149	146·0	146·0
Lower limit ...	—	124·3	124·4
Upper limit ...	—	171·5	172·3

Subject to the reservations already made on account of the excessive range of responses for the test preparation, the vitamin content of the cod-liver oil is estimated as 146·0 units per g., and, by the fiducial argument (§ 2.4), the assertion is made that the true potency lies between 85 per cent. and 118 per cent. of this. Here and elsewhere, the experimenter should remember that his fiducial limits are calculated from the internal evidence of a single assay, yet their subsequent use is likely to assume that they measure the agreement to be expected between results of repeated assays of the same test preparation (*cf.* Finney, 1952, § 56). Provided that the condition of similarity is fulfilled and that assumptions implicit in the statistical analysis (linearity, homoscedasticity, normality, etc.) are substantially correct, this is justifiable. Potency estimation ought then to be independent of assay technique (§ 3.4), and the assessment of sampling variation expressed by the fiducial limits ought to have

universal validity. Nevertheless, a too ready belief that all conditions
are satisfied, and that repeated assays will agree within the limits
indicated by intra-assay variances, is dangerous. Published examples
are few. Young and Romans (1948) reported satisfactorily consistent
potency estimates for twenty-one insulin samples when each was
assayed several times within a few days. Jones (1945) found X-ray
and line test assays of vitamin D to agree well during a period of more
than three years. Sheps and Munson (1957) proposed a method for
taking account of inter-assay variance of M as well as of intra-assay;
in a series of androgen assays, they found an important inter-assay
component, but did not reconcile this with the general theory of
bioassay. The *British Pharmacopoeia* (1958) explicitly counsels that,
where possible, precision should also be assessed in terms of a simple
error mean square calculated from potency estimates from independent assays.

4.13 Data for a 4-point assay

Much of the complexity in the analysis of the data in Table 4.1
is due to the lack of symmetry in the assay design. The general
principles of good design will be made clear in later chapters
(especially Chapter 6), but the coming discussion may be anticipated
by the statement that symmetry is one desirable feature. The
simplest symmetrical design for parallel line assays is the 4-*point
design*, in which only two doses of each preparation are included ;
the high and low doses of the two preparations have the same
difference on the logarithmic scale, and the total number of subjects
is divided equally between doses. Bliss and Marks (1939*a*, *b*) and
Schild (1942) have given good accounts of the statistical analysis
appropriate to assays of this design, essentially the same as will be
described here but with some differences of notation.

The data in Table 4.5 relate to an assay of oestrone by means
of the responses of ovariectomized female rats (Bülbring and Burn,
1935) ; the response recorded was the weight of the uterus,
expressed as mg. per 100 g. body weight and measured at a fixed
number of days after treatment of the animals. This method of
adjusting for inequalities in the sizes of the subjects will be criticized
in Chapter 12 ; here there was no possibility of using a covariance
analysis on body weight, since only the records in Table 4.5 are
available. Rats were injected daily with one of the four experimental

doses, 0·2μg. and 0·4μg. of the standard oestrone and 0·0075 c.c.
and 0·015 c.c. of the preparation to be assayed, the same dose being
given to any one rat throughout the experiment.

TABLE 4.5—Weights of uteri of ovariectomized rats

(In mg. per 100 g. body weight)

Litter	Daily dose				Totals	
	Oestrone 0·2μg.	0·4μg.	Test preparation 0·0075 c.c.	0·015 c.c.	Totals	
I	54	152	61	92	359	
II	49	71	74	63	257	
III	51	112	51	(87)	214	(301)
IV	(50)	58	60	102	220	(270)
V	81	102	(82)	120	303	(385)
VI	63	(111)	83	105	251	(362)
VII	126	(133)	83	108	317	(450)
Totals ...	424	495	412	590	1,921	
	(474)	(739)	(494)	(677)		(2,384)
Means ...	(67·7)	(105·6)	(70·6)	(96·7)		

Values in brackets in the body of the table have been calculated. Totals
without brackets exclude, totals within brackets include the calculated values.

Rats from seven litters were used. There was reason to expect
that litters would differ in mean uterine weight quite apart from any
effect of oestrone, an opinion confirmed by the results ; in order
to eliminate ill effects of inter-litter differences upon the precision
of the assay, a randomized block design was adopted, and one
animal from each litter, selected at random, was assigned to each
of the four doses. Unfortunately, either because some litters

contained only three females or because some animals were lost during the course of the experiment, the records from five litters relate only to three animals.

Most 4-point assays will have completely balanced designs, with equal numbers of subjects at all doses and in all blocks, and the first concern of the reader should be to master the statistical analysis of these. The data in Table 4.5 have been augmented by five values, shown in brackets, that complete the symmetry of the design ; the bracketed totals for litters and for doses include these extra ' data '. The justification for inserting these particular values is discussed in § 4.14. The reader who is unfamiliar with the standard method of analysis for a 4-point assay should proceed immediately to §§ 4.16–4.18, where he will find Table 4.5 analysed as though all the data were from independent observations. He must remember, however, that this is only for the convenience of exposition; in reality, if the symmetry of an assay is marred by missing values, the methods of §§ 4.14, 4.19, 4.20 (or equivalents) must be applied before conclusions can safely be drawn. A 4-point assay free from these complications is described in § 5.3.

4.14 Missing values

Even in the most carefully conducted experiment, an accident or unforeseeable circumstance may cause the loss of one subject, and so destroy the symmetry of the design. Severe limitation of the total number of subjects may also force the adoption of an unsymmetrical design. In the oestrone assay, for example, if five of the seven litters available for use contained only three females, the design adopted was about the best that could be contrived ; certainly it was a better choice than a design omitting one dose of the test preparation entirely or from each of the five litters. When the design fails to achieve symmetry only because of one or two gaps in the complete table of responses, a method of statistical analysis based upon reconstruction of the missing entries is usually the most convenient.

The analysis of this oestrone assay requires that special measures be taken in order to prevent the conclusions from being biased by the absence of some records. Inspection of the genuine data in Table 4.5 indicates large differences between litters, so that simple averaging of columns would give an unfair representation of the effects of doses. Litter IV, for example, gave low results, and therefore the average of the responses of the other six litters for the lower dose of the standard preparation would give too high a value relative to other doses. The difficulty is overcome by calculating from the data values which, when inserted in the empty spaces of the table, will remove any distortion in the means. The general procedure is to use symbols $y_1, y_2, y_3, \ldots$ to represent the missing values, to perform an analysis of variance of all the data in terms of these symbols, to express the error sum of squares as a quadratic function of the unknowns, and then to determine $y_1, y_2, y_3, \ldots$ by the condition that the error sum of squares shall be a minimum. The same method has been used in many other applications of statistical science, notably in agricultural field-plot experiments, and, for some standard experimental designs, simple formulæ have been developed (Snedecor, 1956, §§ 11.6, 11.7); papers by Anderson (1946) and Yates (1933a) may be noted as giving more detail than is usually to be found in text-books. For example, when a single value must be calculated in a randomized block design, the formula

$$y = \frac{rR + cC - G}{(r-1)(c-1)} \tag{4.15}$$

may be used; r is the number of rows (here litters) in the table of results and R the total of all data in the same row as the missing entry*, c is the number of columns (here doses) and C the total of all data in the same column as the missing entry, and G is the total of all the data. Equation (4.15) can be seen to represent a compromise between the average of all other entries in the same row and the average of all other entries in the same column. When more than one entry is missing, the formula may be applied iteratively. Values are guessed for all except the first, and the formula is used to calculate the first; the result, together with all guessed values except that for the second missing entry, is then used in a calculation of the second, and so on until all have been calculated. The process is repeated so as to revise the first, second, . . . values with the aid of the results of the first set

---

* This momentary use of R in a sense entirely different from that of a relative potency should not confuse the reader; it will occur only when missing data have to be discussed.

of calculations, and the iteration is continued until two successive cycles agree closely. The values then attained are independent of the initial guesses. In the present assay, the formula

$$y = \frac{7R + 4C - G}{18}$$

is used to give

	y_1	y_2	y_3	y_4	y_5
Guesses :—	—	30	92	91	154
Cycle I :—	87	50	81	114	133
Cycle II :—	87	50	81	111	133
Final :—	87	50	82	111	133

(The reader may verify that any other set of ' guesses ' yields the same final line.)

The possibility of calculating ' missing values ' in this manner must not be thought a justification for careless experimentation, either in choice of a design or in failure to make complete records. Though the calculated values are estimates of the responses that would have been found in a complete experiment, they do not create information by some statistical trick. Their primary function is to eliminate bias in the comparison of means, and Table 4.5 has been completed by the insertion of the values just calculated. If an analysis of variance is performed, using the calculated entries as though they were genuine, the error mean square is an unbiased estimate of the variance per response provided that the number of degrees of freedom for error is reduced by the number of missing entries inserted. The loss of information is felt, however, when mean responses for different doses are compared. In particular, though the functions of mean responses used in the formation of $(\bar{y}_S - \bar{y}_T)$ and b are unbiased, their variances are increased to an extent that must be carefully considered (§§ 4.19, 4.20).

4.15 The dose-response diagram

The reader should draw a dose-response diagram for the mean responses in Table 4.5. A convenient dose scale, using logarithms to base $\sqrt{2}$, makes $(x - \bar{x})$ equal to -1 for the lower, $+1$ for the upper dose of either preparation. Different origins may be used for the x scale of the two preparations, and a simple choice is that which makes the two lower doses have the same scale point.

A rough estimate of potency can be derived from parallel regression lines drawn by eye in this diagram. One version of the diagram had lines 0·18 apart in a direction parallel to the axis of x. Hence

$$M = \bar{x}_S - \bar{x}_T - 0{\cdot}18,$$

and, using a formula similar to equation (4.5),

$$\log_{10} R = \log_{10} 0{\cdot}2 - \log_{10} 0{\cdot}0075 - 0{\cdot}18 \times \tfrac{1}{2} \times \log_{10} 2, \quad (4.16)$$

since symmetry makes $(\bar{x}_S - \bar{x}_T)$ equal to the difference in x values for corresponding doses. Therefore

$$R = \frac{0{\cdot}2}{0{\cdot}0075} \text{ antilog } \bar{1}{\cdot}973$$

$$= 25,$$

and 1 c.c. of the test preparation is estimated to contain 25μg. oestrone.

4.16   Analysis of variance

The calculations will now be completed as though the five calculated responses in Table 4.5 were genuine measurements. The only allowance made for the effect of their insertion will be reductions in the degrees of freedom for error from 18 to 13, and the total from 27 to 22. As an approximation to the correct analysis this is crude, and in practice it should not be adopted if more than one response is 'missing'. It is given here in order to illustrate the simplicity of the analysis for a symmetrical 4-point assay without obscuring the discussion by complications that should seldom arise. In § 4.19, the exact analysis appropriate to an assay with missing values will be considered, and in § 4.20 a useful approximate method will be proposed.

Table 4.6 shows the analysis of variance. The total sum of squares is formed from the 28 entries in the body of Table 4.5. The subdivision of the total into components 'between doses', 'between litters', and 'error' follows the familiar procedure for a randomized block design: for example, the sum of squares between doses is

$$(474^2 + 739^2 + 494^2 + 677^2 - 7 \times 202{,}981) \div 7.$$

The subdivision of the component for doses into squares for three separate degrees of freedom can be effected by the same steps as were used to give lines 4, 5, 6 in Table 4.2. For a symmetrical design, the device of orthogonal contrasts, illustrated in Table 4.7, is more convenient. The dose totals are multiplied in turn by each set of coefficients and summed to give the sums of products in the last column, each of which will be denoted by the letter L with some distinguishing affix. These sums are squared and divided by the 'divisors' shown, and the quotients are the components required in Table 4.6.

TABLE 4.6—Analysis of variance for the data of Table 4.5

Adjustment for mean		202,981	Mean square
Nature of variation	d.f.	Sum of squares	
Preparations	1	63	63
Regression	1	7,168	7,168
Parallelism	1	240	240
Between doses	3	7,471	
Between litters	6	7,069	
Error	13	7,165	551·2
Total	22	21,705	

The conditions to be fulfilled in order that a set of coefficients such as those in Table 4.7 shall lead to a subdivision of the sum of squares for doses are :

(i) Each set of coefficients shall represent a *contrast* amongst the individual responses ; that is to say, if each sum in Table 4.7 is expressed in terms of individual responses, the set of coefficients for these responses shall add to zero.

(ii) Every pair of contrasts shall be *orthogonal* ; that is to say, if each contrast is expressed in terms of individual responses, the products of corresponding coefficients for any two contrasts shall add to zero.

TABLE 4.7—Coefficients of orthogonal contrasts for the 4-point design
Applied to the data of Table 4.5

Doses	S_1	S_2	T_1	T_2	Divisor	Sum
Response totals ...	474	739	494	677		
Preparations (L_p)	−1	−1	1	1	28	− 42
Regression (L_1) ...	−1	1	−1	1	28	448
Parallelism (L_1') ...	1	−1	−1	1	28	− 82

Because each dose total in a symmetrical design contains the same number of individual responses, these conditions may be applied to the coefficients of dose totals instead. Therefore, since

$$-1 + 1 - 1 + 1 = 0$$

the line for ' Regression ' represents a contrast, and since

$$(-1) \times 1 + 1 \times (-1) + (-1) \times (-1) + 1 \times 1 = 0$$

the contrasts for ' Regression ' and ' Parallelism ' are orthogonal. The divisors are calculated as the sums of the squares of the coefficients of individual responses, a rule which gives for ' Regression '

$$7 \times (-1)^2 + 7 \times 1^2 + 7 \times (-1)^2 + 7 \times 1^2 = 28.$$

A consequence of these conditions is that the squares for the separate contrasts must add to the sum of squares for doses ; here

$$\frac{(-42)^2}{28} + \frac{448^2}{28} + \frac{(-82)^2}{28} = 7,471.$$

The set of orthogonal contrasts is not unique. A sum of squares of deviations can be subdivided into single squares for mutually orthogonal contrasts, in number equal to the degrees of freedom, in an unlimited number of ways ; the set chosen here is peculiarly relevant to the object of the analysis of variance. The three squares are exactly the same as would have been obtained if the general method of § 4.4 had been used. The first contrast in Table 4.7

gives the difference between totals for the two preparations, the second has $(x - \bar{x})$ as its coefficients, so that the sum is ΣS_{xy}, and the third gives the difference between values of S_{xy} for the preparations. Bliss and Marks (1939a, b) showed the advantages of polynomial coefficients in the analysis of assays (cf. Chapter 5).

4.17 Validity tests

As in §§ 4.7, 4.8, the mean squares for preparations and parallelism must be compared with the error mean square. Neither is significantly large, so that on these counts the validity of the assay need not be doubted. Use of the five calculated values will to some extent bias these tests of significance, but could scarcely do so to an extent sufficient to mask genuine effects under the guise of the small mean squares in Table 4.6. Anderson (1946) and Yates (1933a) have described the calculations for unbiased tests of significance when missing values have been inserted.

The great flaw in the 4-point design is that it gives no test for linearity, since only two points on each response curve are studied. A genuinely non-linear regression might manifest itself as non-parallelism, at least if the doses had been so unsuccessfully chosen as to give also a large difference between preparations (Fig. 4.4). On the other hand, if doses of the test preparation were so chosen that they were almost equal in effect to corresponding doses of the standard, the fitted lines would appear as satisfactorily parallel even though the true relationship was far from linear (Fig. 4.2). As pointed out in § 4.10, this will not bias the estimation of potency appreciably, but may upset the assessment of precision. Because a 4-point design usually fails to detect non-linearity, assays should be planned to include at least three doses of each preparation (§ 6.10), unless the material under assay is so well understood as to remove all fear of non-linearity.

4.18 Potency estimation and precision

The mode of construction of Table 4.7 makes clear that the contrast labelled L_p is simply the difference in total responses for the two preparations. Hence

$$\bar{y}_T - \bar{y}_S = L_p/14$$
$$= -42/14$$
$$= -3 \cdot 00.$$

Moreover, the divisor and sum for the regression contrast, L_1, are ΣS_{xx} and ΣS_{xy} respectively, and therefore, by equation (4.8),

$$b = L_1/28$$
$$= 448/28$$
$$= 16 \cdot 00.$$

Equation (4.11) now gives

$$M = \bar{x}_S - \bar{x}_T - 0 \cdot 1875,$$

and, by equation (4.16),

$$R = \frac{0 \cdot 2}{0 \cdot 0075} \text{ antilog} (- 0 \cdot 1875 \times 0 \cdot 1505)$$
$$= 25 \cdot 0.$$

Still ignoring the fact of five responses having been calculated, the fiducial limits of R may be found by use of Fieller's theorem. This involves using the error mean square in Table 4.6,

$$s^2 = 551 \cdot 2,$$

as the variance per response with 13 degrees of freedom, but otherwise acting as though the data of Table 4.5 were complete. By the well-known elementary property of a linear function of independent observations, the variance of any contrast sum can be written as the variance per response multiplied by the sum of the squares of the coefficients of individual responses in the contrast. The rule in § 4.16 by which the divisors in Table 4.7 are calculated shows this to be expressible as

$$V(L) = s^2 \times \text{Divisor} \qquad (4.17)$$

for any contrast, or

$$V\left(\frac{L}{\text{Divisor}}\right) = \frac{s^2}{\text{Divisor}}. \qquad (4.18)$$

Consequently, because of the way in which $(\bar{y}_T - \bar{y}_S)$ and b for this assay have been formed,

$$V(\bar{y}_T - \bar{y}_S) = s^2/7$$

and

$$V(b) = s^2/28.$$

By equation (4.13)

$$g = \frac{(2 \cdot 160)^2 \times 551 \cdot 2}{(16 \cdot 00)^2 \times 28}$$
$$= 0 \cdot 3588,$$

or, from Table 4.6 and the alternative method proposed in § 4.12,

$$g = \frac{4 \cdot 67 \times 551 \cdot 2}{7,168}$$

$$= 0 \cdot 3591,$$

a value that is arithmetically slightly less accurate. From equation (4.12), the fiducial limits to $(M - \bar{x}_S + \bar{x}_T)$ are

$$\left[- 0 \cdot 1875 \pm \frac{2 \cdot 160}{16 \cdot 00} \left\{ \left(\frac{0 \cdot 6412}{7} + \frac{0 \cdot 1875^2}{28} \right) \times 551 \cdot 2 \right\}^{\frac{1}{2}} \right] \div 0 \cdot 6412$$

$$= [- 0 \cdot 1875 \pm 0 \cdot 9658] \div 0 \cdot 6412$$

$$= - 1 \cdot 799, \ 1 \cdot 214.$$

Therefore

$$R_L = \frac{0 \cdot 2}{0 \cdot 0075} \text{ antilog } \bar{1} \cdot 729 = 14 \cdot 3,$$

$$R_U = \frac{0 \cdot 2}{0 \cdot 0075} \text{ antilog } 0 \cdot 183 = 40 \cdot 6.$$

Thus the potency is estimated to be $25 \cdot 0 \mu g.$ per c.c., with fiducial limits at $14 \cdot 3 \mu g.$ and $40 \cdot 6 \mu g.$ per c.c.

4.19 Exact analysis for missing entries

The contrasts expressed by the orthogonal coefficients in Table 4.7 satisfy the condition of mutual orthogonality only when the calculated values inserted into Table 4.5 are regarded as genuine. If instead these three contrasts are written in full as functions of the twenty-three true data, they are seen not to be orthogonal. Exact analysis of the assay, taking account of the five missing values, is complicated by the impossibility of using Table 4.7, or any simple alternative, in the construction of orthogonal components of an analysis of variance. Yates (1933b) and Snedecor (1956, § 11.10) have described a general procedure, the *fitting of constants*, for the analysis of non-orthogonal data. For the oestrone assay, this would involve the solution of linear equations for six parameters representing differences between the seven litters and three representing differences between the four doses, and the inversion of a 9×9 matrix (albeit a simple one) in order to obtain variances.

An easier method in an instance such as this, where differences between litters are of no direct concern and the whole interest devolves upon three special contrasts between the doses, is to set up equations for the estimation of these three contrasts alone. This may be done formally by multiple regression. Introduce three ' independent variates ' x_1, x_2, x_3, defined to take the following values at the four dose levels :

	S_1	S_2	T_1	T_2
$x_1 =$	-1	-1	1	1
$x_2 =$	-1	1	-1	1
$x_3 =$	1	-1	-1	1

Thus the three variates have the same values as the polynomial coefficients in Table 4.7, and x_2 is the $(x - \bar{x})$ of the earlier analysis. For complete data with no missing entries, the regressions on x_1, x_2, x_3, would give the sums in the last column of Table 4.7 as the various S_{xy} ; because of the orthogonality of the independent variates, the three squares for preparations, regression, linearity in Table 4.6 would then be computed as the squares attributable to the separate regressions.

The method may be applied to the genuine data of Table 4.5, after omission of all bracketed entries ; indeed it may be shown to be equivalent to the fitting of constants. An analysis of variance and covariance for x_1, x_2, x_3, y is made, all distinction between columns (doses) being dropped since these are taken account of by the independent variates. Sums of squares and products are calculated for the 22 degrees of freedom between the 23 responses, and components with 6 degrees of freedom for litter differences are subtracted. It must be remembered that some litters contain four responses and some only three ; for y, for example, the sum of squares for litters is

$$\tfrac{1}{4}\,(359^2 + 257^2) + \tfrac{1}{3}\,(214^2 + 220^2 + 303^2 + 251^2 + 317^2)$$
$$- \frac{1{,}921^2}{23} = 4{,}786.$$

Similarly, the sum of products of x_2, y for litters is

$$\tfrac{1}{3}\,(-1 \times 214 + 1 \times 220 + 1 \times 303 - 1 \times 251$$
$$- 1 \times 317) - \frac{(-1) \times 1{,}921}{23} = -2{\cdot}81.$$

The reader should have no difficulty in checking the details of the analysis, shown in Table 4.8.

TABLE 4.8—Analysis of variance and covariance in an exact analysis for the data of Table 4.5

Adjustments for means ...		0·0435	0·0435	0·0435	−0·0435	0·0435
Nature of variation	d.f.	$S_{x_1 x_1}$	$S_{x_2 x_2}$	$S_{x_3 x_3}$	$S_{x_1 x_2}$	$S_{x_1 x_3}$
Between litters ...	6	1·6232	1·6232	1·6232	−0·2898	0·2898
Within litters ...	16	21·3333	21·3333	21·3333	1·3333	−1·3333
Total	22	22·9565	22·9565	22·9565	1·0435	−1·0435

Adjustments for means ...		−0·0435	83·52	−83·52	83·52	160,445
Nature of variation	d.f.	$S_{x_2 x_3}$	$S_{x_1 y}$	$S_{x_2 y}$	$S_{x_3 y}$	S_{yy}
Between litters ...	6	−0·2898	6·81	− 2·81	62·15	4,786
Within litters ...	16	1·3333	−7·33	335·33	−38·67	12,652
Total	22	1·0435	−0·52	332·52	23·48	17,438

The equations giving the regression coefficients b_1, b_2, b_3 are

$$\frac{64}{3} b_1 + \frac{4}{3} b_2 - \frac{4}{3} b_3 = -7·33,$$

$$\frac{4}{3} b_1 + \frac{64}{3} b_2 + \frac{4}{3} b_3 = 335·33,$$

$$-\frac{4}{3} b_1 + \frac{4}{3} b_2 + \frac{64}{3} b_3 = -38·67.$$

On the left-hand sides of these equations, exact numerical values of the coefficients have been inserted (instead of their decimal expressions in Table 4.8) because they happen to be so simple in form. By solving the three sets of three equations corresponding to $i = 1$, $i = 2$, and $i = 3$

		$i = 1$	$i = 2$	$i = 3$
$\dfrac{64}{3}v_{i1} + \dfrac{4}{3}v_{i2} - \dfrac{4}{3}v_{i3}$	$=$	1	0	0
$\dfrac{4}{3}v_{i1} + \dfrac{64}{3}v_{i2} + \dfrac{4}{3}v_{i3}$	$=$	0	1	0
$-\dfrac{4}{3}v_{i1} + \dfrac{4}{3}v_{i2} + \dfrac{64}{3}v_{i3}$	$=$	0	0	1

the inverse matrix

$$V = \begin{pmatrix} 0\cdot0472\ 6891 & -0\cdot0031\ 5126 & 0\cdot0031\ 5126 \\ -0\cdot0031\ 5126 & 0\cdot0472\ 6891 & -0\cdot0031\ 5126 \\ 0\cdot0031\ 5126 & -0\cdot0031\ 5126 & 0\cdot0472\ 6891 \end{pmatrix}$$

is obtained (*cf.* Fisher, 1958, § 29). In analyses of this kind, retention of a large number of decimal places is desirable as an aid to checking and as a guard against irregularities due to the taking of differences between nearly equal large quantities. The regression coefficients are obtained as

$$b_i = -7\cdot33v_{i1} + 335\cdot33v_{i2} - 38\cdot67v_{i3},$$

and are therefore

$$b_1 = -1\cdot5251,$$
$$b_2 = 15\cdot9956,$$
$$b_3 = -2\cdot9077.$$

The sum of squares accounted for by this regression is

$$-7\cdot33b_1 + 335\cdot33b_2 - 38\cdot67b_3 = 5,487.$$

The regression on log dose alone would account for a square obtained by omission of x_1, x_3, namely

$$(335\cdot33)^2 \div \frac{64}{3} = 5,271.$$

The difference, with two degrees of freedom, is a composite test of preparations and parallelism, which cannot be separated completely because of non-orthogonality. As Table 4.9 shows, the two together are too small to occasion any alarm here ; a test of either could be made by omitting x_2 or x_3 and finding out how much of the 5,487 is left when a regression on x_1 and the other is formed, but the portions so obtained would not be independent and additive (*cf.* Table 2.5). Note that the error sum of squares is identical with that in Table 4.6, since both are obtained by choice of parameters to minimize them and the two procedures are algebraically identical. Table 4.9, however, gives unbiased validity tests.

TABLE 4.9—Final analysis of variance in an exact analysis for the data of Table 4.5

Adjustment for mean		160,445	Mean square
Nature of variation	d.f.	Sum of squares	
Regression on log dose ...	1	5,271	
Preparations and parallelism	2	216	108
Doses	3	5,487	
Litters, ignoring doses ...	6	4,786	
Error	13	7,165	551·2
Total	22	17,438	

The definitions of x_1 and x_2 show that the regression coefficient on x_2 is an estimate of the regression of response on log dose, the quantity usually called b, and that the regression coefficient on x_1 is an estimate of one-half the difference in mean responses for the two preparations, the quantity usually called $(\bar{y}_T - \bar{y}_S)$. The method of calculation has ensured that these estimates are adjusted for the non-orthogonality ; they differ from those in § 4.18 only because of the rounding of decimal figures in that section. Hence M is taken as

$$M = \bar{x}_S - \bar{x}_T - \frac{2 \times 1\cdot5251}{15\cdot9956}$$

$$= \bar{x}_S - \bar{x}_T - 0\cdot1907.$$

In order to construct the fiducial limits for M, the variances and covariance of $2b_1$ and b_2 are needed. They are obtained from the matrix V as

$$V(2b_1) = 4s^2v_{11} = \quad 0 \cdot 18908s^2,$$
$$V(b_2) = \quad s^2v_{22} = \quad 0 \cdot 04727s^2,$$
$$C(2b_1, b_2) = 2s^2v_{12} = -\ 0 \cdot 00630s^2.$$

Hence

$$g = \frac{(2 \cdot 160)^2 \times 0 \cdot 04727 \times 551 \cdot 2}{(15 \cdot 9956)^2}$$
$$= 0 \cdot 4751,$$

a value considerably higher than that in § 4.18. Again Fieller's theorem may be applied to give fiducial limits for $(M - \bar{x}_S + \bar{x}_T)$; these are

$$\left[-\ 0 \cdot 1907 + \frac{0 \cdot 4751 \times 0 \cdot 00630}{0 \cdot 04727} \pm \frac{2 \cdot 160}{15 \cdot 9956} \left\{ (0 \cdot 18908 \right. \right.$$
$$-\ 2 \times 0 \cdot 1907 \times 0 \cdot 00630 + 0 \cdot 1907^2 \times 0 \cdot 04727$$
$$\left. \left. -\ 0 \cdot 4751 \times 0 \cdot 18824) \times 551 \cdot 2 \right\}^{\frac{1}{2}} \right] \div 0 \cdot 5249$$

$$= [-\ 0 \cdot 1907 + 0 \cdot 0633 \pm 0 \cdot 9973] \div 0 \cdot 5249$$
$$= -\ 2 \cdot 1427,\ 1 \cdot 6573.$$

Hence, again using equation (4.16),

$$R = \frac{0 \cdot 2}{0 \cdot 0075} \text{ antilog } \bar{1} \cdot 9713 = 25 \cdot 0,$$

and similarly

$$R_L = \frac{0 \cdot 2}{0 \cdot 0075} \text{ antilog } \bar{1} \cdot 6775 = 12 \cdot 7,$$

$$R_U = \frac{0 \cdot 2}{0 \cdot 0075} \text{ antilog } 0 \cdot 2494 = 47 \cdot 4.$$

The estimate of potency could differ from that in § 4.18 only on account of the retention of more digits in the present calculations ; to the accuracy that may reasonably be reported, it is identical with that obtained earlier. The widening of the limits to $12 \cdot 7 \mu g$. and $47 \cdot 4 \mu g$. per c.c., 51 per cent. and 190 per cent. of the estimate instead of 57 per cent. and 162 per cent., represents the effect of failure to adjust the first analysis adequately because of the missing entries in Table 4.5.

4.20 Approximate analysis for missing entries

The example just discussed is peculiarly unfavourable from the point of view of approximating in a simple manner to the proper treatment of assay data from which some entries are missing. Of the twenty-eight responses needed for a fully symmetrical design, five were missing, a proportion much higher than would often be encountered in practice. Moreover, the high variability of the responses makes g large, and the analysis in § 4.18 omits any adjustment to g needed on account of the missing entries.

Nevertheless, a simple modification to the calculations of § 4.18 is likely to give conclusions near enough to those from the complete analysis, at least in assays for which only a small proportion of the fully symmetrical design has been lost. This approximation consists in calculating the difference in mean responses and the regression coefficient exactly as in § 4.18, but, in the calculation of variances and fiducial limits, replacing equation (4.18) by

$$V\left(\frac{L}{\text{Divisor}}\right) = \frac{s^2}{\text{Adjusted divisor}} \; ; \qquad (4.19)$$

the adjusted divisor is defined to be the sum of the squares of the coefficients of individual responses in the contrast, omitting those inserted by calculation of missing values. In this assay, for L_p

$$\text{Adjusted divisor} = 6 \times (-1)^2 + 5 \times (-1)^2 + 6 \times 1^2 + 6 \times 1^2$$
$$= 23,$$

and for L_1 the adjusted divisor is also 23. Hence

$$V\left(\frac{L_p}{28}\right) = V\left(\frac{L_1}{28}\right) = \frac{s^2}{23} \; .$$

For the quantities used in the calculation of M, this rule now gives

$$V(\bar{y}_T - \bar{y}_S) = \frac{4s^2}{23}$$

and

$$V(b) = \frac{s^2}{23} \; ;$$

zero covariance between the two contrasts is assumed. Recalculation by the procedure of § 4.18 yields

$$g = 0 \cdot 4368.$$

The potency is still estimated to be 25·0μg. per c.c., but the limits are now obtained as 12·8μg. per c.c. and 44·0μg. per c.c.

The limits found by this approximate method are a little narrower than the correct ones found in § 4.19, but are close enough for practical purposes. Had only one or two entries been missing, the approximation would have been still more satisfactory. On the other hand, had the missing entries left the design even more unbalanced (as, for example, if three of the five had been in the S_1 group and the other two in the T_2 group), it might not have been good enough. Yates (1933a) has described a better, but more complicated, approximate method for calculating the variances of contrasts between means after adjustment for missing entries, and his proposals could be adapted for use here. In an assay for which this was really better than the crude method just illustrated, however, the exact method by regression on x_1, x_2, x_3 might be preferred as being little more laborious.

4.21 Constraints of design

The design of the oestrone assay is an example of the device of litter-mate control, adopted so that differences between litters will not affect the estimate of potency or the assessment of its precision. The design of any experiment determines the character of the proper statistical analysis ; to analyse the data of Table 4.5 ignoring the litter classification would be entirely wrong and possibly very misleading.

This point should become clearer from a reading of later chapters (especially Chapter 9), but a warning must be given here against the neglect of other constraints in an experiment. The experimenter might find it convenient to put all identically treated animals into one cage (or, in a microbiological assay, to put all tubes of the same dose in adjacent positions in the incubator). If he does so, he must recognize that he thereby *confounds* (§ 9.2) differences between doses with differences between cages : the several animals in one cage are not true replicates of the treatment for comparison with differently treated animals in another cage. Any interaction between the animals in one cage, such as competition for food, may make individual responses different from what they would have been had all animals been caged separately, and so produce a variance between cages differing from that within cages. The experimenter who analyses the responses without regard to cage differences is in effect asserting that these differences are negligible, and that he may legitimately assess the precision of his potency estimate from variation *within* cages in spite of the fact that his dose comparisons are made *between* cages ; the experiment itself can provide no test of the validity of this assumption, unless each dose group is spread over two or more cages. Even though the animals were caged individually, the same difficulty would arise if all cages for one dose were placed close together in the animal house. Writing from extensive experience of the practice of biological assay and other types of animal experimentation, Emmens (1948, § 13.5) said ' There has been in biological work a considerable tendency to ignore the possibility of differences in reaction due to animals being caged in distinct groups and it seems to have been tacitly assumed that variation between cages must be negligible. It must be a rarely designed animal house in which conditions are so uniform that this assumption can be justified, and in the light of our knowledge that a variety of responses are influenced by health, temperature, light, feeding and many other factors, it would always seem worth while so to arrange our preliminary trials that the contributions of these factors to differences in the location of test objects may be examined '

On questions of the arrangement of subjects in cages, the randomization of order in an animal house, or the randomization of order of testing, the convenience or even the practicability of an experiment may conflict with the ideal statistical conditions. Complex designs, such as are described in Chapters 9 and 10, may sometimes enable the statistician to overcome these difficulties, but on other occasions the very complexity of a design may make it impossible of application. In general, the labour of statistical analysis for an important experiment is a small part of the total labour involved, and considerations of its complexity should not influence the choice of design (§ 6.6). Individual caging of subjects, or a complicated arrangement of tests, however, may sometimes so much increase the danger of gross mistakes or the costliness of an experiment as to make it completely impracticable. The statistician must recognise that these situations do arise, and must be prepared for some compromise with the exigencies of experimentation. He will need to make clear to the experimenter the price that must be paid for the use of a statistically inferior design ; the price may be loss of precision or, more serious, the production of results whose validity rests upon an assertion about the unimportance of certain sources of variation which cannot be tested in the experiment. If the experimenter is satisfied that these disadvantages do not outweigh the advantages of the design, the statistician's responsibility is ended.

Ideally, the animals used in an assay should be caged individually, caged in groups corresponding to one of the uninformative classifications of the experiment (such as litters), or caged in some new grouping, orthogonal with all others, for which a sum of squares can be isolated in the analysis of variance. If the use of individual cages is impracticable, and the experimenter is reluctant to cage together animals that are being differently treated (possibly for the very good reason that they would interact in some manner), he should at least aim at dividing each dose group between two or more cages. The analysis of variance will then show separate residual mean squares between and within cages ; if the first is significantly larger than the second, it must be used as the basic s^2 for subsequent calculations.

When faced with the results of an assay for the detailed design of which he was not responsible, the statistician must make strenuous efforts to discover exactly how the experiment was arranged and conducted. Bitter experience will teach him how easily an experimenter may fail to mention the existence of some constraint in a design, because of failure to realize its relevance to the statistical analysis : in some instances, the appearance of the data may be such as to arouse the suspicions of an alert statistician in the course of the analysis, but in others only the most careful discussion of the experiment with the person responsible for its execution will elicit information on points of design which modify the form of that analysis.

4.22 Heterogeneous deviations from linearity

The test of significance of deviations from linearity of regression has been discussed in § 4.6. If a significant result is obtained from an assay in which several doses of each preparation were included, inspection of the dose-response diagram may show either of two situations. Systematic deviation of the points from the calculated straight lines may indicate that the true regressions are curved, perhaps in the manner shown in Fig. 4.2 ; the statistical invalidity is then such that the linear regression model is wrong, and must be rejected in favour of a different metametric transformation or method of analysis. Alternatively, the points may show considerable scatter about the regression lines yet appear to be completely erratic in their deviations ; this may be a manifestation of an unusually complicated dose-response relationship, but often a more plausible explanation is heterogeneity of the batches of subjects at different doses. If the selection of subjects for each dose is not strictly random, or if indeed the batches are knowingly made up from different sources, even though the true regression be linear, the deviations of mean responses from the regression lines will be greater than is predicted from variations within batches. A similar effect may occur if different doses have to be tested on different occasions, and experimental conditions change in some unexpected way between occasions.

If the experimenter is prepared to accept heterogeneity between the dose groups, rather than a very complex regression curve, as the explanation of erratic deviations from linearity, and provided that there was a proper randomization in the allocation of groups, occasions, or other classifications, to doses, the mean square for deviations from linearity may be used as the estimated variance per response in all subsequent tests and assessments of fiducial limits. That some randomization be present is essential. For example, if only one dose per day can be tested, and the set of doses to be included are used in systematic order on successive days, any secular trend in experimental conditions will bias the estimation of the regression coefficient ; on the other hand, a random order of doses will ensure that deviations about regression lines give a valid estimate of the random errors of experimentation. Again, in an assay of an insecticide, successive batches of insects withdrawn from a single culture might show a steady trend in some factor, such as sex-ratio, that could be correlated with response, and random allocation of batches to doses is necessary if the assessment of precision (and even the estimation of potency itself) is to be unbiased (Bliss, 1939 ; Murray, 1937).

When only two or three doses of each preparation are tested, discrimination between the two types of significant deviation from linearity is impossible. This might appear to be a consideration opposed to the recommendations of § 6.10 on the number of dose levels to be included. In reality, the right course is almost always to choose an assay design that makes proper randomness throughout consistent with inevitable restrictions on experimental technique, and so to avoid the necessity for an estimate of variance based upon deviations from linearity. Occasionally this may be impossible, and the case for four or more doses of each preparation is then strengthened. The critical reader will appreciate the dangers of using the mean square for deviations from linearity as his value of s^2, for the temptation to accept the arguments justifying this course is bound to be strong when the only alternative is to reject a set of data as worthless. To assume randomness when no random element has been consciously incorporated into the design is a risk. Moreover, even if the logic is unassailable, the estimate of error will not be very satisfactory unless many doses have been used. The data of Table 4.1, for example, give only 3 degrees of freedom for the linearity mean square ; if fiducial limits had had to be based on this, they would have suffered from the imprecision in the estimate of variance.

An illustration of the use of the linearity mean square as s^2 occurs in § 16.2. In assays using quantal responses, the same problem may arise : the heterogeneity factor (§ 18.1) has the same function, and the same unsatisfactory basis, as the variance estimate just described.

It is important to avoid any automatic rule of rejecting assays on account of non-linearity or other aspects of statistical invalidity. As Humphrey et al. (1953) have emphasized, any rule based solely on individual significance tests would merely result in the most precise assays being rejected! A truly linear regression is a rarity, and to penalize all assays in which high precision detects non-linearity is folly. To formulate an ideal policy is difficult, as significant non-linearity at least indicates that precision is less good than the error mean square at first suggests. Humphrey's practice seems somewhat less desirable than the use of a different mean square for s^2, but the question deserves closer study by those concerned with large numbers of related routine assays.

CHAPTER 5

SYMMETRICAL DESIGNS FOR PARALLEL LINE ASSAYS

5.1 A 6-point assay

The last chapter has indicated the advantages of symmetry in the design of biological assays, but has also illustrated the inadequacy of the simplest symmetrical design, the 4-point, in respect of validity tests. Before a general discussion of symmetrical designs is begun, an example of the analysis of the next simplest type, the 6-point, is given.

TABLE 5.1—Increase in (Length + Height) of comb of capons injected with testosterone propionate

Measured in mm.

Dose	Standard preparation			Test preparation		
	20μg.	40μg.	80μg.	20μg.	40μg.	80μg.
Responses ...	6	12	19	6	12	16
	6	11	14	6	11	18
	5	12	14	6	12	19
	6	10	15	7	12	16
	7	7	14	4	10	15
Totals ...	30	52	76	29	57	84
Means ...	6·0	10·4	15·2	5·8	11·4	16·8

The data in Table 5.1 (Pugsley, 1946) relate to the assay of a test preparation of testosterone propionate against a standard, using three doses of each. Each of the six doses was injected into five capons, and the birds responded by showing a growth of comb. The response used for assay purposes is the increase in the sum of the length and height of the comb ; possibly some other combination of length and height would be a more sensitive metameter (Chapter 13), but this expression has the merit of

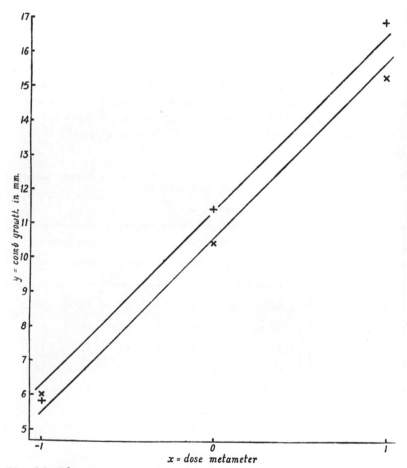

Fig. 5.1—Linear dose-response regressions for the assay of testosterone propionate, Table 5.1

×: Mean responses to standard preparation

+: Mean responses to test preparation

The straight lines are those found from the calculations in § 5.1.

simplicity and is likely to pick up the main features of the response to injection. Fuller data are not available for analysis. When log dose to base 2 is used as a metameter, and 40μg. is taken as the zero of the scale for both preparations, the values of x are −1, 0, 1. Fig. 5.1 shows mean responses plotted against x. Pugsley's paper seems to imply that experience has indicated approximate linearity of regression of this response on log dose ; the first impression of Fig. 5.1 is that the data will both confirm this linearity and show little deviation from parallelism.

TABLE 5.2—Analysis of variance for the data of Table 5.1

Adjustment for mean		3,586·13	Mean square
Nature of variation	d.f.	Sum of squares	
Preparations	1	4·80	4·80
Regression	1	510·05	510·05
Parallelism	1	4·05	4·05
Quadratic	1	0·02	0·02
Difference of quadratics ...	1	0·15	0·15
Between doses	5	519·07	
Error	24	56·80	2·367
Total	29	575·87	

Table 5.2 shows the analysis of variance of the data for this assay. Subdivision of the total sum of squares into components for ' between doses ' and ' error ' (within doses) presents no novel features ; the assay has no classification analogous to litters in the example of § 4.13. The five degrees of freedom between doses can be analysed into five orthogonal components, each of which is of interest in the interpretation of the assay. Again the method of orthogonal coefficients may be used for obtaining the appropriate

squares. One contrast must be chosen as the difference between preparations, and a second must represent the average linear regression of response on x ; for the latter, the coefficients are the values of $(x - \bar{x})$. By changing the signs of the coefficients for the standard preparation in the regression component, but leaving those for the test preparation unaltered, a contrast for the difference in regressions, leading to a test of parallelism, is obtained. The remaining two degrees of freedom measure deviations from linearity of regression. Tables of orthogonal polynomials (Fisher and Yates, 1963, Table XXIII) give 1, -2, 1 as the coefficients for the quadratic component in a set of three equally spaced levels, and assignment of these values to both preparations leads to a component corresponding to the average quadratic curvature. Reversal of signs for the standard preparation gives the last component, the difference between quadratic curvatures for the two preparations. Details of the five contrasts are shown in Table 5.3, where it is easily verified that every pair satisfies the condition for orthogonality in § 4.16 ; hence the rules of that section give a subdivision of the sum of squares between doses into squares for each of these five contrasts. The contrasts for a 6-point design may conveniently be referred to as L_p (preparations), L_1 (regression), L_1' (parallelism), L_2 (quadratic curvature), L_2' (difference of quadratics).

TABLE 5.3—Coefficients of orthogonal contrasts for the 6-point design, applied to the data of Table 5.1

Dose	S_1	S_2	S_3	T_1	T_2	T_3	Divisor	Sum
Response totals	30	52	76	29	57	84	Divisor	Sum
L_p	-1	-1	-1	1	1	1	30	12
L_1	-1	0	1	-1	0	1	20	101
L_1'	1	0	-1	-1	0	1	20	9
L_2	1	-2	1	1	-2	1	60	1
L_2'	-1	2	-1	1	-2	1	60	-3

Before making any estimate of potency, the validity of the assay must be considered. Freedom from any serious heterogeneity of variance may be seen by inspection of Table 5.1, without recourse to formal test. The mean squares for preparations and for parallelism in Table 5.2 are a little larger than the error, though not sufficiently so to cause any alarm. As a test of non-linearity of regression, the mean square for the quadratic component is compared with the error ; here the mean square is small. A large mean square for the component L_2' is unlikely to arise (except by chance) unless the quadratic component itself is large, in which case it would indicate a difference in curvature for the two regression equations over the range of responses studied ; if it did occur alone, it would certainly give rise to grave doubts about validity. Here this mean square also is small.

Users of the analysis of variance are often unduly alarmed by small mean squares ; that for the quadratic component in Table 5.2, for example, is less than 0·01 times the error mean square. The variance ratio test is a *one-tail test* ; that is to say, as ordinarily applied it serves only to detect mean squares significantly larger than the error mean square and the probability levels relate to this use. If it is to be used for examining mean squares that are smaller than the error, the ratio of the mean squares must be taken upside down (so as to keep the larger value on top) and compared with a tabular value in which the usual order of the degrees of freedom is reversed. Thus the quadratic mean square in Table 5.2, for which a more exact value is 0·0167, gives

$$F = \frac{2 \cdot 367}{0 \cdot 0167}$$

$$= 142 \text{ with } (24,1) \text{ degrees of freedom.}$$

The appropriate tabular entry in tables of the 5 per cent. significance level (Appendix Table II ; Fisher and Yates, 1963, Table V) is 249, so that the value of F found here need occasion no surprise.*

---

* The significance test as now used would allow extremes on either side of the error mean square to be judged significant, and is a *two-tail* test at the 10 per cent. probability level. In order to provide a test of this kind at the 5 per cent. level, a variance ratio table like Appendix Table II but computed for a one-tail probability of 2·5 per cent. is needed ; that of Merrington and Thompson (1943) gives 997 as the significance level for (24,1) degrees of freedom.

Moreover, special attention has been directed to the mean square for quadratic curvature not because of its intrinsic importance but because it is the most extreme criterion encountered in validity tests for this assay. If allowance were made for this selection, the probability assigned to the variance ratio would be even less extreme (Finney, 1941). Nevertheless, significantly small mean squares for important contrasts undoubtedly sometimes occur. When asked to explain one, the experienced statistician will first suspect a mistake (arithmetical or theoretical) in the statistical analysis, but, if this has been adequately checked, the possibility of non-independence of observations or lack of proper randomization must be investigated (*cf.* §§ 6.7, 15.3). Though the explanation of a significantly small mean square for, say, parallelism, will be entirely different from that of a large mean square, the same result, namely, rejection of the assay as invalid, may sometimes follow.

The data of Table 5.1 have shown no suspicion of invalidity for the assay. From Table 5.3, since the coefficients of L_1 are values of $(x - \bar{x})$, the regression coefficient is

$$b = \frac{101}{20}$$
$$= 5\cdot050.$$

Both preparations had the same zero for x, the value corresponding to a dose of $40\mu g$. Hence equation (4.11) gives

$$M = -\frac{\bar{y}_S - \bar{y}_T}{b}$$
$$= \frac{11\cdot33 - 10\cdot53}{5\cdot050}$$
$$= 0\cdot1584 \;;$$

the mean responses may be determined from Table 5.1, or $(\bar{y}_{T'} - \bar{y}_S)$ may be calculated from the L_p total in Table 5.2 (by division by 15, half the 'divisor' in that table). Equation (4.13) gives

$$g = \frac{(2\cdot064)^2 \times 2\cdot367}{(5\cdot050)^2 \times 20}$$
$$= 0\cdot0198.$$

By equation (4.12), therefore,

$$M_L, M_U = \left[0.1584 \pm \frac{2.064}{5.050} \left\{ \left(0.9802 \times \frac{2}{15} + \frac{(0.1584)^2}{20} \right) \times 2.367 \right\}^{\frac{1}{2}} \right] \div 0.9802$$

$$= [0.1584 \pm 0.2284] \div 0.9802$$

$$= -0.0714, \; 0.3946.$$

Of course, with so small a value for g, equation (2.9) might have been used in the determination of fiducial limits without appreciably affecting the results. Multiplication by $\log_{10} 2$ converts M, M_L, M_U into logarithms to base 10, and thence are obtained

$$R = \text{antilog } 0.0477 = 1.12,$$
$$R_L = \text{antilog } \bar{1}.9785 = 0.95,$$
$$R_U = \text{antilog } 0.1188 = 1.31.$$

Thus 1μg. of the test preparation of testosterone propionate is estimated to be the equivalent of 1.12μg. of the standard, and the true potency is very likely to lie between 0.95μg. and 1.31μg.

5.2 The symmetrical $2k$-point design

Discussion of the 4-point and 6-point designs naturally leads to the idea of a symmetrical $2k$-point design. This will have k doses of each preparation such that successive doses bear a ratio D to one another ($D > 1$), and n subjects at each dose. The total number of subjects is

$$N = 2nk, \tag{5.1}$$

divided into nk for each preparation. Let any pair of corresponding doses of the two preparations—for convenience, say the largest— be Z_S, Z_T. The doses of the test preparation will usually be chosen in such a way as to make Z_S/Z_T equal to R_0, a value for the relative potency guessed from any evidence that may be available (§ 6.8).

Write S_i, T_i for the totals of responses to the n subjects on the ith dose of each preparation. Then, as in the 6-point assay of § 5.1, the contrast between preparations is defined to be

$$L_p = (-S_1 - S_2 \ldots - S_k) + (T_1 + T_2 + \ldots + T_k), \tag{5.2}$$

and consequently

$$\bar{y}_S - \bar{y}_T = -L_p/nk. \tag{5.3}$$

In order to find the regression coefficient, designs with k even and with k odd must be distinguished. When k is even, the most convenient dose metameter is the logarithm to base $D^{\frac{1}{2}}$, giving as values of $(x - \bar{x})$

$$- (k - 1), - (k - 3), \ldots - 3, - 1, 1, 3, \ldots (k - 3), (k - 1).$$

The regression contrast is then

$$L_1 = - (k - 1)(S_1 + T_1) - (k - 3)(S_2 + T_2) - \ldots$$
$$+ (k - 1)(S_k + T_k). \quad (5.4)$$

The divisor for this contrast is

$$4n\{1^2 + 3^2 + 5^2 \ldots (k - 1)^2\} = \tfrac{2}{3}nk\,(k^2 - 1). \quad (5.5)$$

Hence

$$b = \frac{3L_1}{2nk\,(k^2 - 1)}. \quad (5.6)$$

When k is odd, log dose to base D will be the natural metameter to use, giving the values of $(x - \bar{x})$

$$- \tfrac{1}{2}(k - 1), - \tfrac{1}{2}(k - 3), \ldots - 2, - 1, 0, 1, 2, \ldots \tfrac{1}{2}(k - 3),$$
$$\tfrac{1}{2}(k - 1).$$

The regression contrast is then

$$L_1 = - \tfrac{1}{2}(k - 1)(S_1 + T_1) - \tfrac{1}{2}(k - 3)(S_2 + T_2) - \ldots$$
$$+ \tfrac{1}{2}(k - 1)(S_k + T_k), \quad (5.7)$$

with divisor

$$4n\left\{1^2 + 2^2 + 3^2 + \ldots \left(\frac{k - 1}{2}\right)^2\right\} = \tfrac{1}{6}nk\,(k^2 - 1). \quad (5.8)$$

Hence

$$b = \frac{6L_1}{nk\,(k^2 - 1)}. \quad (5.9)$$

Write $d = \log_{10} D$. \hfill (5.10)

Then, by equations (4.4) and (4.11),

$$R = \frac{Z_S}{Z_T} \text{ antilog } \left\{\frac{d\,(k^2 - 1)\,L_p}{3L_1}\right\} \text{ } (k \text{ even})$$

and

$$R = \frac{Z_S}{Z_T} \text{ antilog } \left\{\frac{d\,(k^2 - 1)\,L_p}{6L_1}\right\} \text{ } (k \text{ odd}).$$

$$(5.11)$$

Bliss (1944b) mentions a suggestion of L. C. Miller that D be taken as a simple power of 10. For penicillin assays, for example, instead of the common practice of taking $D = 2$ or 4, D might be taken as $10^{\frac{1}{2}}$, or 3·16, so giving $d = \tfrac{1}{2}$ and simplifying the subsequent arithmetic. The simplification may be dearly bought, however, if it involves using a much wider or a much narrower range of doses than would otherwise be chosen. Too wide a range will introduce a danger of non-linearity, and a range narrower than necessary reduces the precision of the assay (Chapter 6): a little extra arithmetic in the evaluation of R is a small price to pay for the avoidance of these evils.

Equations (5.11) enable R to be calculated directly from two easily constructed contrasts, L_p and L_1, without any intermediate steps and without an analysis of variance. This is both useful and dangerous—useful because of the time it saves in routine assays, dangerous because it may encourage neglect of important tests of validity and uncritical acceptance of estimates based on faulty premises. The formulæ will always give an answer, but whether or not the answer has any meaning is uncertain without validity tests. Moreover, evaluation of fiducial limits for the estimate requires further calculations.

In order to make validity tests and to form fiducial limits, the variance per response must be calculated. The full analysis of variance is not always required for this. For example, in the assay of testosterone propionate (Table 5.1) s^2 may be obtained by combining sums of squares, each with 4 degrees of freedom, from within the six dose groups :

$$24s^2 = \left(6^2 + 6^2 + 5^2 + 6^2 + 7^2 - \frac{30^2}{5}\right) + \ldots$$
$$= 56 \cdot 80,$$

whence

$$s^2 = 2 \cdot 367, \text{ with } 24 \text{ degrees of freedom},$$

as before. If there were some constraint in the assay design, such as a balancing over litters, this cannot be done ; an alternative that is sometimes useful is illustrated in § 5.3 for the popular 4-point design.

The contrast L_1' measuring deviation from parallelism can be constructed as

$$\left.\begin{aligned}
L_1' &= (k-1)(S_1 - T_1) + (k-3)(S_2 - T_2) + \ldots \\
&\qquad - (k-1)(S_k - T_k) \text{ for } k \text{ even,} \\
L_1' &= \tfrac{1}{2}(k-1)(S_1 - T_1) + \tfrac{1}{2}(k-3)(S_2 - T_2) + \ldots \\
&\qquad - \tfrac{1}{2}(k-1)(S_k - T_k) \text{ for } k \text{ odd.}
\end{aligned}\right\} \quad (5.12)$$

Two important validity tests are given by testing the deviations from zero of L_p, L_1', by means of their standard errors :

$$\text{S.E. of } L_p = sN^{\frac{1}{2}},\tag{5.13}$$

and

$$\left.\begin{array}{l}\text{S.E. of } L_1' = s\{\tfrac{1}{3}N(k^2-1)\}^{\frac{1}{2}} \text{ for } k \text{ even,} \\ \text{S.E. of } L_1' = s\{\tfrac{1}{12}N(k^2-1)\}^{\frac{1}{2}} \text{ for } k \text{ odd.}\end{array}\right\}\tag{5.14}$$

A t test, using these standard errors, is exactly equivalent to a variance ratio test in the analysis of variance. Linearity tests could be made in similar form, using L_2, L_2' ; if all these tests are wanted, however, the analysis of variance is the best procedure.

As a preliminary to evaluation of the fiducial limits of R, g should be calculated :

$$\left.\begin{array}{l}g = \dfrac{Nt^2s^2(k^2-1)}{3L_1^2} \text{ for } k \text{ even,} \\[3mm] g = \dfrac{Nt^2s^2(k^2-1)}{12L_1^2} \text{ for } k \text{ odd,}\end{array}\right\}\tag{5.15}$$

as may be found from equation (4.13). Equation (4.12) then shows the limits to be

$$\left.\begin{array}{l}R_L, R_U = \dfrac{Z_S}{Z_T} \text{ antilog } \left[\dfrac{d(k^2-1)}{3L_1(1-g)}\left\{L_p \right.\right. \\[3mm] \qquad\qquad \left.\left. \pm ts\sqrt{N\left\{(1-g)+\dfrac{(k^2-1)L_p^2}{3L_1^2}\right\}}\right\}\right] \\[2mm] \qquad\qquad\qquad\qquad \text{for } k \text{ even,} \\[4mm] R_L, R_U = \dfrac{Z_S}{Z_T} \text{ antilog } \left[\dfrac{d(k^2-1)}{6L_1(1-g)}\left\{L_p \right.\right. \\[3mm] \qquad\qquad \left.\left. \pm ts\sqrt{N\left\{(1-g)+\dfrac{(k^2-1)L_p^2}{12L_1^2}\right\}}\right\}\right] \\[2mm] \qquad\qquad\qquad\qquad \text{for } k \text{ odd.}\end{array}\right\}\tag{5.16}$$

5.3 The 4-point design

Undoubtedly the most popular assay design is the 4-point. Its limitations will be considered in Chapter 6 ; for the present the only concern is with the analysis. The coefficients for the contrasts are given in Table 5.4 (*cf.* Table 4.7). The estimation of potency may proceed by way of an analysis of variance, as in

§§ 4.16–4.18, or the contrasts may be used directly to give R, R_L, R_U. By equation (5.11), the estimate of potency is

$$R = \frac{Z_S}{Z_T} \text{ antilog } \frac{dL_p}{L_1}. \tag{5.17}$$

For the validity tests

$$\text{S.E. of } L_p = \text{S.E. of } L'_1 = sN^{\frac{1}{2}}. \tag{5.18}$$

Moreover,

$$g = \frac{Nt^2s^2}{L_1^2}, \tag{5.19}$$

and the fiducial limits, equation (5.16), are

$$R_L, R_U = \frac{Z_S}{Z_T} \text{ antilog } \left[\frac{d}{L_1(1-g)} \left\{ L_p \pm ts \sqrt{N \left(1 - g + \frac{L_p^2}{L_1^2}\right)} \right\} \right] \tag{5.20}$$

which may be written

$$R_L, R_U = \frac{Z_S}{Z_T} \text{ antilog } \left[\frac{d\{L_pL_1 \pm \sqrt{Nt^2s^2 (L_p^2 + L_1^2 - Nt^2s^2)}\}}{L_1^2 - Nt^2s^2} \right]. \tag{5.21}$$

TABLE 5.4—Coefficients of orthogonal contrasts for the 4-point design

Contrast	S_1	S_2	T_1	T_2	Divisor
L_p	−1	−1	1	1	$4n$
L_1	−1	1	−1	1	$4n$
L'_1	1	−1	−1	1	$4n$

Table 5.5 shows the results of an assay of penicillin reported by de Beer and Sherwood (1945). The doses of the standard preparation are not stated in the original publication, but for convenience of description here will be assumed to be 50 units per ml. and 200 units per ml. ; the doses of the test preparation were a 1 in 4 dilution and the basic 'undiluted' preparation. Tests were made by placing paper discs, damped with penicillin solution, on agar plates inoculated with *Bacillus subtilis*. Four plates were used, each having one circle of each of the four doses. The responses measured, diameters of the zones of growth, are shown in Table 5.5 in units of 0·25 mm. so as to be expressed as integers.

TABLE 5.5—Diameters of zones of inhibition in an assay of penicillin

In units of 0·25 mm.

Plate no.	S.P. (units per ml.) 50	S.P. (units per ml.) 200	T.P. (dilution) 0·25	T.P. (dilution) 1	$L^p = -S_1 - S_2 + T_1 + T_2$	$L_1 = -S_1 + S_2 - T_1 + T_2$	$L_1' = S_1 - S_2 - T_1 + T_2$
I	92	108	68	90	− 42	38	6
II	95	111	74	91	− 41	33	1
III	93	108	72	91	− 38	34	4
IV	90	107	75	88	− 34	30	−4
Total	370	434	289	360	−155	135	7

From equation (5.17) and the totals at the foot of Table 5.5,

$$R = \frac{200}{1} \text{ antilog} \left\{ -\frac{155}{135} \log_{10} 4 \right\}$$
$$= 200 \times 0.2036$$
$$= 40.7.$$

Thus the undiluted test preparation is estimated to contain 40.7 units per ml. The design of the assay was in randomized blocks, each plate being a block ; differences between plates must be eliminated before an estimate of variance is formed, and s^2 therefore cannot be calculated from within dose groups. Consideration of the structure of the analysis of variance shows that s^2 should have 9 degrees of freedom, and these can be obtained as comparisons between contrasts L_p, L_1, L_1' formed for each plate separately. Thus, from the separate values for L_p shown in Table 5.5, a sum of squares

$$(-42)^2 + (-41)^2 + (-38)^2 + (-34)^2 - \tfrac{1}{4}(-155)^2 = 38.75$$

may be formed ; similarly from L_1 and L_1' are obtained 32.75 and 56.75 respectively. Each of these sums of squares has 3 degrees of freedom. Moreover, any contrast between entries in one of the columns L_p, L_1, L_1' in Table 5.5 is orthogonal with all contrasts between doses, between plates, and between entries in either of the other two columns, as may be seen by application of the rule of orthogonality (§ 4.16). The three sums of squares must therefore belong to the error component of the analysis of variance, and, since they are mutually orthogonal, must account for all the 9 degrees of freedom for that error. Each entry in the L_p, L_1, L_1' columns is formed by additions and subtractions amongst four responses, so that mean squares formed from the sums of squares just described would be estimates of $4\sigma^2$. Hence, on pooling the three items,

$$4s^2 = \frac{38.75 + 32.75 + 56.75}{3 + 3 + 3},$$

and

$$s^2 = 3.562,$$

as may be verified by an analysis of variance.* From equation (5.18),

---

* The analysis of variance for the data of this assay is shown in Table 5.6. The reader is advised to verify it for himself, by the method of § 4.16, and to study the relationship between it and the computations described in the text.

$$L_p = - 155 \pm 7\cdot5,$$
$$L_1' = 7 \pm 7\cdot5.$$

(The squares of the ratios of L_p, L_1' to their standard errors are the corresponding variance ratios in Table 5.6.) Clearly L_p is highly significant, and gives rise to some fear that the doses of the test preparation may have run outside the region of linearity. Indeed,

TABLE 5.6—Analysis of variance for the data of Table 5.5

Adjustment for mean		1,870·56	
Nature of variation	d.f.	Sum of squares	Mean square
Preparations	1	1,501·56	1,501·56
Regression	1	1,139·06	1,139·06
Parallelism	1	3·07	3·07
Between doses	3	2,643·69	
Between plates	3	24·69	
Error	9	32·06	3·562
Total	15	2,700·44	

the upper dose of the test preparation gave smaller responses than the lower dose of the standard. On the other hand, L_1' shows no indication of non-parallelism and, in view of past good experience of linearity in penicillin assays based upon circles of growth inhibition, acceptance of the assay as valid seems reasonably justifiable.

Now s^2 is based on 9 degrees of freedom, and therefore $t = 2\cdot262$. Hence

$$Nt^2s^2 = 291\cdot6,$$

and

$$g = \frac{291\cdot6}{135^2}$$
$$= 0\cdot0160 \; ;$$

g is so small that it might be neglected, and the fiducial limits calculated from the approximate form of equation (5.21):

$$R_L, R_U = \frac{Z_S}{Z_T} \text{ antilog} \left[\frac{d \left\{ L_p L_1 \pm \sqrt{N t^2 s^2 (L_p^2 + L_1^2)} \right\}}{L_1^2} \right] \quad (5.22)$$

$$= 200 \text{ antilog} \left[\log 4 \times \left(\frac{-20{,}925 \pm 3{,}510}{18{,}225} \right) \right]$$

$$= 200 \text{ antilog } \bar{1} \cdot 1928, \; 200 \text{ antilog } \bar{1} \cdot 4247$$

$$= 31 \cdot 2, \; 53 \cdot 2.$$

Use of the full formula, equation (5.21), occasions little extra work, and is generally to be preferred:

$$R_L, R_U = 200 \text{ antilog} \left[\log 4 \times \left(\frac{-20{,}925 \pm 3{,}498}{17{,}933} \right) \right]$$

$$= 200 \text{ antilog } \bar{1} \cdot 1801, \; 200 \text{ antilog } \bar{1} \cdot 4149$$

$$= 30 \cdot 3, \; 52 \cdot 0.$$

Thus the potency of the test preparation seems almost certain to lie between 30·3 units per ml. and 52·0 units per ml.

5.4   The 6-point design

The coefficients for the five contrasts in their most useful form have been given in Table 5.3. By equation (5.11)

$$R = \frac{Z_S}{Z_T} \text{ antilog} \left(\frac{4 d L_p}{3 L_1} \right). \quad (5.23)$$

By equations (5.13), (5.14)

$$\text{S.E. of } L_p = s N^{\frac{1}{2}}, \quad (5.24)$$

$$\text{S.E. of } L_1' = s \, (2N/3)^{\frac{1}{2}}, \quad (5.25)$$

and the two curvature contrasts may be tested for significance with the aid of

$$\text{S.E. of } L_2 = \text{S.E. of } L_2' = s \, (2N)^{\frac{1}{2}}. \quad (5.26)$$

For g, equation (5.15) gives

$$g = \frac{2 N t^2 s^2}{3 L_1^2} \quad (5.27)$$

and the formula for the fiducial limits, equation (5.16), may be reduced to

R_L, R_U

$$= \frac{Z_S}{Z_T} \text{ antilog} \left[\frac{4d \left\{ L_p L_1 \pm \sqrt{\tfrac{1}{3} N t^2 s^2 \left(2L_p^2 + 3L_1^2 - 2N t^2 s^2 \right)} \right\}}{3L_1^2 - 2N t^2 s^2} \right] \quad (5.28)$$

These formulæ may be applied to the testosterone propionate assay discussed in § 5.1, using $s^2 = 2\cdot367$ from an analysis of variance or from direct calculation of the sum of squares within doses, and $N = 30$. Hence

$$L_p = 12 \pm 8\cdot4,$$
$$L_1' = 9 \pm 6\cdot9,$$
$$L_2 = 1 \pm 11\cdot9,$$
$$L_2' = -3 \pm 11\cdot9,$$

which give the same significance tests as did the analysis of variance in Table 5.2. Also

$$g = \frac{60 \times (2\cdot064)^2 \times 2\cdot367}{3 \times (101)^2}$$
$$= 0\cdot0198$$

as before. For the potency,

$$R = 1 \times \text{antilog} \frac{4 \log 2 \times 12}{3 \times 101}$$
$$- 1\cdot12,$$

with limits at

$R_L, R_U = 1 \times \text{antilog}$

$$\left[\frac{4 \log 2 \left\{ 12 \times 101 \pm \sqrt{100\cdot84 \times (2 \times 12^2 + 3 \times 101^2 - 605)} \right\}}{3 \times 101^2 - 605} \right]$$

$$= 0\cdot95,\ 1\cdot31$$

as before. The simplified formulæ have thus given exactly the same results as did the analysis in § 5.1.

5.5   The 8-point design

Formulæ similar to those already given can readily be written down for higher values of k. Though no general account will be given here, the orthogonal coefficients for a full set of contrasts in the next member of the series, the 8-point design, may be of some interest. These are shown in Table 5.7. The method of construction is explained by Fisher and Yates (1963) in connexion with their Table XXIII. In addition to the contrasts previously used, a component of cubic curvature, L_3, and another for the difference between cubics for the two preparations, L_3', are now required. Significance of L_3 or L_3' bears much the same interpretation as significance of L_2 or L_2', though it conveys rather different information on the form of the non-linear response curve. The estimate of potency is

$$R = \frac{Z_S}{Z_T} \text{ antilog } \frac{5dL_p}{L_1} ; \qquad (5.29)$$

other formulæ may be written down by insertion of $k = 4$ in equations (5.13)–(5.16).

TABLE 5.7—Coefficients of orthogonal contrasts for the 8-point design

Contrast	S_1	S_2	S_3	S_4	T_1	T_2	T_3	T_4	Divisor
L_p	-1	-1	-1	-1	1	1	1	1	$8n$
L_1	-3	-1	1	3	-3	-1	1	3	$40n$
L_1'	3	1	-1	-3	-3	-1	1	3	$40n$
L_2	1	-1	-1	1	1	-1	-1	1	$8n$
L_2'	-1	1	1	-1	1	-1	-1	1	$8n$
L_3	-1	3	-3	1	-1	3	-3	1	$40n$
L_3'	1	-3	3	-1	-1	3	-3	1	$40n$

5.6 Streamlined computations

When a large number of assays of the same simple design must be analysed, the investigator is bound to be impressed by the magnitude of his task (especially if he has no pretensions to being a statistician !) and to wish for the most expeditious scheme of computing. As emphasized in § 6.6, statistical analysis is usually only a small charge on the total cost of an assay ; in a long series of routine assays, however, the cost of analysis is likely to be of greater importance to the economy than in a single assay for a special purpose. The development of routine assay procedures for use in association with factory production of penicillin and other antibiotics has brought this question into prominence, and numerous suggestions for dealing with it have been made.

The most obvious step to take in order to reduce the labour of analysing routine assays is to standardize the computations. The data may consist of a series of 4-point or 6-point assays, all with the same number of subjects and the same spacing of log doses. A printed or duplicated form that provides spaces for insertion of the data and each step of the calculation will enable a great amount of time to be saved. These steps are all simple arithmetical operations, and an assistant with no knowledge of their meaning can easily be instructed in their performance ; a calculating machine, of course, should be part of the equipment of any laboratory engaged in routine assay. Each completed analysis must be inspected and interpreted by someone qualified to understand it, in order to avoid the danger that unexpected peculiarities in a set of data escape detection.

The formulæ and examples in §§ 5.1–5.5 indicate how this ' streamlining ' of computations may be effected for symmetrical parallel line assays. These or similar formulæ have been proposed by various authors for use in specific types of assay. Naturally the 4-point design has been most frequently discussed, and formulæ essentially the same as those in § 5.3 have been put forward by Bliss (1944b, c ; 1945), Bliss and Marks (1939a, b), Finney (1944b), Gridgeman (1944a, b), Knudsen and Randall (1945), Schild (1942), Sherwood, Falco, and de Beer (1944). Formulæ for R in 6-point and 8-point assays have been given by Sherwood (1947) though these have little novelty as they merely employ orthogonal coefficients in the same way as was suggested earlier by Bliss and Marks (1939a, b). The search for ' simple ' methods of analysis can lead to such extraordinary suggestions as those of Osgood (1947) and Osgood and Graham (1947) ; results obtained by the calculations they suggest appear to depend upon the scale of measurement of responses, and the method cannot be recommended.

The purpose of this book is to set out general principles and methods of analysis, and not to discuss schemes of computation especially suited for particular routine applications. The reader who has mastered the general methods will have no difficulty in understanding and developing further the suggestions of these and other authors for streamlined computing. The only source of confusion is the excessive variety of notations that have been devised ; unfortunately, a writer on streamlined methods usually adopts a notation convenient to his immediate needs, without thought of whether his use of symbols conflicts with the current practice for less specialized designs or with other schemes of streamlining.

On the other hand, those who are not thoroughly familiar with the general methods are unwise to rely on their own judgments in deciding to use formulæ such as have been mentioned. To the user, the most attractive method is that which demands least arithmetical labour, but all tempting simplifications of arithmetic require critical examination if the dangers of wrong method or serious loss of information are to be avoided. Writers on streamlined computations for bioassay sometimes omit all mention of the precision of their potency estimates, and are often content to assess fiducial limits with the aid of a formula based on equation (2.9), so neglecting g ; validity tests also are usually neglected. Consequently, a method that may be safely used in, say, penicillin assay, because variances are low and validity well-established, may be completely untrustworthy if applied to an assay of the same design that is based on a much more variable dose-response relationship. Moreover, the streamlined method can never take account of accidents that disturb the symmetry of the designs. The penicillin assay in Table 5.5 and the oestrone assay in Table 4.5 are almost the same in design, from the statistical point of view (they differ only in that the oestrone assay has more blocks and has some observations ' missing ') ; streamlined computing is very suitable for the one, but little use for the other.

5.7 Nomographic analysis

The evaluation of formulæ such as equation (5.11) can be made largely graphical by the use of a nomograph or specially constructed chart. Such a chart is used by locating the values of L_p and L_1 on two linear scales, joining the points by a straight edge, and reading the value of RZ_T/Z_S from the intersection of this join with a third scale. A different nomograph is needed for each value of k and for each dose interval, d. Since the most important types are few in number, a set of nomographs could easily be prepared ; the most popular designs are the 4-point (*i.e.* $k = 2$) with simple dose intervals such as a ratio of 2 (*i.e.* $d = 0.301$).

Additional nomographs can be prepared for aiding the computation of $V(M)$, where g is small enough to permit the use of this, and hence the fiducial limits of R.

Bliss (1946a) has given nomographs for a 4-point assay with a dose ratio of 2·0 ($k = 2$, $d = 0·301$). Anon (1946), Knudsen (1945a), and Knudsen and Randall (1945) have given nomographs of slightly different form for a 4-point assay with a dose ratio of 1·5 ($k = 2$, $d = 0·176$), and Knudsen, Smith, Vos, and McClosky (1946) and Knudsen (1950) have done the same for a dose ratio of 4·0 ($k = 2$, $d = 0·602$). Other variants have been proposed by Harte (1948), Koch (1947), and Sherwood (1951).

Unless drawn to a very large scale, potency estimation from a nomograph suffers from arithmetical inaccuracy, although it can often be made as accurate as the data justify. More important criticisms are the neglect of validity tests and the use of the so-called naïve variance formula. Developments by Healy (1949) and Gridgeman (1951) indicate how, at the expense of a small amount of extra arithmetic, validity tests may be made and fiducial limits based upon Fieller's theorem may be found from a more elaborate nomograph. Healy has illustrated his type of chart for a 6-point assay with dose ratio 1·5 ($k = 3$, $d = 0·176$); Gridgeman's scheme, a full account of which is published elsewhere (1951), may require more calculation for the first construction of the nomograph, but appears likely to be particularly convenient in use. All who wish to analyse routine assays nomographically should consider carefully the merits of these last two types of chart, relative to the simplicity of others mentioned above.

5.8 Mechanical aids to analysis

In 1938, Morrell, Chapman and Allmark could fairly state that ' a calculating machine is an instrument not often found in a biological laboratory '. Today, no biological laboratory concerned with extensive numerical records can afford the inaccuracy and inefficiency consequent upon the lack of a relatively inexpensive desk calculator; the major academic and industrial research centres are increasingly able to use electronic computers for routine and standardized calculations (§ 1.7).

The object of this section, however, is to draw the attention of the reader to various suggestions for simple pieces of mechanism for use in biological assays only. De Beer (1941) has proposed a special type of protractor for direct reading of regression coefficients on a dose-response diagram. Goyan and Dufrenoy (1947), and Dufrenoy and Goyan (1947) have described a device of movable scales which, when superimposed on a dose-response diagram, enable the estimate of relative potency to be read. Lees (1949) has described a rotating drum, to the surface of which is attached a specially prepared table, that replaces ' the conventional slide rule and semi-logarithmic paper techniques . . . by the simple operation of turning two wheels on a machine ' ; his explanation is not very clear, but the machine appears to be closely related to a nomograph. All these devices suffer from the disadvantage that they deal only with estimation and take no account of validity or precision.

5.9 Range estimation for standard deviations

The calculation of sums of squares of deviations is an easy process, but, in routine assays as simple as that described in § 5.3, the formation of s (the standard deviation per response) is one of the most time-consuming parts of the analysis. Various writers,

TABLE 5.8—The estimation of a standard deviation
from a range in a sample of normally
distributed observations

No. of observations	Factor by which range must be multiplied
2	0·887
3	0·591
4	0·486
5	0·430
6	0·395
7	0·370
8	0·351
9	0·337
10	0·325

including Knudsen (1945a), Bliss (1946a), and Wood (1947b) have proposed that the standard deviation per response might be estimated from a range instead of from a sum of squares. The range of a set of values is the difference between the highest and the lowest, and is clearly a measure of variability. Its use in the estimation of a standard deviation is common in many branches of statistical work. On the assumption that the distribution of individual deviations is normal, the best estimate that can be formed from the range is less efficient than the root mean square estimate, but the efficiency is high when the number of values involved is small. Table 5.8 shows the factor by which the range must be multiplied, in order to estimate the standard deviation ; it relates only to a normal distribution, and to the small numbers of observations likely to be needed in bioassay analyses.

The ranges of the four values in the columns L_p, L_1, L_1' in Table 5.5 are 8, 8, 10 respectively, the average being 8·67. The true standard deviation of each column is 2σ, where σ is the standard deviation per response, since the values are compounded by additions and subtractions of four responses. Hence σ may be estimated by

$$s = \tfrac{1}{2} \times 0\cdot486 \times 8\cdot67$$
$$= 2\cdot11,$$

instead of 1·89 as in § 5.3. An estimate so obtained should not be used in the formulæ for tests of validity and fiducial limits, because these relate to an s based upon sums of squares of deviations. Tables analogous to the t table have been calculated (Lord, 1947) for use with the range, and tests of significance for validity might be based upon these. Their use in the derivation of limits of error, however, is less easily justified, though so long as g is reasonably small the values so obtained should be a reasonable indication of the precision. All the authors mentioned in § 5.7 in connexion with nomographic analysis used ranges as the basis of their assessments of precision.

Though the method has been described for the 4-point design, it can easily and obviously be applied to others. Its uncritical adoption is not recommended, however, because non-normality of distribution is likely to have more serious consequences for range estimation than for mean square estimation.

5.10 Control charts

If a standard pattern of assay has been adopted as a routine in factory production, a system of control charts should be instituted, in order to check that experimental conditions and processes are being maintained satisfactorily constant. This book is primarily concerned with bioassay in research problems, and no detailed discussion of routine applications is attempted. Of the many books on industrial quality control, that of Shewhart (1931) may be mentioned here; methods particularly relevant to control charts for s^2, b, s/b have been excellently described by Bliss (1952a) and further discussed by Bliss and Pabst (1955).

Knudsen and Randall (1945), in describing the practice of the United States Food and Drug Administration for the control of cylinder plate antibiotic assays, advise that

'Separate control charts should be kept for 3-plate assays, 5-plate assays, etc., and as each assay is run, the values . . . are plotted on the proper control chart. If they fall outside the control limits, some cause of trouble must be looked for, and, when it is found, the assay should be repeated. Contamination of the plates by bacteria from the air may be a cause of trouble, although this can usually be observed. A variation in thickness of the inoculated agar layer may result in excessive variation in zone size, and unapparent " leakers " where the leakage is symmetrical around one or more of the cups may also result in larger circular zones. Of course errors of dilution or weighing will not be pointed out by the control chart method '.

Noel (1945) has also made use of the quality control technique. In a series of assays like that for penicillin discussed in § 5.3, if the number of plates and the dose interval be constant, s^2, L_1, and L_1' ought all to remain in control, and each might be made the basis of a control chart ; the chart for s^2 might be replaced by one for range, if range estimation of the standard deviation were in use. A paper by Jones (1945) is also of interest in this connexion. Knudsen (1945b) has made a further suggestion about the use of control charts in biological laboratories, this time not directly in connexion with bioassay, but obviously of interest in this field as well as in others. She says ' The weights of mature rats and the numbers of animals in each litter could be plotted on a control chart, to insure a continual supply of uniform animals and to spot any defects in diet and care that may be causing an untoward variation in the animals, or in the sizes of litters '. Cohen *et al.* (1959) have presented a chart showing b excellently in control over a series of 39 assays of tetanus toxoids.

When the assay technique is satisfactorily in control, some gain may be expected from pooling estimates of s^2, and perhaps also of b, from the two or three assays preceding the current one, so as to gain precision on these quantities (Gridgeman, 1944b). This may be particularly useful in assays of a kind for which sampling variation in s^2 or in L_1 is largely responsible for low precision in R. To give exact expression to the errors of estimation after such pooling is not easy, but the obvious modifications in the degrees of freedom and in $V(b)$ are unlikely to be far wrong. If the control is completely satisfactory, a long series of results may be pooled in order to give what are effectively population values, σ^2 and β, instead of estimates s^2 and b.

5.11   Quadratic regression and the 4-point design

Suppose that the regression equation for the standard preparation is quadratic rather than linear (§ 3.8), so that the true equation is

$$Y_S = a + \beta x + \gamma x^2. \tag{5.30}$$

Then for the test preparation

$$Y_T = a + \beta (x + \log \rho) + \gamma (x + \log \rho)^2. \tag{5.31}$$

In general, an assay would give data from which the four parameters, a, β, γ, ρ, would have to be estimated simultaneously, and the equations of estimation would be complicated. For a 4-point symmetrical design, however,

$$R = \frac{Z_S}{Z_T} \text{ antilog } \frac{dL_p}{L_1} \tag{5.17}$$

is an estimate of ρ just as it is for a linear regression equation, L_p and L_1 being the contrasts defined in Table 5.4 (Gridgeman, 1943; Wood, 1944a). The remaining contrast between doses, L_1', no longer gives a validity test, as it is now utilized in the estimation of the extra parameter. The conclusion that, if there are no additional constraints in the design, equations (5.17), 5.21) give the potency estimate and fiducial limits even though the true regression is quadratic, is surprising. Constraints such as litter-mate control, or grouping of antibiotic tests on plates would upset this, however, as their effects on response would probably not be linear. No such simple method can be used if the design is other than a symmetrical 4-point, or if the regression equation is more complicated than a quadratic.

This result is unlikely to be of great practical use, and is little more than a mathematical accident. Knowledge that a non-linear regression is really quadratic rather than some other curve must be rare! If a dose-response regression is known to deviate from linearity only slightly, over a moderate range of doses a quadratic equation should be an adequate approximation; provided that the doses for a 4-point assay have been well chosen, the result stated above does then give some assurance that conclusions based upon an analysis made as though the regression were linear will not be seriously wrong.

CHAPTER 6

EFFICIENCY, RELIABILITY, AND SENSITIVITY

6.1 The purpose of an assay

The great developments in statistical science since 1920 sometimes leave the unwary with the impression that statistical analysis is now more concerned with standard errors and tests of significance than with the mean values to which the standard errors relate. This misconception arises because the technical difficulties and labour are usually greater for the assessment of precision than for the evaluation of means. Nothing in this book must be allowed to obscure the fact that the primary object of every biological assay is

(i) To obtain a valid estimate of the potency of the test preparation.

Generally the potency will be assessed relative to a standard, but an example of estimation in absolute terms is discussed in § 21.5. The estimate itself is of little use unless the investigator is able

(ii) To ensure that the potency estimate is of adequate precision.

By ' adequate precision ' is meant a deviation of the estimate from the true value almost certainly too small to be of practical importance in affecting any action to be based upon the assay. A vague assurance that the estimate is reasonably precise is seldom sufficient ; usually the assay must be planned

(iii) To provide a numerical assessment of the precision of the potency estimate.

Indeed, (ii) can rarely be accomplished without (iii), for in few circumstances has an investigator confidence in the precision of his assay unless the data themselves give him a measure of that precision. In (i) the need for a *valid* estimate was stated, and this means that the estimate must be not merely the result of applying a formula to a set of observations, but also correctly interpretable as a property of the test preparation. The implications of this are discussed more thoroughly in Chapter 15. The point to be stressed here is that, unless the investigator's belief in the validity of his assay *a priori* is so strong as to make the precaution unnecessary, he will wish

> (iv) To include tests of the fundamental validity of the assay and of the validity of the statistical analysis used in the calculation of the potency estimate.

6.2 Validity

By a valid assay is meant one that leads to a consistent estimate of ρ, the relative potency that it is intended to measure. Consistency is to be interpreted in its strict statistical sense of convergence in probability (§ 3.12; Cramér, 1946, § 20.3; Kendall & Stuart, 1961); if the size of the assay were increased by the inclusion of more and more subjects at each dose, the estimate, R, would tend to the true value, ρ. ' Tend ' is here used in the sense that, in the fair tossing of a well-balanced coin, the proportion of heads tends to 0.5 as the number of trials is increased: occasional runs will take the proportion further from 0.5, but the general trend is towards 0.5, and, in the language of the mathematical statistician, this value is approached as a limit ' almost certainly ' or ' with a probability approaching unity '.

In an analytical dilution assay, the test preparation is known to be identical with the standard except for a different amount of inert diluent. Any method of estimating equally effective doses must lead to a valid estimate of relative potency and the choice between alternatives may be made entirely from considerations of precision and economy. If the conditions for an analytical assay are not known to be strictly fulfilled, because of the presence in the test preparation of impurities or other constituents that may affect the response, the assay should be so designed as to be able to indicate disturbances from this cause. No statistical analysis can detect the action of constituents of the test preparation that produce responses whose relationship to dose is of the same kind as for the substance to be estimated. Wood (1946), writing of slope ratio assays, said : ' If, for example, in a riboflavine assay the test preparation should happen to contain not only riboflavine, but also some other growth stimulating factor, and if this factor stimulated growth proportionally to the dosage at all dosage levels, no statistical test and no method of calculating the result could possibly detect anything suspicious in the result obtained. The combined riboflavine and other factor would be estimated as riboflavine '. The validity tests that can be incorporated into a statistical analysis, however, do give some chance of detecting disturbances in the character of the response ; for parallel line assays, the test of parallelism is particularly important. In a comparative dilution assay, for which the effective constituents of the two preparations are not chemically identical, the importance of a test of deviations from the hypothesis of similarity as a check on the validity of all conclusions is even greater.

Most methods of statistical analysis of assay data depend upon representation of the dose-response relationship, in metametric form, by a simple algebraic equation, usually a straight line. Though an assay be fundamentally valid, the statistical analysis will be invalid if the data show this representation to be wrong. For many of the commoner assay techniques, experience has taught the right form of relationship to use as a reasonably adequate representation of the truth ; even then, linearity or similar validity tests are valuable safeguards against the misuse of data from an assay with some previously unsuspected abnormal feature. For newer techniques which at present lack a sufficient experience, these tests must be regarded as essential. Small deviations from an ideal relationship may have no great effect, but serious discrepancies are a warning that some other specification of the characteristics of the data must be sought, and statistical analysis based upon that, before valid inferences can be drawn.

6.3 The economics of design

By the design of an assay is meant the choice of the levels of dose to be tested, the scheme of allocation of subjects to doses, the arrangement of all other experimental constraints such as litter-mate control, the order in which doses are given or measurements made, the subdivision of labour between collaborating observers, and other matters relating to the structure of the experiment rather than to the technical details of its execution. The selection of a design for a particular purpose necessarily involves a compromise between the conflicting interests of the precision of estimation, the sensitivity of validity tests, and factors representative of the convenience, difficulty, and expense of the experimental procedure and the statistical analysis ; these last may be described in general terms as relating to the *cost* of the assay, whether this cost be measured in monetary units or on any other scale that allows the total expenditures of time, labour, and materials to be compounded into a single figure. The experimenter will wish either to obtain the best possible results, in respect of precision and sensitivity, for a specified cost, or to minimize the cost of obtaining results of specified precision and sensitivity. The two requirements, which are in reality different aspects of the same conditions for an optimal design, are never fulfilled perfectly, because measurement of the precision and sensitivity of an assay depends upon the particular numerical results obtained. Nevertheless, useful general indications can be based upon even a slight previous knowledge of some of the relevant quantities.

To make a full analysis of the economics of design for all the complicated types of design that can be contrived is impracticable, but consideration of the principles governing choice of the number and spacing of doses for the simplest types of assay gives useful guidance in other situations. For a parallel line assay, the demands that, for a given cost, both the most reliable estimate of ρ and an assessment of its precision shall be obtained are compatible ; for a slope ratio assay (Chapter 7), this is not true. On the other hand, few assays can provide adequate validity tests unless the design be of less than optimal efficiency as judged purely by the estimation of ρ. Provided that the condition of similarity is satisfied, (and, if the experimenter did not believe this, he would not be planning a dilution assay), by a prodigal expenditure of time, labour, and materials, any desired reliability of estimation coupled with any desired sensitivity of validity tests can be obtained. In practice, the limited resources of an experimenter require that he choose the dose levels and the numbers of subjects at each dose in relation to any pre-existing knowledge of the potency of the test preparation, knowledge of the appropriate metametric transformations, and his degree of certainty in respect of the conditions of monotony and similarity. If previous experience makes him almost certain of his choice of metameters, of the range of doses over which a linear regression obtains, and of the condition of similarity, he need not reduce his precision by insistence on tests of validity, or at least he can be content with crude tests. If he lacks this certainty, some sacrifice of precision is necessary, but he must not lose sight of his primary object.

6.4 Pilot investigations

As in so many types of statistical enquiry (for example, sampling surveys), the optimal design cannot be stated unless the answer is already known, since the conditions for maximum precision themselves involve ρ. However, an assay is seldom undertaken without some knowledge of the potency of the test preparation, and even a very little information can help greatly in the planning of an efficient assay. If absolutely nothing is known about ρ, as may happen in the first assay of material from an entirely new source, the investigator should begin with a small *pilot assay*, involving the determination of only a few responses, which will serve to indicate the order of magnitude of ρ. No rules on the design of such a pilot assay can be formulated, except that the doses should be chosen so as to explore the widest conceivable range for the potency of the test preparation ; even if ρ is located only within a ten-fold range on either side, plans for the main assay will be greatly assisted.

In general, the data from the pilot assay will not be combined with those of the main assay, and so will not contribute directly to the precision of the potency estimate. The question of the best subdivision of a fixed total number of subjects between the pilot and the main assays therefore arises. No simple answer can be given, though a fraction of between one-fourth and one-tenth of the total number of subjects may be suggested as a working rule. If the experimental technique is such that each response is measured before treatment of the next subject is begun, the development of sequential methods of statistical analysis may offer some hope of combining the two stages, so that the early tests in the main assay are used as guides to progressive modifications in design. Staircase methods for quantal responses (§ 19.6) are of this kind, and analogous procedures for quantitative responses might be developed.

6.5 Symmetry

In general, symmetrical designs ought always to be chosen. Thus, for parallel line assays, the basic pattern will always be that of the symmetrical $2k$-point, k doses of each preparation, equally spaced on the log scale and with equal numbers of subjects (or responses per subject ; see Chapter 10) at each dose. Of course, further complications may be imposed on top of this. For example, whenever differences between litters (or other natural groupings of the subjects) are likely to be large, some form of litter-mate control or other block restriction should be incorporated into the assay ; the simplest form is that of the randomized block design, in which group differences are balanced over levels and so do not affect the precision of the potency estimate. Again, if all the tests cannot be made on one day, or by one observer, balance may be secured by the use of randomized blocks. Limitations of resources may prevent the complete realization of this symmetry, and compel the use of, say, a balanced incomplete block design (§§ 9.5–9.7). If the available subjects do not permit even this degree of symmetry, there is no objection to a non-symmetrical design ; the oestrone assay in § 4.13, for example, has a perfectly legitimate design, but the computations are more laborious than if the five gaps in Table 4.5 had been filled. On the other hand, there is seldom any real advantage, and usually some disadvantage, in unnecessary departures from symmetry ; there may be a small gain in precision or in one validity test, with a loss on something else, but much the same flexibility of aim is given by the choice for k. The vitamin D_3 assay discussed in § 4.2 was poor in design, though it was saved from disaster by the fact that N_S and N_T were nearly equal and that, in spite of badly chosen doses, the mean difference in log dose was almost equal to M.

Symmetrical designs are usually the easiest to use in an experiment, and the easiest for statistical analysis. Of course, accidents during an assay may convert a symmetrical design into an unsymmetrical.

6.6 The cost of statistical analysis

The labour and cost of a statistical analysis is generally only a small part of the total expenditure on an assay, and the marginal savings that might be effected by modifications in design (at least within the field of symmetrical designs) are unlikely to be sufficiently important to influence the choice of design. This will always be true of an assay carried out as a research project, in which the cost of securing and measuring each response will be high : every effort should then be made so to design the assay as to make each response as useful as possible, and no considerations of computational labour should be allowed to prevent a fully efficient analysis. Even in routine assays of a preparation manufactured in large batches (for example, penicillin), in which the whole assay technique may be simplified and ' streamlined ', suggestions for omitting some parts of the statistical analysis should be viewed with suspicion until they are proved not to be false economies : as has been shown in §§ 5.3–5.6, the amount of arithmetic required in such a routine assay can be made quite small by careful arrangement of the calculations, and may be reduced still further if approximations such as range estimation of the standard deviation are permissible.

No doubt the chemist, biochemist, or microbiologist whose own statistical experience is small would object to some of the designs discussed in later chapters, on the grounds that, however theoretically efficient they may be in special circumstances, they are valueless to him, because when he had obtained the data he would have no idea how to analyse them. This difficulty illustrates the need for close collaboration between the experimental scientist and the statistician. To reject a good design for such a reason would be short-sighted ; the right policy is surely either to learn how to analyse the data or to obtain assistance from a professional statistician. Statistical science is one of the precision instruments available to the experimenter, who, if he is to make proper use of the knowledge at his disposal, must either learn to handle it himself or find someone else to do so for him. Experimenters who will put themselves to great trouble in acquiring skill with some difficult biological or chemical technique often deny themselves the benefits of statistical techniques because they consider these beyond their understanding. The fault may lie in part with statisticians, in that they fail to make their methods sufficiently clear to the non-mathematician, but the loss is entirely the experimenters'. An appreciation of the principles of experimental design and a familiarity with the commoner techniques of statistical analysis are within the competence of any scientist, however restricted his mathematical education may have been ; with this basis, he will be content to accept the advice of a statistician on more abstruse matters

A more serious problem arises when the experimental design that appears theoretically ideal for a certain purpose is so complex in its structure that its execution in the laboratory would be technically difficult or attended by the risk of frequent errors. This may happen if a design requires a complicated sequence of doses to be applied to each subject, with different sequences for different subjects. Mistakes in dosing might occur and would destroy the intended symmetry ; even if the experimental programme were carried out without mistakes, the precision might be much less than was expected because of the difficulties of running the experiment. In framing his advice, the statistician needs to remember that a simple design can give better results than one for which the complexity defeats its own ends.

6.7 Randomization

In all subsequent discussion of designs, every choice in the selection of a design or in the allocation of subjects to a place in the design will be assumed to be made at random unless there is explicit statement to the contrary. Thus, in an assay such as that of § 5.1, the thirty capons would be divided into six sets of five entirely at random. In a randomized block design, using litters as blocks, one member of each litter would be selected at random for the first dose, a second member at random for the second dose, and so on. If the design is based upon a Latin square, that square will be selected at random either from all squares of the same size or at least from all of a particular transformation set (Fisher and Yates, 1963, Introduction). Every randomization should be made independently of others in the same assay ; in a series of assays of the same design, each will have its own randomization. Moreover, by randomization is meant a strict process of selection by lot, using a table of random numbers or equivalent machinery, and not merely a haphazard selection according to the whim of the experimenter. In theory, the order in which the subjects receive their doses should be random. If all subjects in one dose-group are treated in succession, a correlation between their responses may be introduced, and may pass undetected though it would affect the true experimental errors. To give doses in random order, however, may introduce a risk of gross blunders, and some discretion must be exercised in the enforcement of this requirement (*cf*. § 11.3). The reasons for this insistence on randomization are not peculiar to biological assay, but are fundamental to the probabilistic interpretation of statistical data ; Fisher (1960) should be consulted for a fuller explanation.

Any departure from proper randomization may have serious effects on the validity of experimental comparisons. Emmens (1948, § 6.1) quotes an instance of an attempted ' random ' selection of mice from a cage, in which an assistant picked the mice haphazardly ; a significant correlation between the weights of the mice and the order in which they were taken from the cage appeared. A selection of insects for tests of insecticides which allows the more active individuals in a culture a greater chance of appearance in the first batches may produce heterogeneity of sex-ratio, or of age distribution, between batches (§ 4.22). Deliberate omission of a randomization is equivalent to an assertion that the responses will be independent of the systematic element introduced, or at least that any correlation is negligible in comparison with the experimental errors. In microbiological assays, for example, the placing of replicate tubes adjacent to one another in the incubator, on the assumption that position in the incubator is without effect on bacterial growth, might be thought convenient and has been customary in some laboratories. Alternative, and far preferable, procedures are to number the tubes for identification and then to randomize completely, to immerse them in a water-bath, with forced circulation, providing far more accurate thermostatic control than is possible when the tubes are surrounded by air, or to move the tubes around the incubator by means of a revolving holder, so ensuring the balancing of environmental differences.* The responsibility for a decision to omit a randomization rests with the experimenter : the data will give the statistician no means of checking the assumption that no bias is introduced, though, without strong supporting evidence from previous experiments, his experience will generally lead him to be a little sceptical of it.

A good illustration of the effects of a failure to randomize is provided by a series of agar-plate assays of penicillin. In an assay

---

* I am indebted to Dr. E. C. Wood (personal communication) for notes on these alternatives, and for drawing my attention to the advantages of the revolving holder.

such as that discussed in § 5.3, the circles are placed symmetrically on the plate at angles of $0°$, $90°$, $180°$, $270°$ from a fixed radius. If the four dose levels were assigned to the four positions on a plate entirely at random, and independently for each plate, the three contrasts L_p, L_1, L_1' would necessarily have equal variances. For convenience in the execution of an assay, however, an experimenter might standardize the order of doses ; he might perhaps always take the order round the plate as S_1, T_1, S_2, T_2. The fact that S_1, S_2 and T_1, T_2 were always further apart than other pairs of circles would make the mean squares derived from L_p, L_1, L_1' have expectations $\sigma^2 (1 + r_2 - 2r_1)$, $\sigma^2 (1 - r_2)$, $\sigma^2 (1 - r_2)$ respectively, where r_1, r_2 are the correlation coefficients between responses for adjacent circles and between responses for non-adjacent circles respectively. Since r_1 would normally exceed r_2, the variance of L_p would be less than that of L_1 or L_1'. The two variances would have to be estimated separately, by computation of values for the contrast from each plate, as in Table 5.5 ; validity tests and fiducial limits would have to make allowance for this complication, the latter by use of the first analogue of Fieller's theorem. In these circumstances, the precision of an assay like that in § 5.3 would have to be assessed from two variance estimates, each with only 3 degrees of freedom, a very unsatisfactory situation even with variances as small as are usually found for penicillin responses. An assay sufficiently precise for practical purposes would then scarcely be obtained with less than eight plates.

In a series of penicillin assays whose design was similar to that used by de Beer and Sherwood (§ 5.3), though the experimental details were a little different, Knudsen and Randall (1945) found evidence of heterogeneity of variability in the contrasts L_p, L_1. Miss Knudsen (private communication) has confirmed that a systematic order of doses was adopted ; the order, however, was S_1, S_2, T_2, T_1 on each plate ; for which the variances of L_p, L_1, L_1' must be $\sigma^2 (1 - r_2)$, $\sigma^2 (1 - r_2)$, $\sigma^2 (1 + r_2 - 2r_1)$ respectively. Thus, for these assays, lack of randomization cannot be responsible for a difference in variance between L_p and L_1. Knudsen and Randall used range estimates of standard deviations (§ 5.9), and their control charts showed clearly that the range for L_1 was the greater. Non-normality of the distribution of responses may have caused inequality of the mean ranges even though the mean variances must be equal, but this does not seem a very plausible explanation ; examination of L_1', which contrast was not discussed by the authors, might give some clue to what has happened (see also § 14.4). Enough has been said here to draw attention to the dangers of assuming that randomization is an unimportant refinement, or an unnecessary complication, of an experimental programme.

6.8 Parallel line assays

The remainder of this chapter is concerned only with parallel line assays. The optimal design for a projected assay depends upon existing knowledge about the standard and test preparations, and any rules given here are liable to modification to meet special circumstances. Nevertheless, a useful guide to good design can be based upon consideration of the policy to adopt when

(a) Past experience (or preliminary study of responses to the standard preparation) has shown a linear regression on log dose to be a satisfactory approximation to the truth over a moderately wide range of doses ;

(b) The same experience or study has given some indication of the magnitudes of the regression coefficient and the standard deviation of responses about the regression (though any change in the source of the subjects or the conditions of experimentation may affect these quantities) ; and

(c) The experimenter is not entirely ignorant of the potency of the test preparation, and a pilot assay (or other information) enables a rough estimate, R_0, to be made.

The basic problem of design then confronting the experimenter is that of how best to use a total of N subjects. The first point to be considered is the error of estimation, for, if the assay is to be of any use, there must be a high probability that R is close to the true unknown value ρ. From (4.12), the quarter-square of the fiducial interval for M is

$$I = \frac{t^2 s^2}{b^2 (1-g)^2} \left[(1-g) \left(\frac{1}{N_S} + \frac{1}{N_T} \right) + \frac{(M - \bar{x}_S + \bar{x}_T)^2}{\Sigma S_{xx}} \right], \quad (6.1)$$

and the aim is to keep this quantity small, with the restriction that $N_S + N_T = N$ (Bliss, 1950). The experimenter will therefore wish to choose his design so that

(i) t is small,

(ii) s is small,

(iii) b is large,

(iv) g is small,

(v) $\left(\dfrac{1}{N_S} + \dfrac{1}{N_T}\right)$ is small,

(vi) $(M - \bar{x}_S + \bar{x}_T)$ is small,

(vii) ΣS_{xx} is large,

a formidable list, but fortunately not all are independent.

(i) t is determined by the number of degrees of freedom for s^2 (and, of course, by the probability level chosen for the fiducial limits, but that may be supposed fixed by the use to which the potency estimate is to be put). A minimum of 10 degrees of freedom for t is generally desirable, but increase beyond that will seldom be important by comparison with the other factors. If the N subjects are arranged in a $2k$-point design without further constraints, t will have $(N - 2k)$ degrees of freedom ; if the subjects are divided into l blocks, this will be reduced to $(N - 2k - l + 1)$. This suggests that satisfactory assays are scarcely possible unless N is at least 20.

(ii) s depends upon homogeneity of subjects, good choice of design, and care in the conduct of the assay. Use of a highly inbred line of animals appears to be undesirable, because of reduced vigour and possibly increased variability in some physiological responses, and F_1 hybrids of inbred lines may give lower values of s^2 (McLaren and Michie, 1954; Biggers and Claringbold, 1954). Control of environment and nutrition, before and during an assay, and accuracy in experimental technique are important. Blocks of litter-mates (§ 6.7, Chapter 9) and other constraints may eliminate irrelevant variability.

(iii) b is the increase in response per unit increase in dose, in terms of the metameters, and is a measure of the *sensitivity* (§ 1.9) of the subjects to changes in dose. Any breeding of subjects for assays should aim at high values of b as well as low values of s. Note that the word ' sensitivity ' is used to refer to rate of change of response with dose, as explained in § 1.9.

(iv) Since

$$g = \frac{t^2 s^2}{b^2 \Sigma S_{xx}},$$

all measures taken under the headings (i), (ii), (iii), (vii) will also benefit g. Whereas the width of the fiducial interval is directly proportional to s, t, and $1/b$, for g all that is necessary is a reasonably small value, say 0·05, and further reduction below this gives a negligible return. In a well-planned assay, the second term in (6.1) will be small by comparison with the first, and I will therefore be inversely proportional to $(1 - g)$; for small g, the width of the fiducial interval will be approximately proportional to $(1 + \frac{1}{2}g)$. If the second term in (6.1) is not small, this factor of proportionality will increase, but cannot exceed $1/(1 - g)$.

(v) For a fixed N, $\left(\dfrac{1}{N_S} + \dfrac{1}{N_T}\right)$ has the minimum value $4/N$ when $N_S = N_T = \frac{1}{2}N$: subjects should therefore be divided equally between the two preparations unless there are strong reasons to the contrary. The loss through a small departure from equality will be trivial, but, except in the simplest designs, an unequal division will not easily fit in with the structure and will increase the labour of statistical analysis. The oestrone assay in § 4.13 illustrates this : the design used there, which represents a good attempt to come near to symmetry with awkward material, is obviously better than if all incomplete litters had been rejected (in which case, only eight subjects could have been used), and better than if all the missing entries had occurred for the same dose. In some circumstances, rejection of a few subjects which are superfluous to a good design may be preferable to adoption of an inferior design that uses all available subjects. Of course, these remarks relate to self-contained assays of a single test preparation. If information from previous tests of the standard preparation can be used in the current assay, or if several test preparations are to be assayed simultaneously (Chapter 11), the situation will be different.

(vi) The aim of making $(M - \bar{x}_S + \bar{x}_T)$ small in absolute magnitude will best be achieved by first choosing the doses of the standard and then dividing each by R_0 to give corresponding doses of the test preparation, so that

$$x_T = x_S - \log R_0. \qquad (6.2)$$

If equal numbers of subjects are assigned to corresponding doses,

$$M - \bar{x}_S + \bar{x}_T = M - \log R_0,$$

an expression which will not be far from zero unless R_0 is a bad estimate.

(vii) Since the largest contributions to S_{xx} come from doses far from $\bar{x}$, ΣS_{xx} will be maximized by testing all subjects at the extremes of the region of linearity. Even if this could be done satisfactorily for the standard preparation, an attempt to use an equal range of x for the test preparation, about which less is known, would involve serious risk that one or more doses might fall outside the region of linearity. To use unequal ranges of x for the two preparations is generally inconvenient. Instead, the dose range for the standard preparation must be made a little less than the maximum, in such a way that the doses for the test preparation, obtained by division by R_0 as just described, are unlikely to be too extreme for the linear regression.

The maximum value for ΣS_{xx} will then be given by assigning $N/4$ subjects to the highest and lowest doses of each preparation, so giving a 4-point design. The validity tests can be improved only at the expense of ΣS_{xx}, and consequently also of g ; use of a symmetrical 6-point design, for example, will reduce ΣS_{xx} to $2/3$ of its maximum. If the choice of doses is successful in making $(M - \bar{x}_S + \bar{x}_T)$ small, the second term in (6.1) may be able to suffer a decrease in ΣS_{xx} without affecting I seriously, and control of g may often be effected in other ways. Nevertheless, there are types of assay in which the responses are so variable as to make any decrease in ΣS_{xx} have unfortunate consequences for g. This should not in itself be regarded as justification for the use of a 4-point design rather than a 6-point. A large g is then a characteristic of the technique, and can be overcome only by increasing the size of the assay. A potency estimate of low precision with a reasonable assurance of validity is preferable to one of apparently higher precision that may be entirely irrelevant because of invalidity. An argument that, in a particular assay, since the precision is low there is no need to be strict about validity would be better replaced by an assertion that the assay in question is worthless because of the inherent variability of the technique.

6.9   Symmetrical $2k$-point designs

In general, doses will be spaced at equal intervals on the log scale, and equal numbers of subjects will be assigned to each dose. As noted in § 6.5, the advantages of this policy are many, the advantages of departing from it few and infrequently occurring. The desiderata of a good assay will now be examined for the symmetrical $2k$-point design (§ 5.2) more fully than was practicable for the general design in § 6.8.

Suppose that the highest and lowest doses, of either preparation, differ by X on the log scale. The interval between successive doses will therefore be $X/(k - 1)$, and

$$\left.\begin{aligned} d &= \frac{X}{2(k - 1)} \quad (k \text{ even}) \\ d &= \frac{X}{k - 1} \quad (k \text{ odd}) \end{aligned}\right\} \tag{6.3}$$

may be used in the formulæ of § 5.2. In that section, the dose metameter was chosen to make the values of $(x - \bar{x})$ simple integers ; in the present discussion, X will be regarded as fixed for different choices of k, and no scale of measurement can make the $(x - \bar{x})$ take integral values for all possible k. On the logarithmic scale used for X, the values of $(x - \bar{x})$ are those in § 5.2 multiplied by d, and therefore $\mathit{\Sigma}S_{xx}$ is the divisor for L_1 multiplied by d^2. Equations (5.5) and (5.8) both give

$$\mathit{\Sigma}S_{xx} = \frac{NX^2}{12} \times \frac{k + 1}{k - 1} . \tag{6.4}$$

Hence

$$g = \frac{12t^2s^2}{Nb^2X^2} \times \frac{k-1}{k+1}.$$ (6.5)

Write

$$A = \frac{12t^2s^2}{Nb^2X^2},$$ (6.6)

and also

$$h = (M - \bar{x}_S + \bar{x}_T)/X,$$ (6.7)

the deviation of M from the provisional log R_0 expressed as a proportion of the total range of doses. Then, since $N_S = N_T = N/2$, equation (6.1) may be written

$$I = \frac{AX^2\left[1 - \dfrac{k-1}{k+1}\left(A - 3h^2\right)\right]}{3\left(1 - \dfrac{k-1}{k+1}A\right)^2}.$$ (6.8)

Most discussions of the relative merits of alternative assay designs and techniques have in the past been based upon what in this book is called a naive variance formula (*cf.* Finney, 1947*a*). The variance formula for the symmetrical 2k-point design is

$$V(M) = \frac{4s^2}{Nb^2}\left[1 + 3h^2\left(\frac{k-1}{k+1}\right)\right],$$ (6.9)

which can legitimately be used only when A is small enough for terms in A^2 or higher powers in equation (6.8) to be neglected; this condition is equivalent to the condition that g be small, and when it obtains

$$I = t^2V(M).$$

The precision of an estimate is defined as the reciprocal of the sampling variance, and therefore can be given meaning only when use of a variance is permissible. Before the more general situation (g not negligible) is considered, designs for different values of k will be compared on the assumption that the assay is one for which equation (6.9) can be used. From the point of view of precision alone, the best assay using N subjects will be that having $k = 2$, $h = 0$; the precision of the 2k-point design relative to it is given by

$$\text{Relative precision} = \frac{1}{1 + 3h^2\left(\dfrac{k-1}{k+1}\right)},$$ (6.10)

since s and b are unaffected by the choice of h and k. This relative precision is tabulated in Table 6.1 ; values are shown for h less than 1·0 in absolute magnitude, and for $k = 2, 3, 4, 5, 10$, and the limit as k is increased indefinitely.

TABLE 6.1—Percentage precision of the symmetrical $2k$-point design relative to the optimal 4-point

g is assumed to be small

Values of k	Values of $\mid h \mid$					
	0·0	0·1	0·2	0·3	0·5	1·0
2	100	99	96	92	80	50
3	100	99	94	88	73	40
4	100	98	93	86	69	36
5	100	98	93	85	67	33
10	100	98	91	82	62	29
Limit	100	97	89	79	57	25

If h is small in absolute magnitude, the ill effects of using a large k are slight. An assay in which a bad choice of doses, attributable to poor information on R_0, causes $\mid h \mid$ to exceed 0·3 should be regarded as very unsatisfactory ; its analysis of variance is likely to show a significant difference between preparations, a recognized danger signal for invalidity (§ 4.7). The 6-point assay of testosterone propionate (§ 5.1), for example, had $h = 0·08$, an excellent value ; nothing appreciable would have been gained by arranging the same number of subjects in a 4-point assay, and little would have been lost if the subjects had been distributed between a larger number of doses. In the penicillin assay (§ 5.3), even though g was small, $h = -1·1$, and equation (6.10) shows that the precision has been reduced to 45 per cent. of the maximum by the poor choice of doses : had a 6-point design been used, the precision would have fallen to 36 per cent.

When A is not very small, the increase in g as k increases is liable to make the ill-effects of using a large k more marked. The exact concept of precision, as measured by the reciprocal of the variance of M, must be abandoned, since no true variance exists. Instead, the *reliability* of an assay may be defined as the reciprocal of I (Finney, 1947a). This definition is not entirely satisfactory, as the relative reliability of two designs then depends upon the probability used in defining the fiducial limits, but no better measure of the quality of an assay in respect of its closeness of estimation has yet been proposed. Provided that the number of degrees of freedom in both designs is large enough for t to be practically independent of its degrees of freedom, the reliability of the symmetrical $2k$-point relative to the optimal design with $k = 2$, $h = 0$, is

$$\text{Relative reliability} = \frac{\left(1 - \dfrac{k-1}{k+1} A\right)^2}{\left(1 - \dfrac{1}{3} A\right)\left[1 - \dfrac{k-1}{k+1}(A - 3h^2)\right]} . \quad (6.11)$$

In Tables 6.2, 6.3, 6.4, the relative reliability is shown for $A = 0.2$, 0.4, 1.0 respectively, and for the same values of k, h as were used in Table 6.1 ; for $A = 0$, of course, equation (6.11) reduces to equation (6.10). These tables all relate to the 95 per cent. fiducial limits adopted throughout this book, and similar tables for a higher probability, say 99 per cent., would show lower reliabilities.

TABLE 6.2—Percentage reliability of the symmetrical 2k-point design relative to the optimal 4-point

For $A = 0.2$

Values of k	Values of $\lvert h \rvert$					
	0·0	0·1	0·2	0·3	0·5	1·0
2	100	99	96	91	79	48
3	96	95	90	84	68	36
4	94	92	87	80	62	31
5	93	91	85	77	59	28
10	90	87	80	71	52	23
Limit	86	83	75	64	44	18

TABLE 6.3—Percentage reliability of the symmetrical 2k-point design relative to the optimal 4-point

For $A = 0.4$

Values of k	Values of $|h|$					
	0·0	0·1	0·2	0·3	0·5	1·0
2	100	99	96	91	78	46
3	92	91	86	79	63	32
4	88	86	80	72	55	26
5	85	82	76	68	50	23
10	78	75	68	58	41	17
Limit	69	66	58	48	31	12

TABLE 6.4—Percentage reliability of the symmetrical 2k-point design relative to the optimal 4-point

For $A = 1.0$

Values of k	Values of $|h|$					
	0·0	0·1	0·2	0·3	0·5	1·0
2	100	99	94	88	73	40
3	75	73	67	59	43	19
4	60	57	51	43	28	11
5	50	47	40	32	20	7
10	27	24	18	12	6	2
Limit	0	0	0	0	0	0

Inspection of these tables indicates that, broadly speaking, if $A < 0.2$, the value of h is the most serious cause of reduced liability ; if $|h|$ is also small, variation in the number of dose levels is not very important, at least up to $k = 5$. Even for $A = 0.4$, however, the fall in reliability as k increases is much more marked than for $A = 0$. If A is large, any increase in k reduces the reliability seriously when $|h|$ is small, a trend that becomes still more rapid when $|h|$ also is large. An assay of reasonable size, using subjects and responses of the low variability desirable in bioassay, should seldom have A greater than 0·2, though much larger values will sometimes be encountered.

6.10 The choice of k

The results presented in § 6.9 make clear that, if there were no doubts about the statistical validity of the analysis of an assay, the 4-point design ($k = 2$), would always be chosen. Only when there is very extensive experience of an assay technique, however, can statistical validity over the range of doses tested be practically certain. In general, the contention that at least three doses of each preparation should be used must still be upheld ; the increase in fiducial range may be a small price to pay for the gain of linearity tests, even under conditions in which $|h|$ and A are both large. On the other hand, assuming that the recommended policy of preliminary investigations into the character of the response curve and the choice of metameters (§ 3.5) has been followed, there is little to be said for the use of more than three levels. The loss in reliability as k increases makes clear the harm that results from confusion of purpose : too often, experimenters fail to distinguish between the need to study the response curve as a preliminary to the establishment of an assay procedure and the need for an efficient allocation of subjects in an assay. For complex assay designs, $k = 4$ is sometimes useful, because $4 = 2^2$ and more satisfactory factorial and confounding schemes can be based upon this number than upon 3 (§ 9.9), but a larger k should rarely be required (cf. § 4.22). The practice of using a few subjects at each of many dose levels, which is undoubtedly essential for a proper study of a response curve, seems to merit general condemnation for assays.

The argument in §§ 6.8, 6.9, has been based upon the simplest type of design, in which the subjects tested at each dose are random selections from all those available. Nevertheless, the essential features of the conclusions are applicable to designs of more complex character, in which block constraints are introduced. Even in the incomplete block designs described in Chapter 9, the same considerations govern the choice between 4-point, 6-point, 8-point, and other schemes.

These points are well illustrated by consideration of the uterine weight assay for oestrone. The assay data in Table 4.5 led to

$$s^2 = 551 \cdot 2$$

and

$$bX = 16 \cdot 00 \times 2$$
$$= 32 \cdot 00.$$

If a symmetrical 4-point assay were to be performed with six litters of four rats and the same dose range as in Table 4.5, the value of A might be expected to be about

$$A = \frac{12 \times (2 \cdot 131)^2 \times 551 \cdot 2}{24 \times (32 \cdot 00)^2}$$
$$= 1 \cdot 2.$$

Equation (6.11) shows that use of a 6-point design with the same total number of subjects would have a relative reliability of 67 per cent. if $|h|$ were negligible and only 34 per cent. if $|h|$ were as much as 0·5 (from § 4.18, $h = -0 \cdot 1$ for the data of Table 4.5). Moreover, this estimate assumes that only intra-litter variance is involved, as would be true if four litters of six rats were available ; if the subjects to be used were again six litters of four, an incomplete block design (Chapter 9) would be necessary, and might cause a further loss in reliability (but see § 9.9). Thus the minimum price to be paid for the 6-point design is a 22 per cent. increase in the fiducial range of M, and unfavourable circumstances might make this much worse. This is inevitable if adequate validity tests are to be incorporated into the assay. A further increase in k so as to give an 8-point design would reduce the reliability to 47 per cent. at most, and increase the fiducial range by 46 per cent. at least, with correspondingly worse results in unfavourable circumstances, but such extravagance of design is rarely commendable.

6.11 The comparison of assay techniques

Earlier sections of this chapter have been concerned with the purely statistical aspects of assay design, the effects of the structure of the experiment on its efficiency as a method of assay. Implicit in this discussion was the assumption that all comparisons referred to alternative designs for the same subjects, using the same manipulative techniques and making the same measurements, the only permissible variations being in the allocation of subjects to doses. Most of the factors listed in § 6.8 depend only on this structure, and not on the choice of a response for measurement ; s, b, and indirectly g, however, are functions of the particular responses measured, and will be altered by a change in the stock of subjects or in the property of the subjects that is chosen for measurement.

In a good assay, for which g and $|h|$ are both small, not only is the use of a variance formula for M permissible, but the standard error may be written

$$\text{S.E.} (M) \doteq \frac{s}{b}\left(\frac{1}{N_S} + \frac{1}{N_T}\right)^{\frac{1}{2}}. \tag{6.12}$$

Hence s/b, which is measured in the same units as x, may be regarded as an inherent standard error per response in respect of the measure of log potency; interpreted in this sense, equation (6.12) has the form of a standard error of the difference of two means of N_S and N_T observations. Alternative experimental techniques for the estimation of the potency of a particular stimulus may therefore be compared in terms of the magnitudes of s/b. The physical dimensions of this quantity are those of a log potency, and before values from different sources are compared they must be converted to the same base for their dose metameters; logarithms to base 10 are usually preferred. Apart from complications caused by g and h, the number of subjects required in order to secure a specified precision of estimation is inversely proportional to the square of s/b. Choice of technique cannot be based entirely on this quantity, as, unless the range of linearity of response, X, is reasonably large, the variance formula on which equation (6.12) is based cannot be used, but at least it is a major factor to be considered. Bliss and Cattell (1943) summarized values of s/b ranging from 0·03 to 0·5 in a series of forty-five parallel line assays for various drugs; five different methods of vitamin D assay showed values between 0·07 and 0·34. Jones (1945) reported two long series of values obtained in routine tests of vitamin D using line test and X-ray methods. Somers (1950) discussed the relative merits of alternative techniques for the assay of thyroid preparations in terms of values of s/b.

In making a choice of assay technique, the cost of alternatives must be considered in conjunction with their inherent precisions. An assay using cats may have a lower value of s/b than a similar technique using rats, but against this must be balanced the higher cost of a cat. Again, for any one species of subject, the stimulus may have a general effect on many measurable characteristics as well as a specific effect on some particular organ. The specific effect is likely to show greater sensitivity to change in dose, and so to give a smaller value of s/b, but a general body measurement can be made more easily, without destruction of the subject. The experimenter must choose that species and characteristics which are 'best' in the widest sense, balancing the more costly animal or the more laborious measurement against its possibly higher inherent precision. A response specific to the stimulus may carry less risk of invalidity because its magnitude is less likely to be modified by other constituents of the test preparation. In some circumstances, human volunteers can be used as subjects, without danger and with the advantage of coming closer to the conditions of clinical use of a drug, which may be important if there is any doubt about the analytical dilution property; Mongar (1959), Myerscough and Schild (1958), and Schild (1959) have given examples. Every new measurement or assay technique should have its own study of the dose-response relation, although often the metametric transformation can have the simplicity of equation (3.71).

Sometimes several different measures of response to each dose can be measured on each subject, so as to specify a multivariate response $y_1, y_2, y_3, \ldots$. The possibility of improving assay precision by a combination of these values involves construction of a *discriminant function* (Chapter 13).

CHAPTER 7

SLOPE RATIO ASSAYS

7.1 The power dose metameter

The assays discussed in Chapters 4–6 have used equation (3.7) as the dose response regression relationship, and have therefore made use of a logarithmic dose metameter. The alternative form of regression in equation (3.6), with $\lambda \neq 0$, must now be considered. This naturally leads to the dose metameter

$$x = z^\lambda \qquad (7.1)$$

and the regression lines for the two preparations, in terms of the response metameter,

$$\left. \begin{array}{l} Y_S = a + \beta x, \\ Y_T = a + \beta \rho^\lambda x. \end{array} \right\} \qquad (7.2)$$

Instead of two parallel lines, these equations represent two lines of different slope, β and $\beta \rho^\lambda$ respectively, intersecting at $x = 0$; this intersection accords with commonsense, for the response to zero dose must be the same for the two preparations. If b_S, b_T are estimates of the two regression coefficients,

$$R = \left(\frac{b_T}{b_S} \right)^{1/\lambda} \qquad (7.3)$$

is an estimate of the relative potency; assays of this type are therefore known as *slope ratio assays*. In all current uses of this type, $\lambda = 1$ appears to be an adequate approximation to the truth, and throughout this book the assumption that $\lambda = 1$ will be made. The restriction is not very serious, however, for results appropriate to any other value of λ can be derived by using exactly the same methods to give estimates of R^λ and its fiducial limits; the final step is then to raise each of these to the power $1/\lambda$. If λ itself had to be estimated for each assay, instead of being regarded as a part of the definition of the dose metameter with a value determined from preliminary investigations, the analysis would be more difficult. The method of calculation for this problem will not be described here, but the interested reader may like to note what has been written elsewhere about the Parker-Rhodes equation (Finney, 1952, § 45).

The first recorded use of a slope ratio assay appears to be that of Birch and Harris (1934), though their discussion did not explicitly recognize the nature of the analysis. They found the duration of cure of bradycardia in vitamin B_1 deficient rats, resulting from treatment with the vitamin, to be directly proportional to dose ; they therefore proposed to estimate the potency of a test preparation by adjusting the dose scales until its response curve coincided with that for the standard—essentially the procedure now used, but performed graphically rather than arithmetically. Later, equations (7.2) were found to be suitable for the analysis of many micro-biological assays, and they were first systematically discussed in this connexion (Burn *et al.* 1950, Chapter III ; Emmens, 1948, Chapter 20 ; Finney, 1945a, 1947d ; Wood, 1945, 1946a).

Since the chief use of slope ratio assays now seems to be for microbiological techniques, the terminology of microbiological assays will be adopted in this chapter and the next. In a micro-biological assay, the test subject is no longer a single animal, but is an inoculum (of specified size) of a bacterial culture, which is added to a dose of the standard or test preparation and incubated under standard conditions. The response is some measure of the bacterial growth that takes place in a fixed time, often a measurement of turbidity or of the amount of alkali required to neutralize the acid formed during growth. The theory, of course, remains unaltered if required for macrobiological techniques such as that of Birch and Harris. Moreover, the response as actually measured seems usually to show a homoscedastic linear regression without transformation, so that

$$Y = U \qquad (7.4)$$

gives the response metameter. Equation (7.4) will be assumed in these two chapters.

7.2 The multiple regression equation

Let x_S, x_T represent the doses of the two preparations. Then (with $\lambda = 1$) equations (7.2) may be written in the single equation

$$Y = a + \beta x_S + \beta \rho x_T. \qquad (7.5)$$

This equation shows that the dose–response relationships may be expressed as a multiple linear regression equation. If the relationship represented by equations (7.2) remains valid down to $x_S = x_T = 0$, it will be natural to run some tests on 'blank' or control subjects with zero dose, and, as will be shown in Chapter 8, this is also expedient from the point of view of efficiency. Even if the equations are not valid down to zero dose, estimation of the parameters by the fitting of separate regressions to the data from the two preparations would still be improper, since it would ignore the restriction that both of equations (7.2) have the same a. This restriction is analogous to the constraint of fitting parallel lines when a logarithmic dose metameter is used. Whether or not responses at $x_S = x_T = 0$ have been measured, the equation

$$Y = a + b_S x_S + b_T x_T \qquad (7.6)$$

may be fitted to the data by the ordinary procedure of multiple linear regression, such as has been used for another purpose in § 4.19. The equations for determining the regression coefficients are

$$\left.\begin{aligned} b_S S_{x_S x_S} + b_T S_{x_S x_T} &= S_{x_S y}, \\ b_S S_{x_S x_T} + b_T S_{x_T x_T} &= S_{x_T y}. \end{aligned}\right\} \qquad (7.7)$$

The summations are to be taken over all subjects, in the manner illustrated in § 7.4. When b_S, b_T have been found, the estimate of ρ may be formed as

$$R = \frac{b_T}{b_S}, \qquad (7.8)$$

and limits of error can be assigned by applying Fieller's theorem to this ratio.

7.3   Data for an unsymmetrical slope ratio assay

Kent-Jones and Meiklejohn (1944) have described an assay of nicotinic acid in a meat extract. The design adopted is scarcely ideal, as will be apparent from a study of Chapter 8. The intention of its authors was to use the doses of the standard preparation in order to fix the one regression line and then to compare each response to the test preparation with this standard curve, afterwards averaging the several estimates of potency ; such a method of analysis is in general to be deprecated, although in this instance it gives about the right answer. The lack of symmetry, however, may be a help in emphasizing the main features of the full statistical analysis.

The data from Kent-Jones and Meiklejohn are reproduced in Table 7.1. The solution of meat extract used in the assay was a dilution containing 1 g. per 5,000 ml. Duplicate assay tubes were prepared for each of five doses of standard nicotinic acid and three doses of the test preparation, as well as for a ' blank ' or zero dose. The eighteen tubes were inoculated from a culture of *Lactobacillus arabinosus*, and incubated at 37° C. for 72 hours. The acidity of each tube was then measured by titration with N/14 sodium hydroxide, bromothymol blue being used as an indicator in a colour comparator.

TABLE 7.1—Responses in an assay of nicotinic acid in
a meat extract
(ml. N/14 NaOH)

Dose of standard preparation (μg. per tube)				
0·05	0·10	0·15	0·20	0·25
3·5	5·0	6·2	8·0	9·4
3·2	4·7	6·1	7·7	9·5

Dose of test preparation (ml. per tube)			Blanks
1·0	1·5	2·0	
4·9	6·3	7·7	1·5
4·8	6·5	7·7	1·4

Fig. 7.1 shows each response plotted against dose, independent common-zero scales being used for the two preparations. The two sets of points lie close to two straight lines, intersecting near the points for blanks ; of course, the mean response for $x_S = x_T = 0$ has no more reason for lying absolutely on the lines than has any other point. Lines drawn by eye in Fig. 7.1 show

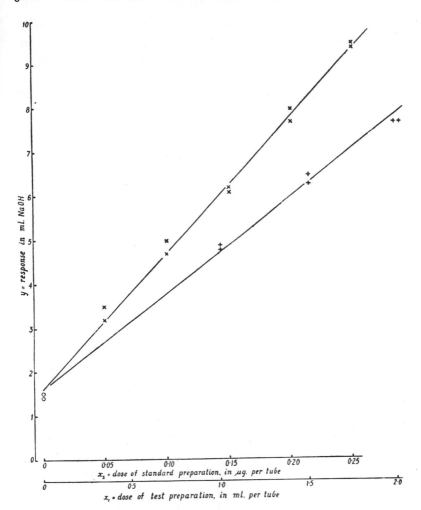

Fig. 7.1—Linear dose-response regressions for the assay of nicotinic acid, Table 7.1

  × : Responses to standard preparation

  + : Responses to test preparation

  ⊙ : ' Blanks '

  The straight lines are those mentioned in § 7.3 as having been drawn by eye, but are very close to the lines on which equation (7.16) is based.

for the standard preparation an increase in response of about 31 units. (ml. NaOH) per $0.1\mu g.$, and for the test preparation an increase in response of about 3.1 units per ml. Hence the potency of the test preparation is about $0.1\mu g.$ per ml., and, making allowance for the dilution factor, 1 g. of the meat extract contains about $500\mu g.$ nicotinic acid.

7.4 Analysis of variance

As usual, an analysis of variance is an aid to examination of the validity of the assay. The regression coefficients must first be calculated. If S be used to represent summation over the eighteen tubes,

$$\left.\begin{array}{l} Sx_S = \quad 1.5 \\ Sx_T = \quad 9.0 \\ Sy = 104.1, \end{array}\right\} \tag{7.9}$$

since $x_S = 0$ except for tubes of the standard and $x_T = 0$ except for tubes of the test preparation. Moreover, the sums of squares and products of deviations are

$$\left.\begin{array}{l} S_{x_S x_S} = 0.2750 - \dfrac{(1.5)^2}{18} \\ \qquad = 0.15, \\ S_{x_S x_T} = -\dfrac{1.5 \times 9.0}{18} \\ \qquad = -0.75, \\ S_{x_T x_T} = 10.00, \\ S_{x_S y} = 2.34, \\ S_{x_T y} = 7.65. \end{array}\right\} \tag{7.10}$$

The two regression coefficients are therefore the solutions of

$$\left.\begin{array}{l} 0.15b_S - \quad 0.75b_T = 2.34, \\ -0.75b_S + 10.00b_T = 7.65, \end{array}\right\} \tag{7.11}$$

and are found to be

$$\left.\begin{array}{l} b_S = 31.080, \\ b_T = \quad 3.096. \end{array}\right\} \tag{7.12}$$

The analysis of variance in Table 7.2 can now be constructed. The total sum of squares and the sum of squares between doses are found in the usual manner. The sum of squares accounted for by the regression, 2 degrees of freedom out of the 8 between doses, is

$$b_S S_{x_S y} + b_T S_{x_T y} = 31 \cdot 080 \times 2 \cdot 34 + 3 \cdot 096 \times 7 \cdot 65 \qquad (7.13)$$
$$= 96 \cdot 412.$$

TABLE 7.2—Analysis of variance for the data of Table 7.1

Adjustment for mean		602·045	Mean square
Nature of variation	d.f.	Sum of squares	
Regression	2	96·412	
Deviations from regression	6	0·278	0·0463
Between doses	8	96·690	
Error	9	0·175	0·0194
Total	17	96·865	

7.5 Validity tests

The absence of any appreciable heteroscedasticity may be seen by inspection of Table 7.1. The error sum of squares in Table 7.2 is composed of nine single degrees of freedom, one from each of the doses, and to apply to these the heterogeneity test used in § 3.10 would scarcely be satisfactory because each response was measured only to the nearest 0·1 ml. If there were any doubt, a test might be made on, say, three mean squares, each with 3 degrees of freedom, obtained by pooling the squares from doses giving the three lowest, the three highest, and the other three pairs of responses.

The component of the sum of squares representing deviations from the linear regression equation gives a composite validity test relating to linearity of the regressions for the two preparations and intersection of these lines in a point estimated by the blanks. As for parallel line assays, linearity is a requirement for statistical validity ; intersection of the lines in the right point is a requirement for fundamental validity, analogous to parallelism in parallel line assays, since it derives from the condition of similarity. The sum of squares for deviations from the linear regression does not divide into components appropriate to different validity tests as easily as does the corresponding sum of squares in a parallel line assay, and users of an assay such as that under discussion may often rest content with the composite test. In the present instance, the ratio of the mean square to that for error is 2·4, as compared with 3·4 for significance at the 5 per cent. level (Appendix Table II). Though not significant, the ratio is sufficiently large to arouse the suspicion that at least one large component may be concealed in the sum of squares for deviations, and a full analysis should be undertaken.

From the sum of squares for deviations from regression, two components to be briefly described as ' Blanks ' and ' Intersection ' may be separated, each with one degree of freedom. These were first suggested by Bliss (1947b), and were discussed more generally by Finney (1951a). The component for blanks represents the deviation of the mean response to zero dose from a new version of equation (7.6) fitted to the data from the non-zero doses only, and is used as a test of whether or not equation (7.5) remains valid down to zero dose. The component for intersection depends upon the difference in the expected responses for zero dose calculated from lines fitted to the two preparations separately, and is thus a specific test of fundamental validity (cf. Wood, 1945). The remaining degrees of freedom comprise the curvature components for the two preparations separately, excluding zero dose. For an unsymmetrical design, computation of the squares for blanks and intersection is tedious.

The easiest general procedure for deriving the blanks component is to introduce a new variate, x_0, defined to have the value unity for the blanks, zero elsewhere. Calculate then a multiple linear regression on x_S, x_T, x_0 : equations (7.11) are easily seen to be extended to

$$\left.\begin{array}{l} 0{\cdot}1500b_S - 0{\cdot}7500b_T - 0{\cdot}1667b_0 = 2{\cdot}3400, \\ -\,0{\cdot}7500b_S + 10{\cdot}0000b_T - 1{\cdot}0000b_0 = 7{\cdot}6500, \\ -\,0{\cdot}1667b_S - 1{\cdot}0000b_T + 1{\cdot}7778b_0 = -\,8{\cdot}6667. \end{array}\right\} \quad (7.14)$$

The values of b_S, b_T are no longer those of equations (7.12), but the same notation is retained. The solutions of equations (7.14) are

$$\left. \begin{array}{l} b_S = 30\cdot1253, \\ b_T = 2\cdot9874, \\ b_0 = -0\cdot3704 \; ; \end{array} \right\} \tag{7.15}$$

note the necessity for a large number of decimal places in order to give sufficient accuracy in the next calculation. The sum of squares for the new regression is

$$2\cdot3400b_S + 7\cdot6500b_T - 8\cdot6667b_0 = 96\cdot556.$$

The difference between this result and the sum of squares with 2 degrees of freedom in equation (7.13) is the required component for blanks. That for intersection is obtained indirectly, by finding the residual sum of squares after the fitting of linear regressions to the non-zero doses for the two preparations separately. By calculation from the dose totals for the five doses of the standard preparation and the three of the test preparation, the sums of squares between doses are found to be 46·296 and 8·143, with 4 and 2 degrees of freedom respectively. Linear regressions account for

$$(-2 \times 6\cdot7 - 9\cdot7 + 15\cdot7 + 2 \times 18\cdot9)^2/20 = 46\cdot208$$

and

$$(-9\cdot7 + 15\cdot4)^2/4 = 8\cdot122$$

respectively. The residual for all types of curvature is therefore

$$(46\cdot296 - 46\cdot208) + (8\cdot143 - 8\cdot122) = 0\cdot109$$

with 4 degrees of freedom. This could be further split into quadratic, cubic, and other components if desired. The square for intersection is now obtained by subtraction, and Table 7.3 is completed.

As was feared, the complete analysis discloses serious evidence of invalidity. Fortunately, this is only statistical invalidity, the mean response for the blanks being appreciably lower than is predicted by the fitting of equation (7.6) to the other data. The mean square for blanks is significant at the 5 per cent. level. This phenomenon of a slight curvature at very low doses is not infrequently encountered. Wood (1946) suggests that, for riboflavin assays using

Lactobacillus helveticus as test subject, the difficulty might be overcome by adding a small amount of the standard preparation, say $0.03\mu g$. per tube, to the basal medium, and regarding as experimental doses only quantities in excess of this. The conventional zero dose should then be brought on to the linear portions of both response curves. For a true analytical dilution assay, this seems an unexceptionable procedure, and might be adapted to assays of materials other than riboflavin. For a comparative assay, the danger of chemical or biological complications through the mixing of the standard and test preparations must be considered by the experimenter.

TABLE 7.3—Complete analysis of variance for the data of Table 7.1

Adjustment for mean		602·045	Mean square
Nature of variation	d.f.	Sum of squares	
Regression	2	96·412	
Blanks	1	0·144	0·144
Intersection	1	0·025	0·025
Curvature	4	0·109	0·027
Between doses	8	96·690	
Error	9	0·175	0·0194
Total	17	96·865	

One possible cause of variance heterogeneity in microbiological assays is that some experimenters place replicate tubes of each dose adjacent to one another in the incubator (§§ 4.21, 6.7). Unless the incubator temperature is absolutely uniform, a local irregularity may affect all tubes of a certain dose. The mean square for deviations from regressions in Table 7.2 will thereby be increased relative to the error, and it would then become the appropriate mean square for use in assessing the fiducial limits of the relative potency. A similar danger is introduced by Kent-Jones and Meiklejohn in their recommendation that, in titrating the acidity after incubation, duplicate tubes should be matched for colour with one another rather than independently with a standard. Unless the colour change is very sharply defined, a correlation between duplicates in respect of their response measurements may be produced, and this will result in underestimation of the error variance. Experimenters are tempted to believe that consecutive treatments of, or consecutive measurements on, duplicate tubes may be regarded as giving independent observations, and to ignore the possible occurrence of correlated subjective errors ; this may be often justifiable, but the dangers of faulty interpretation of data are always present when proper randomization in space and time is abandoned. In the present assay, curvature at very low doses seems a more plausible explanation of the evidence for invalidity, since only the square for blanks is much greater than the error mean square.

7.6   Potency estimation

In view of the anomalous behaviour of the responses at zero dose, estimation of potency from the non-zero dose levels seems desirable. The effect of omission of the blanks is trivial so far as R itself is concerned, but it does make some difference to the precision ; use of the blanks would give an apparently more precise estimate, but Table 7.3 shows evidence that the conclusion would be misleading. The natural method of computation is to proceed exactly as in § 7.4 but to use only the data from the sixteen tubes. These calculations verify what is already theoretically apparent, namely, that the values of b_S, b_T are those in equations (7.15). Therefore

$$R = \frac{2\cdot987}{30\cdot125}$$

$$= 0\cdot0992, \tag{7.16}$$

which gives an estimate of $496\mu g$. per g. for the potency of the meat extract.

Evaluation of variances requires the inverse matrix of the coefficients in equation (7.14) ; by the procedure illustrated in § 4.19, this is found to be

$$V = \begin{pmatrix} 16\cdot9663 & 1\cdot51685 & 2\cdot44382 \\ 1\cdot51685 & 0\cdot241573 & 0\cdot278090 \\ 2\cdot44382 & 0\cdot278090 & 0\cdot948034 \end{pmatrix} . \qquad (7.17)$$

In routine computation, V would be found first, and the regression coefficients obtained from it, as

$$b_S = 2\cdot3400v_{11} + 7\cdot6500v_{12} - 8\cdot6667v_{13}, \text{ etc.}$$

Multiplication of s^2 by v_{11}, v_{22}, and v_{12} in turn gives the variances of b_S, b_T and their covariance. For s^2, there appears to be no objection to using the error mean square in Table 7.3, in spite of its inclusion of 1 degree of freedom from the blanks:

$$s^2 = 0\cdot0194. \qquad (7.18)$$

Fieller's theorem, equation (2.6), then gives the fiducial limits of R as

$$R_L, R_U =$$

$$\left[R - \frac{gv_{12}}{v_{11}} \pm \frac{ts}{b_S} \left\{ v_{22} - 2Rv_{12} + R^2v_{11} - g\left(v_{22} - \frac{v_{12}^2}{v_{11}}\right) \right\}^{\frac{1}{2}} \right]$$

$$\div (1-g), \quad (7.19)$$

where

$$g = \frac{t^2 s^2 v_{11}}{b_S^2}. \qquad (7.20)$$

In a good microbiological assay, the variation between replicate tubes should be relatively much less than that between animals in a macrobiological assay. Consequently, g is usually negligible, and fiducial limits may be based upon the variance formula

$$V(R) = \frac{s^2}{b_S^2} [v_{22} - 2Rv_{12} + R^2v_{11}]. \qquad (7.21)$$

The complete formula (7.19) must be used for any slope ratio assay in which g is not small. In the example under discussion,

$$g = \frac{(2\cdot262)^2 \times 0\cdot0194 \times 16\cdot966}{(30\cdot125)^2}$$

$$= 0\cdot0019,$$

which is sufficiently small to be neglected. If (7.19) is applied, the fiducial limits are found as

$$R_L, R_U = \left[0\cdot09915 - 0\cdot00017 \pm \frac{2\cdot262}{30\cdot125} \left\{ 0\cdot0194 \times (0\cdot24157 \right. \right.$$

$$\left. \left. - 0\cdot30079 + 0\cdot16679 - 0\cdot00020) \right\}^{\frac{1}{2}} \right] \div 0\cdot9981$$

$$= 0\cdot0957, \ 0\cdot1026.$$

Since the meat extract was diluted 5,000-fold for use as a test preparation, it is estimated to contain $496\mu g$. per g., with fiducial limits at $478\mu g$. and $513\mu g$. per g. The same result may be obtained by using equation (7.21) to give a standard error of $7\cdot6\mu g$. per g. to the potency estimate. Had the indications of invalidity been ignored and the data from the blanks used, R would have been obtained from equations (7.12) ; the estimate of potency would then have been $498 \pm 7\cdot3\mu g$. per g., with limits at $482\mu g$. and $514\mu g$. per g. In spite of the significance of ' blanks ' in Table 7.3, the difference in conclusion is clearly unimportant here.

7.7 General formulae

Slope ratio assays should give no difficulty to those who are accustomed to the technique of multiple linear regression, but the formulæ are necessarily a little more cumbrous than for parallel line assays. With the notation already introduced, the general variance and covariance matrix may be written

$$V = \begin{pmatrix} \dfrac{S_{x_T x_T}}{\varDelta} & -\dfrac{S_{x_S x_T}}{\varDelta} \\[2ex] -\dfrac{S_{x_S x_T}}{\varDelta} & \dfrac{S_{x_S x_S}}{\varDelta} \end{pmatrix} \qquad (7.22)$$

where $\varDelta$ is defined by

$$\varDelta = S_{x_S x_S} S_{x_T x_T} - \left(S_{x_S x_T}\right)^2. \qquad (7.23)$$

The regression coefficients, obtained by solving equations (7.7), are

$$\left.\begin{aligned} b_S &= v_{11} S_{x_S y} + v_{12} S_{x_T y} , \\ b_T &= v_{12} S_{x_S y} + v_{22} S_{x_T y} , \end{aligned}\right\} \qquad (7.24)$$

and equation (7.8) gives R. Moreover, g is given by equation (7.20), and, if it is small, the variance formula

$$V(R) = \frac{s^2}{b_S^2 \varDelta}\left(S_{x_S x_S} + 2RS_{x_S x_T} + R^2 S_{x_T x_T}\right) \qquad (7.25)$$

may be used ; if g is not small, the fiducial limits are given by equation (7.19). Formula (7.13) gives the amount of the sum of squares between doses accounted for by the regression, and an analysis of variance like that in Table 7.2 can readily be constructed.

If the replicates are not classified into blocks, the error sum of squares can be calculated directly from the pooled variation within doses. The general procedure of analysis of variance is always available for the elimination of block effects, as would have been necessary, for example, if the tubes in the assay just discussed had been arranged in the incubator in two randomized blocks of nine.

These formulæ are perfectly general ; they apply to any spacing of doses, to any numbers of tubes at each dose, and whether or not tests are made at zero dose. If the sum of squares for deviations from regression is to be subdivided as in Table 7.3, the formulæ may be applied twice, once including and once excluding the blanks, so as to give the one degree of freedom for blanks as the difference between two residual sums of squares, but the procedure illustrated in § 7.5 is preferable.

Important though these general formulæ are, symmetrical designs should be adopted whenever possible, both because of their efficiency and because of their relative simplicity of execution and analysis. For them, the calculations can be put into simpler form.

7.8   The symmetrical $(2k + 1)$-point design

The slope ratio design analogous to the $2k$-point for parallel lines is the $(2k + 1)$-point. In its symmetrical form, equal numbers of subjects are assigned to zero dose and to k equally spaced doses of each preparation. Without loss of generality, the scales may be so chosen that the highest dose of each preparation is unity ; if on the original scales these doses are X_S, X_T, the relative potency calculated on the conventional scales must finally be multiplied by X_S/X_T. The total number of subjects is

$$N = n\,(2k + 1), \tag{7.26}$$

divided into nk for each preparation and n for the blanks or controls ; thus there are n subjects at zero dose and at doses $\dfrac{1}{k}$, $\dfrac{2}{k}$, $\cdots$ $\dfrac{k-1}{k}$, 1 of each preparation.

The general algebraic theory may be developed as in § 5.2. If the dose totals are represented by C for the blanks, S_1, S_2, $\cdots$ S_k and T_1, T_2, $\cdots$ T_k for the two preparations,

$$\left.\begin{aligned}
S_{x_S y} &= \frac{1}{k}\left(S_1 + 2S_2 + \ldots + kS_k\right) - \frac{(k+1)G}{2(2k+1)} \\
S_{x_T y} &= \frac{1}{k}\left(T_1 + 2T_2 + \ldots + kT_k\right) - \frac{(k+1)G}{2(2k+1)},
\end{aligned}\right\} \quad (7.27)$$

where G is the grand total of all responses:

$$G = C + S_1 + S_2 + \ldots + S_k + T_1 + T_2 + \ldots + T_k.$$

The matrix V, defined in equation (7.22), becomes

$$V = \frac{3k}{N(k+1)(k^2+k+1)}\begin{pmatrix} 5k^2+5k+2 & 3k(k+1) \\ 3k(k+1) & 5k^2+5k+2 \end{pmatrix}, \quad (7.28)$$

the factor outside the matrix being understood as multiplying each of the elements. The regression coefficients are obtained from equations (7.24). The components of the analysis of variance for blanks and intersection are given by two orthogonal contrasts, L_B and L_I, defined by

$$\begin{aligned}
L_B = k(k-1)C &- (2k-2)(S_1+T_1) \\
&- (2k-5)(S_2+T_2) - (2k-8)(S_3+T_3) + \ldots \\
&+ (k-1)(S_k+T_k)
\end{aligned} \quad (7.29)$$

for which the divisor is $Nk(k-1)(k^2+k+1)/(2k+1)$, and

$$\begin{aligned}
L_I = (2k-2)(S_1-T_1) &+ (2k-5)(S_2-T_2) \\
&+ (2k-8)(S_3-T_3) + \ldots - (k-1)(S_k-T_k)
\end{aligned} \quad (7.30)$$

for which the divisor is $Nk(k-1)$. The sum of squares for the remaining $(2k-4)$ degrees of freedom between doses is then found by subtraction of

$$b_S S_{x_S y} + b_T S_{x_T y} \qquad \text{(2 degrees of freedom)},$$

$$\frac{(2k+1)L_B^2}{Nk(k-1)(k^2+k+1)} \qquad \text{(1 degree of freedom)},$$

and

$$\frac{L_I^2}{Nk(k-1)} \qquad \text{(1 degree of freedom)}$$

from the complete sum of squares between doses with $2k$ degrees of freedom ; it may be further partitioned into quadratic, cubic and higher order components for each preparation, by applying to the S totals and the T totals *separately* the same orthogonal coefficients as were discussed in Chapter 5.

In the absence of evidence of invalidity, the estimate and its fiducial limits are assessed by the equations (7.8) and (7.19). The variances and covariance of the regression coefficients are obtained from V as

$$
\left.\begin{aligned}
V\,(b_S) &= s^2 v_{11}, \\
V\,(b_T) &= s^2 v_{22}, \\
C\,(b_S,\,b_T) &= s^2 v_{12},
\end{aligned}\right\} \tag{7.31}
$$

whence

$$
g = \frac{3 t^2 s^2 k\,(5k^2 + 5k + 2)}{N b_S^2\,(k+1)(k^2 + k + 1)}. \tag{7.32}
$$

The formulæ for $V(R)$ and the fiducial limits can be written in terms of k, but they do not take any particularly simple form and the general expressions are more easily remembered.

If the assay is statistically invalid because of the significance of L_B, the data for the blanks may be rejected and the remainder treated as a $2k$-point design. A new analysis as described in § 7.12 may then be tried, remembering that the total number of subjects is now only $2kN/(2k+1)$ or $2nk$.

7.9   The 3-point design

The simplest special case of the $(2k+1)$-point design, the 3-point, is even less satisfactory as a general assay procedure than is the 4-point parallel line assay, since it provides no validity tests of any kind. Nevertheless, it is of interest as a standard of comparison, since, if the experimenter were certain of validity *a priori*, it would lead to the most reliable estimate of potency. In any 3-point design, the two regression lines will be obtained by joining the points representing mean responses to the two preparations to the point for the blanks, so giving a perfect fit of the data to the regression equations ; no degrees of freedom remain for tests of statistical or fundamental validity.

In the symmetrical design, $\tfrac{1}{3}N$ subjects will be tested at zero dose and at unit dose of each preparation. If the totals of the responses at the three doses are C, S, T, either the commonsense argument of the last paragraph or the general equations of § 7.8 give

$$
\left.\begin{aligned}
b_S &= 3\,(S - C)/N, \\
b_T &= 3\,(T - C)/N,
\end{aligned}\right\} \tag{7.33}
$$

and
$$R = (T - C)/(S - C). \qquad (7.34)$$

Moreover
$$g = \frac{6t^2s^2}{Nb_S^2}$$
$$= \frac{2Nt^2s^2}{3(S-C)^2} . \qquad (7.35)$$

The fiducial limits might be expressed directly in terms of the totals C, S, T, but they are more conveniently written

$$R_L, R_U = \left[R - \tfrac{1}{2}g \pm \frac{t}{b_S} \left\{ \frac{3s^2}{2N}(4 - 4R + 4R^2 - 3g) \right\}^{\frac{1}{2}} \right]$$
$$\div (1 - g). \qquad (7.36)$$

When g is small,

$$V(R) = \frac{6s^2(1 - R + R^2)}{Nb_S^2} \qquad (7.37)$$

may be used.

7.10   The 5-point design

The 5-point design possesses most of the advantages that the 3-point lacks, though, as will be shown in Chapter 8, the gain is achieved at the cost of a reduction in reliability. The symmetrical form is perhaps the most useful of all slope ratio designs. The five doses may be taken as zero and $\tfrac{1}{2}$, 1 unit of each preparation, and $N/5$ subjects are assigned to each. Equation (7.28) reduces to

$$V = \frac{4}{7N} \begin{pmatrix} 16 & 9 \\ 9 & 16 \end{pmatrix} \qquad (7.38)$$

The regression coefficients are usually calculated from $S_{x_S y}$, $S_{x_T y}$ by means of equations (7.24); formula (7.13) gives the sum of squares (2 degrees of freedom) for the regression.

Alternatively, the calculations may be made directly by the formation of contrasts between responses. This is analogous to the procedure for parallel line assays in Chapter 5, but now, unfortunately, the contrasts for b_S and b_T are not mutually orthogonal (§ 4.16) ; consequently, the two regression coefficients cannot be made to give independent squares for the analysis of variance, and use of formula (7.13) is unavoidable. The method is convenient, however, because the remaining dose contrasts can be subdivided into components orthogonal with one another and with b_S and b_T. Table 7.4 shows the contrasts required, as obtained by the method of § 7.8 ; the column headed 'divisor' is to be used only for forming b_S and b_T from the first two lines of the table, and only for forming the appropriate squares from the other lines. (The reader should verify the non-orthogonality of b_S and b_T, the orthogonality of every other pair.) The contrasts L_B and L_I, together with the regression, account for the whole of the sum of squares between doses, as will be numerically verified in Tables 7.5 and 7.6.

TABLE 7.4—Coefficients of regression and orthogonal contrasts for the 5-point design

Contrast	C	S_1	S_2	T_1	T_2	Divisor
b_S	-15	1	17	-6	3	$35n/2$
b_T	-15	-6	3	1	17	$35n/2$
L_B	2	-2	1	-2	1	$14n$
L_I	0	2	-1	-2	1	$10n$

The analysis of variance analogous to that in Table 7.3 may now be completed. If examination of L_B, L_I and any other relevant tests does not indicate invalidity, the fiducial limits to R are assessed as

$$R_L, R_U = \left[R - \frac{9g}{16} \pm \frac{t}{b_S} \left\{ \frac{8s^2}{7N} \left(8 - 9R + 8R^2 - \frac{175g}{32} \right) \right\}^{\frac{1}{2}} \right]$$
$$\div (1 - g), \quad (7.39)$$

where

$$g = \frac{64t^2s^2}{7Nb_S^2} \quad (7.40)$$

When g is small,

$$V(R) = \frac{8s^2 (8 - 9R + 8R^2)}{7Nb_S^2} \quad (7.41)$$

may be used. Wood and Finney (1946) have given general formulæ for unsymmetrical 5-point designs ; these are rarely needed and will not be reproduced here.

The computational simplicity of the symmetrical 5-point design, by comparison with a design such as that of the assay in Table 7.1, may be illustrated on data relating to the assay of a sample of malt

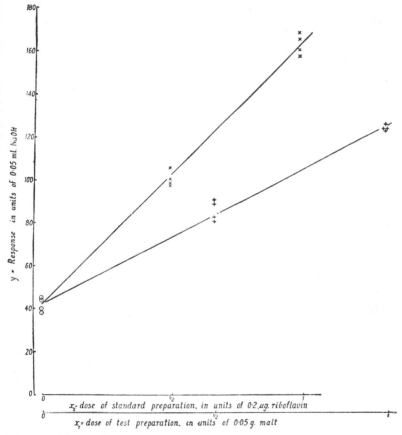

Fig. 7.2—**Linear dose-response regressions for the assay of riboflavin, Table 7.5**

     × : Responses to standard preparation

     + : Responses to test preparation

     ○ : 'Blanks'

     The straight lines are those calculated from the analysis in § 7.10.

for its riboflavin content. The data in Table 7.5 were reported by Wood (1946a) ; they were obtained by using *Lactobacillus helveticus* as the test organism, and titrating for acidity with sodium hydroxide. Twenty tubes were used, four for blanks and four each at 0·1, 0·2μg. of standard riboflavin and 0·025, 0·05 g. malt per tube. Responses were measured to the nearest 0·05 ml., and for arithmetical convenience this may be taken as the unit of response so that all values of y are integers (Fig. 7.2).

TABLE 7.5—Responses in an assay of riboflavin in malt
(In units of 0·05 ml. N/10 NaOH)
Standard preparation : 1 unit = 0·2μg. riboflavin
Test preparation : 1 unit = 0·05 g. malt

Blanks	Standard		Test	
$x_S = 0$	$x_S = \frac{1}{2}$	$x_S = 1$	$x_S = 0$	$x_S = 0$
$x_T = 0$	$x_T = 0$	$x_T = 0$	$x_T = \frac{1}{2}$	$x_T = 1$
38	97	167	80	121
45	100	164	88	124
40	105	159	90	122
44	98	156	82	122
167	400	646	340	489

The regression coefficients may be found as the solutions of equations (7.7), which here take the form

$$3·2b_S - 1·8b_T = 233·4,$$
$$- 1·8b_S + 3·2b_T = 46·4.$$

Alternatively, the dose totals in Table 7·5 may be used with the contrasts defined in Table 7·4 to give directly

$$b_S = \frac{8,304}{70}$$
$$= 118·629,$$
$$b_T = \frac{5,686}{70}$$
$$= 81·229.$$

Formula (7.13) then gives 31,456·9 as the sum of squares for the regression. Moreover, the blanks and intersection contrasts in Table 7.4 here give

$$L_B = - 11,$$
$$L_I = - 37,$$

and these make contributions $11^2/56$, $37^2/40$ to the analysis of variance in Table 7.6. The sum of squares between doses, computed directly from the five dose totals, gives a check on the total of these three items. The sum of squares for error may be obtained by subtraction, or by the pooling of contributions with 3 degrees of freedom from each column of Table 7.5. The second method is interesting because it shows (as indeed is evident by inspection)

TABLE 7.6—Analysis of variance for the data of Table 7.4

Adjustment for mean		208,488·2	Mean square
Nature of variation	d.f.	Sum of squares	
Regression	2	31,456·9	
Blanks	1	2·2	2·2
Intersection	1	34·2	34·2
Between doses	4	31,493·3	
Error	15	216·5	14·43
Total	19	31,709·8	

that the variance between responses at the upper dose level of the malt is less than in any of the other groups : the estimates for the five columns are 10·9, 12·7, 24·3, 22·7, and 1·6 respectively. These figures show no steady trend, such as would arise if the variance tended to increase (or to decrease) as the response increased, and application of the test used in § 3.10 discloses no heterogeneity.

Table 7.6 shows no indications that the blanks or intersection component is large enough to be a source of danger.

The estimate of potency, in the units used for analysis, is, by equation (7.8),

$$R = 81\cdot229/118\cdot629$$
$$= 0\cdot6847.$$

Equation (7.40) gives

$$g = \frac{16 \times (2\cdot131)^2 \times 14\cdot43}{35 \times (118\cdot63)^2} = 0\cdot0021,$$

so small that the standard error $0\cdot0181$ could safely be assigned to R. Equation (7.39) is little more trouble to compute, and gives

$$R_L, R_U = 0\cdot6464, 0\cdot7235$$

as the fiducial limits. In order to express the results as μg. of riboflavin per g. malt, they must be multiplied by the ratio of units, $0\cdot2/0\cdot05$. The conclusion is that the malt contains $2\cdot74\mu$g. riboflavin per g. with fiducial limits at $2\cdot59$ and $2\cdot89\mu$g. per g.

7.11 Other $(2k + 1)$-point designs

Designs with higher values of k will seldom be required in ordinary assay practice. As shown in Chapter 8, they are appreciably less efficient, and their additional validity tests are not often needed. Uncertainty about the upper limit of the range of linearity may occasionally make desirable an assay with one or two high dose levels that may be rejected from the analysis if they are clearly beyond the linear region.

The 7-point design is unlikely to be popular, because it involves the awkward division of the whole dose interval into thirds. For it, equation (7.28) becomes

$$V = \frac{9}{26N} \begin{pmatrix} 31 & 18 \\ 18 & 31 \end{pmatrix}. \tag{7.42}$$

Table 7.7 shows the non-orthogonal contrasts required in forming the regression coefficients. The remaining 4 degrees of freedom between doses may be divided orthogonally into blanks, intersection, and quadratic components for each preparation ; since the regression curves are not parallel, there is no meaning to be attached to average measures of curvature, and the use of separate components for the two preparations seems preferable. These contrasts are also shown in Table 7.7, L_{2S} and L_{2T} denoting the two quadratic components. The divisors are used to give the magnitudes of b_S and b_T, and to give the squares for the other contrasts ; the sum of squares for the regression must as usual be calculated from formula (7.13).

TABLE 7.7—Coefficients of regression and orthogonal contrasts for the 7-point design

Contrast	C	S_1	S_2	S_3	T_1	T_2	T_3	Divisor
b_S	− 42	− 11	20	51	− 24	− 6	12	$182n/3$
b_T	− 42	− 24	− 6	12	− 11	20	51	$182n/3$
L_B	6	− 4	− 1	2	− 4	− 1	2	$78n$
L_I	0	4	1	− 2	− 4	− 1	2	$42n$
L_{2S}	0	1	− 2	1	0	0	0	$6n$
L_{2T}	0	0	0	0	1	− 2	1	$6n$

The 9-point design is easily incorporated into a programme that ordinarily uses 5-points, as it requires only that additional tests be made at doses one-quarter and three-quarters of the highest for each preparation. For this design,

$$V = \frac{24}{35N} \begin{pmatrix} 17 & 10 \\ 10 & 17 \end{pmatrix}. \qquad (7.43)$$

The regression and other contrasts are shown in Table 7.8 ; a factor 3 has been removed from L_B and L_I. The additional degrees of freedom are associated with cubic components for the two preparations, L_{3S} and L_{3T}. The relationship of the quadratic and cubic components to L_2 and L_3 in Table 5.7 should be clear. For most purposes, however, a composite test of residual curvatures, with 4 degrees of freedom, will suffice ; the sum of squares is obtained by subtraction of the regression, blanks, and intersection components from the total between doses.

TABLE 7.8—Coefficients of regression and orthogonal contrasts for the 9-point design

Contrast	C	S_1	S_2	S_3	S_4	T_1	T_2	T_3	T_4	Divisor
b_S	-30	-13	4	21	38	-20	-10	0	10	$105n/2$
b_T	-30	-20	-10	0	10	-13	4	21	38	$105n/2$
L_B	4	-2	-1	0	1	-2	-1	0	1	$28n$
L_I	0	2	1	0	-1	-2	-1	0	1	$12n$
L_{2S}	0	1	-1	-1	1	0	0	0	0	$4n$
L_{2T}	0	0	0	0	0	1	-1	-1	1	$4n$
L_{3S}	0	-1	3	-3	1	0	0	0	0	$20n$
L_{3T}	0	0	0	0	0	-1	3	-3	1	$20n$

7.12   The symmetrical $2k$-point design

For slope ratio assays, a second type of symmetrical design is possible. This is the symmetrical $2k$-point, in which no blanks are tested. If the scales are again chosen to make the highest doses tested one unit of either preparation, the design will use k doses of each, equally spaced between some low level, say c, and unity. Thus the doses will be

$$c, \ c + \frac{1-c}{k-1}, \ c + \frac{2(1-c)}{(k-1)}, \ \ldots \ c + \frac{(k-2)(1-c)}{k-1}, \ 1,$$

with $N/2k$ subjects at each. This design would not be chosen if the linear regression of response on dose were believed to hold down to zero dose, for it would then fail to make use of the whole range of linearity and so would give results less precise than the best obtainable. On the other hand, if an assay is based upon a response which is known to depart from a linear regression at low doses, and if the trick of adding a small amount of the standard preparation to all tubes (§ 7.5) is not used, a $2k$-point design would be the best choice ; the value of c would be taken as small as possible, perhaps about 0·1.

General formulæ for this design will not be given here. They involve both c and k, and offer no particular advantages over the complete regression calculation. One special case is that of a $(2k + 1)$-point converted into a $2k$-point by the necessity of rejecting the tests on the blanks, because of significant deviation from the linear regression equation (*cf.* § 7.5). This design has $c = 1/k$. If N now represents the total number of subjects excluding those for the blanks, and is therefore the original N multiplied by $2k/(2k + 1)$, the variance matrix is found to be

$$V = \frac{6k^2}{N\,(k^2 - 1)(2k + 1)} \begin{pmatrix} 5k + 1 & 3(k + 1) \\ 3(k + 1) & 5k + 1 \end{pmatrix}. \quad (7.44)$$

The blanks contrast no longer occurs ; that for intersection is still L_I as defined by (7.30), and, in terms of the new N, its divisor is $\frac{1}{2}N(k - 1)\,(2k + 1)$. With these formulæ, the analysis is easily completed.

For ease of reference, the contrasts required in analysis of the 4-point, 6-point, and 8-point designs resulting from rejection of the blanks in a $(2k + 1)$-point design are summarized in Tables 7.9–7.11. These are arranged to correspond to Tables 7.4, 7.7, and 7.8 respectively. The variance matrices are

$$V = \frac{8}{5N} \begin{pmatrix} 11 & 9 \\ 9 & 11 \end{pmatrix} \quad (7.45)$$

for the 4-point,

$$V = \frac{27}{7N} \begin{pmatrix} 4 & 3 \\ 3 & 4 \end{pmatrix} \quad (7.46)$$

for the 6-point, and

$$V = \frac{32}{15N} \begin{pmatrix} 7 & 5 \\ 5 & 7 \end{pmatrix} \quad (7.47)$$

for the 8-point. In these formulæ, N always represents the total number of subjects in the assay as analysed, n the number of subjects per dose, so that equation (7.26) must be replaced by

$$N = 2nk. \quad (7.48)$$

7.13 Routine assays

If a particular design is being used frequently as a routine method of potency estimation, the calculations may be standardized and reduced to a minimum of labour (*cf.* § 5.6). In its statistical analysis, a slope ratio assay is necessarily a little more trouble than

TABLE 7.9—Coefficients of regression and orthogonal contrasts for the 4-point design with $c = \frac{1}{2}$

Contrast	S_1	S_2	T_1	T_2	Divisor
b_S	-4	7	-6	3	$5n$
b_T	-6	3	-4	7	$5n$
L_I	2	-1	-2	1	$10n$

TABLE 7.10—Coefficients of regression and orthogonal contrasts for the 6-point design with $c = \frac{1}{3}$

Contrast	S_1	S_2	S_3	T_1	T_2	T_3	Divisor
b_S	-3	1	5	-4	-1	2	$14n/3$
b_T	-4	-1	2	-3	1	5	$14n/3$
L_I	4	1	-2	-4	-1	2	$42n$
L_{2S}	1	-2	1	0	0	0	$6n$
L_{2T}	0	0	0	1	-2	1	$6n$

TABLE 7.11—Coefficients of regression and orthogonal contrasts for the 8-point design with $c = \frac{1}{4}$

Contrast	S_1	S_2	S_3	S_4	T_1	T_2	T_3	T_4	Divisor
b_S	-8	-1	6	13	-10	-5	0	5	$15n$
b_T	-10	-5	0	5	-8	-1	6	13	$15n$
L_I	2	1	0	-1	-2	-1	0	1	$12n$
L_{2S}	1	-1	-1	1	0	0	0	0	$4n$
L_{2T}	0	0	0	0	1	-1	-1	1	$4n$
L_{3S}	-1	3	-3	1	0	0	0	0	$20n$
L_{3T}	0	0	0	0	-1	3	-3	1	$20n$

a parallel line. A 5-point, however, which is one of the most popular and convenient designs, can be rapidly analysed by the scheme illustrated in § 7.10; further savings may be effected by approximations such as using a range-estimate of standard deviation (Wood, 1947*b*; *cf*. § 5.9). Nomographic methods might also be developed (*cf*. § 5.7).

For a series of routine assays, a system of control charts should prove a valuable guard against unsuspected changes in experimental conditions. Control charts might be set up for s^2 and b_S, and also for L_B and L_I or for the ratios of these two quantities to their standard errors. In order to give better values for s^2 and b_S, some pooling of estimates from previous assays might be permitted in a series of assays showing satisfactory control. The suggestions made for parallel line assays (§ 5.10) are readily adapted to these slope ratio designs.

7.14   Other slope ratio problems

Whereas the study of parallel regression lines preceded their special use in biological assays, development of statistical methods for concurrent pencils of regression lines seems to have begun with slope ratio assays. However, neither the designs nor the arrangements of the analysis of variance suited to assays are necessarily the most useful in other circumstances. Claringbold (1959) has pointed out that, when chief interest lies in tests of significance of slope differences, sets of mutually orthogonal contrasts may be preferable and also that the blanks may give little relevant information. His valuable paper should be seen by any who have problems allied to the slope ratio situation but not strictly of an assay type. Extensive accounts of other special methods of analysis appropriate to pencils of lines have been well presented by Williams (1959).

CHAPTER 8

EFFICIENCY IN SLOPE RATIO ASSAYS

8.1 General principles

Most of what has been written in §§ 6.1–6.7 on the principles of assay design is as relevant and as important in slope ratio as in parallel line assays. The application of those principles leads to different results, because the formulæ expressing precision and reliability are different. In this chapter, the requirements of good design for slope ratio assays are discussed, with the assumption that the experimenter is again working under conditions (a), (b), and (c) of § 6.8 (except that the regression is now known to be linear on the absolute measure of dose). The problem facing the experimenter is still that of making the best use of a total of N subjects.

Suppose that the highest doses of the two preparations used in an assay are X_S, X_T. As in § 7.7, define v_{11}, v_{12}, v_{22} to be the elements of the variance matrix obtained when the dose scales are changed so as to make the highest doses of both preparations unity ; that is to say, these quantities relate to an assay in which all doses of the standard preparation have been divided by X_S, all doses of the test preparation by X_T. Then, for the assay as actually performed,

$$V = \begin{pmatrix} \dfrac{v_{11}}{X_S^{\,2}} & \dfrac{v_{12}}{X_S X_T} \\[2ex] \dfrac{v_{12}}{X_S X_T} & \dfrac{v_{22}}{X_T^{\,2}} \end{pmatrix} \tag{8.1}$$

This definition enables the effect of changing the range of doses to be kept distinct from that of changing the distribution of doses over their range. From equation (7.19), the quarter-square of the fiducial interval for R is

$$I = \frac{t^2 s^2}{b_S^2 (1 - g)^2} \left[\frac{v_{22}}{X_T^{\,2}} - \frac{2R v_{12}}{X_S X_T} + \frac{R^2 v_{11}}{X_S^{\,2}} - \frac{g}{X_T^{\,2}} \left(v_{22} - \frac{v_{12}^{\,2}}{v_{11}} \right) \right], \tag{8.2}$$

where

$$g = \frac{t^2 s^2 v_{11}}{b_S^2 X_S^2} \tag{8.3}$$

Equation (8.2) may be written

$$I = \frac{R^2 t^2 s^2}{b_S^2 X_S^2 h^2 (1 - g)^2} \left[v_{22} - 2hv_{12} + h^2 v_{11} - g\left(v_{22} - \frac{v_{12}^2}{v_{11}} \right) \right] ; \tag{8.4}$$

here

$$h = RX_T/X_S, \tag{8.5}$$

the ratio of the relative potency to relative magnitudes of the highest doses, is introduced to play a part similar to that of h in Chapter 6. Since R is a property of the test preparation, and is not at the experimenter's choice, his influence on the reliability of the estimate will be restricted to attempts to ensure that

(i) t is small,

(ii) s is small,

(iii) $b_S X_S$ is large,

(iv) g is small,

(v) h is large,

(vi) $\left[v_{22} - 2hv_{12} + h^2 v_{11} - g\left(v_{22} - \frac{v_{12}^2}{v_{11}} \right) \right]$ is small.

Several of these are similar to the requirements listed in § 6.8, and need not be discussed again in detail.

(i) The need of having enough degrees of freedom for t again indicates that at least twenty subjects will be required for a good assay, unless, as may happen in microbiological work, s is exceedingly small.

(ii) Genetic and environmental homogeneity of subjects are important to the control of the size of s ; in some types of assay, adoption of a randomization restricted by suitable block constraints may be valuable as a method of eliminating irrelevant variation.

(iii) $b_S X_S$ is the total increment in response to the standard preparation between zero dose and the highest dose used in the assay, as estimated from the regression ; the fact that curvature may prevent the use of very small doses does not enter into this stage of the argument. In parallel line assays, a high value of b itself is desirable : in slope ratio assays, an increase in b_S is no use if it is accompanied by a compensating reduction in the upper limit of doses for which the regression is linear. For a slope ratio assay, X_S should be chosen to have the largest possible value consistent with existing evidence of linearity of regression, and efforts to improve the subjects or the conditions of experiment should be directed at increasing the total increment in response, $b_S X_S$.

(iv) Equation (8.3) shows that g will be reduced by measures taken under the headings (i), (ii), and (iii). A small value of v_{11} will also benefit g, and this will be ensured by a wide spread of doses between 0 and X_S, as is also found to be desirable under heading (vi). The width of the fiducial interval will be approximately proportional to $1/(1 - g)$, so that any reduction in g below 0·05 can give little return.

(v) Since R is outside control and X_S has already been chosen to be as large as possible, h can be increased only by making X_T large. The greatest value for X_T consistent with the need for remaining on the linear portion of the regression for the test preparation is X_S/ρ. The experimenter will estimate this quantity by X_S/R_0 ; he will then presumably choose X_T a little less in order to guard against the possibility that an accidentally low value of R_0 may take him beyond the range of linearity. He should thereby obtain a value of h near to, but rather less than, unity.

(vi) This expression will be minimized by using extremes of dose, so concentrating the subjects at X_S, X_T and the lowest doses of the two preparations that do not go outside the region of linearity at that end of the scale. Provided that the region of linearity extends to zero dose, tests at this level are desirable because the subjects used there do double duty by occurring at the lower extremes of dose for both preparations. The ideal distribution of subjects between these doses will not be discussed here, as, in practice, the need for validity tests conflicts with the ideals of reliability : allocation of some subjects to intermediate levels of dose is essential if any validity tests are to be made, and should be regarded as a prerequisite of a good assay unless validity is certain *a priori*. Some further account is given in § 8.4.

8.2 Symmetrical $(2k + 1)$-point designs

Considerations of symmetry suggest that a $(2k + 1)$-point design should be adopted for any assay in which tests on blanks can be included. The possible advantages in departing from symmetry will be discussed in § 8.3, but for the present the symmetrical design may be regarded as the standard. For a symmetrical $(2k + 1)$-point design having X_S, X_T as the highest doses of the two preparations, equation (7.28) may be modified to the form

$$V = \begin{pmatrix} \dfrac{K_1}{NX_S^2} & \dfrac{K_2}{NX_S X_T} \\[2ex] \dfrac{K_2}{NX_S X_T} & \dfrac{K_1}{NX_T^2} \end{pmatrix}, \tag{8.6}$$

in which

$$K_1 = \frac{3k\,(5k^2 + 5k + 2)}{(k + 1)(k^2 + k + 1)}, \tag{8.7}$$

$$K_2 = \frac{9k^2}{k^2 + k + 1}. \tag{8.8}$$

Now

$$g = AK_1, \tag{8.9}$$

where

$$A = \frac{t^2 s^2}{N b_S^2 X_S^2}, \tag{8.10}$$

and equation (8.4) may therefore be written

$$I = \frac{AR^2\,[K_1\,(1 + h^2) - 2K_2 h - A\,(K_1^2 - K_2^2)]}{h^2\,(1 - AK_1)^2}. \tag{8.11}$$

From the point of view of precision, the best assay of this class will be that which has X_S and X_T at the highest values possible for linearity of regression, $h = 1$, and $k = 1$; this will be taken as the standard of comparison.

When A is small enough for g to be negligible, a variance formula may be used for R, based upon equation (7.25). The precision of the design for any values of k and h relative to the standard is then

$$\text{Relative precision} = \frac{6h^2}{K_1 - 2K_2h + K_1h^2}. \tag{8.12}$$

Values of this expression are shown in Table 8.1 for h equal to or less than unity, and for $k = 1, 2, 3, 4, 5, 10$ and the limit as $k \rightarrow \infty$.

TABLE 8.1—Percentage precision of the symmetrical $(2k + 1)$-point design, relative to the optimal symmetrical 3-point

(g is assumed to be small)

Values of k	Values of h				
	1·0	0·9	0·8	0·7	0·5
1	100	89	76	62	33
2	75	67	57	46	24
3	67	59	50	40	21
4	62	56	47	38	19
5	60	53	45	36	19
10	55	49	41	33	17
Limit	50	44	38	30	15

When A is not small, the increase in K_1 from its minimum of 6 to its maximum of 15 as k increases may have serious effects ; g is no longer negligible, and the strict concept of precision must be abandoned. As in Chapter 6, the reliability may be defined as the reciprocal of I. The reliability of the design for any values of k and h relative to the standard is

Relative reliability

$$= \frac{3h^2 (2 - 9A)(1 - AK_1)^2}{(1 - 6A)^2 [K_1 (1 + h^2) - 2K_2h - A (K_1^2 - K_2^2)]}. \tag{8.13}$$

If $A = 1/15$, the factor $(1 - AK_1)$ will tend to zero as k becomes large, and for larger values of A the reliability will fall to zero even for quite small k. In microbiological assays, values of A of this size ought never to be encountered ; the riboflavin assay discussed in § 7.10, for example, had A only about 0·0002. For $A = 0$, the formula for the reliability reduces to that for the precision ;

Tables 6.2, 6.3, 6.4 show the relative reliability for $A = 1/75$, 2/75, and 1/15 respectively, and for the same values of k and h as were used in Table 8.1.

TABLE 8.2—Percentage reliability of the symmetrical $(2k + 1)$-point design, relative to the optimal symmetrical 3-point

For $A = 1/75$

Values of k	Values of h				
	1·0	0·9	0·8	0·7	0·5
1	100	90	77	63	34
2	71	64	55	44	23
3	61	55	47	38	20
4	56	51	44	35	18
5	54	48	42	34	17
10	48	43	37	30	15
Limit	42	38	33	27	14

TABLE 8.3—Percentage reliability of the symmetrical $(2k + 1)$-point design, relative to the optimal symmetrical 3-point

For $A = 2/75$

Values of k	Values of h				
	1·0	0·9	0·8	0·7	0·5
1	100	90	78	64	35
2	66	60	52	43	22
3	55	50	44	36	19
4	49	45	39	32	17
5	46	42	37	30	16
10	39	36	32	26	13
Limit	33	31	27	22	11

TABLE 8.4—Percentage reliability of the symmetrical $(2k + 1)$-point design, relative to the optimal symmetrical 3-point

For $A = 1/15$

Values of k	Values of h				
	1·0	0·9	0·8	0·7	0·5
1	100	93	83	70	39
2	42	41	39	33	18
3	24	25	24	21	11
4	16	17	17	15	8
5	11	12	13	12	6
10	4	4	5	5	3
Limit	0	0	0	0	0

Tables 8.1 to 8.4 indicate that, even when A is small, the loss in reliability as the number of dose levels increases is more serious than for parallel line assays. Low values of h are also important factors in the reduction of reliability. These trends are accentuated at large values of A.

8.3 The unsymmetrical 3-point design

If the formula for $V(R)$, equation (7.25), is written down for the special case of the 3-point design, with n_0, n_S, n_T subjects at the three doses $(n_0 + n_S + n_T = N)$, it may be shown to be minimized by taking

$$\frac{n_0}{1 - h} = \frac{n_S}{h} = n_T = \tfrac{1}{2}N. \qquad (8.14)$$

Under the optimal condition of $h = 1$, this leads to the surprising conclusion that $\tfrac{1}{2}N$ subjects should be assigned to the doses of the two preparations and none to the blanks! Common sense shows that such an arrangement could not in reality be satisfactory, since it cannot give any information on b_S and b_T. The explanation lies in the neglect of g : as n_0 is reduced to zero, g increases without limit.

Any proper examination of the efficiency of unsymmetrical 3-point designs is thus impossible without use of the full formula for fiducial limits. The type of chief interest is the semi-symmetrical design having equal numbers of subjects for the standard and test preparations :

$$n_0 = Np \\ n_S = n_T = \tfrac{1}{2}N(1-p), \Bigg\} \qquad (8.15)$$

where p is some fraction which will presumably be less than $1/3$ for maximum reliability. The quarter-square of the fiducial interval may again be represented by equation (8.11), but now with

$$K_1 = \frac{1+p}{p(1-p)}, \qquad (8.16)$$

and

$$K_2 = \frac{1}{p}. \qquad (8.17)$$

The optimal fully symmetrical design, which has $h = 1$, $p = 1/3$, was taken as the standard in § 8.2 and may be so used again here. The relative reliability of the general semi-symmetrical 3-point is then given by equation (8.13), but with the changed definitions of K_1, K_2. This expression, evaluated for $p = 0.5$, $1/3$, 0.2, 0.1, 0.05, is tabulated in Tables 8.5–8.8.

TABLE 8.5—Percentage precision of the semi-symmetrical 3-point design, relative to the optimal symmetrical 3-point

(g is assumed to be small)

Values of p	Values of h				
	1·0	0·9	0·8	0·7	0·5
0·5	75	67	58	48	27
1/3	100	89	76	62	33
0·2	120	106	89	70	34
0·1	135	118	95	70	28
0·05	142	121	90	60	20

TABLE 8.6—Percentage reliability of the semi-symmetrical 3-point design, relative to the optimal symmetrical 3-point

For $A = 1/75$

Values of p	Values of h				
	1·0	0·9	0·8	0·7	0·5
0·5	74	67	58	48	28
1/3	100	90	77	63	34
0·2	118	105	89	70	34
0·1	123	109	88	64	25
0·05	109	95	69	43	13

TABLE 8.7—Percentage reliability of the semi-symmetrical 3-point design, relative to the optimal symmetrical 3-point

For $A = 2/75$

Values of p	Values of h				
	1·0	0·9	0·8	0·7	0·5
0·5	74	67	58	49	28
1/3	100	90	78	64	35
0·2	115	104	88	70	34
0·1	109	98	80	58	21
0·05	68	62	43	24	6

TABLE 8.8—Percentage reliability of the semi-symmetrical 3-point design, relative to the optimal symmetrical 3-point

For $A = 1/15$

Values of p	Values of h				
	1·0	0·9	0·8	0·7	0·5
0·5	72	66	60	51	31
1/3	100	93	83	70	39
0·2	100	95	84	68	32
0·1	35	39	34	21	5
0·05	0	0	0	0	0

Table 8.5 ignores g, and the steady increase in the column for $h = 1 \cdot 0$ as p decreases must not be misunderstood ; a reduction in p from $1/3$ to $0 \cdot 05$ increases K_1 from 6 to 22, and further reduction will eventually make even a very small value of A give rise to an appreciable g. Nevertheless, if h is near to unity and A is not unduly large, the reliability is increased by taking p about $0 \cdot 2$ or $0 \cdot 1$; thus, for $A = 1/75$, as much as 23 per cent. may be gained by allotting only one-tenth of the subjects to zero dose instead of one-third. This gain is reduced, however, if a poor choice of doses produces a low value of h. If A happened to be much larger than was expected, the effect of having assigned very few subjects to the blanks might be disastrous, as may be seen from comparisons between $p = 1/3$ and $p = 0 \cdot 1$ in Table 8.8. In practice, the simplicity of the fully symmetrical design, and the fact that its reliability is seldom much below the maximum, will make it usually preferable to other 3-point designs. The semi-symmetrical design with $p = 0 \cdot 2$, $n_0 = N/5$, $n_S = n_T = 2N/5$ is about the most valuable alternative. This is convenient for the experimenter who is frequently employing the symmetrical 5-point, because the only change he has to make is to assign to each double dose the subjects that are normally given a single dose ; unless A is very large, even a small value of h will not make it less reliable than the fully symmetrical 3-point.

8.4   The choice of k

So much has been said about the choice of k in § 6.10, that the topic can be dismissed briefly here, for the needs of slope ratio assays are in this respect very similar to those of parallel line assays. The results presented in §§ 8.2, 8.3 show that, if there were no doubts of statistical validity, a 3-point design would always be chosen, and that allocation of about twice as many subjects to the two non-zero doses as to the blanks would be desirable in the interests of precision. Unfortunately, such certainty of validity is rare, and the conflict between the ideal conditions for precision and the need for validity tests must be resolved by choosing $k \geqslant 2$. In general assay practice, a value greater than 2 is seldom desirable ; as suggested in § 7.11, the most useful alternative, when a larger number of doses is wanted, is $k = 4$, the 9-point design.

8.5 Symmetrical 2k-point designs

If knowledge that the linear regression of response on dose is not valid at very low doses, or any other circumstances, prevent the inclusion of tests on blanks, the natural design to adopt is a symmetrical $2k$-point (§ 7.12) with its lowest doses, cX_S and cX_T, as small as the experimenter dare risk without fear of their falling outside the region of linearity. The reliability depends upon c as well as upon k. As an illustration, the case of $c = 0\cdot1$ has been studied, for which the effect of the non-linearity at low doses is to remove one-tenth of the dose range from experimental use. For purposes of comparison, the symmetrical 3-point with $h = 1$ is again taken as the standard of reliability, even though, if a common-zero design were not permissible, the best symmetrical scheme would be a 4-point ; the advantage of this procedure is that the reliability values also give a measure of the loss due to the shortening of the available dose range. The relative reliability is again given by equation (8.13), but now with

$$K_1 = \frac{200\,(k - 1)\,(175k - 67)}{27\,(k + 1)\,(74k - 47)} \tag{8.18}$$

and

$$K_2 = \frac{24{,}200\,(k - 1)^2}{27\,(k + 1)\,(74k - 47)} . \tag{8.19}$$

Tables 8.9–8.12 show numerical values comparable with those in Tables 8.1–8.4.

TABLE 8.9—Percentage precision of the symmetrical 2k-point design, relative to the optimal symmetrical 3-point

For $c = 0\cdot1$

(g is assumed to be small)

Values of k	Values of h				
	1·0	0·9	0·8	0·7	0·5
2	76	68	58	48	26
3	66	58	50	40	21
4	62	55	47	38	20
5	61	54	46	37	19
10	58	51	43	34	17
Limit	56	49	41	32	15

TABLE 8.10—Percentage reliability of the symmetrical $2k$-point design, relative to the optimal symmetrical 3-point

For $c = 0.1$ and $A = 1/75$

Values of k	Values of h				
	1·0	0·9	0·8	0·7	0·5
2	74	67	58	48	27
3	61	55	48	39	21
4	57	51	44	36	18
5	54	49	42	34	17
10	49	45	38	30	15
Limit	45	41	35	27	13

TABLE 8.11—Percentage reliability of the symmetrical $2k$-point design, relative to the optimal symmetrical 3-point

For $c = 0.1$ and $A = 2/75$

Values of k	Values of h				
	1·0	0·9	0·8	0·7	0·5
2	72	65	57	48	27
3	56	51	45	37	20
4	50	46	40	33	17
5	46	42	37	30	15
10	39	36	32	26	13
Limit	32	31	27	21	10

TABLE 8.12—Percentage reliability of the symmetrical $2k$-point design, relative to the optimal symmetrical 3-point

For $c = 0.1$ and $A = 1/15$

Values of k	Values of h				
	1·0	0·9	0·8	0·7	0·5
2	64	60	54	47	27
3	32	31	29	26	15
4	18	19	19	17	9
5	11	12	12	12	6
10	0	0	1	1	0
Limit	0	0	0	0	0

These tables indicate that, with $c = 0.1$, a symmetrical $2k$-point design has at best 76 per cent. reliability relative to the symmetrical 3-point, and that the loss in reliability increases rapidly as k or A is increased. Comparison with Tables 8.1–8.4, however, reveals the surprising fact that, for low values of A, the reliabilities of corresponding $(2k + 1)$-point and $2k$-point designs are almost equal ; indeed, the $2k$-point may have a slight advantage, presumably because it allots more subjects to high doses. If c were larger, this would not be true ; for the small value of c discussed here, however, tests of blanks can be replaced by tests on low doses of each preparation without ill-effect on reliability. If A is as large as $1/15$, the $2k$-point design is appreciably more reliable than the $(2k + 1)$-point for small k ; for large k, the situation is reversed, but the reliability of either design is then so low as to make both assays of no practical use.

In the light of the last paragraph, what has been said in (vi) of § 8.1 about tests of blanks may be explained further. The merit of using blanks appears to be not that they increase reliability but that they represent a cheap method of obtaining validity tests without sacrifice of reliability. The 4-point has the highest reliability of all $2k$-point designs, but it permits no test of statistical validity (the 'intersection' contrast gives a test of fundamental validity).

As Tables 8.9–8.12 show, replacement of a 4-point by a 6-point design, in order to obtain linearity tests, will involve a serious loss of reliability, especially if A is large. Much the same end can be achieved at a lesser cost in reliability by using a 5-point design, for test of the ' blanks ' contrast is in reality a test of linearity of regression. From this point of view, the most interesting way of using Tables 8.9–8.12 with Tables 8.1–8.4 is to compare a $(2k + 2)$-point design with a $(2k + 1)$-point for any value of k.

8.6   The comparison of assay techniques

The argument of §§ 8.1–8.5 has been concerned primarily with the relative efficiencies of different experimental designs based upon the same subjects, techniques, and measurements. Just as for parallel line assays (§ 6.11), questions may arise as to which of two or more alternative assay techniques for estimating the same potency is preferable. In a good assay, for which g is small and h near to unity, equation (8.4) shows that the standard error of R is proportional to $s/b_S X_S$. This quantity is a measure of the intrinsic quality of the technique for the purposes of assay, whereas its multiplier depends only upon the number of subjects used and their distribution between doses. It plays a part analogous to that of s/b in parallel line assays, though no simple interpretation such as is suggested by equation (6.12) can be given. Its physical dimensions are those of a pure ratio, so that not only does it provide a scale of comparison for alternative assays of the same potency but it also enables the efficiencies of slope-ratio assays for entirely different purposes to be compared. The value of X_S used is assumed to be the largest possible ; data that do not extend over the whole region of linearity can therefore give only an upper limit for $s/b_S X_S$. Apart from complications introduced by g and h, the number of subjects needed in order to secure a specified precision, by use of a particular set of doses and proportional allocation between doses, is inversely proportional to the square of $s/b_S X_S$. Hence consideration of this intrinsic error enables the economics of alternative techniques to be compared. No simple comparison between a parallel line assay and a slope ratio assay for estimation of the potency of the same preparation can be made in this way.

The remarks on the choice of a response, in the second half of § 6.11, are equally applicable to slope ratio assays.

CHAPTER 9

INCOMPLETE BLOCK DESIGNS

9.1 Complex designs

The general principles of good design for assays based on quantitative responses have been discussed in Chapters 6 and 8. The desiderata in respect of symmetry, number of dose levels, choice of doses, magnitudes of regression coefficients and variance, and so on must be borne in mind in any consideration of designs more complex than the completely randomized or randomized block types that have been described in earlier chapters. They are not in themselves sufficient to determine the ideal design for a particular assay. Limitations of the test subjects, in respect of either their total number or the numbers in different litters or other classes ; restrictions on the number of tests that can be performed simultaneously, or on the same day, or by the same operator ; a limit to the total amount of a preparation available for testing ; and any other conditions imposed upon the conduct of the experiment, will often affect the design to be recommended as likely to give the best results.

The theory of experimental design came into existence largely because of the needs of agricultural field experiments, but it is applicable to many other branches of research. To give a full account of that theory here is impossible, and even a complete bibliography would be very extensive. The early chapters of R. A. Fisher's *The Design of Experiments* (1960) make an excellent introduction to the subject, but the statistician will need to be familiar with the detailed methods such as are described by Cochran and Cox (1957), Fisher and Yates (1963), Yates (1937*a*), and in papers in many journals. The biologist or other user of biological assay can scarcely hope himself to be an expert in experimental design, but he ought to be aware of the basic principles and of the characteristics of the more important designs. Though many different types of design have been studied, these do not provide for every need. The statistician should regard it as his duty to supply a design 'tailored' for a special purpose rather than to rely upon a published catalogue of designs. Knowledge of the basic designs is, of course, essential to him, but often the ideal scheme for his purpose, bearing in mind the imposed conditions, will be compounded of ideas from different sources.

A good illustration of how even a simple assay may require a complicated design, in order that the heterogeneity of the subjects may be eliminated and an estimate of reasonable precision obtained, has been described by Fisher (1949a). This 4-point assay of a tuberculin preparation was arranged in such a way that each of the four doses was injected once on each side of the neck of 120 cows, the eight sites being balanced over doses by means of a Latin square scheme. The response measured was the thickening of the skin at a fixed time after injection. The responses varied very widely, and the variance was obviously correlated with the response ; Fisher adopted an exceedingly ingenious method of analysis for overcoming this difficulty. Much the same results would be obtained, however, by using a logarithmic or square-root response metameter and analysing according to the methods of this book. The reader who studies the structure of the design should have little difficulty in making that analysis for himself.

In this and in subsequent chapters will be given examples of designs that are useful in biological assay. The statistical analysis for these is much the same as would be needed if they were used for other purposes, such as comparing the crop yields obtained from different qualities and quantities of fertilizer, though some features are peculiar to assays. In the examples that follow, the analysis of variance will be described only briefly, since full accounts can be found elsewhere, and the emphasis will be placed on those points of especial importance for assays. The assays discussed are almost all of the parallel line type ; the same ideas might be adapted to slope ratio assays, but satisfactory symmetry is less easy to arrange and at present the need seems less.

9.2 Confounding

The major reason for interest in experimental designs more complex than those already discussed is that only by their use can certain sources of variability in response be prevented from exercising an undesirable influence on the precision of potency estimates, and on the sensitivity of validity tests. The device of litter-mate control, introduced in § 4.13 in order to eliminate the effects of differences between litters, led to the use of a randomized block design ; the same type of design was adopted in a penicillin assay (§ 5.3) in order to eliminate differences between plates. This extremely useful design is such that any contrast between doses is orthogonal with every contrast between blocks (litters, plates, etc.). The estimate of potency can be formed regardless of the block classification ; its precision and the sensitivity of validity tests are determined by the average variation within blocks. Application of the design is restricted, however, to assays in which the number of doses is equal to the number of subjects per block.

Unfortunately, the subjects available to an experimenter for an assay are not always so obliging as to fall into blocks of the right size. Litters may be too small, or agar plates may be incapable of taking the total number of doses to be tested. An *incomplete block* design must then be adopted. The oestrone assay discussed in Chapter 4 (Table 4.5) was in fact an example of this, since some litters consisted of only three rats. The complete orthogonality of dose and block contrasts is then destroyed, though the disturbance need not always be as severe as it was for the oestrone assay. In particular, if the blocks are all of the same size, conditions of symmetry may be imposed in such a way as to simplify the analysis and its interpretation.

In an incomplete block design, contrasts between doses are of three kinds :

(i) A contrast that is identical with some contrast between blocks (*i.e.* has its coefficients proportional to those of the block contrast) is said to be *confounded* with block differences (Fisher, 1960, Chapter VII).

(ii) A contrast that is not identical with any block contrast, but is not orthogonal with every block contrast, so that condition (ii) of § 4.16 is not satisfied, is said to be *partially confounded*.

(iii) A contrast that is orthogonal with every block contrast is said to be *unconfounded*.

When a confounded contrast is used in the construction of an analysis of variance it will take its place as a component of the sum of squares between blocks, and a residual mean square between blocks must be used in the assessment of its precision or the testing of its significance. A partially confounded contrast can be divided into two parts, one of which is unconfounded and the other completely confounded, and each part contributes to the appropriate section of the analysis of variance ; a partially confounded contrast may be either unconfounded in one group of blocks, confounded in another, or partially confounded for all blocks. In general, the precision of estimation of a contrast will be greater if it is unconfounded than if it is confounded, and much of the art of experimental design consists in the choice of a scheme of confounding that will sacrifice only the least interesting contrasts. Yates (1937*a*) and Cochran and Cox (1957) have discussed the construction and analysis of many confounded designs, and Finney (1947*b*) has given an elementary account of the rules on which these are based.

9.3 An incomplete block assay of vitamin A

The data in Table 9.1 are a simple example of an incomplete block design used for a 6-point assay of vitamin A (Gridgeman, 1944*b*). The response to be measured was the weight increase in rats in a period of three weeks. Since bucks have a higher growth rate than does, the experimenter wished to use bucks only, and in consequence he found that many of his litters would not provide more than two subjects. He therefore arranged that the blocks should be pairs of litter-mates. He had thirty litters available, and chose to assign ten to comparisons of the lowest doses of the two preparations, ten to comparisons of the middle doses, and ten to comparisons of the highest doses ; the doses of the test preparation were chosen in the belief that its potency was about 2,000 units per gram. Successive doses of either preparation were in the ratio 5 : 3.

The standard set of five orthogonal contrasts to be used in the analysis of the sum of squares between doses in a 6-point design has been shown in Table 5.3. Inspection of these shows that L_p, L_1', L_2' are orthogonal with all block contrasts, whereas L_1, L_2 between them make up the two degrees of freedom for contrasts between the three types of block S_1, T_1 ; S_2, T_2 ; S_3, T_3. In fact, as is obvious from the way in which the design was formed, differences between levels of dose have been confounded between the three types of block ; the difference between preparations is

TABLE 9.1—Increases in weight of male rats during three weeks of dosage with vitamin A

(Weights in g.)

Each pair of columns contains the responses for ten litters

S_1 0·9 units	T_1 0·45 mg.	S_2 1·5 units	T_2 0·75 mg.	S_3 2·5 units	T_3 1·25 mg.
20	15	43	35	51	37
22	8	37	30	45	34
18	18	38	37	46	23
26	14	40	37	48	44
30	15	47	31	55	39
29	35	27	35	35	46
47	34	41	48	49	41
16	20	43	47	51	51
16	19	35	18	43	36
30	23	30	30	27	28
254	201	381	348	450	379

unconfounded, as also must be what would be called in the general terminology of experimental design the interaction Preparations × Levels and in this assay the components for parallelism and difference of quadratics.

The analysis of variance divides into two sections, the inter-block and the intra-block variation. From total sums of squares between and within litters, the squares for the dose contrasts are subtracted in accordance with the confounding scheme just described, and the two error sums of squares are found as residuals. The easiest procedure is to tabulate sums and differences of the pairs of responses for each litter, as in Table 9.2. The sum of squares of deviation of the thirty litter totals, divided by 2, is the total sum of squares for the inter-litter section of the analysis. The sum of squares of the thirty differences within litters (with no adjustment for a mean), divided by 2, is the total sum of squares within litters.

These two make up the complete sum of squares of deviations with 59 degrees of freedom. By application of the coefficients in Table 5.3 to the dose totals in Table 9.1, or directly from the litter totals and differences in Table 9.2,

$$
\begin{array}{llll}
 & & & \textit{Divisor} \\
L_p = & - 53 - 33 - 71 & = - 157 & 60 \\
L_1 = & - 455 + 829 & = 374 & 40 \\
L_1' = & 53 - 71 & = - 18 & 40 \\
L_2 = & 455 - 2 \times 729 + 829 & = - 174 & 120 \\
L_2' = & - 53 + 2 \times 33 - 71 & = - 58 & 120 \\
\end{array}
$$

The squares for the dose contrasts are formed from these quantities in the same way as in § 5.1, and the analysis of variance, Table 9.3, may then be completed.

TABLE 9.2—Sums and differences of responses for litter-mates in Table 9.1

	$S_1 + T_1$	$S_2 + T_2$	$S_3 + T_3$	$T_1 - S_1$	$T_2 - S_2$	$T_3 - S_3$
	35	78	88	− 5	− 8	− 14
	30	67	79	− 14	− 7	− 11
	36	75	69	0	− 1	− 23
	40	77	92	− 12	− 3	− 4
	45	78	94	− 15	− 16	− 16
	64	62	81	6	8	11
	81	89	90	− 13	7	− 8
	36	90	102	4	4	0
	35	53	79	3	− 17	− 7
	53	60	55	− 7	0	1
Totals :	455	729	829	− 53	− 33	− 71

TABLE 9.3—Analysis of variance for the data of Table 9.1

Adjustment for mean		67,536	Mean square
Nature of variation	d.f.	Sum of squares	
Regression	1	3,497	3,497
Quadratic	1	252	252
Error (1)	27	2,663	98·63
Between litters	29	6,412	
Preparations	1	411	411
Parallelism	1	8	8
Difference of quadratics ...	1	28	28
Error (2)	27	1,062	39·33
Total	59	7,921	

Each validity test must be made by comparison of the mean square with the error mean square in the same section of the analysis. The mean square for preparations is significantly greater than the error within litters ; the parallelism mean square is small, however, and that for quadratic curvature is not sufficiently in excess of the error between litters to be alarming. Taken together, the tests do not suggest invalidity, and, provided that the experimenter began in the belief that he was performing an analytical dilution assay (§ 15.5), estimation may proceed.

The value of R might be determined by calculation of $\bar{y}_S$, $\bar{y}_T$, b, and M in the standard manner, but calculation may be simplified by use of equation (5.23), the applicability of which is not disturbed by the confounding since the definitions of L_p, L_1 are unaltered. Hence

$$R = \frac{Z_S}{Z_T} \text{ antilog } \left\{ \frac{4L_p}{3L_1} \log \left(\frac{5}{3} \right) \right\}$$

$$= \frac{2 \cdot 5}{1 \cdot 25} \text{ antilog} \left\{ \frac{- 4 \times 157 \times 0 \cdot 2218}{3 \times 374} \right\}$$

$$= 2 \text{ antilog } \bar{1} \cdot 8759$$

$$= 1 \cdot 503.$$

The fiducial limits cannot be computed directly from equation (5.28), because the variances of L_p and L_1 are based upon different mean squares. In fact, if s_1^2, s_2^2 represent the error mean squares between and within litters, then

$$V(L_p) = 60s_2^2,$$
$$V(L_1) = 40s_1^2.$$

Limits to L_p/L_1 must therefore be obtained from the first analogue of Fieller's theorem (§ 2.7). Since s_1^2 and s_2^2 are both based on 27 degrees of freedom, the value of Sukhatme's d-deviate is almost independent of the angle θ, and as a first approximation may be taken as 2·05 (Appendix Table III ; Fisher and Yates, 1963, Table V$_1$). Hence

$$g = \frac{d^2 V(L_1)}{L_1^2} \text{ by equation (2.20)}$$

$$= \frac{(2 \cdot 05)^2 \times 40 \times 98 \cdot 63}{(374)^2}$$

$$= 0 \cdot 1185.$$

Limits to L_p/L_1, whose numerical value is $- 0 \cdot 4198$, are then given by equation (2.19), as

$$\left[- 0 \cdot 4198 \pm \frac{2 \cdot 05}{374} \left\{ 0 \cdot 8815 \times 60 \times 39 \cdot 33 \right. \right.$$

$$\left. \left. + (0 \cdot 4198)^2 \times 40 \times 98 \cdot 63 \right\}^{\frac{1}{2}} \right] \div 0 \cdot 8815$$

$$= - 0 \cdot 8039, \ - 0 \cdot 1486.$$

These are in reality only approximations, to be used in equation (2.17) in order to give angles θ_L, θ_U for the two limits :

$$\tan \theta_L = \frac{1}{0 \cdot 8039} \left(\frac{60s_2^2}{40s_1^2} \right)^{\frac{1}{2}} = 0 \cdot 96,$$

$$\tan \theta_U = \frac{1}{0 \cdot 1486} \left(\frac{60s_2^2}{40s_1^2} \right)^{\frac{1}{2}} = 5 \cdot 20,$$

whence $\theta_L = 44°$, $\theta_U = 79°$. Interpolation in Fisher and Yates's Table V$_1$ then gives d for these angles as 2·046 and 2·051, values so close to 2·05 as to make recalculation unnecessary ; the result of recalculation of the two limits, each with its own values of d and g, is to give $- 0·8029$, $- 0·1485$. The limits may then be inserted in place of L_p/L_1 in the formula for R to give

$$R_L = 2 \text{ antilog } \bar{1}·7625 = 1·158,$$
$$R_U = 2 \text{ antilog } \bar{1}·9561 = 1·808.$$

The test preparation is therefore estimated to contain 1,500 units of vitamin A per g., with limits at 1,160 and 1,810 units per g. The estimate of 2,000 units per g. used in determining the doses of the test preparation appears to have been substantially wrong, as was demonstrated by the significance of the component for preparations in Table 9.3.

9.4 Criticism of the design for the assay of vitamin A

In the assay for which the responses are shown in Table 9.1, the necessity of estimating the regression coefficient from differences between litters has lowered the reliability of the estimated potency relative to the results that would be obtainable with litters of six. The loss in this instance is not very great, since s_1^2 is only about 2·5 times s_2^2 ; inspection of the calculations in § 9.3 shows that replacement of s_1^2 by s_2^2 would reduce g from 0·118 to about 0·047, and would narrow the fiducial range by about 5 per cent. Consequently the possible gain from an alternative design is here not very great.

Nevertheless, a design in which L_p and L_1 appear as contrasts of different types, one within and the other between litters, is obviously undesirable. For some data, the difference between s_1^2 and s_2^2 might be very great, and for others a relatively higher variability than was encountered in § 9.3 might make the value of g of critical importance for reliability. The need for more laborious calculations in the assessment of fiducial limits is an additional objection to designs of the type discussed, though not a very serious one because s_1^2 and s_2^2 will have equal numbers of degrees of freedom and the dependence of the d-deviate upon the angle θ is therefore slight.

Provided that proper randomizations have been made, a value of L_1 measured as an inter-litter contrast estimates exactly the same quantity as if it were intra-litter. In the vitamin A assay,

$L_1/40$ is an estimate of the increase in response per unit increase in dose (the unit being an increase by a factor of $5/3$), for animals chosen at random from the population ; the fact that L_p is an intra-litter contrast does not invalidate the use of L_p/L_1 in the formula for relative potency. Any departure from proper randomization of litters, however, would destroy the validity of the argument : the ten litters to be assigned to doses S_1, T_1 must be selected at random from the thirty available. Without condoning deliberate non-random allocation of litters, it must be admitted that departures from randomness sometimes occur accidentally or unavoidably, and for this reason also the investigation of designs in which L_p and L_1 are both intra-litter contrasts is to be desired.

9.5   A balanced incomplete block assay of vitamin A

One method of overcoming the objections to the design used in § 9.3 would be to adopt a *balanced incomplete block design*. Designs may be constructed to have any convenient number of subjects per block, with the condition that the number of blocks in which two doses both occur is the same for every pair of doses. For a fixed number of subjects per block and a fixed number of doses to be tested, certain restrictions must be placed on the number of replications of each dose if perfect balance is to be achieved (Fisher and Yates, 1963, Introduction ; Yates, 1937b, 1940). The mean difference in response between any two doses is measurable by a contrast within blocks, with precision independent of the two doses chosen ; consequently contrasts L_p, L_1 can be formed orthogonal with block differences, as also can the other contrasts L_1', L_2, L_2'. In addition, if the allocation to blocks has been randomized, independent contrasts measuring the same features of the dose-response relationships can be formed between blocks. A second estimate of relative potency is therefore obtainable, though it is likely to be of lower precision than that calculated within blocks. The two estimates may be combined in order to summarize the whole information from the assay.

A selection of balanced incomplete block designs suitable for biological assays is given in § 9.7. Here an artificial example will be discussed. This purports to be the result of an assay like the vitamin A assay in § 9.3, but having all possible types of block instead of only three. The same six doses are used, and each of the fifteen possible pairs of doses occurs in two of the thirty blocks. For illustrative purposes, numerical values of the responses have been constructed so as to have the same totals for the ten animals at one dose and about the same variances between and within blocks as in § 9.3. Table 9.4 contains the data.

TABLE 9.4—Artificial data for increases in weight of male rats during three weeks of dosage with vitamin A

(Weights in g.)

Blocks are denoted by numbers I to XXX

Block no.	S_1 0·9 units	S_2 1·5 units	S_3 2·5 units	T_1 0·45 mg.	T_2 0·75 mg.	T_3 1·25 mg.
I	20	33	—	—	—	—
II	18	36	—	—	—	—
III	16	—	44	—	—	—
IV	22	—	33	—	—	—
V	29	—	—	35	—	—
VI	26	—	—	14	—	—
VII	47	—	—	—	48	—
VIII	30	—	—	—	30	—
IX	16	—	—	—	—	38
X	30	—	—	—	—	41
XI	—	40	47	—	—	—
XII	—	40	59	—	—	—
XIII	—	35	—	4	—	—
XIV	—	47	—	16	—	—
XV	—	27	—	—	35	—
XVI	—	43	—	—	35	—
XVII	—	43	—	—	—	50
XVIII	—	37	—	—	—	33
XIX	—	—	44	26	—	—
XX	—	—	48	28	—	—
XXI	—	—	35	—	43	—
XXII	—	—	43	—	33	—
XXIII	—	—	46	—	—	23
XXIV	—	—	51	—	—	51
XXV	—	—	—	20	37	—
XXVI	—	—	—	12	30	—
XXVII	—	—	—	21	—	33
XXVIII	—	—	—	25	—	40
XXIX	—	—	—	—	39	43
XXX	—	—	—	—	18	27

For this relatively simple example, although the analysis of variance may be performed by the general method for balanced incomplete blocks (Yates, 1940), the nature of the analysis may be made clearer to those unfamiliar with complex experimental designs if it is developed from first principles. The subdivision of the total sum of squares of deviations into a section between litters (29 degrees of freedom) and a section within litters (30 degrees of freedom) proceeds exactly as in § 9.3, using sums and differences for the two animals in each litter. Complications arise when the dose contrasts are considered, for none of those in Table 5.3 is orthogonal with blocks ; all are partially confounded. Consequently, both sections of the analysis contribute information on

TABLE 9.5—Orthogonal coefficients for contrasts between litters for the data of Table 9.3

Doses	Totals	L_p	L_1	L_1'	L_2	L_2'
$S_1 + S_2$	107	-2	-1	1	-1	1
$S_1 + S_3$	115	-2	—	—	2	-2
$S_1 + T_1$	104	—	-2	—	2	—
$S_1 + T_2$	155	—	-1	1	-1	-3
$S_1 + T_3$	125	—	—	2	2	—
$S_2 + S_3$	186	-2	1	-1	-1	1
$S_2 + T_1$	102	—	-1	-1	-1	3
$S_2 + T_2$	140	—	—	—	-4	—
$S_2 + T_3$	163	—	1	1	-1	3
$S_3 + T_1$	146	—	—	-2	2	—
$S_3 + T_2$	154	—	1	-1	-1	-3
$S_3 + T_3$	171	—	2	—	2	—
$T_1 + T_2$	99	2	-1	-1	-1	-1
$T_1 + T_3$	119	2	—	—	2	2
$T_2 + T_3$	127	2	1	1	-1	-1
Divisor	...	96	64	64	192	192
Sum ...	...	-126	301	-31	-93	-57

each contrast. The components of the sum of squares might be found by a multiple regression procedure like that in § 4.19. Five independent variates would be used, each variate taking the values of the coefficients of one of the contrasts in Table 5.3. The multiple regression calculations for the litter-mate sums would give the inter-litter components, and those for the differences the intra-litter components. The symmetry of the design is such as to make evaluation of the regression coefficients very simple, since each set of five corresponds to a set of mutually orthogonal contrasts.

The calculations can be simplified by the use of two modified sets of orthogonal contrasts. Table 9·5 contains the coefficients for inter-block dose contrasts, these being constructed to correspond with the preparations, regression, parallelism, and other components. The first column in the table shows the fifteen types of total that can be formed from litters, and the totals of four responses from the two litters of each type are entered in the second column. The coefficients for L_p, L_1, L_1', L_2, L_2' may be obtained by adding the coefficients in Table 5.3 for the two doses in each litter ; thus, in the L_2' column, successive entries are obtained as $(-1 + 2)$, $(-1 - 1)$, $(-1 + 1)$, etc. A factor of 2 could be removed from the L_p column, but the explanation is clearer if this is retained. The divisors are obtained, as in § 4.16, by summing the squares of coefficients and noting that each entry in the second column is a total of four responses. Each pair of columns is orthogonal ; therefore, the square of each contrast may be divided by the corresponding divisor, entered in the analysis of variance (Table 9.7), and subtracted from the sum of squares between litters, in order to leave an error sum of squares for inter-litter variation. The reader should verify that the six components of the inter-litter section of the analysis are exactly the same as would be given by the regression technique described in the preceding paragraph.

The intra-litter section of the analysis of variance may be calculated in a similar manner. Table 9·6 shows the fifteen types of difference between the two doses assigned to a litter and the totals of these differences for the two litters of each type. The coefficients for the contrasts are the differences of the coefficients in Table 5.3 corresponding to the pair of doses in a litter. In Table 9.6, the coefficients need not add to zero in each column, because each row of the table itself refers to a difference between

TABLE 9.6—Orthogonal coefficients for contrasts within litters for the data of Table 9.3

Doses	Totals	L_p	L_1	L_1'	L_2	L_2'
$S_2 - S_1$	31	—	1	-1	-3	3
$S_3 - S_1$	39	—	2	-2	—	—
$T_1 - S_1$	-6	2	—	-2	—	2
$T_2 - S_1$	1	2	1	-1	-3	-1
$T_3 - S_1$	33	2	2	—	—	2
$S_3 - S_2$	26	—	1	-1	3	-3
$T_1 - S_2$	-62	2	-1	-1	3	-1
$T_2 - S_2$	0	2	—	—	—	-4
$T_3 - S_2$	3	2	1	1	3	-1
$T_1 - S_3$	-38	2	-2	—	—	2
$T_2 - S_3$	-2	2	-1	1	-3	-1
$T_3 - S_3$	-23	2	—	2	—	2
$T_2 - T_1$	35	—	1	1	-3	-3
$T_3 - T_1$	27	—	2	2	—	—
$T_3 - T_2$	13	—	1	1	3	3
Divisor	...	144	96	96	288	288
Sum ...	...	-188	447	-5	-255	-59

two pairs of responses and the condition for a contrast is maintained. Again the contrasts are mutually orthogonal. The divisors are found as for Table 9.5, and the analysis of variance may then be completed. The reader may note that the sum of values for any pair of corresponding contrasts in Tables 9.5 and 9.6 is twice the corresponding value in the analysis of § 9.3 ($-126 - 188 = -2 \times 157$): dose totals are identical for the two sets of data, and in the present analysis each response is used twice.

TABLE 9.7—Analysis of variance for the data of Table 9.4

Adjustment for mean		67,536	
Nature of variation	d.f.	Sum of squares	Mean square
Preparations	1	165	165
Regression	1	1,416	1,416
Parallelism	1	15	15
Quadratic	1	45	45
Difference of quadratics ...	1	17	17
Error (1)	24	2,590	107·92
Between litters	29	4,248	
Preparations	1	245	245
Regression	1	2,081	2,081
Parallelism	1	0	0
Quadratic	1	226	226
Difference of quadratics ...	1	12	12
Error (2)	25	1,039	41·56
Total	59	7,851	

If the error variance between litters, s_1^2, were much larger than that within litters, s_2^2, the first part of the analysis would be ignored as uninformative and all conclusions based on the second. For the sake of simplicity, although s_1^2 is here only 2·6 times s_2^2, conclusions will be first obtained from the intra-litter analysis alone. If the data were genuine, validity tests would be made in the usual manner : in Table 9.7, both the preparations and the quadratic mean square are significantly greater than s_2^2, but, since the data are artificial, this may be attributed to the difficulty of manufacturing a realistic example! The very small mean square for parallelism is more exactly 0·26, a value not significantly less than s_2^2. By inspection of Table 9.6, L_p is seen to represent a difference between thirty-six responses to the test, and thirty-six to the standard preparation. Therefore, in terms of responses adjusted so as to eliminate litter differences,

$$\bar{y}_T - \bar{y}_S = \frac{L_p}{36} = -5\cdot2222, \qquad (9.1)$$

with a variance

$$V(\bar{y}_T - \bar{y}_S) = \frac{144s_2^2}{36^2} = \frac{s_2^2}{9}. \qquad (9.2)$$

Also, L_1 is in essence a difference between twenty-four responses to high doses and twenty-four to low doses; the responses to middle doses that occur in its definition were introduced in order to eliminate litter differences, and their total expectation is zero since S_2 and T_2 occur as often with negative as with positive signs. The ratio of successive doses was 5/3, and therefore the logarithm to base 5/3 will be taken as the dose metameter. On this scale, the difference between high and low doses is 2; consequently the expected value of L_1 is 2×24 times the true regression coefficient. Hence the regression coefficient is estimated as

$$b = \frac{L_1}{48} = 9\cdot3125, \qquad (9.3)$$

with variance

$$V(b) = \frac{96s_2^2}{48^2} = \frac{s_2^2}{24}. \qquad (9.4)$$

An estimate of relative potency may be formed from equation (4.11):

$$M = \bar{x}_S - \bar{x}_T - \frac{5\cdot2222}{9\cdot3125}$$

$$= \bar{x}_S - \bar{x}_T - 0\cdot5608.$$

Moreover, since $t = 2\cdot060$ for 25 degrees of freedom,

$$g = \frac{(2\cdot060)^2 \times 41\cdot56}{(9\cdot3125)^2 \times 24} = 0\cdot0847,$$

and application of Fieller's theorem to the ratio $(\bar{y}_T - \bar{y}_S)/b$ gives

$$M_L, M_U = \bar{x}_S - \bar{x}_T - \left[0.5608 \pm \frac{2.060 s_2}{9.3125} \left\{ \frac{0.9153}{9} \right. \right.$$
$$\left. \left. + \frac{(0.5608)^2}{24} \right\}^{\frac{1}{2}} \right] \div 0.9153$$
$$= \bar{x}_S - \bar{x}_T - 1.1406, \quad \bar{x}_S - \bar{x}_T - 0.0848.$$

These quantities must be multiplied by $\log(5/3)$, or 0.22185, in order to convert them to logarithms to base 10. Hence

$$R = 2 \text{ antilog } \bar{1}.8756 = 1.502,$$
$$R_L = 2 \text{ antilog } \bar{1}.7470 = 1.117,$$
$$R_U = 2 \text{ antilog } \bar{1}.9812 = 1.915.$$

Contrasts between litters provide entirely independent information on differences between doses, and, in particular, on relative potency. Examination of the first part of Table 9.7 shows no indications of invalidity, and calculations similar to those just described may be used to give a second potency estimate. From Table 9.5, L_p is seen to be a difference between two sets of twenty-four responses, and therefore

$$\bar{y}_T - \bar{y}_S = \frac{L_p}{24} = 5.2500, \tag{9.5}$$

with

$$V(\bar{y}_T - \bar{y}_S) = \frac{96 s_1^2}{24^2} = \frac{s_1^2}{6}. \tag{9.6}$$

A similar argument shows that

$$b = \frac{L_1}{32} = 9.4062, \tag{9.7}$$

with

$$V(b) = \frac{s_1^2}{16}. \tag{9.8}$$

Hence

$$M = \bar{x}_S - \bar{x}_T - 0.5581.$$

For 24 degrees of freedom $t = 2.064$, and therefore

$$g = 0.3248,$$

a value that leads to

$$M_L, M_U = \bar{x}_S - \bar{x}_T - 2.0532, \quad \bar{x}_S - \bar{x}_T + 0.4000,$$

by the usual procedure of applying Fieller's theorem to $(\bar{y}_T - \bar{y}_S)/b$.

The estimate and its fiducial limits are

$$R = 2 \text{ antilog } \bar{1}\cdot 8762 = 1\cdot 504,$$
$$R_L = 2 \text{ antilog } \bar{1}\cdot 5445 = 0\cdot 701,$$
$$R_U = 2 \text{ antilog } 0\cdot 0887 = 2\cdot 454.$$

The very close agreement between the two values of R is fortuitous, or rather is due to the artificiality of the data ; the two are statistically just as truly independent of one another as if they had been derived from separate experiments. As might be expected, the second estimate is much less reliable than the first, yet it certainly conveys some information. The experimenter will naturally desire to combine the two, in the hope that he will thereby obtain an estimate better than either one separately. The general problem of combining potency estimates is considered in Chapter 14, and, even though the two values of R now under discussion have arisen from one experiment, the method in § 14.3 may be adopted.

If the error variances in the two parts of Table 9.7 were equal, the variances of corresponding quantities estimated from inter- and intra-block contrasts would be in the ratio 3 : 2, as is evident from equations (9.2), (9.4), (9.6), and (9.8). If the design were without confounding, the variance of the mean response at any dose would be $s^2/10$, and variances for other contrasts would be constructed from this. In fact, variances for intra-block contrasts can be calculated on the basis of a variance $s_2^2/6$ for a mean response at any dose. For example, equation (9.2) may be obtained as

$$V(\bar{y}_T - \bar{y}_S) = V\left[\tfrac{1}{3}(\bar{y}_{T_1} + \bar{y}_{T_2} + \bar{y}_{T_3}) - \tfrac{1}{3}(\bar{y}_{S_1} + \bar{y}_{S_2} + \bar{y}_{S_3})\right]$$
$$= \frac{2}{3} \times \frac{s_2^2}{6}$$
$$= s_2^2/9.$$

Variances for inter-block contrasts may be similarly constructed from a basic variance $s_1^2/4$. This may be expressed by the statement that 40 per cent. of the information on contrasts between doses is confounded between blocks and 60 per cent. is unconfounded, so that intra-block estimates have variances which are those of an unconfounded design divided by 0·6.

Composite validity tests may be made with the aid of the Behrens distribution (§ 2.6). For example, from Table 9.5, the inter-litter L_2 is seen to be made up of forty-eight responses to S_1, S_3, T_1, or T_3 taken positively, sixteen of these taken negatively, and thirty-two responses to S_2 or T_2 taken negatively ; consequently, the measure of curvature in units of a mean difference between subjects, is $L_2/32$, with

$$V(L_2/32) = \frac{192s_1^2}{32^2} = \frac{3s_1^2}{16}.$$

The corresponding measure from intra-litter comparisons (Table 9.6) is $L_2/48$, with

$$V(L_2/48) = \frac{s_2^2}{8}.$$

Equations (2.13)–(2.16) therefore give, as a weighted mean measure of curvature,

$$\frac{-\dfrac{93}{32} \times \dfrac{16}{3s_1^2} - \dfrac{255}{48} \times \dfrac{8}{s_2^2}}{\dfrac{16}{3s_1^2} + \dfrac{8}{s_2^2}} = -\frac{0 \cdot 1436 + 1 \cdot 0226}{0 \cdot 0494 + 0 \cdot 1925}$$

$$= -4 \cdot 821,$$

with variance

$$\frac{1}{0 \cdot 0494 + 0 \cdot 1925} = 4 \cdot 134$$

$$= (2 \cdot 033)^2,$$

and

$$\tan \theta = \left(\frac{2s_2^2}{3s_1^2}\right)^{\frac{1}{2}} \qquad (9.9)$$

$$= 0 \cdot 51,$$

whence

$$\theta = 27°.$$

By interpolation in Fisher and Yates's Table V_1, the 5 per cent. value of d for 24, 25 degrees of freedom and 27° is 2·056 ; the weighted mean curvature is more than 2·056 times its standard error, and the assay thus shows significant deviation from linearity. Other validity tests could be similarly examined, but the results are of no real interest for these artificial data.

If the assay were valid, the second analogue of Fieller's theorem could be applied to the estimation of potency and the assessment of fiducial limits ; the process is an adaptation of the general method in § 14.3 to a situation in which pooling of variance estimates is not permissible, but only two sets of data are to be combined and these conform to certain conditions of symmetry set out in § 2.7. If $(\bar{y}_T - \bar{y}_S)$ and b for the two sections of the analysis, as defined by equations (9.1), (9.3), (9.5), and (9.7) play the roles of a_2, a_1, b_2, b_1 in the second analogue of Fieller's theorem, then, in the notation of § 2.7,

$$v_{11} = 1/6,$$
$$v_{12} = 0,$$
$$v_{22} = 1/16,$$
$$k = 2/3,$$

and, by equation (2.26),

$$s^2 = \left(\frac{1}{s_1^2} + \frac{3}{2s_2^2}\right)^{-1}$$
$$= (0 \cdot 00927 + 0 \cdot 03609)^{-1}$$
$$= 22 \cdot 05.$$

The mean values of the response difference and the regression coefficient are

$$\bar{y}_T - \bar{y}_S = \frac{-5 \cdot 2500 \times 0 \cdot 00927 - 5 \cdot 2222 \times 0 \cdot 03609}{0 \cdot 00927 + 0 \cdot 03609}$$
$$= -5 \cdot 2279,$$
$$b = \frac{9 \cdot 4062 \times 0 \cdot 00927 + 9 \cdot 3125 \times 0 \cdot 03609}{0 \cdot 00927 + 0 \cdot 03609}$$
$$= 9 \cdot 3316.$$

Hence

$$M = -\frac{5 \cdot 2279}{9 \cdot 3316}$$
$$= -0 \cdot 5602.$$

Moreover

$$V(\bar{y}_T - \bar{y}_S) = \frac{s^2}{6},$$
$$V(b) = \frac{s^2}{16},$$

and the orthogonality of the design ensures that the covariance is zero. By equation (2.25),

$$\tan \theta = \left(\frac{2s_2^2}{3s_1^2}\right)^{\frac{1}{2}},$$

a repetition of equation (9.9) which therefore again gives 2·056 as the 5 per cent. d-deviate. Equation (2.28) then becomes

$$g = \frac{(2\cdot056)^2 \times 22\cdot05}{(9\cdot3316)^2 \times 16}$$
$$= 0\cdot0669,$$

and, by substitution in equation (2.27),

$$M_L, M_U = \bar{x}_S - \bar{x}_T - \left[0\cdot5602 \pm \frac{2\cdot056s}{9\cdot3316} \left\{ \frac{0\cdot9331}{6} + \frac{(0\cdot5602)^2}{16} \right\}^{\frac{1}{2}} \right] \div 0\cdot9331$$

$$= \bar{x}_S - \bar{x}_T - 1\cdot0644, \quad \bar{x}_S - \bar{x}_T - 0\cdot1363.$$

Thus, finally,

$$R = 2 \text{ antilog } \bar{1}\cdot8757 = 1\cdot502,$$
$$R_L = 2 \text{ antilog } \bar{1}\cdot7639 = 1\cdot161,$$
$$R_U = 2 \text{ antilog } \bar{1}\cdot9698 = 1\cdot866.$$

The conclusion from the assay data in Table 9.4 is therefore an estimate of potency of 1,500 units of vitamin A per g. with fiducial limits at 1,160 and 1,870 units per g. The fiducial interval is 12 per cent. narrower than that from intra-litter analysis alone, and the additional calculations are not heavy. However, Fisher (1961b) has indicated the flaw in applying Behrens's theory to weighted means and has shown that the effective precision may be lower than at first appears, especially when degrees of freedom are few. The 8 per cent. increase in width of interval relative to that in § 9.3 results from the insistence that all dose contrasts be equally confounded. Had inter-litter variance been relatively greater, the loss from partial confounding of $(\bar{y}_T - \bar{y}_S)$ might have been more than balanced by gain in the precision of b; in this instance, the only advantages in the balanced incomplete block design are the greater sensitivity of the test of curvature and any logical preference for having numerator and denominator of M contrasts of the same type.

9.6 The statistical analysis of balanced incomplete block designs

Although the method of obtaining the final potency estimate has been based upon the general principle adopted in § 14.3, the symmetry of the design causes the result to be exactly the same as if weighted mean responses to each of the six doses had been calculated and equation (5.23) had been applied to these. When an incomplete block design is used in an ordinary experiment for the comparison of treatments, as distinct from an assay, the results are summarized in terms of weighted means of inter- and intra-block estimates of treatment differences. The statistical analysis might therefore be expected to be identical with that described by Yates (1940 ; Cochran and Cox, 1957, Chapter 11 ; Fisher and Yates, 1963, pp. 28-31), except for the final stages relating to the calculation of M and its limits. The reader familiar with Yates's method will notice one small difference ; Yates devised an ingenious scheme for obtaining additional information on the inter-block variance from the sum of squares between treatments (in the present terminology, between doses) in the inter-block section of the analysis. This may be important if the number of degrees of freedom for the inter-block error is small, as it will be for some experiments, but in the example in § 9.5 the advantage is trivial. The disadvantages are that the fiducial limit formulæ do not apply and that the structure of the analysis is less easily understood. In most biological assays with balanced incomplete block designs, s_1^2 will have enough degrees of freedom for this refinement of analysis to be ignored. If preferred, Yates's method may be followed exactly until adjusted mean responses to each dose have been formed ; an estimate of potency is then calculated from these as if they were responses in an assay with one subject per dose. Though no existing theory enables fiducial limits to be formed, provided that the number of degrees of freedom involved is reasonably large, a deviate taken from Fisher and Yates's Table V_1 as roughly representative of the appropriate part of the table might perhaps be used in equation (2.27) without great harm. For the data of Table 9.4, for example, the Yates analysis with 2·06 used for d gives $R = 1·503$ with limits at 1·166, 1·860, which scarcely differ from the results of the other analysis.

Bliss (1947a) has published details of the statistical analysis of two balanced incomplete block designs, both of which are also cross-over designs (Chapter 10). He followed the procedure advocated by Yates. The rather simpler computations for these assays that are needed if the procedure of § 9.5 be adopted are described in §§ 10.6 and 12.5.

In all incomplete block designs, random allocation of the blocks of subjects to the several types of block constitution, as well as random allocation of doses to subjects within blocks, is essential if both inter- and intra-block information are to be utilized.

9.7   Catalogue of balanced incomplete block designs

No general rules can be given for the construction of balanced incomplete block designs, but the lists given by Cochran and Cox (1957 ; Tables 9.5, 11.3) and by Fisher and Yates (1963, Tables XVII–XIX) include all that are likely to be required in biological assay.   Indeed, if the recommendations in Chapters 6 and 8 on numbers of doses are followed, only the simplest designs will be needed, except, perhaps, for multiple assays (Chapter 11).   The most useful designs, for both parallel line and slope ratio assays, are here classified according to the number of dose levels in a symmetrical assay ; they may be used for unsymmetrical sets of doses if required.   For each, a minimal number of blocks is stated, and if greater replication is desired this should be obtained by using a multiple of that number.

(i) 4-*point designs.*—The design for blocks of 2 is that which uses all possible blocks of this size, the property that defines an *unreduced* design.   Six blocks would be S_1, S_2 ; S_1, T_1 ; S_1, T_2 ; S_2, T_1 ; S_2, T_2 ; T_1, T_2 ; this would be repeated on further sets of six blocks, if more were available.   The design is very similar to that discussed in § 9.5, with the simplification that it has only four doses instead of six.   For blocks of 3, a set of four blocks is obtained by omitting each dose in turn, and the arrangement is repeated on further sets of four blocks if possible.

(ii) 6-*point designs.*—The only design for blocks of 2 is unreduced and has been described in § 9.5 ; it consists of a set of fifteen blocks making up all possible pairs.   For blocks of 3, a design in ten blocks is possible, this being half the total number of different blocks of 3 that can be formed (Table 9.8) ; each dose is used for five subjects, and each pair of doses occurs in two blocks.   If twenty blocks were available, all possible combinations of three doses would be used, but the design in Table 9.8 is equally amenable to analysis by the standard procedure.   The only design for blocks of 4 is unreduced ; it can be formed by omission of every pair of doses in turn, and requires fifteen blocks. For blocks of 5, a set of six blocks is given by omitting each dose in turn.

TABLE 9.8—Balanced incomplete block 6-point design in ten blocks of three

Block no.	S_1	S_2	S_3	T_1	T_2	T_3
I	×	×		×		
II	×	×				×
III	×		×	×		
IV	×		×			×
V	×			×	×	
VI		×	×	×		
VII		×	×		×	
VIII		×			×	×
IX			×	×		×
X				×	×	×

(*iii*) 8-*point designs.*—For blocks of 2, 3, 5, 6, or 7, the only possible designs are unreduced ; hence the number of blocks must be a multiple of 28, 56, 56, 28, or 8 respectively. For blocks of 4, a design in fourteen blocks, with only seven subjects at each dose, is possible (Table 9.9).

Designs for larger numbers of doses might be needed for multiple assays, but will not be listed here. Some $(2k + 1)$-point designs, which might prove useful if slope ratio assays had to be subjected to block restrictions, are as follows :

(*iv*) 3-*point designs.*—A design in blocks of 2 is obtained by omitting each dose in turn, so giving a set of three blocks ; these may be replicated as often as desired in order to give an experiment of reasonable precision.

(*v*) 5-*point designs.*—Designs in blocks of 2, 3, or 4 are unreduced ; the number of blocks must therefore be a multiple of 10, 10, or 5 respectively.

TABLE 9.9—Balanced incomplete block 8-point design
in fourteen blocks of four

Block no.	S_1	S_2	S_3	S_4	T_1	T_2	T_3	T_4
I	×	×	×	×				
II	×	×			×	×		
III	×	×					×	×
IV	×		×		×		×	
V	×		×			×		×
VI	×			×	×			×
VII	×			×		×	×	
VIII		×	×		×			×
IX		×	×			×	×	
X		×		×	×		×	
XI		×		×		×		×
XII			×	×	×	×		
XIII			×	×			×	×
XIV					×	×	×	×

TABLE 9.10—Balanced incomplete block 7-point design
in seven blocks of three

Block no.	C	S_1	S_2	S_3	T_1	T_2	T_3
I	×	×	×				
II	×			×	×		
III	×					×	×
IV		×		×		×	
V		×			×		×
VI			×	×			×
VII			×		×	×	

(*vi*) *7-point designs*.—As stated in § 7.11, 7-point designs are not likely to be wanted often. For blocks of 2, 5, or 6, only the unreduced type is possible. For blocks of 3, the design in Table 9.10 is balanced in seven blocks, instead of the thirty-five that would be required if all possible sets of 3 were used. A design for blocks of 4 is obtainable by using the doses omitted from each block of Table 9.10.

(*vii*) *9-point designs*.—For blocks of 2, 7, or 8, only unreduced designs are possible. For blocks of 3, the twelve blocks in Table 9.11 form a balanced design with four subjects on each dose. A design in blocks of 6 consists of the doses omitted in this. For blocks of 4, Table 9.12 shows a balanced design in eighteen blocks with eight subjects on each dose. The doses omitted from the blocks of Table 9.12 form a design in blocks of 5.

TABLE 9.11—Balanced incomplete block 9-point design

in twelve blocks of three

Block no.	C	S_1	S_2	S_3	S_4	T_1	T_2	T_3	T_4
I	×	×					×		
II	×		×					×	
III	×			×		×			
IV	×				×				×
V		×	×	×					
VI	×				×	×			
VII	×							×	×
VIII			×		×		×		
IX			×			×			×
X				×	×			×	
XI			×				×		×
XII						×	×	×	

TABLE 9.12—Balanced incomplete block 9-point design in eighteen blocks of four

Block no.	C	S_1	S_2	S_3	S_4	T_1	T_2	T_3	T_4
I	×	×		×				×	
II	×	×			×	×			
III	×	×					×		×
IV	×		×	×	×				
V	×		×			×	×		
VI	×		×					×	×
VII	×			×		×			×
VIII	×				×		×	×	
IX		×	×	×			×		
X		×	×		×			×	
XI		×	×			×			×
XII		×		×	×				×
XIII		×				×	×	×	
XIV			×	×		×		×	
XV			×		×		×		×
XVI				×	×	×	×		
XVII				×			×	×	×
XVIII					×	×		×	×

The number of blocks in any balanced incomplete block design must be a multiple of some minimal number, and, even if no more than eight or nine doses are to be included, this minimum may be quite large. What is to be done if the number of blocks available is less than the minimum, or is not an exact multiple of the minimum? The experimenter must be content with contrasts of unequal precision, and possibly with much more laborious calculations consequent upon the lesser symmetry of any design he may adopt. Partially balanced designs (Cochran and Cox, 1957) may sometimes be useful ; abandonment of all attempt at balance, and adoption of some simpler confounding scheme on the lines of § 9.8, will often be preferred.

A type of design that might occasionally be needed is the ' super-complete ' block. If for a particular assay a 4-point scheme of doses were considered desirable, in the light of the arguments of Chapter 6, the fact that the most convenient blocks contained six subjects should not be regarded as a reason for adopting instead a 6-point design. The better procedure would be to make each block consist of one subject per dose plus two extra subjects assigned to doses in accordance with a balanced incomplete block scheme for blocks of two. The statistical analysis would present no special difficulties (§ 14.4).

9.8 An alternative scheme of confounding for the assay of vitamin A

The objections to the design used in § 9.3 can be overcome in another way. Instead of seeking equal precision on all dose contrasts, the experimenter may choose an alternative scheme of confounding that will give L_p and L_1 entirely as intra-block contrasts. This must involve the relegation of certain validity tests to dependence upon inter-block contrasts. As will be seen from the example that follows, the computations are very much simpler than for balanced incomplete block designs, and simpler even than those of § 9.3 because Fieller's theorem can always be used in its original form. Considerations of simplicity of analysis naturally appeal to the experimenter, but (cf. § 6.6) should not be allowed to persuade him to adopt a design other than the best for his purpose. If he can afford some sacrifice on validity tests, the designs described in this and the next section are excellent : if his knowledge of his materials and experimental conditions are insufficient, he must be content with a more laborious balanced incomplete block design.

For a 6-point design in blocks of two, a very simple modification makes the required change in confounding. Suppose that three types of block are used again, but that, instead of the block constitutions in § 9.3, they are made up as S_1, T_3 ; S_2, T_2 ; S_3, T_1 : the contrasts L_1 and L_1' now change places in the analysis, the former becoming intra-block and the latter inter-block. In other respects the analysis is unaltered, so that the transfer of the regression contrast to the intra-block analysis is accomplished at the price of reduced sensitivity in the test of parallelism. Once again an artificial example will be discussed, in order to emphasize the similarity to the analysis in § 9.3. The data in Table 9.13 purport to be from an assay of this design used in exactly the same circumstances as was the assay of vitamin A in Table 9.1 ; numerical values have been constructed so as to have the same dose totals and about the same variances between and within blocks.

TABLE 9.13—Second set of artificial data for increases of weight of male rats during three weeks of dosage with vitamin A

(Weights in g.)

Each pair of columns contains the responses for ten litters

S_1 0·9 units	T_3 1·25 mg.	S_2 1·5 units	T_2 0·75 mg.	S_3 2·5 units	T_1 0·45 mg.
20	33	43	35	51	19
22	26	37	30	45	17
18	35	38	37	46	5
26	32	40	37	48	27
30	32	47	31	55	21
29	53	27	35	35	28
47	52	41	48	49	23
16	38	43	47	51	33
16	37	35	18	43	18
30	41	30	30	27	10
254	379	381	348	450	201

The analysis of the data in Table 9.13 proceeds like that for Table 9.1. The same device of forming sums and differences of pairs aids the subdivision of the total sum of squares into the components between and within litters. Since the dose totals are the same as before, the values of L_p, L_1, L_1', L_2, L_2' are unaltered, but, as already stated, L_p, L_1, L_2' are now orthogonal with litter contrasts. The analysis of variance is shown in Table 9.14.

TABLE 9.14—Analysis of variance for the data of Table 9.13

Adjustment for mean		67,536	
Nature of variation	d.f.	Sum of squares	Mean square
Parallelism	1	8	8
Quadratic	1	252	252
Error (1)	27	2,680	99·26
Between litters	29	2,940	
Preparations	1	411	411
Regression	1	3,497	3,497
Difference of quadratics ...	1	28	28
Error (2)	27	1,067	39·52
Total	59	7,943	

For this artificial example, no discussion of validity tests is needed. The potency estimate is calculated exactly as in § 9.3, and so is again

$$R = 1·503.$$

Since L_p and L_1 are both intra-block contrasts, only the one variance,

$$s_2^2 = 39·52$$

enters into the fiducial limit calculations. In the simple form of Fieller's theorem,

$$g = \frac{(2·052)^2 \times 40 \times 39·52}{374^2}$$

$$= 0·0476,$$

a substantial improvement on the value of 0·1185 in § 9.3.   Fiducial limits to L_p/L_1 may then be calculated, and in the usual manner converted into limits for R.   The results are

$$R_L = 1\cdot216,$$
$$R_U = 1\cdot805.$$

Equations (5.23) and (5.28) may legitimately be applied to the calculation of R, R_L, and R_U when, as here, L_p and L_1 are completely unconfounded.

The fiducial range is about 10 per cent. narrower than that in § 9.3, the gain being due in part to the reduction in g, in part to the reduction in the second term within the square root in the fiducial limit formula.   In this instance, the change is not dramatic, because the two error mean squares in the analysis of variance, though clearly different, are of the same order of magnitude.   Probably the gain here would scarcely outweigh the loss of sensitivity on the test of parallelism.   On other occasions, however, the change of design might make all the difference between a hopelessly imprecise estimate of potency and one of some practical value.

9.9   Catalogue of confounded designs

The design used in § 9.8 is one of a series that can be used for $2k$-point parallel line assays in such a way as to leave L_p, L_1 unconfounded with blocks.   Provided that the experimenter does not object to some loss of sensitivity in validity tests, designs of this class are preferable to the balanced incomplete blocks, and a list of the more important ones follows ; these may be used only for assays with symmetrical sets of regularly spaced doses.

(*i*) *4-point designs.*—The balanced design for blocks of 2 requires sets of six blocks.   The precision of the preparations contrast is increased, at the price of confounding the parallelism contrast, if only two of these block types are used.   A design in which pairs of blocks are assigned to S_1, T_2, and S_2, T_1 gives L_p, L_1 as intra-block contrasts and L_1' as an inter-block contrast.   The squares are computed in the usual manner, as illustrated in § 4.16, but are allocated to the appropriate section of the analysis of variance table as in § 9.8.

As an illustration of the application of the principle of this design, the assay of preparations of plant viruses may be considered. Price (1946) described a design that used two leaves from each plant and regarded the two halves of each leaf as separate ' subjects ' ; the two halves of one leaf received doses S_1, T_1, and the two halves of the other leaf from the same plant received S_2, T_2, with the result that the regression contrast was confounded with differences between leaves. He noted that a better scheme might have been to assign one of the two leaves (chosen at random) to S_1, T_2 and the other to S_2, T_1, in order that only the parallelism contrast would be confounded. The use of two leaves from each plant enables the parallelism contrast to have the precision of an intra-plant comparison. Table 9.15 shows part of a suitably randomized design, for which the analysis of variance would have its degrees of freedom partitioned as in Table 9.16. These tables assume that the numbering of the leaves and the labelling of the two sides of each leaf is entirely conventional. If leaf 2 is always taken higher on the plant than leaf 1, if the ' left half ' of a leaf is always defined as the half nearer to the light, or if in some similar way these names represent identifiable positions instead of arbitrary distinctions, the number of plants should be a multiple of 2 or of 4 and the arrangement should be balanced for positional effects ; components for them, and for their interactions with dose effects, must then be isolated in the analysis of variance. Price (1945) and Price and Spencer (1943) have given the numerical results of assays with this design.

TABLE 9.15—Randomized 4-point design for the assay of a plant virus
L_p and L_1 unconfounded

Plant no.	Leaf 1		Leaf 2	
	Left half	Right half	Left half	Right half
I	S_2	T_1	T_2	S_1
II	T_2	S_1	T_1	S_2
III	S_1	T_2	T_1	S_2
IV	T_2	S_1	S_2	T_1
V	T_1	S_2	T_2	S_1

TABLE 9.16—Partition of the degrees of freedom in the analysis of variance for the design of Table 9.15 with K plants

Nature of variation	d.f.
Between plants	$K - 1$
Parallelism	1
Error (1)	$K - 1$
Between leaves	$2K - 1$
Preparations	1
Regression	1
Error (2)	$2K - 2$
Total	$4K - 1$

(*ii*) 6-*point designs.*—The design for blocks of 2, using three block types, S_1, T_3 ; S_2, T_2 ; S_3, T_1, has been discussed in § 9.8. A design in blocks of 4 is given by omitting each of these pairs of doses in turn, and so has the three block types shown in Table 9.17.

TABLE 9.17—6-point design in $3K$ blocks of four

L_2 and L_1 unconfounded

Block type	S_1	S_2	S_3	T_1	T_2	T_3
I	×	×			×	×
II	×		×	×		×
III		×	×	×	×	

This design ought to be of considerable practical use, especially as it is very easily analysed. It would be the ideal design, for example, in a cylinder-plate assay for antibiotics in which not more than four tests could be accommodated on one plate. The reader accustomed to problems of experimental design should have no difficulty in verifying that L_p, L_1, L_2' are completely free of confounding, and are therefore estimated in the usual manner from dose totals. The parallelism and quadratic contrasts are partially confounded: the intra-block estimates must be based on

$$L_1' = L_1' \text{ (crude)} + \tfrac{1}{2} (B_{\text{III}} - B_{\text{I}}),$$
$$L_2 = L_2 \text{ (crude)} + \tfrac{1}{2} (B_{\text{I}} - 2B_{\text{II}} + B_{\text{III}}),$$

where the crude values are formed by application of the coefficients in Table 5.3, and B_{I}, B_{II}, B_{III} represent totals of all blocks of the three types. If the assay consists of K blocks of each type, the analysis of variance has the following squares for intra-block dose contrasts:—

Preparations:	$L_p^2/12K$,
Regression:	$L_1^2/8K$,
Parallelism:	$L_1'^2/6K$,
Quadratic:	$L_2^2/18K$,
Difference of quadratics:	$L_2'^2/24K$.

Additional information on the two partially confounded contrasts can be obtained from the inter-block section of the analysis. In this section,

$$L_1' = \tfrac{1}{2} (B_{\text{III}} - B_{\text{I}}), \text{ with square } L_1'^2/2K,$$

and

$$L_2 = \tfrac{1}{2} (B_{\text{I}} - 2B_{\text{II}} + B_{\text{III}}), \text{ with square } L_2^2/6K$$

may be used, these forming 2 of the $(3K - 1)$ degrees of freedom between blocks. However, even if the inter-block variance were no greater than the intra-block, only one-quarter of the information on L_1', L_2 would reside in the inter-block contrasts; if the inter-block variance is much larger, this part of the information may be trivial. For most purposes, the intra-block analysis should suffice, and this, except for the slight modification in the definitions of L_1', L_2, is as simple as if complete blocks of 6 were used.

(*iii*) 8-*point designs.*—For blocks of 2, the number of blocks should be a multiple of four, equal numbers being assigned to the types S_1, T_4; S_2, T_3; S_3, T_2; S_4, T_1; this design leaves L_p and L_1 unconfounded, as also are L_2' and L_3, while L_1', L_2, and L_3' are completely confounded between blocks. For blocks of 4, a design having equal numbers of blocks of each of the two types shown in Table 9.18 has L_p, L_1, L_1', L_2, L_3, and L_3' unconfounded, and L_2' completely confounded between block types. A design for blocks of 6 in sets of four blocks is given by omitting in turn each of the pairs of doses used for the design in blocks of 2. The analyses will not be discussed, as they should cause no great difficulty to those who have mastered the 6-point design in blocks of 4.

Other schemes for blocks of 4 or 6 might be developed, if additional information on validity tests were required.

TABLE 9.18—8-point design in $2K$ blocks of four
All contrasts unconfounded, except L_2'

Block type	S_1	S_2	S_3	S_4	T_1	T_2	T_3	T_4
I	×			×		×	×	
II		×	×		×			×

Nothing has been said in this section about blocks of 3, 5, or 7. If the number of subjects per block is odd, partial confounding of L_p is unavoidable. Nevertheless, some improvement in the precision of L_p and L_1, as compared with the balanced incomplete block design, is possible, at the usual price of reduced sensitivity in the validity tests. For example, a 6-point design in blocks of 3 could be arranged in blocks of the two types shown in Table 9.19 ; L_1, L_1' and L_2 are unconfounded, and the confounding of information on L_p is minimized. Provided that L_2' can be ignored, an intra-block estimate of L_p may be formed as

$$L_p = L_p \text{ (crude)} + \tfrac{1}{3}(B_\text{I} - B_\text{II})$$

where B_I and B_II are totals of all blocks of the two types. If the whole assay has $2K$ blocks, the components of the intra-block sum of squares are

Preparations : $3L_p^2/16K$,
Regression : $L_1^2/4K$,
Parallelism : $L_1'^2/4K$,
Quadratic : $L_2^2/12K$.

The L_2' component is indistinguishable from L_p. The inter-block contrasts can yield information on the difference of preparations, provided that the difference of quadratics is ignored, but the additional information is too small to be worth recovery. In order to obtain the intra-block estimate of $(\bar{y}_T - \bar{y}_S)$, L_p must be divided by $8K/3$. Again the method proposed is equivalent to the general regression procedure in § 9.5.

TABLE 9.19—6-point design in $2K$ blocks of three
L_1 unconfounded and L_p minimally confounded

Block type	S_1	S_2	S_3	T_1	T_2	T_3
I	×		×		×	
II		×		×		×

Additional difficulties arise in the confounding of slope ratio assays, since, at least for the common-zero type, the total number of doses is odd. Undoubtedly some restriction of types of block below the total required for a balanced incomplete block design could be used to increase the precision of estimation of the two regression coefficients, but the possibility does not at present seem of great practical importance and will not be discussed further here.

Enough has been said to show the advantages of choosing an assay design which takes account of existing knowledge of the assay technique and of the preparations under examination, and which concentrates information on those matters of chief interest to the experimenter. If validity were highly suspect, the emphasis of the designs in this section might have to be reversed, in order to plan for high sensitivity at the price of low precision. Each new situation encountered calls for a careful choice of the optimal design, and competent statistical advice is at least as important to an experimenter at this stage of his investigations as it is during the evaluation of the results.

9.10 Blocks of unequal size

A problem that appears to have escaped the attention of statisticians is that of the optimal utilization of blocks of different sizes. In agricultural experimentation, for the needs of which modern ideas of experimental design have largely been developed, the number of units per block can usually be held constant, but in animal experimentation this may involve a regrettable extravagance with material. For example, if each block is to consist of litter-mates, the available subjects are likely to include potential blocks of several different sizes. The smallest size could be chosen as a standard, and all others reduced to this number by discarding animals, but this might be very wasteful. An alternative would be to use several incomplete block designs of the types described in §§ 9.7, 9.9, one for each size of litter, and to combine the results into a single statistical analysis ; in practice, the number of litters of each size would seldom be enough to give satisfactory symmetry in this way. The oestrone assay in Table 4.5 is an illustration of the difficulty : the design adopted omitted each dose in turn from the litters of three, and would have been symmetrical if the number of these litters had been a multiple of four, but inclusion of the last litter spoiled the symmetry. No detailed advice can be given here, as the number of possibilities is too great, but the general principle should be to approach as closely as possible to symmetry (as was done in Table 4.5). Not only will the results then be as precise as possible, but the statistical analysis will be less laborious. ' Symmetry ', however, is to be interpreted widely as relating either to the complete balance of the designs in § 9.7 or to the carefully selected confounding in § 9.9, according to whichever best suits the needs of the projected assay.

The assumption of an intra-litter variance independent of litter size, which is theoretically a requirement for the estimation of precision by the formulæ of this book, is likely to be more nearly correct than would be the corresponding assumption in an agricultural field trial.

CHAPTER 10

CROSS-OVER DESIGNS

10.1 The cross-over principle

In all the indirect assays discussed in earlier chapters, an assumption has been made that only one response is measured on each subject : the chosen dose of the stimulus is applied, the response is measured, and the subject is discarded. This discarding of subjects after one use is unavoidable in many assay techniques, either because the response can be measured only when the subject is dead (as in the oestrone assay of § 4.13) or because a subject is likely to have been so affected by the dose it has received as to make it no longer useful for further tests.

From the point of view of precision, this is unfortunate, because the natural variation between subjects is usually responsible for a large part of the variance, σ^2 or s^2. Some types of test that are used to provide assay responses can be applied repeatedly to one subject without any appreciable disturbance of that subject's reactions. For example, one of the standard techniques for the assay of insulin takes as the response the change in blood sugar concentration of a rabbit, after injection with a dose of insulin (Burn *et al.*, 1950, Chapter V) ; provided that several days elapse between successive tests, one rabbit can be used a number of times. The responsiveness of a subject may vary from one occasion of testing to another, and the statistical analysis must take account of this. If the design of the assay has been well chosen, the precision of the potency estimate will depend only upon the variance 'within subjects' (that is to say, the variance between repeated tests on one subject), and will be independent of the variance between subjects. The assay should therefore be more precise than one in which each subject is used once only.

Arrangements in which each subject is made to give two responses, one for the standard and one for the test preparation, are known as *cross-over designs*. The simplest type is that in which one group of subjects receives a dose of the standard preparation followed by an approximately equipotent dose of the test preparation, while a second group receives the same doses in reverse order. Unless a form of the standard slope method (§ 3.15) is acceptable, the relative potency cannot be estimated. If a series of such trials is made, with a fixed dose of the standard and different doses of the test preparation, estimation becomes possible (Fieller *et al.*, 1939*a*, *b*; Fieller, 1940), but the rather specialized analysis will not be described here.

In the more symmetrical cross-over designs presented in this chapter, statistical independence of successive responses is assumed. The level of response may change from one occasion to another, as balance over occasions permits such effects to be eliminated. Non-independence can take such forms as additive residual effects of each dose on subsequent occasions, correlation between successive experimental error components, and autoregressive effects. Although these features may not greatly affect potency estimation, they can lead to heterogeneity of components of error and inflate some of the mean squares ordinarily included in error. If there is any reason to suspect their occurrence, a more cautious arrangement of the analysis of variance should be adopted; it is usually possible to make validity tests and to calculate limits valid under any of these more complicated models, although they sacrifice information if independence is complete (Finney, 1956).

10.2 The twin cross-over design

The minimal requirement for a satisfactory parallel line assay is a 4-point design, and the twin cross-over design (Smith, Marks, Fieller, and Broom, 1944) is therefore the simplest useful type. This has sets of four subjects assigned to doses according to the scheme in Table 10.1. The subjects should be numbered in random order, and the arrangement is repeated on sets of four subjects. The difference in response for doses S_1, T_2, and also that for doses T_1, S_2, can be estimated from comparisons between tests on one subject. From the total of these two is derived the average difference between high and low doses, or the regression coefficient ; from their difference is derived the mean difference in response between the two preparations. The contrast for parallelism is confounded between subjects, so that the validity test has only the sensitivity of a non-cross-over design, but the gain in respect of the other two contrasts may be great. The balance over the two occasions of experiment eliminates any effect of a change in the general level of responsiveness, provided that the response on the second occasion is unaffected by what happened on the first. The modified calculations are illustrated in § 10.3.

TABLE 10.1—The twin cross-over design

Subject no.	Dose on occasion no.	
	1	2
I	S_1	T_2
II	S_2	T_1
III	T_1	S_2
IV	T_2	S_1

Repeat the arrangement with each randomized set of four subjects

The design of an experiment always determines the form of the statistical analysis : though the twin cross-over is a 4-point assay, it cannot be analysed in the same way as a simple 4-point, for that would fail to take account of the constraints imposed upon the design. The estimation of a relative potency can be made according to any of the usual formulæ for 4-point assays, except that if any observations are missing special calculations will be needed, but the analysis of variance and the validity test require modification of the procedures given previously.

10.3 A twin cross-over assay of insulin

Smith *et al.* (1944) have described an assay of insulin with a twin cross-over design. The doses were 1 and 2 units per ml. of a standard insulin preparation and doses of the test preparation calculated as equivalent to these on the basis of an assumed potency of 22 units per mg. Twelve rabbits were used, and the second day of testing was one week after the first. The metameter usually chosen for insulin assays is the percentage reduction in blood sugar. In a series of experiments of which that under discussion was one, however, Fieller (1940) found a correlation between the initial blood sugar and the percentage reduction after injection with insulin. By means of covariance analyses, he showed that the metameter

$$y = \text{per cent. reduction} - 30 \times \text{initial value in}$$
$$\text{parts per 100,000} \qquad (10.1)$$

gave more precise estimates of potency. The method of obtaining such a metameter will be discussed later (Chapter 12). The values of y are shown in Table 10.2. The records for rabbit VII were not obtained : for the purpose of this example, values have been inserted by an extension of the method in § 4.14, and are used as though they were genuine. The exact analysis needed to take account of the missing values is described in § 10.8.

TABLE 10.2—Response metameters in a twin cross-over assay of insulin

Rabbit no.	Day 1	Day 2	Day 1 + Day 2
I II III	$S_1 \begin{cases} 47 \\ 48 \\ 38 \end{cases}$	$T_2 \begin{cases} 52 \\ 46 \\ 34 \end{cases}$	99 94 72
Totals	133	132	265
IV V VI	$S_2 \begin{cases} 38 \\ 53 \\ 38 \end{cases}$	$T_1 \begin{cases} 26 \\ 34 \\ 29 \end{cases}$	64 87 67
Totals	129	89	218
VII VIII IX	$T_1 \begin{cases} 34 \\ 26 \\ 43 \end{cases}$	$S_2 \begin{cases} 34 \\ 24 \\ 43 \end{cases}$	68 50 86
Totals	103	101	204
X XI XII	$T_2 \begin{cases} 34 \\ 40 \\ 39 \end{cases}$	$S_1 \begin{cases} 22 \\ 25 \\ 18 \end{cases}$	56 65 57
Totals	113	65	178
Grand totals	478	387	865

The design of this assay is closely related to a form of 4-point design mentioned earlier (§ 9.9), in which the contrast for parallelism is confounded. The data may be analysed by the methods used

for a $2 \times 2 \times 2$ factorial experiment ; here the three factors are P (preparation), B (dose level), and D (day). The ingenious scheme of additions and subtractions suggested by Yates (1937a, § 3) may be used to form seven orthogonal contrasts between the totals for the eight combinations of these factors. Yates's monograph must be consulted for a description of this type of calculation. Briefly, what is done is to write the totals for the eight combinations of factors in a systematic order obtained by changing each factor in turn, then to form a new column of which the top half is the sum of successive pairs, the bottom half the differences of successive pairs of these totals. Two more columns are formed by repetition of the same process ; the last column may easily be verified to contain the values for the contrasts in systematic order (Table 10.3). As already noted, the contrast L_1' is confounded between subjects. The interactions DL_p, DL_1, measuring respectively the difference between the preparation contrasts for the two days and the difference between the regression contrasts for the two days, are also confounded : for example, DL_p can be formed from rabbit totals as
$$265 + 218 - 204 - 178 = 101.$$

TABLE 10.3—Calculation of contrasts for the data of Table 10.2

| Factors | | | Combination total | Additions | | | Contrast in (3) |
P	B	D		(1)	(2)	(3)	
S	1	1	133	236	478	865	(Total)
T	1	1	103	242	387	9	L_p
S	2	1	129	154	− 46	85	L_1
T	2	1	113	233	55	21	L_1'
S	1	2	65	− 30	6	− 91	Days
T	1	2	89	− 16	79	101	DL_p
S	2	2	101	24	14	73	DL_1
T	2	2	132	31	7	− 7	DL_1'

All other contrasts between the eight totals are intra-rabbit. Each contrast involves every response with a multiplier of 1 or − 1, and the divisor for the square of each is therefore 24. The sum of squares of deviations for the twenty-four responses is divided into inter-rabbit and intra-rabbit sections in the obvious manner and the analysis of variance (Table 10.4) is then easily completed.

TABLE 10.4—Analysis of variance for the data of Table 10.2

Adjustment for mean		31,176·04	Mean square
Nature of variation	d.f.	Sum of squares	
Parallelism	1	18·38	18·38
Days × Preparations ...	1	425·04	425·04
Days × Regression ...	1	222·04	222·04
Error (inter-rabbit) ...	8	711·00	88·88
Between rabbits	11	1,376·46	
Preparations	1	3·38	3·38
Regression	1	301·04	301·04
Days	1	345·04	345·04
Days × Parallelism ...	1	2·04	2·04
Error (intra-rabbit) ...	8	71·00	8·875
Total	23	2,098·96	

As always in a 4-point assay, no test of the linearity of the regression is possible. One of the disadvantages of the present design is that the contrast to be used in the test of parallelism is confounded with differences between rabbits, in consequence of which the test is not very sensitive. Here, however, the mean square for parallelism not only is smaller than the inter-rabbit error mean square but would not be judged significant even if it were compared with the intra-rabbit error : clearly there is no cause for alarm in respect of deviations from parallelism. The mean square for preparations is small, indicating a satisfactory choice of doses. The large mean square for days confirms what is apparent from Table 10.2, namely that the rabbits were much less responsive on the second occasion than on the first. The mean squares for the interactions, Days × Preparations and Days × Regression, are fairly large but not significant: they suggest that the difference between preparations and the regression coefficient may change from day to day, but the variation here is not sufficient to require any special treatment. The component for the Days × Parallelism interaction should be separated in the analysis, even though it is small, as to leave it in the intra-rabbit error because of its smallness would bias the estimation of the error mean square.

Unlike some of the incomplete block designs discussed in Chapter 9, all information on L_p and L_1 comes from the same section of the analysis, namely from intra-rabbit contrasts. Hence equation (5.17) can be applied, and gives

$$R = 22 \text{ antilog } \frac{9 \times 0.3010}{85}$$

$$= 23.7.$$

Moreover,

$$Nt^2s^2 = 24 \times (2.306)^2 \times 8.875$$
$$= 1,132.7,$$

and therefore, by equation (5.21),

$R_L, R_U = 22 \text{ antilog}$

$$\left[\frac{\{9 \times 85 \pm \sqrt{1,132.7 \times (9^2 + 85^2 - 1,132.7)}\} \times 0.3010}{85^2 - 1,132.7} \right]$$

$$= 22 \text{ antilog } \bar{1}.9072, \quad 22 \text{ antilog } 0.1684$$

$$= 17.8, \quad 32.4.$$

The conclusion drawn is that the estimate of potency is 23.7 units per mg., and that the true value is almost sure to lie between 17.8 units per mg. and 32.4 units per mg.

Had the twelve rabbits consisted of three litters of four, the four sequences of dose would naturally have been assigned to one rabbit from each litter. A sum of squares for litter differences, orthogonal with the dose contrasts, would then have had to be isolated in the inter-rabbit section of the analysis. This would not affect the estimation of ρ, but might be expected to improve the sensitivity of the test of parallelism.

10.4   The efficiency of cross-over designs

The gain from the use of a cross-over design may be assessed by comparison of the inter-subject and intra-subject error mean squares. In the insulin assay analysed in § 10.3, if σ^2 be the variance between repeated responses to a fixed dose in the same rabbit and σ_r^2 is the additional variance per response for differences between rabbits, then

$$\sigma^2 \text{ is estimated by error (2)}$$
$$\text{and } \sigma^2 + 2\sigma_r^2 \text{ is estimated by error (1) ;}$$

the second of these follows because contrasts between rabbits involve two responses per rabbit (see, for example, Snedecor, 1956, § 11.4). Hence s^2, s_r^2, estimates of σ^2, σ_r^2, may be taken as

$$s^2 = 8\cdot88,$$
$$s_r^2 = 40\cdot00.$$

In an assay which did not use the cross-over principle, but instead based all conclusions on contrasts between rabbits, the basic variance per response would be $(\sigma^2 + \sigma_r^2)$, estimated by

$$s^2 + s_r^2 = 48\cdot88,$$

a quantity 5·5 times greater than s^2, the intra-rabbit variance that applied to both L_p and L_1 in § 10.3. Thus, in order to obtain a potency estimate whose fiducial range would be as narrow as that in the cross-over assay, a non-cross-over design based on 5·5 times as many responses would be needed : twelve rabbits with two tests on each have led to a potency estimate as good as if 132 rabbits had been tested once each.

This argument is a convincing demonstration of the superiority of the cross-over design. The gain depends upon the relative magnitudes of the two components of variance, which will vary from one stock of subjects to another ; it is likely to be large in a heterogeneous stock, small in a closely inbred stock. A cross-over design can scarcely ever lead to a loss of precision, and will usually give some increase. Nevertheless, it has its defects : in order to ensure that the correct sequence of doses is followed for each

subject, extra care in organization is needed, and also the obtaining
of conclusions is delayed until the second day of the experiment.
Each investigator must balance for himself the advantages against
the defects, in the light of his knowledge of the circumstances in
which the assay is to be conducted.

10.5   Catalogue of cross-over designs

Many other cross-over designs can be devised and the possibilities
of these have not yet been fully exploited.   If the number of
occasions is equal to the number of doses, a Latin square design
ensures that on each occasion all doses are tested on equal numbers
of subjects and every subject receives each dose once.   The design
in Table 10.1 makes the allocation of doses to subjects follow an
incomplete block scheme, actually that for a 4-point design in blocks
of two listed in § 9.9.   Other designs in §§ 9.7 and 9.9 can be used
as bases for cross-over designs, the number of occasions being
always the number of doses per incomplete block ;   the balanced.
incomplete blocks lead to Youden squares (Youden, 1937, 1940).
If the number of occasions that could be used exceeded the number
of doses, a super-complete block scheme would be required ;   it
could be obtained by using a Latin square design for a number of
occasions equal to the number of doses, and appending an
incomplete block scheme for the remaining occasions (Table 10.8 ;
cf. Cochran and Cox, 1957, Chapter 13).

These ideas will become clearer from consideration of the
following catalogue of designs, which includes most of the types
likely to be of practical use.   Statistical analysis should present
few difficulties, as it is always very similar to that for the corresponding non-cross-over design except for the isolation of the
inter-occasion component of the sum of squares ;   an example is
given in § 10.6.   Except for the 4-point, Latin square designs will
not be discussed, since Fisher and Yates (1963, Table XV) have
provided adequate tables.   No designs for which the minimum
number of subjects is greater than twenty are listed here.

(i) 4-*point designs*.—If each subject can be used four times,
and the investigator is prepared to wait as long as that for his
results, a Latin square design is the ideal.   Moreover, the statistical
analysis is much simpler than for any of the incomplete block
designs.   For example, a set of four subjects (numbered in random

order) might be assigned to doses and occasions as shown in Table 10.5. All contrasts between doses are then intra-subject. If more than four subjects are to be used, a new Latin square for each set of four ought to be chosen at random from all possible squares, according to the rules given by Fisher and Yates (1963, Introduction). A design with $4K$ subjects would have its degrees of freedom partitioned as shown in Table 10.6. Bliss and Rose (1940) have given an example of the application of this design to

TABLE 10.5—Cross-over design for a 4-point assay with four responses per subject

Subject no.	Dose on occasion no.			
	1	2	3	4
I	S_1	T_2	T_1	S_2
II	S_2	T_1	T_2	S_1
III	T_1	S_2	S_1	T_2
IV	T_2	S_1	S_2	T_1

TABLE 10.6—Partition of degrees of freedom in the analysis of variance for the design of Table 10.5 with $4K$ subjects

Nature of variation	d.f.
Subjects	$4K - 1$
Occasions	3
Preparations	1
Regression	1
Parallelism	1
Error	$12K - 6$
Total	$16K - 1$

the assay of a parathyroid extract, by means of serum calcium determinations in dogs (§ 10.6).

For twelve subjects, the design in Table 10.7 has some advantages. In it are used three Latin squares, which together include twelve out of the twenty-four possible different orders of giving the four doses. Moreover, each dose on occasion 1 is followed by each of the others on occasion 2 (thus subjects I, V, IX have S_1 followed by T_2, S_2, T_1 respectively), and similarly for the other two pairs of successive occasions. Consequently, with a little extra ingenuity, not only may differences between occasions and differences between subjects be eliminated from effect on the assay but also any residual (additive) influences of one dose on the response to the next. For example, if a high dose on one day still has some effect on the next day of testing, and reduces the apparent response to the dose then given, disturbance from this cause can be eliminated. Designs of this kind are important for nutritional experiments, but the possibility of taking account of residual effects does not at

TABLE 10.7—**Balanced cross-over design for a 4-point assay with four responses per subject**

Subject no.	Dose on occasion no.			
	1	2	3	4
I	S_1	T_2	T_1	S_2
II	S_2	T_1	T_2	S_1
III	T_1	S_2	S_1	T_2
IV	T_2	S_1	S_2	T_1
V	S_1	S_2	T_2	T_1
VI	S_2	S_1	T_1	T_2
VII	T_1	T_2	S_2	S_1
VIII	T_2	T_1	S_1	S_2
IX	S_1	T_1	S_2	T_2
X	S_2	T_2	S_1	T_1
XI	T_1	S_1	T_2	S_2
XII	T_2	S_2	T_1	S_1

present seem of great interest in biological assay. Further information on methods of construction and analysis has been given by Williams (1949, 1950) and Patterson (1950, 1951).

If each subject is to be used only twice, the design in Table 10.1 will usually be the best. A design based upon the balanced incomplete block design in § 9.7 requires twelve (or a multiple of twelve) subjects; it can be read from the first two occasions in Table 10.7. If each subject is to be used three times, designs are obtained by omitting the last occasion in Table 10.5. Omission of the last occasion in Table 10.7 leaves a design with three tests per subject that is balanced for residual effects. The method of construction of the super-complete block designs is illustrated by Table 10.8, which is compounded of Tables 10.1 and 10.5 to give a design with six tests on each subject.

TABLE 10.8—Cross-over design for a 4-point assay with six responses per subject

Subject no.	Dose on occasion no.					
	1	2	3	4	5	6
I	S_1	T_2	T_1	S_2	S_2	T_1
II	S_2	T_1	T_2	S_1	T_2	S_1
III	T_1	S_2	S_1	T_2	T_1	S_2
IV	T_2	S_1	S_2	T_1	S_1	T_2

(*ii*) 6-*point designs*.—A 6-point design with tests on two occasions may be based upon the confounded design discussed in § 9.8, and is shown in Table 10.9. The number of subjects must be a multiple of six, and the analysis of variance will be like that in Table 9.14 except that a degree of freedom for the difference between occasions must be isolated in the intra-subject section. The design is very similar to the 4-point design discussed in § 10.3. A balanced incomplete block scheme can easily be constructed ; thirty subjects are necessary and the fifteen pairs of doses in Table 9.4 are used in both orders.

TABLE 10.9—Cross-over design for a 6-point
assay with two responses per
subject

L_p and L_1 orthogonal with subjects

Subject no.	Dose on occasion no.	
	1	2
I	S_1	T_3
II	S_2	T_2
III	S_3	T_1
IV	T_1	S_3
V	T_2	S_2
VI	T_3	S_1

If each subject is to be used three times, a neatly confounded design is impossible, and a design based on Table 9.19 is the best for intra-subject information on L_p and L_1. Table 10.10 shows this design, which is constructed by forming two 3×3 Latin squares with the two types of block in Table 9.19. The recom-

TABLE 10.10—Cross-over design for a 6-point assay
with three responses per subject

L_1 orthogonal with subjects and L_p minimally confounded

Subject no.	Dose on occasion no.		
	1	2	3
I	S_1	S_3	T_2
II	S_3	T_2	S_1
III	T_2	S_1	S_3
IV	S_2	T_1	T_3
V	T_1	T_3	S_2
VI	T_3	S_2	T_1

mended confounding scheme in Table 9.17 can be incorporated into a design with four tests per subject, in the manner shown in Table 10.11 ; it is of interest to note that Tables 10.9 and 10.11 together form a 6×6 Latin square. Balanced incomplete block (Youden square or generalized Youden square) designs for three or four tests per subject require at least thirty subjects.

TABLE 10.11—Cross-over design for a 6-point assay with four responses per subject

L_p and L_1 orthogonal with subjects

Subject no.	Dose on occasion no.			
	1	2	3	4
I	S_2	S_3	T_1	T_2
II	S_3	S_2	T_2	T_1
III	T_1	T_2	S_1	S_3
IV	T_3	T_1	S_3	S_1
V	T_2	S_1	T_3	S_2
VI	S_1	T_2	S_2	T_3

The only useful design with five responses per subject is the balanced incomplete block, formed from any 6×6 Latin square by omission of the last column. The complete square, of course, gives a design for six responses per subject.

(*iii*) 8-*point designs.*—Designs for two, four, or six responses per subject can be based upon the confounded designs in § 9.9. These are shown in Tables 10.12–10.14. Designs for three, five, or seven responses per subject cannot be constructed to have very satisfactory confounding schemes, and probably those that use the first three, five, or seven columns of Table 10.15 would be about the best in respect of the freedom of L_p and L_1 from confounding ; this table is an 8×8 Latin square, one of the many that might be used if each subject could be tested on eight occasions. Balanced incomplete block designs all require many subjects, except for that with seven responses per subject obtained by omission of the last column from any 8×8 Latin square.

TABLE 10.12—Cross-over design for an 8-point assay with two responses per subject

L_p and L_1 orthogonal with subjects

Subject no.	Dose on occasion no.	
	1	2
I	S_1	T_4
II	S_2	T_3
III	S_3	T_2
IV	S_4	T_1
V	T_1	S_4
VI	T_2	S_3
VII	T_3	S_2
VIII	T_4	S_1

TABLE 10.13—Cross-over design for an 8-point assay with four responses per subject

L_p and L_1 orthogonal with subjects

Subject no.	Dose on occasion no.			
	1	2	3	4
I	S_1	T_2	S_4	T_3
II	S_2	S_3	T_4	T_1
III	S_3	S_2	T_1	T_4
IV	S_4	T_2	T_3	S_1
V	T_1	T_4	S_2	S_3
VI	T_2	S_1	T_3	S_4
VII	T_3	S_4	S_1	T_2
VIII	T_4	T_1	S_3	S_2

TABLE 10.14—Cross-over design for an 8-point assay with six responses per subject

L_9 and L_1 orthogonal with subjects

Subject no.	Dose on occasion no.					
	1	2	3	4	5	6
I	S_1	S_2	S_3	T_2	T_3	T_4
II	S_2	S_3	T_1	T_3	T_2	S_4
III	S_3	T_2	T_3	S_4	T_1	S_2
IV	S_4	S_1	T_2	S_3	T_4	T_1
V	T_1	T_4	S_4	S_1	S_3	T_2
VI	T_2	T_3	T_4	S_2	S_1	S_3
VII	T_3	T_1	S_3	T_4	S_4	S_1
VIII	T_4	S_4	S_1	T_1	S_2	T_3

TABLE 10.15—Cross-over design for an 8-point assay with eight responses per subject

(To be used also for three, five, or seven responses per subject)

Subject no.	Dose on occasion no.							
	1	2	3	4	5	6	7	8
I	S_1	S_4	T_2	T_3	T_1	T_4	S_2	S_3
II	S_2	S_3	T_1	T_4	S_4	S_1	T_3	T_2
III	S_3	S_2	T_4	T_1	T_3	T_2	S_4	S_1
IV	S_4	S_1	T_3	T_2	S_2	S_3	T_1	T_4
V	T_1	T_4	S_2	S_3	S_1	S_4	T_2	T_3
VI	T_2	T_3	S_1	S_4	T_4	T_1	S_3	S_2
VII	T_3	T_2	S_4	S_1	S_3	S_2	T_4	T_1
VIII	T_4	T_1	S_3	S_2	T_2	T_3	S_1	S_4

(*iv*) 3-*point designs.*—A balanced incomplete block design with two responses per subject is obtained by deletion of the last column from any 3×3 Latin square. This may be repeated for any number of subjects that is a multiple of three.

(*v*) 5-*point designs.*—The balanced incomplete block designs listed in § 9.7 may be arranged to give designs for two, three, or four responses per subject. Tables 10.16 and 10.17 show the designs for two and three responses, these being generalizations of the Youden square principle ; in a set of ten subjects, each dose occurs twice on each occasion. For four responses per subject, the last column of any 5×5 Latin square may be deleted and the remaining columns assigned to a set of five subjects on four occasions.

TABLE 10.16—Cross-over design for a 5-point assay with two responses per subject

Arranged in balanced incomplete blocks

Subject no.	Dose on occasion no.	
	1	2
I	C	S_2
II	C	T_1
III	S_1	C
IV	S_1	T_2
V	S_2	S_1
VI	S_2	T_1
VII	T_1	S_1
VIII	T_1	T_2
IX	T_2	C
X	T_2	S_2

TABLE 10.17—Cross-over design for a 5-point assay with three responses per subject

Arranged in balanced incomplete blocks

Subject no.	Dose on occasion no.		
	1	2	3
I	C	S_2	T_1
II	C	T_2	S_2
III	S_1	S_2	T_1
IV	S_1	T_1	C
V	S_2	C	S_1
VI	S_2	S_1	T_2
VII	T_1	S_1	T_2
VIII	T_1	T_2	S_2
IX	T_2	C	S_1
X	T_2	T_1	C

TABLE 10.18—Cross-over design for a 7-point assay with three responses per subject

Arranged in balanced incomplete blocks

Subject no.	Dose on occasion no.		
	1	2	3
I	C	S_1	S_2
II	S_1	S_3	T_2
III	S_2	T_2	T_1
IV	S_3	S_2	T_3
V	T_1	C	S_3
VI	T_2	T_3	C
VII	T_3	T_1	S_1

(*vi*) 7-*point designs.*—For an assay that is to have two or five responses per subject, at least twenty-one subjects are necessary in order to give a generalized Youden square design. For three or four responses per subject, the balanced incomplete block design in Table 9.10 can be arranged to give simple Youden squares : in a set of seven subjects, each dose is tested on every occasion, and the doses assigned to the subjects form the balanced incomplete blocks. Tables 10.18 and 10.19 show how this can be done. If more than seven subjects are to be used, the designs, or variants of them, may be repeated. In the usual way, a design for six responses per subject is obtainable by deletion of the last column from a 7×7 Latin square.

TABLE 10.19—Cross-over design for a 7-point assay with four responses per subject

Arranged in balanced incomplete blocks

Subject no.	Dose on occasion no.			
	1	2	3	4
I	C	S_2	T_1	T_2
II	S_1	T_3	S_3	C
III	S_2	S_3	S_1	T_1
IV	S_3	T_1	T_3	T_2
V	T_1	T_2	C	S_1
VI	T_3	C	S_2	S_3
VII	T_3	S_1	T_2	S_2

(*vii*) 9-*point designs.*—The number of subjects needed limits the useful 9-point cross-over designs to those for four, five, eight, and nine occasions. The designs for four and five occasions may be based on that for balanced incomplete blocks of four in Table 9.12 and the associated design for blocks of five ; both require eighteen subjects, and Tables 10.20 and 10.21 show the arrangements. Any 9×9 Latin square yields a design for nine occasions with nine subjects, and deletion of the last column reduces this to a design for eight occasions.

TABLE 10.20—Cross-over design for a 9-point assay with four responses per subject

Arranged in balanced incomplete blocks

Subject no.	Dose on occasion no.			
	1	2	3	4
I	C	S_1	S_3	T_3
II	C	S_2	T_1	T_2
III	S_1	S_2	S_3	T_2
IV	S_1	T_3	T_2	T_1
V	S_2	S_3	S_4	C
VI	S_2	T_1	S_1	T_4
VII	S_3	S_4	T_4	S_1
VIII	S_3	T_1	T_3	S_2
IX	S_4	T_2	T_3	C
X	S_4	T_2	T_4	S_2
XI	T_1	C	S_1	S_4
XII	T_1	T_4	C	S_3
XIII	T_2	S_4	T_1	S_3
XIV	T_2	T_4	C	S_1
XV	T_3	S_1	S_2	S_4
XVI	T_3	S_3	T_2	T_4
XVII	T_4	C	S_2	T_3
XVIII	T_4	T_3	S_4	T_1

TABLE 10.21—Cross-over design for a 9-point assay with five responses per subject

Arranged in balanced incomplete blocks

Subject no.	Dose on occasion no.				
	1	2	3	4	5
I	C	S_1	S_4	T_2	T_4
II	C	S_4	T_1	T_3	T_4
III	S_1	S_2	S_3	T_2	C
IV	S_1	T_4	T_3	S_4	S_3
V	S_2	S_3	S_4	T_4	C
VI	S_2	S_4	T_1	C	S_1
VII	S_3	S_1	T_2	S_4	T_1
VIII	S_3	T_1	S_2	T_3	S_4
IX	S_4	T_1	T_4	S_2	T_2
X	S_4	T_2	S_1	S_2	T_3
XI	T_1	S_2	T_4	S_1	S_3
XII	T_1	T_2	T_3	C	S_2
XIII	T_2	S_3	S_2	T_4	T_3
XIV	T_2	T_3	C	S_3	S_4
XV	T_3	C	S_1	S_3	T_1
XVI	T_3	T_4	C	S_1	S_2
XVII	T_4	C	S_3	T_1	T_2
XVIII	T_4	T_3	T_2	T_1	S_1

In the above catalogue of designs, for $(2k + 1)$-point assays only the balanced incomplete block type is shown, as no particularly useful confounding schemes are known. Though all designs are tabulated as for symmetrical assays, those based on balanced incomplete blocks are equally applicable to any unsymmetrical set of doses, since all contrasts are made with the same precision ; the symbols used for the doses of the symmetrical assay should then be replaced by the symbols for the actual doses in random order. Designs based on the confounding schemes in § 9.9, however, would lose their special properties of giving maximal precision to the important contrasts if they were used for unsymmetrical sets of doses.

The designs in Tables 10.1, 10.5 and 10.7–10.21 are arranged in systematic orders. For use, the allocation of subjects to the Roman numerals and the order of the columns should be randomized. If the subjects are to be classified into litters (or other groups), and if the size of the litter is the same as the number of subjects required for a full replication of the design, inter-litter differences may be eliminated ; this will increase the precision of the information given by inter-subject contrasts, and so for the balanced incomplete block designs will increase the precision of the assay but for the others will affect only the sensitivity of the validity tests.

10.6   A cross-over assay of a parathyroid extract

The assay of a parathyroid extract discussed by Bliss and Rose (1940) followed the design in Table 10.5, except that five Latin squares were used. As already noted, the analysis presents little difficulty. Bliss (1947a) has used the responses measured on the first three of the four days of testing as an illustration of the analysis of a 4-point assay with three responses per subject. That analysis will be repeated here, in rather simpler form.

Doses of 0·125 and 0·205 c.c. per kg. of the standard and the test preparations were administered to twenty dogs, each dog receiving three of the four doses with about ten days interval between successive doses. The serum calcium of each dog was determined on the day after treatment, and the sixty values are the responses for analysis. The sequence of doses and the responses are shown in Table 10.22. For that table, the dogs have been rearranged into four groups of five, each group having the same set of doses though not necessarily in the same order ; the five Latin squares, or rather the five Latin squares with final columns omitted, are composed of the first, second, . . . fifth dogs from the groups

TABLE 10.22—Serum calcium values of dogs after injection with parathyroid extract

(Responses in mg. per 100 g.)

Group	Dog no.	Dose on 15 Mar.	Dose on 24 Mar.	Dose on 5 Apr.	Serum calcium on 16 Mar.	Serum calcium on 25 Mar.	Serum calcium on 6 Apr.	Total for dog
I	342	T_1	T_2	S_2	14·7	15·4	14·8	44·9
	287	T_1	T_2	S_2	15·1	15·0	15·8	45·9
	264	T_2	S_2	T_1	14·4	13·8	14·4	42·6
	349	T_2	T_1	S_2	16·2	14·0	13·0	43·2
	247	T_2	S_2	T_1	15·8	16·0	15·0	46·8
II	256	T_2	T_1	S_1	15·8	14·3	14·8	44·9
	317	T_2	T_1	S_1	17·0	16·5	15·0	48·5
	288	T_1	S_1	T_2	13·6	15·3	17·2	46·1
	252	T_1	T_2	S_1	14·0	13·8	14·0	41·8
	308	T_1	S_1	T_2	13·0	13·4	13·8	40·2
III	280	S_1	S_2	T_2	13·8	17·0	16·0	46·8
	244	S_1	S_2	T_2	12·0	13·8	14·0	39·8
	273	S_2	T_2	S_1	14·6	15·4	14·0	44·0
	250	S_2	S_1	T_2	13·0	14·0	14·0	41·0
	271	S_2	T_2	S_1	15·2	16·2	15·0	46·4
IV	320	S_2	S_1	T_1	15·0	14·5	14·0	43·5
	309	S_2	S_1	T_1	15·0	14·0	14·6	43·6
	276	S_1	T_1	S_2	15·8	15·0	15·2	46·0
	278	S_1	S_2	T_1	13·2	16·0	14·9	44·1
	299	S_1	T_1	S_2	14·2	14·1	15·0	43·3
Totals for days of testing					291·4	297·5	294·5	883·4

The analysis of variance for these data may be constructed by the general method outlined in § 9.5, using inter-subject and intra-subject regressions on the variates corresponding to L_p, L_1, L_1'. Table 10.23 contains dose totals for the four groups of subjects and the totals of all responses for these groups, symbolized by B_I, B_{II}, B_{III}, B_{IV}. Those who are inexperienced in the analysis of variance may verify what the more experienced will realize intuitively, namely, that the same analysis will be obtained by forming an intra-subject estimate of the preparations difference:

$$L_p = L_p \text{ (crude)} - \tfrac{1}{3}(B_I + B_{II} - B_{III} - B_{IV}), \qquad (10.2)$$

with a corresponding inter-subject estimate

$$L_p = \tfrac{1}{3}(B_I + B_{II} - B_{III} - B_{IV}), \qquad (10.3)$$

and similar contrasts for L_1 and L_1'. The orthogonality conditions

TABLE 10.23—Dose and group totals for the data of Table 10.22

| Group | Total for | | | | Total of group |
	S_1	S_2	T_1	T_2	
I	—	73·4	73·2	76·8	223·4
II	72·5	—	71·4	77·6	221·5
III	68·8	73·6	—	75·6	218·0
IV	71·7	76·2	72·6	—	220·5
Total	213·0	223·2	217·2	230·0	883·4

TABLE 10.24—Orthogonal coefficients for contrasts within subjects for the data of Tables 10.22 and 10.23

Contrast	Group	S_1	S_2	T_1	T_2	Divisor	Sum
L_0	I	—	− 2	1	1		
	II	− 2	—	1	1		
	III	− 1	− 1	—	2		
	IV	− 1	− 1	2	—	120	13·3
L_1	I	—	1	− 2	1		
	II	− 1	—	− 1	2		
	III	− 2	1	—	1		
	IV	− 1	2	− 1	—	120	34·8
L_1'	I	—	− 1	− 1	2		
	II	1	—	− 2	1		
	III	1	− 2	—	1		
	IV	2	− 1	− 1	—	120	6·1

are satisfied, and the divisors may be found by the usual rules. A still more direct procedure is shown in Table 10.24, where the three intra-subject contrasts are defined in terms of the dose totals in Table 10.23 ; the divisors are as usual the sums of squares of coefficients. The inter-subject contrasts are most easily written as

$$
\begin{aligned}
L_p &= B_{\mathrm{I}} + B_{\mathrm{II}} - B_{\mathrm{III}} - B_{\mathrm{IV}} &&= 6\!\cdot\!4, \\
L_1 &= B_{\mathrm{I}} - B_{\mathrm{II}} + B_{\mathrm{III}} - B_{\mathrm{IV}} &&= -0\!\cdot\!6, \\
L_1' &= -B_{\mathrm{I}} + B_{\mathrm{II}} + B_{\mathrm{III}} - B_{\mathrm{IV}} &&= -4\!\cdot\!4,
\end{aligned}
\qquad (10.4)
$$

with divisor 60 for each (since every response enters with coefficient 1 or -1).

The analysis of variance, Table 10.25, is now rapidly completed. It discloses no sign of invalidity, and the fact that the inter-dog

TABLE 10.25—Analysis of variance for the data of Table 10.22

Adjustment for mean		13,006·5927	Mean square
Nature of variation	d.f.	Sum of squares	
Preparations	1	0·6827	0·6827
Regression	1	0·0060	0·0060
Parallelism	1	0·3227	0·3227
Error (1)	16	33·7159	2·1072
Between dogs	19	34·7273	
Days	2	0·9303	0·4652
Preparations	1	1·4741	1·4741
Regression	1	10·0920	10·0920
Parallelism	1	0·3101	0·3101
Error (2)	35	20·2735	0·5792
Total	59	67·8073	

error is almost four times the intra-dog error indicates a substantial gain in precision as a result of the choice of a cross-over design. In the inter-dog section of the analysis, the regression component is smaller than the error mean square, and indeed, as found above, L_1 has a small negative value. Consequently g is greater than unity and no potency estimate can be obtained from inter-dog contrasts. The inter-dog variation contributes so little information about the potency of the test preparation that an estimate based on intra-dog contrasts alone is likely to be preferable to a compound estimate.

Inspection of Table 10.24 shows the intra-dog L_p to be a difference between forty responses to the test preparation and forty to the standard. Hence the mean difference per observation is estimated to be

$$\bar{y}_T - \bar{y}_S = \frac{L_p}{40} \tag{10.5}$$
$$= 0 \cdot 3325,$$

with

$$V(\bar{y}_T - \bar{y}_S) = \frac{120 s_2^2}{(40)^2}$$
$$= \frac{3 s_2^2}{40}. \tag{10.6}$$

Similarly the regression coefficient, which is exactly the quantity that would be obtained as the intra-dog regression coefficient on a variate that takes the value -1 for every response to S_1 or T_1, $+1$ for every response to S_2 or T_2, is

$$b = \frac{L_1}{80} \tag{10.7}$$
$$= 0 \cdot 4350,$$

with

$$V(b) = \frac{120 s_2^2}{(80)^2}$$
$$= \frac{3 s_2^2}{160}. \tag{10.8}$$

Estimation of potency then proceeds in the usual manner. Thus
$$M = 0 \cdot 7644,$$
$$g = 0 \cdot 2365,$$

and
$$M_L, M_U = (0.7644 \pm 0.9276)/0.7635$$
$$= -0.2138, \; 2.2161.$$

The dose ratio between high and low doses of either preparation was 1·64, so that all log potency values must be multiplied by $\frac{1}{2}$ log 1·64, or 0·1074, in order to convert them to logarithms to base 10. Hence, since the two preparations were given at equal doses,

$$R = \text{antilog } 0.0821 = 1.208,$$
$$R_L = \text{antilog } \bar{1}.9770 = 0.948,$$
$$R_U = \text{antilog } 0.2380 = 1.730.$$

Thus 1 c.c. of the test preparation is estimated to have the potency of 1·208 c.c. of the standard parathyroid extract, with fiducial limits at 0·948 c.c. and 1·730 c.c. of the standard.

If the inter-dog analysis is combined with this, in the manner of § 9.5, the slight improvement in the precision of contrasts is rather more than offset by the lower value of b consequent upon the negative inter-dog L_1. The new value of R is 1·224, with limits a little more widely spaced at 0·956 and 1·788. When one section of the analysis shows so small a regression coefficient, it should be ignored and the estimation based entirely on the other.

10.7   Single subject assays

In cross-over assays, a few subjects are used repeatedly instead of a larger number once only. An extreme form is that in which every response is measured on one subject. For example, histamine may be assayed from contractions of an isolated strip of guinea-pig's gut, which is immersed in a water-bath so as to have one end fixed and the other attached to a writing point that records a constant magnification of any contraction.

Responses to different doses, measured at short intervals of time, are used in the ordinary statistical analysis. The level of response may decline seriously as the assay progresses, and cross-over designs may be adapted for the elimination of trend. Any designs in this chapter can be used by following in succession the sequences previously allotted to different subjects. Thus a 4-point assay using sixteen responses might be based on the Latin square in Table 10.5; if occasions were randomized to the order 4, 2, 3, 1 and subjects to the order 2, 1, 4, 3, the gut would receive in succession the doses

S_1, T_1, T_2, S_2; S_2, T_2, T_1, S_1; T_1, S_1, S_2, T_2; T_2, S_2, S_1, T_1. The standard statistical analysis would eliminate differences between sets of four responses and the average effect of order within sets of four, these corresponding to ' subjects ' and ' occasions '. If changes in responsiveness within the short period of four tests were thought unimportant, a randomized block design could replace the Latin square, with a fresh randomization of order for each four, so increasing flexibility by removing restrictions on the number of replications. Schild (1942) has described clearly assays of this class; Smith and Vos (1943) and Noel (1945) published interesting examples. If one subject cannot be used often enough for the precision desired, two may be used and the results combined.

In § 10.1 was mentioned the possibility of more complex statistical dependence between responses on successive occasions. Reference has been made in § 10.5 to designs specially adapted to balancing effects of preceding doses if there is any reason to suspect that these may influence current responses; Finney (1956) has discussed the consequences for statistical analysis. Analogous designs can be constructed for single subject assays. Consider the sequence

$$S_2; \quad T_1, \ T_2, \ S_2, \ S_1; \quad S_2, \ T_2, \ T_1, \ S_1; \quad T_2, \ S_1, \ T_1, \ S_2.$$

After a first conditioning dose, each dose of a 4-point scheme occurs once in each of three blocks; moreover, each dose is preceded once only by each *other* dose. Finney and Outhwaite (1956) have described the modified statistical analysis that takes account of a simple model in which each expected response includes additive components for the current and immediately preceding dose, with the residual component proportional to the corresponding current one. Even for 4-point assays, this becomes complicated, and since little practical use has been made of the designs no details are presented here. For 6-point assays, slightly better balance may be achieved. The following two sequences might be used on two subjects with nineteen responses measured on each, or they might be put end-to-end for one subject with 37 responses, omitting the first T_3 of (ii):

(i) S_2; $\ S_2$, T_1, T_3, S_1, T_2, S_3; $\ S_3$, T_3, T_2, S_2, S_1, T_1; $\ T_1$, S_2, S_3, T_2, S_1, T_3;

(ii) T_3; $\ T_3$, S_2, T_2, T_1, S_3, S_1; $\ S_1$, S_3, S_2, T_3, T_1, T_2; $\ T_2$, T_3, S_3, T_1, S_1, S_2.

Here each dose is preceded once by *every* dose, including itself.

Sampford (1957) has discussed the construction and properties of these two types of serially balanced sequence.

Designs of the kinds that have been described above are sometimes unsatisfactory for single subject assays because they need a large number of responses per subject for completion, and the computations become troublesome if an accident or sudden deterioration of a piece of tissue forces abandonment before completion. A 6-point assay with measurement of twenty-four responses might be based upon Table 10.11, using in succession the dose sequences allotted to the six subjects in the table; if testing had to stop after eighteen responses, a laborious statistical analysis would be needed. However, designs based on complete or incomplete randomized blocks and lacking the double restriction on order of dosing characteristic of true crossovers are more flexible. For them, changes in plan during the course of experimentation need not be so harmful, and if blocks are small intra-block changes in responsiveness will rarely be important.

Some workers who have been particularly worried by the fear of sudden changes in responsiveness have chosen to proceed by matching doses, adjusting the magnitudes of successive doses of the two preparations in an endeavour to find a pair producing equal responses. Evidently this is wasteful, as many responses contribute nothing to the final potency estimate. Moreover, satisfactory matching will be difficult if the responsiveness of the subject is changing, and any assessment of precision will need extensive additional calculations. Vos (1943, 1950) has objected to cross-over designs because the responsiveness of a subject may not change at a constant rate, and has introduced a *constant standard* design as an improvement on the matching process. A constant standard assay begins with a few preliminary doses of the standard preparation to give some idea of the subject's sensitivity, after which the standard and test preparations are alternated. The standard is held to a constant dose, but doses of the test preparation are varied in such a manner that some responses exceed and some are less than those to the standard, the aim being to choose doses so that mean responses for the two preparations are about equal. A moving average analysis is recommended: each successive (overlapping) pair of standard responses is averaged and subtracted from the intervening test response. The difference is then plotted against the difference of corresponding log doses. A straight line is fitted by least squares, and M is taken to be the value on the dose scale for which the line shows a zero response difference. Vos used this assay design for ergonovine, as did Thompson (1944, 1945) for posterior pituitary and epinephrine.

The constant standard design, at least in the form described, is open to several objections. Because it uses only one dose of the standard preparation, the condition of similarity cannot be tested. The lack of randomization in the order of doses in theory prevents any valid assessment of precision; although this criticism may not always be of great practical importance, internal evidence from an assay is a poor indicator. The obtaining of a standard response comparable with each test response by use of moving averages has obvious merits, but it introduces serial correlations between successive values of Vos's response difference: any estimation of error directly from the least square calculations is therefore additionally suspect. Despite his concern as to whether the responsiveness of such subjects as pieces of animal tissue would change at a constant rate, alternative analyses assuming a linear decrease and avoiding moving averages have been tried for two of Thompson's assays. This method, not described here, gave potency estimates and assessments of precision almost identical with those from Vos's method.

One feature of the constant standard design, the provision for changing the levels of dose in accordance with accumulating knowledge of the subject's responsiveness, may be valuable, especially when little is known initially about the potency of the test preparation. The same convenience may be gained in a randomized block type of design that escapes the difficulties of valid error estimation. Each successive (non-overlapping) pair of responses might be randomized between S and T, to give a dose sequence such as

$$S, T; \quad T, S; \quad T, S; \quad T, S; \quad S, T; \quad T, S; \quad S, T; \quad \ldots$$

Here S could represent a fixed dose of the standard or one that was changed only after evidence of gross change in responsiveness of the subject; T, the dose of the test preparation, could be changed from block to block as information on potency accumulated. A linear regression of $(y_T - y_S)$ on the corresponding $(x_T - x_S)$, each difference being formed for every block of two, would again give M as the intercept of the regression line on the x-axis. As Vos advised, doses of the test preparation should be chosen with the aim of making the mean responses for the two preparations about equal, so that the mean of $(y_T - y_S)$ is near zero. He omitted to mention the need to have a sufficiently wide range of values of x_T, without going outside the region of linearity, for the sum of squares of deviations of $(x_T - x_S)$ to be reasonably large; without this precaution, the estimated regression coefficient may be insufficiently precise. A more sophisticated pattern of design and statistical analysis of this kind, modified to permit the use of a curvilinear regression, has been fully described by Box and Hay (1953).

10.8   Exact analysis with one subject missing

As a final illustration of the analysis of cross-over designs, which throws further light on the general principles of analysis, the insulin assay in § 10.3 will be re-analysed, with proper allowance for the fact that the records for rabbit VII were missing. The method of least squares might be used, as in § 4.14, to provide values for the missing entries which would free the dose contrasts from bias. This would require the choice of numerical values in such a way as to minimize the sums of squares for both error lines in Table 10.4 ; the values are easily seen to be the means of the corresponding entries for rabbits VIII and IX, or 34·5 and 33·5. Except for a rounding to integral values, these are the responses for rabbit VII that were given in Table 10.2, but no allowance for their being calculated values was made in the analysis that followed. In fact, their insertion reduces the number of degrees of freedom for error by 1 in each section of the analysis, so that the mean squares ought to be 101·57 and 10·14. Probably the best procedure is to make the validity tests with the aid of this modified analysis of variance. The tests will not then be entirely unbiased, but will be good enough for practical purposes when only one subject is missing, and are quite adequate when, as here, not a sign of invalidity appears (Anderson, 1946 ; Yates, 1933a).

The estimation of potency needs more careful handling. The method of § 4.19 could be adopted, but, since only intra-rabbit contrasts are involved and only two responses of each rabbit have been measured, an easier process seems to be to form means of intra-rabbit differences for the eleven ' genuine ' rabbits. These differences are of four types, as shown in Table 10.26, where they are listed as (response on day 2 — response on day 1). If A_i, A_{ii}, A_{iii}, A_{iv}, are written for the totals of the intra-rabbit differences of types $(T_2 - S_1)$, $(T_1 - S_2)$, $(S_2 - T_1)$, $(S_1 - T_2)$ respectively, the numbers of these being n_i, n_{ii}, n_{iii}, n_{iv}, an estimate of the preparations difference independent of the difference between occasions and of inter-rabbit differences may be written as the contrast

$$\bar{y}_T - \bar{y}_S = \frac{1}{4} \left(\frac{A_i}{n_i} + \frac{A_{ii}}{n_{ii}} - \frac{A_{iii}}{n_{iii}} - \frac{A_{iv}}{n_{iv}} \right) \qquad (10.9)$$

$$= \frac{1}{4} \times \left(-\frac{1}{3} - \frac{40}{3} + \frac{2}{2} + \frac{48}{3} \right)$$

$$= 0 \cdot 8333.$$

Similarly, on the dose scale that, in the usual manner, makes the low and high doses -1 and $+1$, an estimate of the regression coefficient is the contrast

$$b = \frac{1}{8} \left(\frac{A_i}{n_i} - \frac{A_{ii}}{n_{ii}} + \frac{A_{iii}}{n_{iii}} - \frac{A_{iv}}{n_{iv}} \right) \qquad (10.10)$$

$$= \frac{1}{8} \times \left(-\frac{1}{3} + \frac{40}{3} - \frac{2}{2} + \frac{48}{3} \right)$$

$$= 3 \cdot 500.$$

Hence, by the general formula,

$$M - \bar{x}_S + \bar{x}_T = \frac{0 \cdot 8333}{3 \cdot 5000}$$

$$= 0 \cdot 2381.$$

TABLE 10.26—**Differences between pairs of responses for each rabbit in Table 10.2**
Differences are Day 2 − Day 1

	Type of dose difference			
	$T_2 - S_1$	$T_1 - S_2$	$S_2 - T_1$	$S_1 - T_2$
	5	− 12	—	− 12
	− 2	− 19	− 2	− 15
	− 4	− 9	0	− 21
Totals	− 1	− 40	− 2	− 48

The variance per response can be found from the sum of squares within columns for the differences in Table 10.26. Each difference is based on two responses, three columns contribute 2 degrees of freedom and one contributes 1, so that the value of s^2 with 7 degrees of freedom is

$$s^2 = \frac{1}{2}\left[\left(5^2 + 2^2 + 4^2 - \frac{12^2}{3}\right) + \left(12^2 + 19^2 + 9^2 - \frac{40^2}{3}\right)\right.$$
$$\left. + \left(2^2 + 0^2 - \frac{2^2}{2}\right) + \left(12^2 + 15^2 + 21^2 - \frac{48^2}{3}\right)\right] \div 7$$

$$= 70{\cdot}67/7$$
$$= 10{\cdot}10.$$

The sum of squares here differs from that shown as Error (2) in Table 10.4 only because the missing values in Table 10.2 were each taken as 34 instead of as 34·5, 33·5. Clearly

$$V(A_1) = 2n_1 s^2, \tag{10.11}$$

and similarly for the other totals in Table 10.26. Hence, by reference to their definitions in equations (10.9) and (10.10), the variances and covariance of $(\bar{y}_T - \bar{y}_S)$ and b are seen to be

$$V(\bar{y}_T - \bar{y}_S) = \frac{s^2}{8}\left(\frac{1}{n_1} + \frac{1}{n_{ii}} + \frac{1}{n_{iii}} + \frac{1}{n_{iv}}\right) \tag{10.12}$$

$$= \frac{3s^2}{16},$$

$$V(b) = \frac{s^2}{32}\left(\frac{1}{n_1} + \frac{1}{n_{ii}} + \frac{1}{n_{iii}} + \frac{1}{n_{iv}}\right) \tag{10.13}$$

$$= \frac{3s^2}{64},$$

$$C\{(\bar{y}_T - \bar{y}_S), b\} = \frac{s^2}{16}\left(\frac{1}{n_1} - \frac{1}{n_{ii}} - \frac{1}{n_{iii}} + \frac{1}{n_{iv}}\right) \tag{10.14}$$

$$= -\frac{s^2}{96}.$$

The covariance, equation (10.14), is zero for a symmetrical assay having the same number of subjects in each of the four groups, and the analysis in § 10.3 then applies.

With 7 degrees of freedom, $t = 2 \cdot 365$.   Hence

$$g = \frac{(2 \cdot 365)^2 \times 3 \times 10 \cdot 10}{64 \times (3 \cdot 5000)^2}$$
$$= 0 \cdot 2162,$$

which may be compared with $0 \cdot 1568$ for the analysis in § 10.3. Equation (2.6) gives for the fiducial limits of $(M - \bar{x}_S + \bar{x}_T)$ the values

$$\left[0 \cdot 2381 + \frac{2g}{9} \pm \frac{t}{b} \left\{ s^2 \left(\frac{3}{16} + \frac{0 \cdot 2381}{48} + \frac{3 \times 0 \cdot 2381^2}{64} \right. \right. \right.$$
$$\left. \left. \left. - \frac{5g}{27} \right) \right\}^{\frac{1}{2}} \right] \div (1 - g)$$

$$= \left[0 \cdot 2381 + 0 \cdot 0480 \pm \frac{2 \cdot 365}{3 \cdot 500} \left\{ 10 \cdot 10 \times (0 \cdot 18750 + 0 \cdot 00496 \right. \right.$$
$$\left. \left. + 0 \cdot 00266 - 0 \cdot 04004) \right\}^{\frac{1}{2}} \right] \div 0 \cdot 7838$$

$$= [0 \cdot 2861 \pm 0 \cdot 8457] \div 0 \cdot 7838$$
$$= - 0 \cdot 7140, \; 1 \cdot 4440.$$

Multiplication by $0 \cdot 1505$ converts these to logarithms to base 10, and the potency values are then the antilogarithms multiplied by 22. The result is an estimated potency of $23 \cdot 9$ units per mg., with limits at $17 \cdot 2$ units per mg. and $36 \cdot 3$ units per mg.

The analysis described above is essentially that used by Smith *et al.* (1944). Identical results would be obtained by application of the method of § 4.19 to the intra-rabbit differences. This would require variates x_1, x_2, as in § 4.19 for the preparations and regression and a third variate, x_4, to give the remaining intra-rabbit contrast that is not error, the Days × Parallelism interaction ; thus x_4 would take the values :

	S_1	S_2	T_1	T_2
Day 1	-1	1	1	-1
Day 2	1	-1	-1	1.

Calculation of the multiple regression equation of the eleven differences between days 1 and 2 on x_1, x_2, x_4 gives values for $\frac{1}{2}(\bar{y}_T - \bar{y}_S)$, b, and the Days × Parallelism interaction ; the first two are exactly as obtained in equations (10.12), (10.13), and the third is of no great interest in itself.

The estimate obtained here is almost the same as that in § 10.3. Since the earlier analysis assumed the responses for rabbit VII to be known, its estimate of variance per response was lower than that used here. Had its variance been 10·10 with 8 degrees of freedom, the limits in § 10.3 would have been widened to 17·4 and 33·3 units per mg. The fiducial range calculated in the present section is 20 per cent. wider than the range of these values, although the difference is attributable only to the loss of one subject out of twelve. This loss of 8 per cent. of the information might be expected to increase the fiducial range only by a factor of about $\left(\dfrac{12}{11}\right)^{\frac{1}{2}}$, or by 4·5 per cent; the actual loss incurred in respect of the potency estimate is much greater, because of the manner in which the increase in g and the asymmetry of the design affect M.

CHAPTER 11

MULTIPLE ASSAYS

11.1 The economy of multiple assays

If several test preparations are to be assayed against the same standard preparation, two possible procedures may be considered. Either each test preparation is made the occasion of a separate small assay, or all are included in one *multiple assay*. For example, two or three doses of the standard preparation and of each of three test preparations might be incorporated into a single experiment involving eight or twelve dose levels in all. Naturally, such a multiple assay will be a little more confusing to perform, and the danger of mistakes will be greater than in a simple assay, but, if these difficulties can be overcome, it will have certain advantages. The chief reason for preferring a multiple assay is that it permits a more economical use of subjects. If three test preparations are to be assayed separately against a standard, one-half of the total number of subjects used will be assigned to the standard, and, as has been emphasized in Chapter 3, separate estimates of the regression coefficient will be needed in each assay. In a multiple assay, on the other hand, a more equal division of subjects between all the preparations is possible, and the regression coefficient, now estimated from the combined evidence of all subjects, will be more precisely determined.

The principles of assay design laid down in earlier chapters apply to multiple assays. Contrasts between preparations form a factor in the structure of the design, now having several degrees of freedom instead of only one. Thus the general theory of experimental design for factors at two or more levels may be utilized in order to find the design most suitable for a particular purpose. The statistical analysis introduces no new problems, only additional complexity.

The experimenter may sometimes reject the idea of a multiple assay, because of the impracticability of performing one large experiment ; the nature of his tests may be such that too much labour or space, or more subjects than are available at any one time, would be required for an adequate multiple assay. In these circumstances the advantage may rest with separate assays. Another alternative, however, is that of a series of small multiple assays, whose results will eventually be combined. For example, suppose that three preparations are to be assayed against a standard, and a total of 120 subjects can be spared, although perhaps not all of these are available simultaneously. If separate assays are performed, the best procedure would be to use forty subjects in the assay of the first test preparation, allowing twenty for the standard and twenty for the test preparation. Two further similar assays would be required for the other test preparations. Thus a total of sixty subjects would be assigned to the standard preparation, and only twenty to each of the test preparations. A comprehensive multiple assay might assign thirty subjects to each of the four preparations in a single experiment. Unless the basic variance per response were increased on account of the complexity of the experiment, the precision of the potency estimates would certainly be improved. If a single large experiment were impossible, the alternative of three small multiple assays, each of forty subjects (ten for each preparation) is worth considering. Potency estimates would be calculated separately for each of the three, and eventually combined (by the methods of Chapter 14) to give a single set of estimates based upon all the 120 subjects.

11.2 An assay of two tuberculins

Wadley (1949b) has given data from an assay in which two tuberculins, A and B, were tested against a standard, each being used at three levels of dose. The test subjects were four guinea-pigs ; each had nine points of its skin assigned to applications of the nine doses, the allocation of doses to points being random. After twenty-four hours, the diameter of the irritated area at each spot was recorded as the response (Table 11.1).

The analysis of variance (Table 11.3) for an assay such as this is very similar to that for the 6-point in § 5.1. Indeed, the design is the obvious modification of a randomized block 6-point required in order to include three doses of each of three preparations. The total sum of squares is easily divided into components for guinea-pigs, doses, and error, and the only novelty lies in the subdivision

TABLE 11.1—Responses in a multiple assay of tuberculins

(Diameters of irritated spots, in units of 0·25 mm.)

Guinea-pig no.	Preparation and concentration									Totals
	S			A			B			
	1/2,500	1/500	1/100	1/2,500	1/500	1/100	1/2,500	1/500	1/100	
I	36	52	64	45	40	65	33	44	70	449
II	41	48	62	38	42	65	36	57	63	452
III	44	48	100	45	62	57	33	54	78	521
IV	48	52	59	40	42	70	37	61	70	479
Totals	169	200	285	168	186	257	139	216	281	1,901

of the 8 degrees of freedom between doses. There are now 2 degrees of freedom between preparations. The linear and quadratic components are single degrees of freedom, found in the usual manner from the contrasts ' high dose versus low dose ' and ' high and low doses versus twice middle dose ' totalled over all preparations. The parallelism component, or the difference in regressions for the three preparations, has 2 degrees of freedom, and is most easily obtained as the interaction Preparations × Regression. The component for differences of quadratics is found similarly. The most convenient computing scheme is shown in Table 11.2, where linear and quadratic contrasts are tabulated for each preparation separately as well as for the total. The regression component of the sum of squares is

$$\frac{347^2}{24} = 5,017,$$

and the parallelism component is

$$(116^2 + 89^2 + 142^2 - 8 \times 5,017) \div 8 = 176.$$

The quadratic component and that for differences of quadratics are found in like manner, but with divisors of 72 and 24 respectively.

TABLE 11.2—Dose totals and contrasts for the data of Table 11.1

Preparation	Low	Medium	High	Total	L_1 (= high − low)	L_2 (= low − 2× medium + high)
S	169	200	285	654	116	54
A	168	186	257	611	89	53
B	139	216	281	636	142	− 12
Total	476	602	823	1,901	347	95

Table 11.3 shows no indications of invalidity. The estimation of potency should utilize all available information from the assay, and not (as is suggested by some published analyses) only those portions of it that pertain to the standard and a particular test

TABLE 11.3—Analysis of variance for the data of Table 11.1

Adjustment for mean		100,383	
Nature of variation	d.f.	Sum of squares	Mean square
Preparations	2	78	39
Regression	1	5,017	5,017
Quadratic	1	125	125
Parallelism	2	176	88
Differences of quadratics ...	2	119	60
Doses	8	5,515	
Guinea-pigs	3	371	124
Error	24	1,568	65·33
Total	35	7,454	

preparation. Successive doses differ by a factor of 5, and therefore logarithms to base 5 must be used in order to give a dose metameter that takes values — 1, 0, 1 for the three doses of each preparation. With these units, the average regression coefficient is

$$b = \frac{347}{24}$$
$$= 14\cdot46.$$

Also, for the first test preparation,

$$\bar{y}_A - \bar{y}_S = \frac{611 - 654}{12}$$
$$= -3\cdot583.$$

Hence

$$M = -0\cdot2478.$$

From the usual formula

$$V(b) = \frac{s^2}{24},$$

and s^2 has 24 degrees of freedom, so that

$$g = \frac{(2 \cdot 064)^2 \times 65 \cdot 33}{(14 \cdot 46)^2 \times 24}$$

$$= 0 \cdot 0555.$$

Equation (2.6) then gives for the fiducial limits of M

$$M_L, M_U = -\left[0 \cdot 2478 \pm \frac{2 \cdot 064}{14 \cdot 46} \left\{ \left(0 \cdot 9445 \times \left(\frac{1}{12} + \frac{1}{12} \right) \right. \right. \right.$$
$$\left. \left. \left. + \frac{0 \cdot 2478^2}{24} \right) \times 65 \cdot 33 \right\}^{\frac{1}{2}} \right] \div 0 \cdot 9445$$

$$= -0 \cdot 7509, \; 0 \cdot 2262.$$

Multiplication by $\log_{10} 5$ converts all values of M to common logarithms, whence

$$R = \text{antilog } \bar{1} \cdot 8268 = 0 \cdot 671,$$
$$R_L = \text{antilog } \bar{1} \cdot 4751 = 0 \cdot 299,$$
$$R_U = \text{antilog } 0 \cdot 1581 = 1 \cdot 439.$$

Thus test preparation A is estimated to have a potency $0 \cdot 671$ times that of the standard, with fiducial limits at $0 \cdot 299$ and $1 \cdot 439$. Similar calculations for B give an estimate of potency $0 \cdot 846$ times that of the standard with limits at $0 \cdot 384$ and $1 \cdot 830$.

Some may wonder why the data for A and the standard were not analysed as a 6-point assay, and those for B and the standard as a second assay of the same design. There are a number of objections to this procedure :

(i) Validity tests for either analysis would be less sensitive than those in Table 11.3, because of the fewer degrees of freedom for error ; the analyses would not be completely independent of one another, so that no simple combination of tests would be possible ;

(ii) The regression coefficient in each analysis would be less precisely estimated, having a variance $s^2/16$;

(iii) The quantity g in each analysis would tend to be larger, both because of the greater variance of b and because of the fewer degrees of freedom (15 instead of 24) for t ;

(iv) In consequence of (ii) and (iii), the fiducial range for M would be wider than in the composite analysis ;

(v) Even though in many instances the effects of (i)–(iv) might
be small, the labour of computing two separate analyses
would certainly be greater than is needed for one slightly
more complex analysis.

Wadley (1948) has also mentioned a more complex multiple
assay of tuberculins. Sixteen preparations, each at four levels,
were included, and the sixty-four doses were assigned to sixty-four
sites on each of ten cows. Allowance for differences in responsiveness
between various regions of a cow was made by adoption of a balanced
incomplete block design for the sixteen preparations, the four
doses of a preparation being injected at neighbouring sites. Wadley
states that one such assay showed a 50 per cent. increase in precision
relative to a randomized block design.

11.3   A multiple assay of streptomycin

As a second illustration of the analysis of a multiple assay,
data reported by Brownlee *et al.* (1948) will be used. These relate
to the assay of three preparations of streptomycin against a standard,
by a technique that is a modification of the cylinder-plate method
for penicillin assay. A plate containing 64 cavities in eight rows
of eight was constructed. The cavities were filled with agar and
inoculated with *Bacillus subtilis*. Each cavity received a dose of
streptomycin, for which a response was measured, in the usual
manner, as the diameter of the zone of inhibition of bacterial growth.
The standard preparation, S, was used at two levels, 1 and 10 units
per ml., and the three test preparations, A, B, C, were used at
equivalent levels as calculated from assumed potencies of 24, 360,
and 400 respectively, relative to S. Thus eight doses in all were
included.

Position on the plate was expected to have some effect on
response, and the elimination from the experimental error of the
major variations so caused was secured by arranging the doses in
a Latin square. Moreover, experience of the assay technique had
indicated some danger that the time required for adding the doses
to the plate would influence the responses, so that, irrespective of
their potency, doses applied late would tend to show lower responses
than those applied early. To give the doses in completely random
order was impracticable in an assay design that was intended for
use as a routine, because of the confusion that would be caused

if the operator had to change frequently from one preparation to another. Instead, the effect of order was eliminated by means of a quasi-Latin square (Yates, 1937a). The first thirty-two cells to be filled were four from each of the eight doses, in the following order:

$$S_2, S_1, A_2, A_1, B_2, B_1, C_2, C_1$$

and the remaining thirty-two cells were filled in the reverse order of doses. The mean response to any dose is then freed from the effect of a linear time trend. The thirty-two 'late' filled cells are marked with asterisks in Table 11.4, which table shows the set of 64 responses.

TABLE 11.4—Responses in a multiple assay of three streptomycin preparations

(Diameters of zones of inhibition, expressed for convenience in units of 0·1 mm. minus 100)

A_1^* 9	B_2 44	S_1 11	S_2^* 49	C_1 9	C_2^* 46	B_1^* 11	A_2 52	231
B_2 42	A_1^* 5	C_2^* 40	C_1 7	S_2^* 45	S_1 12	A_2 46	B_1^* 11	208
S_1^* 5	C_2 42	A_1 2	A_2^* 37	B_1 6	B_2^* 45	C_2^* 7	S_2 51	195
A_2 35	B_1^* 3	S_2^* 37	S_1 6	C_2^* 39	C_1 5	B_2 45	A_1^* 9	179
B_1^* 7	A_2 35	C_1 0	C_2^* 36	S_1 6	S_2^* 40	A_1^* 4	B_2 44	172
C_2 32	S_1^* 0	B_2^* 35	B_1 1	A_2^* 35	A_1 1	S_2 42	C_1^* 7	153
C_1^* 0	S_2 36	B_1 2	B_2^* 36	A_1 2	A_2^* 39	S_1^* 6	C_2 41	162
S_2 36	C_1^* 0	C_2^* 35	A_1 2	B_2^* 37	B_1 5	C_2 40	S_1^* 8	163
166	165	162	174	179	193	201	223	1,463

The full set of treatments in this experiment forms a $4 \times 2 \times 2$ factorial scheme, the four preparations in combination with two dose levels and early or late filling. The quasi-Latin square was constructed for this scheme, and the rows and columns were then randomized. Inspection of Table 11.4 shows that columns 1, 2, 7, 8 have S_2, A_2, B_2, C_2 filled early and S_1, A_1, B_1, C_1 filled late ; hence the interaction Order × Regression is confounded with one of the column contrasts. Also, in rows 1, 2, 4, 5, the cells filled early are S_1, A_2, B_2, C_1, and in rows 3, 6, 7, 8, the cells filled early are S_2, A_1, B_1, C_2 ; hence the interaction Order × Regression × $(S - A - B + C)$ is confounded with one of the row contrasts. Since each column (and each row) has eight cells, it contains one-half of the full set of sixteen ' treatments ', and therefore only 1 degree of freedom can be completely confounded with rows (or with columns). Alternatively, 2 degrees of freedom might have been partially confounded with either, but completely confounded contrasts have now been identified and the whole confounding system is known.

Because of the severe restrictions imposed upon it, this design necessarily appears to have a markedly systematic pattern. An alternative procedure would have been to take any 8 × 8 Latin square for the eight doses and impose on it an arbitrary orthogonal partition into two sets of thirty-two cells such that each set consisted of four in each row, four in each column, and four of each dose (Finney, 1945b, 1946c ; orthogonal partitions of 8 × 8 Latin squares have not been investigated, but probably most squares can be so partitioned). The two sets of thirty-two would be used for the early versus late comparison. The structure of this design may be simpler to understand than that based upon the quasi-Latin square, though it is perhaps less elegant in use as it does not permit the isolation of Order × Dose interactions. These interactions, however, ought to be small when the condition of similarity is satisfied and the regression of response on log dose is linear, and little harm should result from leaving them in the error component of the analysis of variance. The quasi-Latin square is a particular instance of the orthogonal partition design, but it has much additional symmetry.

One objection to the design used must be noted. The filling of the thirty-two cells of the early series (and equally, of course, of the late series) ought to be done in random order, whereas in fact it followed a pre-arranged systematic pattern. This pattern secures a balance in order that serves to eliminate any linear time trend from the potency estimate, but it may bias the assessment of error. The contrast between the two sets of thirty-two cells, however, may be expected to isolate a major part of any variation attributable to order, and, if the interactions of the order factor with dose differences have mean squares very similar to that for the residual error, use of the residual error for the calculation of fiducial limits should be fairly safe. This argument has no special reference to multiple assays, but illustrates the remarks in § 4.21 about the occasional need of compromise. If the experimenter contends, as well he may in this type of assay, that an entirely objective and unsystematic order of filling the cells is quite impracticable, the statistician is forced to consent ; both must remember, however, that all conclusions drawn are then subject to assumptions about the unimportance of certain sources of variation. Those to whom these points are new will do well to ignore for the present the order effect, and to concentrate on other aspects of this assay. The effect appears to have been small, and in this instance little difference would have been made to the conclusions had the design been regarded as a simple Latin square.

From Table 11.4, the sums and differences shown in Tables 11.5–11.7 are easily computed. Of these, only Table 11.6 is needed if order is ignored, but all will eventually be wanted for the analysis given here and are therefore conveniently formed at this stage. The analysis of variance when order is ignored is very easily calculated, and appears in Table 11.8. The steps may be summarized as follows (the sets of totals used will be seen immediately in Tables 11.4–11.7) :—

(1) $1,463^2 \div 64 = 33,443 \cdot 27$

(2) $9^2 + 44^2 + 11^2 + \ldots + 40^2 + 8^2 - 33,443 \cdot 27$

(3) $(231^2 + 208^2 + \ldots + 163^2 - 8 \times 33,443 \cdot 27) \div 8$

(4) $(166^2 + 165^2 + \ldots + 223^2 - 8 \times 33,443 \cdot 27) \div 8$

(5) $(54^2 + 336^2 + 34^2 + \ldots + 316^2 - 8 \times 33,443 \cdot 27) \div 8$

(6) $(2) - (3) - (4) - (5)$

(7) $(390^2 + 348^2 + 374^2 + 351^2 - 16 \times 33,443 \cdot 27) \div 16$

(8) $1,125^2 \div 64 = 19,775 \cdot 39$

(9) $(282^2 + 280^2 + 282^2 + 281^2 - 16 \times 19,775 \cdot 39) \div 16$

(10) Check : $(7) + (8) + (9) = (5)$.

As in § 11.2, the sum of squares for parallelism is formed as though it were a sum of squares for the interaction of two factors, preparations and regression, and so is a measure of the extent to which the regression coefficients for the separate preparations differ.

TABLE 11.5—Totals of dose levels and order of filling of cells for the data of Table 11.4

Order of filling	S_1	S_2	A_1	A_2	B_1	B_2	C_1	C_2	Total
Early ...	35	165	7	168	14	175	21	155	740
Late ...	19	171	27	146	32	153	14	161	723
Sum ...	54	336	34	314	46	328	35	316	1,463
Difference	−16	6	20	−22	18	−22	−7	6	−17

TABLE 11.6—Totals of dose levels for the data of Table 11.4, irrespective of order of filling

Level	S	A	B	C	Total
1	54	34	46	35	169
2	336	314	328	316	1,294
Sum	390	348	374	351	1,463
Difference	282	280	282	281	1,125

TABLE 11.7—Differences between late and early filling of cells, totalled over dose levels, for the data of Table 11.4

Level	S	A	B	C	Total
1	− 16	20	18	− 7	15
2	6	− 22	− 22	6	− 32
Sum	− 10	− 2	− 4	− 1	− 17
Difference	22	− 42	− 40	13	− 47

TABLE 11.8—Analysis of variance for the data of Table 11.4, ignoring order of filling of cells

	Nature of variation	d.f.	Sum of squares	Mean square
1	Adjustment for mean		33,443·27	
7	Preparations ...	3	74·29	24·76
8	Regression	1	19,775·39	19,775·39
9	Parallelism	3	0·18	0·06
5	Between doses ...	7	19,849·86	
3	Between rows ...	7	618·86	88·41
4	Between columns ...	7	396·86	56·69
6	Error	42	128·15	3·051
2	Total	63	20,993·73	

If the order factor were absent from the design, validity tests and potency estimates would be based upon Table 11.8. The methods would be essentially the same as are described below after the order analysis has been completed, so that no special account need be given. The calculations for the order of filling and its interactions are most easily made from Table 11.7, which was obtained from Table 11.5 by forming differences, late minus early, instead of sums as in Table 11.6. Calculations analogous to steps (1), (5), (7), (8), (9), (10) enable the sum of squares for Table 11.7 to be partitioned as shown in Table 11.9. But for the confounding, these components would be removed from the sum of squares called 'Error' in Table 11.8. As already noted, however, the contrast representing the interaction Order × Regression is confounded with columns, being identical with the column contrast
$$- 166 - 165 + 162 + 174 + 179 + 193 - 201 - 223 = - 47.$$
The square for this, therefore, has already been extracted and included in the sum of squares for columns. Again, the contrast

Order $\times$ Regression $\times$ $(S - A - B + C)$, for which the numerical value is

$$22 - (-42) - (-40) + 13 = 117,$$

is identical with the row contrast

$$231 + 208 - 195 + 179 + 172 - 153 - 162 - 163 = 117.$$

The square

$$117^2 \div 64 = 213\cdot89$$

has been included in the sum of squares for rows. The unconfounded components may now be inserted into the analysis of variance, which takes the form of Table 11.10.

TABLE 11.9—Partition of the sum of squares for Table 11.7

Nature of variation	d.f.	Sum of squares
Order	1	4·52
Order × Preparations ...	3	3·04
Order × Regression	1	34·52
Order × Parallelism	3	216·54
Total	8	258·62

TABLE 11.10—Complete analysis of variance for the data of Table 11.4

Adjustment for mean		33,443·27	Mean square
Nature of variation	d.f.	Sum of squares	
Preparations	3	74·29	24·76
Regression	1	19,775·39	19,775·39
Parallelism	3	0·18	0·06
Between doses	7	19,849·86	
Between rows	7	618·86	88·41
Between columns	7	396·86	56·69
Order	1	4·52	4·52
Order × Preparations ...	3	3·04	1·01
Order × Parallelism ...	2	2·65	1·32
Error	36	117·94	3·276
Total	63	20,993·73	

From Table 11.10, the following conclusions may be drawn :—

(i) Deviations from parallelism are certainly not significantly greater than may be attributed to random fluctuations. Indeed, the mean square for parallelism is significantly *less* than that for error : the differences between the slopes of regression lines fitted to the preparations separately are less than would be expected on an average. The only explanation that can be suggested for this is some bias in the measurement. As may be seen in Table 11.4, high and low levels of a preparation frequently occurred in adjacent positions in rows. If the person responsible for measuring the zones of inhibition had some preconceived idea of what the mean difference between levels would be, he might subconsciously bias his measurement of the second member of a pair after he had measured the first. A few biases of 0·1 mm. would suffice to produce a markedly subnormal mean square. This possibility cannot easily be tested, as the nature of the quasi-Latin square makes the order of the eight doses in a row semi-systematic, and nothing is known of the order in which the measurements were made. For the sixteen instances in which high and low levels of a preparation were adjacent in rows, the difference between the two was always between 3·1 mm. and 3·9 mm. ; for the other sixteen pairs of doses, it ranged from 2·5 mm. to 4·6 mm. In spite of the unsatisfactory choice of doses of *A* and *C*, the mean square for parallelism gives some assurance that the range of linearity has not been exceeded, but the abnormally low value perhaps gives further reason for preferring a fully randomized Latin square to the quasi-Latin design.

(ii) Differences between preparations are highly significant. The doses chosen for *A* and *C* were clearly based upon over-estimates of the potencies of these preparations. Since no suspicion of invalidity arises, the statistical significance of the preparations component is not of great consequence.

(iii) The very large mean square for regression is satisfactory.

(iv) Order and its interactions appear to be of no importance.

(v) Rows and columns are both highly significant in their effects. Inspection of Table 11.4 suffices to show that zones of inhibition were much smaller in the lower left-hand corner of the plate than elsewhere. Had an arrangement of doses unrestrictedly randomized over the 64 cavities been adopted, its error mean square would presumably have been of the order of

$$3\cdot276 + \tfrac{1}{8}(88\cdot41 - 3\cdot276) + \tfrac{1}{8}(56\cdot69 - 3\cdot276) = 20\cdot60$$

This is six times larger than that in Table 11.10, so that six assays of unrestricted random design would be needed to equal the precision of one of the Latin square type.

In forming the potency estimates and assessing their fiducial limits, simplified formulæ for 4-point assays could be used, but some modifications would be necessary in order to take account of the multiple assay scheme. Whenever an unfamiliar design is encountered, however, the safest procedure is to revert to the basic method of calculation in terms of mean responses and regression coefficients. If an 8×8 Latin square were to be used frequently for the simultaneous assay of three preparations, formulæ analogous to equations (5.17) and (5.21) might profitably be constructed, but in an isolated instance the surest way of avoiding mistakes is to return to first principles.

From the totals of the sixteen responses to each preparation in Table 11.6,

$$\bar{y}_S = 24\cdot375,$$
$$\bar{y}_A = 21\cdot750,$$
$$\bar{y}_B = 23\cdot375,$$
$$\bar{y}_C = 21\cdot938.$$

Also, if the doses be taken to correspond to values of $-1, 1$ on a logarithmic scale, the regression coefficient is

$$b = \frac{\Sigma S_{xy}}{\Sigma S_{xx}}$$
$$= \frac{1,125}{64}$$
$$= 17\cdot578.$$

Hence the three values of M are

$$M_A = \frac{\bar{y}_A - \bar{y}_S}{b}$$
$$= -0.1493,$$
$$M_B = -0.0569,$$
$$M_C = -0.1386.$$

Now the variance per response is the error mean square in Table 11.10 ; hence

$$g = \frac{(2.028)^2 \times 3.276}{(17.578)^2 \times 64}$$
$$= 0.0007,$$

a value so small that it could be ignored. The fiducial limits to the values of M are found to be -0.2234 and -0.0755 for A, -0.1308 and 0.0169 for B, -0.2126 and -0.0755 for C. These are obtained from equation (4.12), with

$$N_S = N_A = N_B = N_C = 16$$

and

$$\Sigma S_{xx} = 64.$$

Multiplication by 0.5 converts to logarithms to base 10, and the antilogarithms must be multiplied by 24, 360, 400 in order to give potencies for A, B, C respectively ; the results are summarized in Table 11.11. Since g is so small, practically the same results would have been obtained from the approximation

$$V(M) = \frac{s^2}{64b^2}(8 + M^2). \tag{11.1}$$

TABLE 11.11—Estimates of potency and fiducial limits for the streptomycin assay in Table 11.4

	Test preparation		
	A	B	C
Estimates of potency (units per ml.)	20·2	337	341
Fiducial limits (units per ml.) ...	18·6–22·0	310–367	313–371
Limits as per cent. of estimate ...	92–109	92–109	92–109

Note that, if separate assays had been used for the three preparations, at the same total cost only ten responses could have been measured for the two preparations in each assay. The approximate variance would then have been

$$V(M) = \frac{s^2}{20b^2}\{4 + (M - \bar{x}_S + \bar{x}_T)^2\}.$$ (11.2)

Comparison of equations (11.1) and (11.2) shows that, if s^2 were the same for both, the use of three separate assays would have increased $V(M)$ by a factor of at least 1·6, and by more than this if $(M - \bar{x}_S + \bar{x}_T)$ were large. This statement, however, over-simplifies the question and may exaggerate the advantage of the multiple assay, as a design with only twenty cells and one test preparation could have a more compact lay-out and might therefore have a smaller s^2.

11.4   Multiple slope ratio assays

The principles illustrated in §§ 11.2 and 11.3 may be applied to the analysis of multiple slope ratio assays. For example, if three test preparations were tested simultaneously, a regression function of the form

$$Y = a + b_S x_S + b_A x_A + b_B x_B + b_C x_C$$ (11.3)

would be estimated, and the ratios of the other three regression coefficients to b_S would be the required estimates of potency. The methods of Chapter 7 may be extended to give validity tests and fiducial limits (Barraclough, 1955; Bliss, 1946b; Clarke, 1952).

11.5   Designs for multiple assays

The number of possible designs for multiple assays is large, and no attempt will be made to discuss and classify them in the same detail as for incomplete block and cross-over designs in Chapters 9 and 10. To those who have understood these earlier chapters, construction of designs for multiple assays should present no special difficulty. Guld et al. (1958) have reported an interesting example.

Equal numbers of doses for all preparations, and regular spacing on the absolute or logarithmic scale are desirable features of these designs. The recommendations on the choice and number of doses made in Chapters 6 and 8 remain applicable. For most purposes, the number of responses measured per dose will be the same for all doses of all preparations ; considerations of symmetry make this desirable, although from the point of view of precision alone this arrangement is not ideal. The advantage of assigning more subjects to the standard than to each of the test preparations is demonstrated in § 11.6, but this modification is rarely convenient in designs other than the completely randomized (like the assay in § 5.1) and the randomized block types.

When the number of responses that can be measured in one block of subjects is as large as the total number of doses, a randomized block design should be used. The assay in § 11.2 was an instance of this, the block there consisting of nine points on one guinea-pig. When the number of responses per block is smaller than the total number of doses, the usual problems of incomplete blocks, balanced or confounded, arise. If equal precision on all dose contrasts is desired, a balanced incomplete block design must generally be chosen, and those in § 9.7 may be applied with appropriate change of nomenclature. For example, if three test preparations are to be assayed against a standard, with two doses of each, the design in Table 9.9 can be used to give an arrangement in blocks of four, the symbols for the eight doses in that table being replaced by those for the two levels of four preparations. The assay of tuberculins in § 11.2 could have been arranged for an experiment with only four tests per guinea-pig by use of the design in Table 9.12. Designs for larger total numbers of doses may be taken from

TABLE 11.12—Design for a multiple assay of three test preparations at two dose levels in blocks of four

Preparations and regression contrasts unconfounded

Block no.	S_1	S_2	A_1	A_2	B_1	B_2	C_1	C_2
I	×		×			×		×
II	×			×	×			×
III	×			×		×	×	
IV		×	×		×			×
V		×	×			×	×	
VI		×		×	×		×	

Cochran and Cox (1957 ; Tables 9.5, 11.3). If the experimenter wishes to increase the precision of estimation of the differences between preparations and the regression coefficient, at the expense of sensitivity in the validity tests, he may use a suitably confounded arrangement analogous to those in § 9.9. Tables 11.12 and 11.13 are examples for three test preparations at two levels in blocks of four and for two test preparations at three levels in blocks of three respectively. The design for the streptomycin assay in § 11.3 is related to that in Table 11.12, and Brownlee, Loraine, and Stephens (1949) have shown how a similar quasi-Latin square may be constructed for the simultaneous assay of seven test preparations against a standard.

TABLE 11.13—Design for a multiple assay of two test preparations at three dose levels in blocks of three

Preparations and regression contrasts unconfounded

Block no.	S_1	S_2	S_3	A_1	A_2	A_3	B_1	B_2	B_3
I	×				×				×
II	×					×		×	
III		×		×					×
IV		×				×	×		
V			×	×				×	
VI			×		×		×		

Cross-over designs may be constructed from these designs in the manner of those in § 10.5. For example, a cross-over design for three responses per subject and using eighteen subjects may easily be constructed from Table 11.13.

11.6 The distribution of responses between preparations

The recommendations on design in § 11.5 have been made with the assumption that the number of responses measured would be the same for every preparation, as indeed was true for the assays discussed in §§ 11.2 and 11.3. For a complicated design, such as that of the streptomycin assay, considerations of symmetry almost force this equality ; for simpler designs, the possibility of gaining in efficiency by unequal distribution must be borne in mind. The situation will be made clear by discussion of the optimal allocation of a fixed total number of subjects, N, in an assay for which only one response per subject can be measured.

Suppose that c preparations are to be assayed against the standard in a parallel line assay. Unless greater precision is desired for some test preparations than for others, the same number of subjects, N_T, will be assigned to each, but this need not be equal to N_S, the number assigned to the standard preparation. Whatever these numbers are,

$$N_S + cN_T = N. \tag{11.4}$$

For any one test preparation, provided that the doses have been well chosen and that g is small, $V(M)$ is approximately proportional to

$$\left(\frac{1}{N_S} + \frac{1}{N_T}\right).$$

Hence, for a fixed value of N, the variance will be a minimum if

$$N_S = c^{\frac{1}{2}} N_T \tag{11.5}$$

(Fieller, 1947) ; the subjects should therefore be distributed as

$$\left. \begin{aligned} N_S &= \frac{N}{1 + c^{\frac{1}{2}}}, \\ N_T &= \frac{N}{c^{\frac{1}{2}} + c}. \end{aligned} \right\} \tag{11.6}$$

The alternative of complete symmetry has

$$N_S = N_T = \frac{N}{1 + c}. \tag{11.7}$$

The distribution now recommended may be seen to reduce the value of $\left(\dfrac{1}{N_S} + \dfrac{1}{N_T}\right)$ by a factor

$$\frac{(1 + c^{\frac{1}{2}})^2}{2(1 + c)};$$

the efficiency of the asymmetrical distribution relative to the symmetrical is therefore*

$$\text{Eff.} = \frac{2(1+c)}{(1+c^{\frac{1}{2}})^2}.$$ (11.10)

When the choice of doses has been less successful, so that $(M - \bar{x}_S + \bar{x}_T)$ is large, $\left(\dfrac{1}{N_S} + \dfrac{1}{N_T}\right)$ plays a less important role in determining the precision or the reliability of M, and the gain from allocating subjects in accordance with equation (11.6) is less. A complete discussion analogous to that in Chapter 6 could be given, but does not seem of great interest.

TABLE 11.14—Precision of a multiple parallel line assay with optimal distribution of subjects, relative to symmetrical distribution

No. of test preparations (c)	% precision	No. of test preparations (c)	% precision
1	100	10	127
2	103	20	140
3	107	30	148
4	111	40	153
5	115	50	157
6	118	60	159
8	123	80	164
10	127	100	167

* If half the subjects were assigned to the standard and the remainder divided equally between the test preparations, so that

$$\left. \begin{array}{l} N_S = N/2, \\ N_T = N/2c, \end{array} \right\}$$ (11.8)

$V(M)$ would be the same as for the distribution in equation (11.7). This might at first suggest that c separate assays would be as good as a multiple assay with a symmetrical distribution of subjects. In reality, the multiple assay is better because all subjects that receive the standard preparation contribute to the one value of $\bar{y}_S$; the efficiency of the separate assays relative to the symmetrical multiple assays is only

$$\text{Eff.} = \frac{1+c}{2c},$$ (11.9)

an expression which is little larger than 0·5 when c is moderately large. Moreover, in the multiple assay, all subjects are used in the determination of b.

Table 11.14 shows some values of the efficiency function, equation (11.10). Unless c is large, the gain is small, but even the 11 per cent. gain for an assay of four test preparations, when interpreted as a 9 per cent. saving of subjects for a specified precision, may be of economic importance, especially if large numbers of routine assays are affected. The very large values of c are scarcely of any practical interest at present, but some assay techniques might one day require them. The exact values of N_S, N_T given by equations (11.6) are often inconvenient, and indeed are seldom integers, but little will be lost by using the nearest convenient integers. For example, for $c = 3$, 4, 5, or 6, the rule of using $N_S = 2N_T$ will be good enough: it gives efficiencies of 107 per cent., 111 per cent., 114 per cent., and 117 per cent. instead of those shown in Table 11.14.

If no block constraints are to be incorporated into the design, the rule expressed by equations (11.6) is very easily applied. Doses are chosen in the usual manner, and each dose of the standard preparation has its number of subjects increased in the same proportion relative to the test preparations. For more complicated designs, perhaps the easiest method of construction is to regard the standard preparation as subdivided into two or more identical treatments. Thus, for a multiple assay of five test preparations, a fully symmetrical design for seven preparations might be formed and the standard preparation included twice ; extra degrees of freedom for error would arise from this duplication of one treatment, but these might be neglected if calculation of the appropriate sum of squares proved awkward.

The analogous semi-symmetrical slope ratio designs would be $(ck + 1)$-point with equal numbers of subjects at each of k regularly spaced doses of every preparation. Discussion of the optimal distribution of a fixed total number of subjects is more difficult, because the variance formulæ are more complex. However, if N_0, N_S, N_T are the numbers of subjects assigned to the blanks, to the standard preparation, and to each test preparation respectively, so that

$$N_0 + N_S + cN_T = N, \qquad (11.11)$$

the variances of b_S and of any b_T will be approximately proportional to $1/N_S$ and $1/N_T$. Under good conditions, for which g is small and h nearly unity, this means that the variance of R will be approximately proportional to

$$\left(\frac{1}{N_S} + \frac{1}{N_T} \right).$$

If N_0 were held fixed, the optimal distribution would again be given by

$$N_S = c^{\frac{1}{2}} N_T.$$

The argument of Chapter 8 showed that there was no merit in making N_0 large, and a reasonable rule would seem to be to take it as equal to the number of subjects on any one dose of a test preparation. Thus the distribution

$$
\begin{aligned}
N_0 &= \frac{N}{1 + k\left(c^{\frac{1}{2}} + c\right)}, \\[2mm]
N_S &= \frac{Nkc^{\frac{1}{2}}}{1 + k\left(c^{\frac{1}{2}} + c\right)}, \\[2mm]
N_T &= \frac{Nk}{1 + k\left(c^{\frac{1}{2}} + c\right)},
\end{aligned}
\left.\rule{0pt}{60pt}\right\} \quad (11.12)
$$

may be expected to be somewhere near the best possible ; if k were large, it would be practically the same as that given by equations (11.6), but for the moderate values of k usually required the difference may be important. Of course, strict adherence to these formulæ is not essential. For $c = 2$, a fully symmetrical design will be almost as good as that recommended here ; for $c = 3, 4, 5,$ or 6, the approximations

$$
\begin{aligned}
N_0 &= \frac{N}{1 + k\left(c + 2\right)}, \\[2mm]
N_S &= \frac{2Nk}{1 + k\left(c + 2\right)}, \\[2mm]
N_T &= \frac{Nk}{1 + k\left(c + 2\right)},
\end{aligned}
\left.\rule{0pt}{60pt}\right\} \quad (11.13)
$$

will be very good.

CHAPTER 12

THE USE OF CONCOMITANT INFORMATION

12.1 The combination of measurements

The discussion of assays based upon quantitative responses has so far assumed that the ' response ' to each application of a dose to a subject is a quantity uniquely defined for the experimenter ; it may be a single measurement, such as uterine weight, or it may be a compound of two or more measurements, such as a percentage reduction in blood sugar. In §§ 6.11, 8.6 the problem of choosing between alternative measures of response and the possibility of combining measurements of different kinds into a single metameter were mentioned ; this chapter and Chapter 13 are concerned with how such a composite metameter may best be constructed from measurements of two or more characteristics of the subjects.

Two distinct situations arise. In the *concomitant problem,* only one measurement that can in the ordinary sense be regarded as a response to the dose is available, but others may be correlated with it. For example, in the rabbit method for insulin assay, the initial blood sugar level cannot be affected by the dose of insulin that is to be given : any association between initial blood sugar and dose either is due to chance or is a consequence of faulty randomization, and the latter explanation ought to be excluded by proper precautions in the planning of the experiment. The final blood sugar level will be affected by the dose of insulin, and may also be correlated with the initial value. The experimenter is not compelled to combine the two by using the percentage change in blood sugar as his metameter, although this is the usual practice. He would be quite in order to use the final value itself, or any function of the two, provided that the validity conditions are satisfied (*cf.* Chapter 15), and he will naturally wish to choose the function that will give him the most reliable estimate of ρ. Again, the response measured may be the body weight, or the weight of a certain organ of the subject, at the end of the experiment, and records of initial body weight may also have been taken. The assumption is often made that the increase in body weight, or the weight of the organ per unit initial body weight, is the ideal metameter, yet in fact this may be no better (it can be even worse) in precision than the unadjusted final weight.

In the *discriminant problem*, on the other hand, there exist records of several measurements made after each application of a dose to a subject, all of which could be affected by that dose. For example, in the assay of testosterone propionate for which data were given in Table 5.1, the response used was the comb growth of capons as represented by (length + height) ; if one of these measurements were more sensitive to dose changes than the other, a compound of the two that gave greater emphasis to the more sensitive would be a better metameter than the sum. When measurements in different units, such as a weight and a length, have been made, there is no obvious method of combining them, and some rule for choosing a metameter is needed.

Arbitrary compounds of the available measurements have often been used as response metameters ; these are usually simple in type, and examples have been given in the two preceding paragraphs. Provided that the usual validity conditions are satisfied, this is perfectly legitimate, but will not lead to the most precise estimates. In the absence of any theoretical reasons for the choice of a particular function, the data themselves should be allowed to indicate the best metameter. If a series of similar assays all point to practically the same metameter, a reasonable approximation for the future may be provided by an average form of the function ; this course was adopted by Fieller (1940 ; *cf.* § 10.3) in a series of insulin assays. Until evidence of this constancy of form of the optimal metameter accumulates, however, the wisest policy is to let each assay determine its own. The statistical techniques appropriate to the two problems are those of covariance analysis and discriminant analysis. Since these are explained in standard text books (Fisher, 1958 ; Mather, 1946), the emphasis here will be placed on the special points arising when they are used in the analysis of assay data. This chapter will be concerned only with the concomitant problem ; discriminants will be discussed in Chapter 13. For neither technique can a choice be made from all possible functions of the measurements, and some restriction to a class of functions must be accepted. In practice, the best linear function is usually good enough ; selection from a larger class would be possible, at the expense of much heavier computations, but is seldom worth while. The phrase ' linear function ' here may be regarded as including linear functions of the logarithms of the original measurements, for situations in which these seem more suitable.

12.2   An assay of prolactin

An assay of prolactin (Finney, 1947e) provides a simple example of the need for taking account of variation in a concomitant measurement not itself responding to the stimulus. The response in this assay was the crop-gland weight of a pigeon injected with one of the six doses tested. A 6-point design was used, with four pigeons at each dose ; seven of the birds were female, the remainder male. The assay was performed by the Research Division of Glaxo Laboratories, Ltd., and the data were originally made available to the author through the kindness of Mr. A. L. Bacharach. Mr. Bacharach described the experimental procedure as follows : ' Suitable doses of the sample to be assayed and of the standard preparation are injected into groups of pigeons, as uniform as possible in respect of weight, age, and general appearance, and preferably of an inbred or " pure " line, the doses being given on six successive days by subcutaneous injection. The resultant enlargement of the crop-gland is established for each animal separately, after it has been killed on the seventh day of the test, by weighing the gland emptied of " pigeon milk ", cleaned of adventitious tissue, and preserved in 70 per cent. ethanol for 24 hours. Except in minor details, the test follows the well-known procedure originally laid down by Riddell and described in more detail by Folley, Turner and others.' The weight of each pigeon at the beginning of the assay was also recorded ; the twenty-four values of body weight (x_1) and crop-gland weight (y) are shown in Table 12.1.

If the crop-gland weights were the only data, analysis would proceed as in § 5.1 or § 5.4. Details need not be given here, though the analysis of variance will appear incidentally in § 12.4. The result is an estimated potency of 6·80 i.u. per mg. for the test preparation, with fiducial limits at 2·36 i.u. per mg. and 13·3 i.u. per mg. In the analysis leading to these values, any sex difference

TABLE 12.1—Body weights and crop-gland weights of pigeons in a prolactin assay

(a) Initial body weights, x_1 (in units of 10 g.)

Dose of standard preparation (i.u.)			Dose of test preparation (mg.)		
1·25	2·50	5·00	0·125	0·250	0·500
49*	49	49	51*	48	45*
53	53	53	51	51	52
44	46*	41*	50	48*	50
49	51*	43	52	50	53
195	199	186	204	197	200

(b) Final crop-gland weights, y (in units of 0·1 g.)

Dose of standard preparation (i.u.)			Dose of test preparation (mg.)		
1·25	2·50	5·00	0·125	0·250	0·500
38*	53	85	28*	48	60*
39	102	144	65	47	130
48	81*	54*	35	54*	83
62	75*	85	36	74	60
187	311	368	164	223	333

Pigeons marked * were female, the others male.

in response has been ignored ; this will be considered further in § 12.4.

The analysis is open to the criticism that the variance of the response increases as the level of response increases. Table 12.2 shows separate estimates of variance for each dose group, each with only 3 degrees of freedom. A correlation of s^2 with $\bar{y}$ is evident ; possibly, therefore, the analysis ought to be modified in order to take account of heteroscedasticity. This matter is further discussed in Chapter 15, and in § 15.6 the conclusion is reached that the estimate of potency in the prolactin assay is little affected by the departure from a strictly homoscedastic regression. Here the usual form of analysis is retained without further discussion, in order to avoid complication of a typical covariance problem by irrelevant issues.

TABLE 12.2—Evidence for the correlation of variance with response for the data of Table 12.1

Dose	S_1	S_2	S_3	T_1	T_2	T_3
Mean response ($\bar{y}$)	47	78	92	41	56	83
Variance (s^2) ...	124	406	1,415	269	158	1,089

12.3 Adjustment by proportionality

On inspection of Table 12.1, a positive correlation of x_1 (initial body weight) and y (final crop-gland weight) within dose groups may be seen. How can this be used for improving the precision of estimation of potency ? A common practice amongst pharmacologists (cf. § 4.13) is to express the weight of the organ used for the assay as a proportion of the body weight, and to use this proportion as a response metameter in place of the absolute weight. To express the gland weights as proportions of final, rather than initial, body weights, may seem more logical, but the sensitivity of the new response metameter to changes in dose might then be reduced if body weight were itself affected by the substance under assay. In this example, the final body weights were also recorded and showed no appreciable effect of prolactin dosage ; nevertheless, the general practice of using initial weights, which necessarily cannot have been influenced by subsequent treatment (assuming that pigeons were allocated to doses by an unbiased randomization procedure), is to be preferred. For arithmetical convenience, the proportions may be calculated to show y as a percentage of x_1 ; the response metameters so obtained are given in Table 12.3.

TABLE 12.3—**Proportional crop-gland weights**

(Calculated as $100y/x_1$)

Dose of standard preparation (i.u.)			Dose of test preparation (mg.)		
1·25	2·50	5·00	0·125	0·250	0·500
78	108	173	55	100	133
74	192	272	127	92	250
109	176	132	70	112	166
127	147	198	69	148	113
388	623	775	321	452	662

The figures in Table 12.3 may be analysed exactly as were those for y in Table 12.1. Again assay validity is not in doubt, except for some indication of heteroscedasticity. Analysis as in § 12.2 gives 6·40 i.u. per mg. as the estimate of potency, with fiducial limits at 2·78 i.u. per mg. and 11·2 i.u. per mg.

12.4 Adjustment by covariance analysis

The adjustment of responses by expressing them as proportions of the concomitant variate may often be very effective in improving the precision of an assay. It is ideal, however, only if the dependence of the response on the concomitant is one of directly proportional variation. If the relationship approximates to proportionality, the effect of the adjustment will still be good, a fact which probably explains its frequent successful employment. Moreover, in an assay such as that in Table 12.1, it might in part adjust for sex differences also, at least in so far as any greater responsiveness of males was due to their generally greater body weights. Nevertheless, it could reduce, rather than increase the precision, even though there was a marked correlation between the response and the concomitant variate ; an obvious example is that of a negative correlation between response and concomitant. A further disadvantage of the method is that its application is restricted to a single concomitant variate, though assays may occur in which simultaneous adjustment for two or more concomitants is desirable.

Bliss and Marks (1939a, especially pp. 97–100) have pointed out that often no sound reason for assuming proportionality exists, and have stated the arguments in favour of a method of adjustment derived by covariance analysis from the internal evidence of the data. They described a system of calculation for use when the response is linearly related to the logarithm of the dose, and illustrated this by numerical results for an insulin assay using two doses of a standard and two of a test preparation ; the percentage fall in blood sugar of injected rabbits was adjusted for inequalities in the initial blood sugar. In a later paper, Bliss (1940a) discussed a similar analysis for an assay of vitamin D based on the ash content of the femur of rats, and showed how allowance could be made for inequalities in the weight of organic matter in the bones, a quantity unaffected by vitamin D. Bliss and Rose (1940) gave examples of assays for parathyroid extracts in which the serum calcium of dogs was adjusted for inequalities in initial body weight ; these are chiefly of interest because incomplete block designs were used. Fieller et al. (1939b) and Fieller (1940), as part of a very full account of insulin assays using cross-over designs, also discussed the adjustment of percentage fall in blood sugar by means of a covariance analysis on initial blood sugar. They estimated a single regression coefficient of response on concomitant from the combined evidence of many assays, and used this in adjusting the response for each assay. If the true regression coefficient does not vary from one assay to another, this adjustment will be more precise than any based on a single assay, and the complications introduced into the assessment of errors and fiducial limits will be less serious.

Provided that a proper randomization has been made, differences between dose groups in respect of a concomitant variate such as initial body weight must be accidental, yet they may indirectly affect the estimation of the dose-response relationship. For example, in Table 12.1, the pigeons receiving the lowest dose of the test preparation were heavy, and the crop-gland weights for this group are probably higher than they would have been if birds of average body weight had been used. The error regression coefficient of y on x_1 may be estimated with the help of an analysis of covariance : the total sum of squares for x_1, $S_{x_1 x_1}$, and the sum of products, $S_{x_1 y}$, may be subdivided in the same manner as was S_{yy} for the analysis mentioned in § 12.2. The ratio of the components of $S_{x_1 y}$ and $S_{x_1 x_1}$ in the error line of the analysis is the required regression coefficient (*cf.* § 2.12) ; it is an estimate of the effect of a change of one unit in x_1 on y, and may be used to adjust each value of y to what would have been expected had x_1 been constant. The quantities $(\bar{y}_T - \bar{y}_S)$ and b may now be re-formed and M re-calculated.

Two alternative procedures may be considered. Though theoretically x_1 is independent of the dose metameter, some small correlation (positive or negative) will generally be found in the short series of observations that constitutes one experiment. The multiple regression equations of y on x_1 and x for the two preparations might therefore be formed as the first stage of the calculations ; insertion of the overall mean value of x_1 would give the regression equations of y on x, subject to the constraint of equal values of x_1, and M would be formed in the usual manner. Alternatively, since theory requires the true regression coefficient of x_1 on x to be zero, a test of significance of the experimental value may be used as an additional check on statistical validity : a significant difference from zero would indicate faulty randomization.* In good assay work, the randomization ought to be satisfactory, and values of y would then be adjusted for their regression on x_1 subject to the condition of a zero regression of x_1 on x.

The first procedure, which was used in an earlier publication (Finney, 1947*e*), may seem to have some advantages, in that it does not invoke the use of the theoretical independence of x_1 and x. Validity tests for parallelism and linearity then require laborious multiple regression calculations. On the other hand, a zero correlation of x_1 and x is demanded by the theory of the assay just as is linearity of the metametric dose-response relationship, and, provided that the appropriate validity test is applied, there seems to be no objection to employing the zero value. This leads to the second procedure, which is essentially that adopted by Bliss and others and for which the validity tests are more rapidly computed. The full calculations for the second procedure will now be illustrated by the prolactin data in Table 12.1.

---

* A covariance analysis would still remove from the apparent relationship of y to x any spurious contribution due to a linear regression of x_1 on x, but it would be unwise to trust the assay if any complications from non-linearity of this regression were suspected.

The possibility that the sex of a pigeon influences its response may be simultaneously considered, by introducing a second concomitant variate, x_2, defined to have the value 0 for a male, 1 for a female. As will be shown later, in the prolactin assay the sex effect is negligible after allowance has been made for body weight ; the more elaborate calculations are presented here, however, because they are of the same kind as would be required if two quantitative concomitant variates had to be used. The generalization to a larger number of concomitants should be obvious.

Application of the orthogonal coefficients in Table 5.3 to the dose totals gives the following values for the contrasts :

	x_1	x_2	y
$L_p =$	21	-1	-146
$L_1 =$	-13	0	350
$L_1' =$	5	0	-12
$L_2 =$	-7	-2	-16
$L_2' =$	27	2	118

The analysis of covariance in Table 12.4 is easily completed ; the calculations follow exactly the pattern of an analysis of variance for y, except that each column is based upon squares or products of the appropriate variates.

The last column of Table 12.4 is the analysis of variance for y, and from it the statements on potency in § 12.2 may be derived. Clearly it shows no evidence of invalidity. The error mean square for x_1 is $205 \cdot 25/18$, or $11 \cdot 40$: none of the dose contrasts for this variate is large enough to cause any worry that the assignment of birds to doses may have been anything but random. The justification for a similar test on x_2 is questionable, because a variate that takes only the values 0, 1 can scarcely be regarded as normally distributed, but, since the mean squares for the dose contrasts are all substantially less than the error mean square, there can scarcely be any evidence of non-random assignment of the sexes to the doses. An exact test, if required, would have to be based upon a contingency table analysis for males and females (Cochran, 1950b).

The error regression coefficients of y on x_1, x_2 are the solutions of

$$205 \cdot 25 b_{1.2} - 13 \cdot 99 b_{2.1} = 749 \cdot 9,$$
$$-13 \cdot 99 b_{1.2} + 4 \cdot 76 b_{2.1} = -84 \cdot 3,$$

TABLE 12.4—Analysis of variance and covariance for the data of Table 12.1

Nature of variation	d.f.	$S_{x_1 x_1}$	$S_{x_1 x_2}$	$S_{x_2 x_2}$	$S_{x_1 y}$	$S_{x_2 y}$	S_{yy}
Adjustments for means		58,115·04	344·46	2·04	78,044·4	462·6	104,808
Preparations	1	18·38	−0·88	0·04	−127·8	6·1	888
Regression	1	10·56	0·00	0·00	−284·4	0·0	7,656
Parallelism	1	1·56	0·00	0·00	− 3·8	0·0	9
Quadratic	1	1·02	0·29	0·08	2·3	0·7	5
Difference of quadratics ...	1	15·19	1·12	0·08	66·4	4·9	290
Between doses	5	46·71	0·53	0·20	−347·3	11·7	8,848
Error	18	205·25	−13·99	4·76	749·9	−84·3	10,382
Total	23	251·96	−13·46	4·96	402·6	−72·6	19,230

and are therefore

$$b_{1.2} = \quad 3 \cdot 0594,$$

$$b_{2.1} = -\ 8 \cdot 718.$$

These account for a portion

$$749 \cdot 9 b_{1.2} - 84 \cdot 3 b_{2.1} = \quad 3,029$$

of the error sum of squares for y.   A test of the significance of
the sex effect may be made by finding also the reduction in the
sum of squares attributable to a regression on x_1 alone (*cf.* Table
2.5).   Table 12.5 makes clear that, though the regression on x_1
is significant, nothing is gained by the inclusion of x_2: allowance
for differences in body weight also takes account of the effect of
sex on response.

TABLE 12.5—Error regression analysis for Table 12.4

Nature of variation	d.f.	Sum of squares	Mean square
Regression on x_1 alone ...	1	2,740	
Additional for x_2	1	289	289
Regression on x_1, x_2 ...	2	3,029	
Residual	16	7,353	459·6
Total	18	10,382	

If sex is ignored, the regression coefficient on x_1 may be
re-estimated as

$$b_1 = \frac{749 \cdot 9}{205 \cdot 25}$$

$$= 3 \cdot 654.$$

The response for each bird will therefore be taken as the crop-gland
weight reduced by 3·654 times the deviation of its body weight from
the general mean body weight (in the units of Table 12.1).   Comparisons between these adjusted values, y', are estimated to be free
from effects of inequalities in initial body weight.   In practice, the

adjustments will be made directly to totals or to means, but consideration of individual subjects assists the understanding of the process. The residual variance is now

$$s^2 = \frac{10,382 - 2,740}{17}$$

$$= 449 \cdot 5$$

with 17 degrees of freedom, and, as in equation (2.33),

$$V(b) = \frac{s^2}{205 \cdot 25} .$$

Since the analysis of y alone showed no evidence of invalidity, and the reduction in residual variance effected by the covariance is not very great, examination of the values of y' is not likely to disclose invalidity. The tests may be made by the general method of testing the significance of treatment contrasts in an analysis of covariance, such as is described in standard text-books. That for a test of parallelism is illustrated in Table 12.6. The parallelism and error components are taken from the $S_{x_1x_1}$, S_{x_1y}, and S_{yy} columns in Table 12.4, and added. Adjusted sums of squares for 'error' and 'parallelism + error' are obtained by subtracting a component with one degree of freedom, calculated as $S^2_{x_1y}/S_{x_1x_1}$, from S_{yy} in each line ; the adjusted square for parallelism is the difference of these two. A variance ratio test for significance follows. As was expected, no indication of non-parallelism is found. The same test could be made by finding the variance of the adjusted contrast for parallelism

$$L_1'(y) - b_1 L_1'(x_1)$$

TABLE 12.6—Parallelism test for adjusted responses in the prolactin assay

Nature of variation	d.f.	$S_{y'y'}$		Mean square
Parallelism ...	1		57	57
Error	17	$10,382 - 2,740 = 7,642$		449·5
Parallelism + Error	18	$10,391 - 2,692 = 7,699$		

(where the symbol $L_1'(y)$ represents the L_1' contrast calculated from the y data) in a manner similar to that used below for L_p and L_1, and examining the significance of the deviation of this contrast from zero. The method based on the analysis of variance is often more convenient, and has the advantage of being applicable to a group of degrees of freedom to be tested together (as in the linearity test in § 4.6 or in a multiple assay).

The adjusted values of the difference in mean responses and the regression coefficient on dose are easily written down, being the same functions of y' as are the unadjusted values of y. Thus

$$\bar{y}_T' - \bar{y}_S' = \frac{L_p(y')}{12}$$

$$= \frac{L_p(y) - b_1 L_p(x_1)}{12} \qquad (12.1)$$

$$= (-146 - 3 \cdot 654 \times 21) \div 12$$

$$= -18 \cdot 561$$

and

$$b' = \frac{L_1(y')}{16}$$

$$= \frac{L_1(y) - b_1 L_1(x_1)}{16} \qquad (12.2)$$

$$= 24 \cdot 844.$$

Hence

$$M' = -\frac{18 \cdot 561}{24 \cdot 844}$$

$$= -0 \cdot 7471.$$

Now, from equation (12.1), since $L_p(y)$ and b_1 are orhtogonal contrasts in y,

$$V(\bar{y}_T' - \bar{y}_S') = s^2 \left[\frac{1}{12} + \frac{1}{12} + \left(\frac{21}{12} \right)^2 \cdot \frac{1}{205 \cdot 25} \right]$$

$$= 0 \cdot 18159 s^2.$$

Similarly, from equation (12.2),

$$V(b') = s^2 \left[\frac{1}{16} + \left(\frac{-13}{16} \right)^2 \cdot \frac{1}{205 \cdot 25} \right]$$

$$= 0 \cdot 06572 s^2.$$

The adjusted values, $(\bar{y}_T' - \bar{y}_S')$ and b', both involve b_1, and are therefore not orthogonal ; their covariance is

$$C\{(\bar{y}_T' - \bar{y}_S'), b'\} = s^2 \left(\frac{21}{12}\right)\left(\frac{-13}{16}\right) \cdot \frac{1}{205 \cdot 25}$$
$$= - \, 0 \cdot 00693 s^2.$$

The value of t for 17 degrees of freedom is $2 \cdot 110$, and therefore

$$g = \frac{(2 \cdot 110)^2 \times 0 \cdot 06572 \times 449 \cdot 5}{(24 \cdot 844)^2}$$
$$= 0 \cdot 2131.$$

Application of Fieller's theorem, equation (2.6), then gives the fiducial limits

$$M_L', M_U' = \left[- \, 0 \cdot 7471 + \frac{0 \cdot 2131 \times 0 \cdot 00693}{0 \cdot 06572} \right.$$
$$\pm \frac{2 \cdot 110}{24 \cdot 844} \Big\{ 449 \cdot 5 \times (0 \cdot 18159 - 2 \times 0 \cdot 7471 \times 0 \cdot 00693$$
$$\left. + \, 0 \cdot 7471^2 \times 0 \cdot 06572 - 0 \cdot 2131 \times 0 \cdot 18086) \Big\}^{\frac{1}{2}} \right] \div 0 \cdot 7869$$
$$= [- \, 0 \cdot 7246 \pm 0 \cdot 7411] \div 0 \cdot 7869$$
$$= - \, 1 \cdot 8626, \; 0 \cdot 0210.$$

Reference to Table 12.1 shows that all M values must be multiplied by $\log_{10} 2$ in order to convert them to logarithms to base 10, and therefore

$$R = 10 \text{ antilog } \bar{1} \cdot 7751 = \;\; 5 \cdot 96,$$
$$R_L = 10 \text{ antilog } \bar{1} \cdot 4393 = \;\; 2 \cdot 75,$$
$$R_U = 10 \text{ antilog } 0 \cdot 0063 = 10 \cdot 1.$$

The estimate now reached is that the test preparation of prolactin contains $5 \cdot 96$ i.u. per mg., with fiducial limits at $2 \cdot 75$ i.u. per mg. and $10 \cdot 1$ i.u. per mg.

The reader unfamiliar with the analysis of covariance may wonder at the complexity of the calculations for validity tests and estimation based on y' ; he may think that a simpler procedure would be to construct the twenty-four adjusted responses and to analyse these in a straightforward manner as for the unadjusted responses in § 12.2. The objection to this is the occurrence of b_1 in each value of y', and the complications shown here are all necessary if proper allowance is to be made for the correlations between responses so introduced. If b_1 were determined very precisely, the simpler analysis would be sufficiently exact, but here it could scarcely be trusted.

TABLE 12.7—Comparison of estimates and fiducial limits in the prolactin assay

		No adjustment	Pro-portionality	Covariance
Estimated potency of test preparation (i.u. per mg.)		6·80	6·40	5·96
5%	g	0·3326	0·2387	0·2131
	limits (i.u. per mg.)	2·36–13·3	2·78–11·2	2·75–10·1
	limits as per cent. of estimate	35–196	43–175	46–169
1%	g	0·6240	0·4479	0·4020
	limits (i.u. per mg.)	0·677–19·0	1·41–14·1	1·54–12·7
	limits as per cent. of estimate	10–279	22–220	26–213

Table 12.7 summarizes the estimates obtained by the three methods of analysis. In order to add to the interest of the comparisons, calculations have also been made for the 1 per cent. limits. Both the proportionality and the covariance adjustments are considerable improvements on the unadjusted analysis, and proportionality has proved almost as good as covariance. The slight advantage for covariance is primarily due to the lower values of g that it has given. The present analyses, taken in conjunction with those of Bliss (1940a) for other data, suggest that the gain in precision is often less than might be expected merely from consideration of the reduction in s^2 due to allowance for the concomitant variate. Even though the regression on the concomitant variate is significant, the benefit of making allowance for it may be nullified by low precision in the estimation of the adjustment, and by the fact that the regression coefficient of response on dose chances to be lower than the regression coefficient when the concomitant

variate is ignored. In such circumstances, no arbitrary adjustment, by proportionality or otherwise, is likely to prove any better. Provided that the regression on the concomitant is significant, adjustment can scarcely lead to any serious *loss* of precision, although there might be a small loss if the number of degrees of freedom for error were few.

The method of analysis described here can easily be extended to give simultaneous adjustment for two or more concomitant variates. If $b_{2.1}$ had been significant, y' would have been defined as the gland weight adjusted to equality of proportions of the two sexes as well as to equality in body weight. The formulæ would have been more complicated, but should present no difficulty to anyone familiar with the calculation of multiple regression equations and their variances. The quantities $(\bar{y}'_T - \bar{y}'_S)$ and b' would be formed by adjustment of L_p, L_1 for both concomitants, and their variances and covariance would easily be written down. Evaluation of M' and its fiducial limits then follows exactly as above.

This example is simple because the assay was fully symmetrical in design, and orthogonal coefficients could readily be used in the subdivision of the degrees of freedom between doses. The method is still applicable, however, even to an unsymmetrical design such as that in § 4.2. The adjustments must then be made directly to $(\bar{y}_T - \bar{y}_S)$ and to b, instead of to the orthogonal contrasts of a symmetrical design. As long as the basic rules of orthogonality are remembered, no serious difficulty should be encountered, even though lack of symmetry makes the arithmetic tedious.

12.5   An assay of parathyroid extract

The procedure illustrated in § 12.4 may be applied to assays of more complex design ; the computations then inevitably become more laborious. An assay of parathyroid extract discussed by Bliss and Rose (1940) provides an interesting example of the use of covariance analysis with a balanced incomplete block design. The response used was the serum calcium level in a dog injected with a dose of the standard or the test preparation. In the belief that large dogs would respond less to a specified dose than would small dogs, the doses for a 4-point assay were chosen as 0·06 c.c. and 0·12 c.c. per kg. body weight. Provided that the dogs used for the two preparations are selected from the same population, this use of a fixed dose per unit body weight does not disturb the validity of the assay, though, as will be shown below, it did not remove all effects of inequalities in weight.

Thirty-six dogs were used, and each was tested twice at an interval of two weeks. A balanced incomplete block cross-over design (§ 10.5) was chosen, so that every pair of doses was assigned to six dogs, three in each of the two possible orders. In order to reduce the amount of labour on any one day, the dogs were divided into three sets of twelve. The arrangement is shown in Table 12.8, which also contains the body weights of the dogs before injection and the final serum calcium values. The close relationship between the design and the twin cross-over design (§ 10.2) should be noted. The twin cross-over would have used only four of the twelve dose sequences. It would have given greater precision on the difference between mean responses to the two preparations and on the dose-response regression coefficient, and therefore greater precision on M, at the expense of a less sensitive test of parallelism. It would also have needed a less troublesome statistical analysis.

Bliss and Rose found that use of the increase in serum calcium as a metameter gave a less precise estimate of potency than the final values alone. Presumably differences between tests made on the same animal on different occasions are not seriously affected by the initial serum calcium status, and use of the increments instead of the final values does more harm than good because it introduces irrelevant variation. The initial serum calcium values have not been published, so that the possibility of there being some regression on that variate cannot be examined. This section is concerned only with the estimation of ρ from the final serum calcium figures, and with the gain in precision resulting from a covariance analysis on body weight.

The first step is to compute the analysis of covariance table. Bliss (1947a) has described the calculations needed for an analysis of variance according to Yates's method for balanced incomplete blocks (§ 9.6), and this could be extended to a covariance analysis. The simpler method used in § 9.5 is again more convenient here. Tables 12.9 and 12.10 show sums and differences of pairs of measurements on each dog. From Table 12.9 it is evident that the difference between pairs of types I and VII and those of types VI and XII estimates the difference between preparations as an

TABLE 12.8—Initial body weight, x_1, and final serum calcium values, y, in an assay of a parathyroid extract
(Units of 0.1 kg. for x_1, 0.1 mg. per cent. for y)

Dog pair no.	Doses First	Doses Second	Body weight Set 1 20/9	Set 1 4/10	Set 2 21/9	Set 2 5/10	Set 3 22/9	Set 3 6/10	Final serum calcium Set 1 20/9	Set 1 4/10	Set 2 21/9	Set 2 5/10	Set 3 22/9	Set 3 6/10
I	T_1	T_2	130	130	130	128	138	132	120	144	140	159	142	146
II	T_1	S_1	120	112	118	118	120	124	134	121	138	138	126	134
III	T_1	S_2	116	118	118	120	116	116	122	122	128	140	134	148
IV	T_2	S_1	118	120	114	114	108	106	134	121	148	140	141	130
V	T_2	S_2	102	116	112	110	104	118	124	142	134	136	130	140
VI	S_1	S_2	120	126	124	124	126	130	120	124	118	122	137	152
VII	T_2	T_1	88	90	96	96	90	90	132	128	136	120	142	138
VIII	S_1	T_1	114	120	86	88	108	112	110	125	129	129	130	133
IX	S_2	T_1	114	120	122	124	102	104	142	122	126	138	154	130
X	S_1	T_2	64	70	82	80	92	100	116	124	116	140	140	188
XI	S_2	T_2	110	118	124	124	162	156	142	148	130	152	144	141
XII	S_2	S_1	160	164	156	148	70	74	134	116	152	140	146	132

TABLE 12.9—Sums of pairs of measurements on each dog for the data of Table 12.8

Pair no.	Doses	Set 1 x_1	Set 1 y	Set 2 x_1	Set 2 y	Set 3 x_1	Set 3 y	Totals x_1	Totals y
I	$T_1 + T_2$	260	264	258	299	270	288	788	851
II	$T_1 + S_1$	232	255	236	276	244	260	712	791
III	$T_1 + S_2$	234	244	238	268	232	282	704	794
IV	$T_2 + S_1$	238	255	228	288	214	271	680	814
V	$T_2 + S_2$	218	266	222	270	222	270	662	806
VI	$S_1 + S_2$	246	244	248	240	256	289	750	773
VII	$T_2 + T_1$	178	260	192	256	180	280	550	796
VIII	$S_1 + T_1$	234	235	174	258	220	263	628	756
IX	$S_2 + T_1$	234	264	246	264	206	284	686	812
X	$S_1 + T_2$	134	240	162	256	192	328	488	824
XI	$S_2 + T_2$	228	290	248	282	318	285	794	857
XII	$S_2 + S_1$	324	250	304	292	144	278	772	820
Totals ...	...	2,760	3,067	2,756	3,249	2,698	3,378	8,214	9,694

TABLE 12.10—Differences of pairs of measurements on each dog for the data of Table 12.8

Pair no.	Doses	Set 1		Set 2		Set 3		Totals	
		x_1	y	x_1	y	x_1	y	x_1	y
I	$T_1 - T_2$	0	-24	2	-19	6	-4	8	-47
II	$T_1 - S_1$	8	13	0	0	-4	-8	4	5
III	$T_1 - S_2$	-2	0	-2	-12	0	-14	-4	-26
IV	$T_2 - S_1$	-2	13	0	8	2	11	0	32
V	$T_2 - S_2$	-14	-18	2	-2	-14	-10	-26	-30
VI	$S_1 - S_2$	-6	-4	0	-4	-4	-15	-10	-23
VII	$T_2 - T_1$	-2	4	0	16	0	4	-2	24
VIII	$S_1 - T_1$	-6	-15	-2	0	-4	-3	-12	-18
IX	$S_2 - T_1$	-6	20	-2	-12	-2	24	-10	32
X	$S_1 - T_2$	-6	-8	2	-24	-8	-48	-12	-80
XI	$S_2 - T_2$	-8	-6	0	-22	6	3	-2	-25
XII	$S_2 - S_1$	-4	18	8	12	-4	14	0	44
Totals ...	...	-48	-7	8	-59	-26	-46	-66	-112

inter-dog contrast ; the other types of pair contribute no information on this difference. On the other hand, from Table 12.10, an intra-dog estimate of the difference between preparations is seen to be obtainable from the contrast of pairs of types II, III, IV, V, with those of types VIII, IX, X, XI. Thus Table 12.11 is constructed to give sets of orthogonal contrasts for the inter-dog and intra-dog sections of the analysis. The coefficients can be obtained exactly as in § 9.5, by addition or subtraction of the coefficients in Table 5.4 corresponding to each dose of a pair ; in Table 12.11 a factor of

TABLE 12.11—Orthogonal coefficients for contrasts between and within dogs for the data of Table 12.8

Pair no.	First dose + second dose			First dose − second dose		
	L_p	L_1	L_1'	L_p	L_1	L_1'
I	1	—	—	—	− 1	− 1
II	—	− 1	—	1	—	− 1
III	—	—	− 1	1	− 1	—
IV	—	—	1	1	1	—
V	—	1	—	1	—	1
VI	− 1	—	—	—	− 1	1
VII	1	—	—	—	1	1
VIII	—	− 1	—	− 1	—	1
IX	—	—	− 1	− 1	1	—
X	—	—	1	− 1	− 1	—
XI	—	1	—	− 1	—	− 1
XII	− 1	—	—	—	1	− 1
Divisor ...	24	24	24	48	48	48
Sum for x_1 ...	− 184	116	− 222	10	6	− 60
Sum for y ...	54	116	32	72	308	− 24

2 has been removed throughout. The results obtained by use of the six mutually orthogonal contrasts in Table 12.11 are identical with the results obtained by forming regressions of the sums and differences in Tables 12.9 and 12.10 on three variates whose values are the coefficients in Table 5.4.

The analysis of covariance, Table 12.12, is now rapidly completed. Total sums of squares and products are calculated, and divided into between dog and within dog portions. For example, the total sum of squares between dogs for x_1 (35 degrees of freedom) is derived from Table 12.9 as

$$[(260)^2 + (232)^2 + (234)^2 + \ldots + (144)^2] \div 2 - (8,214)^2/72$$
$$= 30,573 \cdot 5.$$

Similarly the total sum of squares within dogs (36 degrees of freedom) is derived from Table 12.10 as

$$[0^2 + (8)^2 + (-2)^2 + \ldots + (-4)^2] \div 2 = 494 \cdot 0.$$

Sums of products are obtained by analogous computations on products of corresponding entries. The squares for the preparations contrast are

$$\frac{(-184)^2}{24} = 1,410 \cdot 7$$

and

$$\frac{(10)^2}{48} = 2 \cdot 1$$

for x_1, with similar expressions for y; the corresponding products are

$$\frac{(-184) \times 54}{24} = -414 \cdot 0$$

and

$$\frac{10 \times 72}{48} = 15 \cdot 0.$$

In the inter-dog analysis, a component for differences between the three sets (2 degrees of freedom) must be isolated. In the intra-dog analysis, allowance for a possible change in responsiveness between the first and second injections of each subject must be made. Since the dates of these differ for the three sets, it seemed advisable to calculate the contrast for each set separately, the result being entered in Table 12.12 as 'Dates'; thus for the analysis of x_1 the component entered was

$$[(-48)^2 + (8)^2 + (-26)^2] \div 24 = 126 \cdot 8$$

with 3 degrees of freedom, instead of

$$\frac{(-66)^2}{72} = 60 \cdot 5$$

with 1 degree of freedom (the totals are taken from Table 12.10).

TABLE 12.12—Analysis of variance and covariance for the data of Table 12.8

Adjustments for means	...	937,080·5	1,105,923·8	1,305,189·4
Nature of variation	d.f.	$S_{x_1 x_1}$	$S_{x_1 y}$	S_{yy}
Sets	2	100·3	− 381·8	2,034·5
Preparations	1	1,410·7	− 414·0	121·5
Regression	1	560·7	560·7	560·7
Parallelism	1	2,053·5	− 296·0	42·7
Error (1)	30	26,448·3	2,216·3	3,805·2
Between dogs ...	35	30,573·5	1,685·2	6,564·6
Dates	3	126·8	44·2	235·2
Preparations	1	2·1	15·0	108·0
Regression	1	0·8	38·5	1,976·3
Parallelism	1	75·0	30·0	12·0
Error (2)	30	289·3	339·3	1,840·5
Total	71	31,067·5	2,215·2	10,736·6

As in the example which forms the basis of § 9.5, the information provided by the two portions of the analysis must be separately considered. For the inter-dog analysis, ignoring for the present any covariance adjustment,

$$s_1^2 = \frac{3{,}805 \cdot 2}{30}$$

$$= 126 \cdot 8$$

is the variance per response. No sign of invalidity appears. Moreover, since L_p is a difference between two totals of twelve responses,

$$\bar{y}_T - \bar{y}_S = \frac{54}{12}$$

$$= 4 \cdot 500,$$

and

$$b = \frac{116}{24}$$

$$= 4 \cdot 833.$$

Hence

$$M = \frac{4 \cdot 500}{4 \cdot 833}$$

$$= 0 \cdot 9311.$$

Though the values of L_p, L_1 could be inserted in equation (5.17), in order to give R directly, the confounding makes equation (5.21) inapplicable and development from first principles is safer. From the way in which they have been formed,

$$V(\bar{y}_T - \bar{y}_S) = \frac{s_1^2}{6},$$

and

$$V(b) = \frac{s_1^2}{24}.$$

The two contrasts are, of course, orthogonal, and the covariance is therefore zero. Also

$$g = \frac{(2 \cdot 042)^2 \times 126 \cdot 8}{24 \times (4 \cdot 833)^2}$$

$$= 0 \cdot 9432,$$

a value near to unity since b is only just beyond its significance point. So large a value of g is almost sure to give exceedingly wide fiducial limits to M ; in fact

$$M_L, M_U = \left[0.9311 \pm \frac{2.042}{4.833}\left\{ s_1^2 \times \left(\frac{0.0568}{6} + \frac{0.9311^2}{24}\right)\right\}^{\frac{1}{2}} \right]$$

$$\div 0.0568$$

$$= -1.49, \; 34.28.$$

Multiplication by 0.1505 converts to logarithms to base 10, and therefore

$$R = \text{antilog } 0.140 = 1.38,$$
$$R_L = \text{antilog } \bar{1}.776 = 0.60,$$
$$R_U = \text{antilog } 5.159 = 14{,}400,$$

for the potency of 1 c.c. of the test preparation relative to 1 c.c. of the standard. Because of the low precision of the regression coefficient and the consequent high value for g, the upper limit is so high as to make the result useless. Had any attempt been made to use a variance formula for M, the conclusions reached would have been entirely wrong. As will be seen below, the variances of the numerator and denominator of the intra-dog value for M are about one-quarter those for the inter-dog value, a reduction which brings g to a reasonable level, and leads to an estimate of potency that is at least usable even though still not very precise.

Table 12.13 shows that the error regression of y on x_1 for the inter-dog section of the analysis is not significant. The mean square for the regression is a little greater than the residual, but the difference is certainly not great enough to give any improvement in the precision of potency estimation by adjustment for inequalities in x_1.

TABLE 12.13—Error regression analysis for the inter-dog section of Table 12.12

Nature of variation	d.f.	Sum of squares	Mean square
Regression on x_1	1	185·7	185·7
Residual	29	3,619·5	124·8
Total	30	3,805·2	

For the intra-dog section of the analysis, before any covariance adjustment is tried,

$$s_2^2 = \frac{1,840 \cdot 5}{30}$$
$$= 61 \cdot 35.$$

Again no invalidity appears. Also

$$\bar{y}_T - \bar{y}_S = \frac{72}{24}$$
$$= 3 \cdot 000,$$

and

$$b = \frac{308}{48}$$
$$= 6 \cdot 417.$$

Hence

$$M = 0 \cdot 4675.$$

From the divisors in Table 12.11,

$$V(\bar{y}_T - \bar{y}_S) = \frac{s_2^2}{12},$$

$$V(b) = \frac{s_2^2}{48},$$

and therefore

$$g = \frac{(2 \cdot 042)^2 \times 61 \cdot 35}{48 \times (6 \cdot 417)^2}$$
$$= 0 \cdot 1294.$$

Calculations of the usual type give

$$R = \text{antilog } 0 \cdot 0704 = 1 \cdot 176,$$
$$R_L = \text{antilog } \bar{1} \cdot 9612 = 0 \cdot 915,$$
$$R_U = \text{antilog } 0 \cdot 2005 = 1 \cdot 587.$$

The value of R agrees well with that for the inter-dog analysis, but little importance can be attached to this agreement in view of the wide limits for the latter.

Table 12.14 shows the error regression analysis for y on x_1 in the intra-dog analysis. Adjustment for inequalities in x_1 effects a 20 per cent. reduction in s_2^2, and this is undoubtedly significant. Some improvement in the fiducial limits of the assay is to be

expected if this covariance adjustment is used ; the percentage
narrowing of the limits is likely to be about one-half the percentage
reduction in s_2^2, or about 10 per cent., and possibly a little greater
because of the effect on g. Before proceeding with the adjustment,
however, the validity needs to be re-examined. Reference to Table
12.12 shows a surprisingly large square for parallelism in the analysis
of $S_{x_1 x_1}$; this is balanced by small values for the other two dose
components, so that the mean square for the three degrees of freedom
together is not significant, and there is no special reason to worry
about faulty randomization. Although a test of parallelism for the
adjusted responses, made just as in Table 12.6 for the prolactin
assay, seems desirable, it shows no signs of non-parallelism (Table
12.15). A similar test for the preparations contrast is equally
satisfactory.

TABLE 12.14—Error regression analysis for the intra-dog section of
Table 12.12

Nature of variation	d.f.	Sum of squares	Mean square
Regression on x_1	1	397·9	397·9
Residual	29	1,442·6	49·74
Total	30	1,840·5	

TABLE 12.15—Parallelism test for adjusted responses in the intra-dog
section of the assay of parathyroid extract

Nature of variation	d.f.	Sum of squares	Mean square
Parallelism ...	1	35·5	35·5
Error	29	$1,840·5 - 397·9 = 1,442·6$	49·74
Parallelism+Error	30	$1,852·5 - 374·4 = 1,478·1$	

Now

$$b_1 = \frac{339 \cdot 3}{289 \cdot 3}$$

$$= 1 \cdot 173,$$

an estimate of the increase in serum calcium per unit increase in body weight. Hence, for the adjusted contrasts,

$$\bar{y}_T' - \bar{y}_S' = \frac{72 - 1 \cdot 173 \times 10}{24}$$

$$= 2 \cdot 511,$$

and

$$b' = \frac{308 - 1 \cdot 173 \times 6}{48}$$

$$= 6 \cdot 270.$$

Therefore

$$M' = \frac{2 \cdot 511}{6 \cdot 270}$$

$$= 0 \cdot 4005.$$

Again,

$$V(\bar{y}_T' - \bar{y}_S') = s_2^2 \left[\frac{1}{12} + \left(\frac{10}{24} \right)^2 \cdot \frac{1}{289 \cdot 3} \right]$$

$$= 0 \cdot 08393 s_2^2,$$

$$V(b') = s_2^2 \left[\frac{1}{48} + \left(\frac{6}{48} \right)^2 \cdot \frac{1}{289 \cdot 3} \right]$$

$$= 0 \cdot 02089 s_2^2,$$

and

$$C\left\{ (\bar{y}_T' - \bar{y}_S'), b' \right\} = s_2^2 \left[\left(\frac{10}{24} \right) \left(\frac{6}{48} \right) \cdot \frac{1}{289 \cdot 3} \right]$$

$$= 0 \cdot 00018 s_2^2,$$

where s_2^2 is now the residual variance per response,

$$s_2^2 = 49 \cdot 74.$$

Since s_2^2 has only 29 degrees of freedom, $t = 2 \cdot 045$, and

$$g = 0 \cdot 1105.$$

Calculations exactly like those of § 12.4 then give

$$R = \text{antilog } 0 \cdot 0603 = 1 \cdot 149,$$
$$R_L = \text{antilog } \bar{1} \cdot 9590 = 0 \cdot 910,$$
$$R_U = \text{antilog } 0 \cdot 1762 = 1 \cdot 500.$$

Before comment is made on the gain from the covariance adjustment, it is of interest to combine the information from the two sections of the analysis in a manner similar to that used in § 9.5. Results so far obtained may be summarized as:

	Inter-dog	Intra-dog
$\bar{y}_T - \bar{y}_S$	4·500	2·511
$V(\bar{y}_T - \bar{y}_S)$	21·133	4·175
b	4·833	6·270
$V(b)$	5·283	1·039
$C\{(\bar{y}_T - \bar{y}_S), b\}$	0	0·009

An estimate of log potency may now be formed as the ratio of weighted means of $(\bar{y}_T - \bar{y}_S)$ and b. In the light of considerations advanced in § 14.3, the best weights to use seem to be the reciprocals of the variances of $(\bar{y}_T - \bar{y}_S)$, especially as the variances of b are almost proportional to these. Hence the weighted means are

$$\bar{y}_T - \bar{y}_S = \frac{4 \cdot 175 \times 4 \cdot 500 + 21 \cdot 133 \times 2 \cdot 511}{4 \cdot 175 + 21 \cdot 133}$$
$$= 2 \cdot 839,$$

and similarly

$$b = 6 \cdot 033.$$

Consequently

$$M = \frac{2 \cdot 839}{6 \cdot 033}$$
$$= 0 \cdot 4706.$$

Exact inference about M in terms of fiducial limits is not possible. To use a pooled estimate of variance per response would obviously be inappropriate, and the weights used in forming the final values of $(\bar{y}_T - \bar{y}_S)$ and b are themselves dependent upon the observations. But for the covariance adjustment used in the intra-dog analysis, the second analogue of Fieller's theorem (§ 2.7) would apply. The effect of these adjustments on the variances and covariance is so small, however, that use of the theorem should give sufficiently good guidance, especially as the numbers of degrees of freedom are fairly large. Now, for the weighted means,

$$V(\bar{y}_T - \bar{y}_S) = \left(\frac{4\cdot175}{25\cdot308}\right)^2 \times 21\cdot133 + \left(\frac{21\cdot133}{25\cdot308}\right)^2 \times 4\cdot175 = 3\cdot486,$$

$$V(b) = \left(\frac{4\cdot175}{25\cdot308}\right)^2 \times 5\cdot283 + \left(\frac{21\cdot133}{25\cdot308}\right)^2 \times 1\cdot039 = 0\cdot868,$$

$$C\{(\bar{y}_T - \bar{y}_S), b\} = \left(\frac{21\cdot133}{25\cdot308}\right)^2 \times 0\cdot009 = 0\cdot006.$$

Equation (2.25) may be written approximately here as

$$\tan \theta = \frac{s_2^2}{2s_1^2}$$
$$= 0\cdot196$$

and therefore

$$\theta = 24°.$$

The d-deviate for this angle and (29, 30) degrees of freedom is required, and is about 2·04. Consequently, equation (2.27) gives

$$M_L, M_U = \left[0\cdot4706 - \frac{0\cdot0992 \times 0\cdot006}{0\cdot868} \right.$$
$$\pm \frac{2\cdot04}{6\cdot033} \left\{ 3\cdot486 - 2 \times 0\cdot4706 \times 0\cdot006 \right.$$
$$\left. \left. + (0\cdot4706)^2 \times 0\cdot868 - 0\cdot0992 \times 3\cdot486 \right\}^{\frac{1}{2}} \right] \div 0\cdot9008$$
$$= [0\cdot4699 \pm 0\cdot6167] \div 0\cdot9008,$$
$$= -0\cdot1630, 1\cdot2063,$$

whence

$$R = \text{antilog } 0\cdot0708 = 1\cdot177,$$
$$R_L = \text{antilog } \bar{1}\cdot9755 = 0\cdot945,$$
$$R_U = \text{antilog } 0\cdot1815 = 1\cdot519.$$

Table 12.16 summarizes the four estimations of potency for the assay of the parathyroid extract. The inter-dog estimate alone is clearly useless. Adjustment of the intra-dog estimate for variations in body weight narrows the fiducial range by about 13 per cent., and combination of this estimate with the inter-dog information effects a further 3 per cent. reduction.

TABLE 12.16—Comparison of estimates and fiducial limits in the assay of parathyroid extract

	Inter-dog	Intra-dog No adjustment	Intra-dog Covariance	Combined
Estimated potency of test preparation relative to standard ...	1·38	1·18	1·15	1·18
g	0·9432	0·1294	0·1105	0·0992
Limits	0·60–14,400	0·91–1·59	0·91–1·50	0·95–1·52
Limits as per cent. of estimate ...	43–10,400	77–135	79–130	81–129

12.6   The economics of covariance adjustment

Inspection of Tables 12.7 and 12.16 may suggest that the adjustment of potency estimates by means of covariance analysis gives a small return for a great amount of extra computational labour. That the labour is considerable cannot be denied, but in many circumstances the gain from it is likely to be greater than could be obtained in any other way for the same trouble and labour. For example, in the assay of parathyroid extract the covariance adjustment narrows the fiducial range for the estimate of potency by about 13 per cent. In order to obtain the same reduction by an increase in the size of experiment, about 25 per cent. more observations would be required. Thus the cost of determining body weights and performing the covariance analysis may be compared with that of using an additional nine dogs in the assay and making serum calcium determinations only. For a concomitant that is as easily measured as is body weight, the advantage obviously lies with the saving of subjects ; for a concomitant whose measurement was itself laborious, the experimenter might prefer to be more prodigal in his use of subjects and to omit the covariance entirely (*cf.* § 2.13). No decision about the ideal policy should be based upon analysis of a single assay, for the improvement effected by covariance will vary from one type of assay to another.

Even within one class of assays, it will vary with the stock of animals and the details of assay procedure. All available evidence on assays in which concomitants have been measured should be submitted to statistical examination, in order that, from the collated results of their analyses, experimenters may decide on the most economical future practice.

One further aspect of the use of covariance deserves mention. In the parathyroid assay discussed in § 12.5, the doses used were defined as quantities per kg. body weight of dog. This common practice amongst pharmacologists is itself intended to make allowance for dependence of responsiveness upon size ; it may be compared with the expression of doses in a direct assay as quantities per unit body weight (§ 2.11), and with the expression of responses as proportions of body weight (§§ 4.13, 12.3). If adjustment for inequalities in the weights of subjects is to be made by covariance analysis, the giving of doses proportional to weight is unnecessary, although a reasonable uniformity of weight is desirable in order to avoid the risk of appreciable non-linearity of the weight-response regression. In any evaluation of the economics of covariance analysis for such an assay, therefore, the saving of the labour required for separate measurement of each dose must be credited to the covariance procedure (Jerne and Wood, 1949).

CHAPTER 13

COMPOSITE RESPONSES

13.1 The discriminant problem

The other class of problem mentioned in § 12.1 as involving measurements of several variates on each subject must now be discussed : after every application of the stimulus, two or more different variates are measured, each of which might respond to the stimulus. Calculations of relative potency might be based on any one variate, and a combined estimate might be formed by averaging the several values of M or R. In general, estimates based on different variates would differ in precision, so that some kind of weighted average would be wanted. The precision of the combined estimate could not be assessed in any simple manner, however, since different response variates from one subject are likely to be correlated.

A better procedure is to consider a composite response metameter, y^*, defined as a function of the several response measures y_1, y_2, y_3, ...

$$y^* = y^* (y_1, y_2, y_3, ...). \qquad (13.1)$$

The ideal function will be one leading to an estimate of ρ substantially more precise than if any measure of response were used alone. For obvious practical reasons, some limitation of the class of metameter functions to be considered is inevitable, and in the present discussion only linear functions

$$y^* = p_1 y_1 + p_2 y_2 + p_3 y_3 + \cdots \qquad (13.2)$$

will be used (cf. § 6.11 ; Bliss and Bartels, 1946). All multiples of y^* are equivalent for assay purposes, and an arbitrary standardization of $p_1 = 1$ could be introduced.

For alternative response metameters in a parallel line assay, if the doses have been well chosen and b is large relative to its standard error,

$$V(M) \propto \frac{s^2}{b^2} \qquad (13.3)$$

may be written as an approximate relationship, by equation (6.12).

Hence a reasonable method for determining y^* in equation (13.2) would be to make the routine assay analysis for y^* as a function of p_1, p_2, p_3, ... , and then to determine these coefficients by the condition that s^2/b^2 shall be a minimum.

The non-applicability of a variance formula for M, important though this can be, need not prevent the use of such a working rule for guidance in the choice of y^*. If g is not negligible, the process will not minimize the fiducial range for M exactly, but, since s^2/b^2 is almost always the major influence on precision, it should still give results fairly close to the best possible. Complications will arise with assay designs that have two separate error variances (§§ 9.3–9.7), but these possibilities will not be considered here.

The minimizing of s^2/b^2 is the same as the maximizing of b^2/s^2, a process which amounts to the selection of y^* so as to maximize the ratio of b to its standard error. This is in fact the determination of a *discriminant function* (Fisher, 1958, § 49.2 ; Mather, 1946, § 39) for the contrast representing the regression of response on dose. Theory shows the process to be formally equivalent to the calculation of a multiple linear regression of x, the dose metameter, on y_1, y_2, y_3, ... ; the partial regression coefficients are the required values of p_1, p_2, p_3, ... For imagine an analysis of covariance table to be set up for x and the y_i, in structure like the conventional analysis of variance for the assay except that the single degree of freedom for regression is left in with the error. The analysis of covariance for x and y^* is then obtainable by use of the relationships

$$\left. \begin{array}{l} S_{xy^*} = \sum_i p_i S_{xy_i} \\ S_{y^*y^*} = \sum_i p_i^2 S_{y_iy_i} + 2\sum_i\sum_j p_ip_j S_{y_iy_j}. \end{array} \right\} \quad (13.4)$$

and

The values of the p_i are to be chosen so as to maximize the proportion of the error component of $S_{y^*y^*}$ removed by a linear regression on x. This requirement is equivalent to maximizing the error correlation coefficient between x and y^*, which in turn is equivalent to maximizing the proportion of the error component of S_{xx} removed by linear regression on y^*. In its final version, the condition is exactly that for determining the partial regression coefficients of x on the y_i.

This use of multiple linear regression is purely formal. The values of x cannot be regarded as normally distributed about the regression function ; indeed, since they are selected by the experimenter, they are not 'distributed' in the true statistical sense. Nevertheless, for a test of significance of whether or not certain or the y_i improve the discriminator, the usual regression method is valid. (As for a test of significance of a simple regression or correlation coefficient, the validity of the t test or variance ratio test requires only that either x or y_i should have normally distributed errors.) The regression analogy breaks down, however, for the assessment of the precision of any coefficient, p_i, once it has been shown to deviate significantly from zero.

Discriminant functions seem likely to be less useful in slope ratio assays, because the situations in which the slope ratio model has been found appropriate lend themselves less readily to the making of multiple response measurements. For alternative response metameters in a slope ratio assay, equation (7.21) shows that, approximately,

$$V(R) \propto \frac{s^2}{b_S^2},\qquad (13.5)$$

provided that the value of R is not much altered by the choice of metameter. Hence the coefficients of y^* in equation (13.2) might be determined so as to minimize s^2/b_S^2. The development of the analysis would be a little more complicated than for a parallel line assay, because of the non-orthogonality of b_S and b_T, though the same principles apply ; it will not be discussed further here.

13.2   An example of an assay using a discriminant function

The discriminant function technique has been employed in many fields of statistical inquiry, but apparently no example of its use in biological assay has been published. An artificial numerical example has therefore been constructed, this being based upon the prolactin assay data in Table 12.1. Table 13.1 purports to show data on two response variates in a 6-point assay of design exactly the same as the prolactin assay ; y_1 is identical with the crop-gland weight in Table 12.1, and y_2 is a slightly modified form of the body weight, such as might be found for the final body weight if the stimulus also affected this variate.*

---

* The body weights in the prolactin assay were recorded at the end of the experiment, but showed no sign of response to dose ; the y_2 values in Table 13.1 have been formed by adding 2 to each x_1 at a low dose in Table 12.1, subtracting 2 at each high dose, and leaving the x_1 values unaltered at the middle doses.

TABLE 13.1—Artificial data for an assay giving two response variates

(a) The variate y_1 (in units of 0·1 g.)

Dose of standard preparation (i.u.)			Dose of test preparation (mg.)		
1·25	2·50	5·00	0·125	0·250	0·500
38	53	85	28	48	60
39	102	144	65	47	130
48	81	54	35	54	83
62	75	85	36	74	60
187	311	368	164	223	333

(b) The variate y_2 (in units of 10 g.)

Dose of standard preparation (i.u.)			Dose of test preparation (mg.)		
1·25	2·50	5·00	0·125	0·250	0·500
51	49	47	53	48	43
55	53	51	53	51	50
46	46	39	52	48	48
51	51	41	54	50	51
203	199	178	212	197	192

The dose metameter, x, will as usual be taken as -1, 0, 1 for low, medium, high doses respectively. The contrasts may be summarized as

				x	y_1	y_2
L_p	...	...	...	0	-146	21
L_1	...	...	...	16	350	-45
L_1'	...	...	...	0	-12	5
L_2	...	...	...	0	-16	-7
L_2'	...	...	...	0	118	27

TABLE 13.2—Analysis of variance and covariance for the data of Table 13.1

Nature of variation	d.f.	$S_{y_1 y_1}$	$S_{y_1 y_2}$	$S_{y_2 y_2}$	$S_{y_1 x}$	$S_{y_2 x}$	S_{xx}
Adjustments for means	...	104,808	78,044·4	58,115·04	0	0	0
Preparations	1	888	− 127·8	18·38	0	0	0
Parallelism	1	9	− 3·8	1·56	0	0	0
Quadratic	1	5	2·3	1·02	0	0	0
Difference of quadratics ...	1	291	66·4	15·19	0	0	0
Error	19	18,037	− 234·5	331·81	350	− 45	16
Total	23	19,230	− 297·4	367·96	350	− 45	16

Table 13.2 is the analysis of covariance prepared for examination of the regression of x on y_1, y_2. The subdivision of the degrees of freedom differs from that of Table 12.4 in one important respect : the component for the regression of response on dose is left in the error, because x is now being used as though it were an independent variate. The method of construction of L_1 makes clear that its values for x, y_1, y_2 are S_{xx}, S_{y_1x}, and S_{y_2x} respectively.

The coefficients of the discriminant function are proportional to the linear regression coefficients of x on y_1, y_2. Hence they may be found from

$$18,037p_1 - 234 \cdot 5p_2 = 350, \left. \right\}$$
$$- 234 \cdot 5p_1 + 331 \cdot 81p_2 = -45, \left. \right\}$$

and are

$$p_1 = 0 \cdot 01780,$$
$$p_2 = -0 \cdot 12304.$$

In continuation of the regression analogy, the sum of squares accounted for by the regression of x on y_1, y_2 is calculated as

$$350p_1 - 45p_2 = 11 \cdot 77,$$

as compared with

$$350^2/18,037 = 6 \cdot 79$$

for y_1 alone. The significance of the improvement in discrimination between doses attributable to the use of y_2 as well as y_1 is then tested as shown in Table 13.3 ; in spite of the appearance of the analysis, the usual normality assumptions for y_1, y_2 ensure validity of the significance tests. Clearly y_2 improves discrimination, and a similar test demonstrates that inclusion of y_1 is an improvement on the use of y_2 alone.

Only the ratios of the p_i are really of importance, and for arithmetical purposes the coefficient of y_1 is conveniently reduced to unity, so as to give

$$y^* = y_1 - 6 \cdot 912y_2. \tag{13.6}$$

Equation (13.6) could be approximated by

$$y^* = y_1 - 7y_2$$

with negligible loss in discrimination, but for this example the full version is retained. By the second of equations (13.4), each component of the analysis of variance of x^*, Table 13.4, may be calculated from

$$S_{y^*y^*} = S_{y_1y_1} - 13 \cdot 824S_{y_1y_2} + 47 \cdot 776S_{y_2y_2}. \tag{13.7}$$

TABLE 13.3—Error regression analysis for a discriminant calculated from Table 13.2

Nature of variation	d.f.	Sum of squares	Mean square
Regression on y_1 alone ...	1	6·79	
Additional for y_2	1	4·98	4·98
Regression on y_1, y_2 ...	2	11·77	
Regression on y_2 alone ...	1	6·10	
Additional for y_1	1	5·67	5·67
Regression on y_1, y_2 ...	2	11·77	
Residual	17	4·23	0·249
Total	19	16·00	

The dose components may alternatively be derived from

$$L_p(y^*) = L_p(y_1) - 6·912 L_p(y_2)$$
$$= -291·2,$$
$$L_1(y^*) = 661·0,$$
$$L_1'(y^*) = -46·6,$$
$$L_2(y^*) = 32·4,$$
$$L_2'(y^*) = -68·6.$$

The regression component is assigned two degrees of freedom instead of one, since two variates have been used in the determination of the discriminator ; the justification for this is not immediately obvious, but it will be found to lead to exactly the same variance ratio for a test of significance as would be given by a test of the two degrees of freedom for regression in Table 13.3. The extra degree of freedom is removed from the error line of Table 13.4.

The test of significance for the regression component suggested by Table 13.4 is exact, but other tests of significance from this table and the assessment of fiducial limits that follows are only approximate; the fault lies in assuming the p_i to be known exactly, whereas they are only estimates from the data.

TABLE 13.4—Analysis of variance for the discriminant function, y^*

Nature of variation	d.f.	Sum of squares	Mean square
Preparations	1	3,533	3,533
Regression	2	27,308	13,654
Parallelism	1	136	136
Quadratic	1	22	22
Difference of quadratics ...	1	98	98
Error	17	9,824	577·9
Total	23	40,921	

Table 13.4 gives no indication of invalidity, except for the difference between preparations. From the dose contrasts in the metameter y^*,

$$M = -\frac{291 \cdot 2}{12} \div \frac{661 \cdot 0}{16}$$

$$= -24 \cdot 27 \div 41 \cdot 31$$

$$= -0 \cdot 5875.$$

Moreover, accepting the usual formulae as adequate approximations,

$$g = \frac{(2 \cdot 110)^2 \times 577 \cdot 9}{(41 \cdot 31)^2 \times 16}$$

$$= 0 \cdot 0942,$$

and

$M_L, M_U =$

$$-\left[0.5875 \pm \frac{2.110}{41.31} \times \left\{577.9 \times \left(\frac{0.9058}{6} + \frac{(-0.5875)^2}{16}\right)\right\}^{\frac{1}{2}}\right] \div 0.9058$$

$$= -(0.5875 \pm 0.5100) \div 0.9058$$

$$= -1.2116, -0.0856.$$

Hence
$$R = 10 \text{ antilog } \bar{1}.8231 = 6.65,$$
$$R_L = 10 \text{ antilog } \bar{1}.6353 = 4.32,$$
$$R_U = 10 \text{ antilog } \bar{1}.9742 = 9.42.$$

As is to be expected, these limits are considerably narrower than those based on y_1 alone (§ 12.2), being 65 per cent. and 142 per cent. of R instead of 35 per cent. and 196 per cent. The assumption that the p_i are unknown will lead to overestimation of the precision of estimation, to an extent that would be negligible if the number of degrees of freedom for error were large. Rao (1954) has presented a general theory, in terms of exact multivariate probability distributions, and has illustrated it from Table 13.1. As the exact 95 per cent. fiducial limits, he found 3.70 and 10.35, or 56 per cent. and 156 per cent. of R. The rarity of multivariate response records for bioassays makes unnecessary any full account of his method here, especially as his own paper is very clear.

13.3 Discriminants and concomitants

The two types of problem discussed in Chapter 12 and this chapter might occur simultaneously. If data on concomitant variates, themselves unaffected by the stimulus, are available, as well as two or more response variates, the ideal response metameter will be a discriminant adjusted by covariance. The statistical technique is a little more complicated than the ordinary discriminant function process, but does not involve any essentially new methods. An example which is almost a biological assay, although unfortunately its more interesting features from this point of view are ignored, has been discussed by Cochran and Bliss (1948).

13.4 The economics of discriminant analysis

Like the adjustment of assay data by covariance, the use of a discriminant function as a response metameter increases the computational labour very considerably. Whether or not this labour is worth while can be assessed only by comparison of the cost of measuring the additional variates and computing the discriminant with that of obtaining an equal increase in precision by measurement of one variate for a larger number of subjects (*cf.* § 12.6).

Too few uses of discriminant analysis in assays have been published for any general conclusion to be drawn. Liddle *et al.* (1955) have described a technique for aldosterone assay in which either a potassium response or a sodium response could be used for estimating potency from parallel regression lines. The values of s/b were 0·37 and 0·48 for these responses. An index formed as a linear combination of the two responses had a value of 0·24 for s/b; this suggests that the number of administrations of doses required in order to achieve a stated precision could be reduced to one-half or one-quarter of that needed when account is taken of only one response. Munson and Sheps (1958) found log (comb weight/ body weight) a better metameter than log (comb weight) in a chick assay for androgens. They considered alternatives, but found the simple ratio to be almost as good as a practice of calculating a discriminant function for each assay separately.

CHAPTER 14

THE COMBINATION OF
ESTIMATES

14.1 Weighted means

If the potency of a test preparation is estimated in two or more analytical dilution assays, whether these be assays of the same design and technique or assays by entirely different techniques, the estimates must agree except for differences attributable to sampling error. Hence Fisher (1949) takes the disagreement between two potency estimates for a tuberculin preparation, one by tests on cows and one by tests on guinea-pigs, as evidence of a qualitative difference between the standard and test preparations, When agreement is satisfactory, a composite estimate of ρ that shall summarize all available information in a single precise figure is desirable. Even for comparative assays, if good agreement between several estimates is found, a composite figure will naturally be required. In the formation of the combined estimate, most importance will be attached to the individual values that are most precise or reliable, and some type of weighted mean will therefore be wanted.

The problem is relatively simple if g is small for each assay, and the variance per response is either a known σ^2 (as will often be true for assays based on a quantal response ; see Chapters 17, 18) or is an estimated s^2 with a moderately large number of degrees of freedom. In these circumstances, either M or R can be assigned limits by the use of a variance formula, and $V(M)$ or $V(R)$ is not subject to serious sampling errors. The best procedure then is to take a weighted mean value of the individual estimates, using weights inversely proportional to the variances. For parallel line assays the calculations should be made on M, and for slope ratio assays on R, but otherwise the two types are treated identically.

Under the conditions specified, suppose that the separate values of M, the log potency in a series of parallel line assays of the same preparation, are M_1, M_2, M_3, . . . M_p. Write the weight for the ith assay as the reciprocal of the variance:

$$\omega_i = \frac{1}{V(M_i)}. \tag{14.1}$$

The weighted mean, $\bar{M}$, is then defined by

$$\bar{M} = \frac{\Sigma\omega_i M_i}{\Sigma\omega_i} \tag{14.2}$$

with variance

$$V(\bar{M}) = \frac{1}{\Sigma\omega_i}, \tag{14.3}$$

where Σ denotes summation over all the assays. In the determination of fiducial limits for $\bar{M}$, several cases may be distinguished:

(i) If the ω_i are ' true ' weights, based upon known variances per response, σ_i^2, normal deviates can be used in assigning limits to $\bar{M}$ with rather more justification than they were used for a particular M_i. Hence the 95 per cent. fiducial limits may be taken as

$$\begin{aligned}\bar{M}_L &= \bar{M} - 1\cdot960\,\{V(\bar{M})\}^{\frac{1}{2}}, \\ \bar{M}_U &= \bar{M} + 1\cdot960\,\{V(\bar{M})\}^{\frac{1}{2}}.\end{aligned} \Bigg\} \tag{14.4}$$

Moreover, a test of the homogeneity of the p estimates can be based on reference of

$$\chi^2_{[p-1]} = \Sigma\omega_i M_i^2 - \frac{(\Sigma\omega_i M_i)^2}{\Sigma\omega_i} \tag{14.5}$$

to Appendix Table IV. If the separate M_i came from valid assays, but this χ^2 criterion disclosed differences between them, the hypothesis that all were analytical dilution assays would be contradicted, though they might still be valid comparative assays.

(ii) If the p assays are based upon the same type of response, and the values of s_i^2, the estimated variances per response, are satisfactorily homogeneous (Bartlett's test, §3.11, enables this point to be examined), a pooled variance should be formed;

$$\bar{s}^2 = \frac{\Sigma f_i s_i^2}{\Sigma f_i}, \tag{14.6}$$

where f_i is the number of degrees of freedom for s_i^2. The values of $V(M_i)$ may then be recomputed, using $\bar{s}^2$ in place of s_i^2, so as to give more reliable values. In calculating $\bar{M}$, the factor $1/\bar{s}^2$ may be omitted from each ω_i provided that it is remembered at the end for the formation of $V(\bar{M})$. The fiducial limits are

$$\left. \begin{array}{l} \bar{M}_L = \bar{M} - t\,\{V(\bar{M})\}^{\frac{1}{2}}, \\ \bar{M}_U = \bar{M} + t\,\{V(\bar{M})\}^{\frac{1}{2}}, \end{array} \right\} \qquad (14.7)$$

where t has Σf_i degrees of freedom. Since Σf_i is likely to be fairly large, equations (14.4) will usually be close approximations to equations (14.7) for the 95 per cent. limits. Similarly, equation (14.5) may be used to give an approximate test of homogeneity of the M_i ; more exactly, the expression on the right-hand side of equation (14.5) may be divided by $(p-1)$ and regarded as a variance ratio with $(p-1, \Sigma f_i)$ degrees of freedom (Appendix Table II).

(iii) The instructions given under (i) and (ii) are exact except for the dependence on the smallness of g for each assay and the consequent legitimacy of using $V(M)$. When the s_i^2 cannot be pooled, but each is based upon many degrees of freedom, calculation as for case (ii) is unlikely to be seriously misleading. Probably data for which each f_i is at least 20 can be safely treated in this· manner. If the numbers of degrees of freedom are small, a complete solution can be given only when $p=2$. The problem is then that of § 2.6, so that the Behrens distribution may be used both for testing the significance of the difference between M_1 and M_2 and for assessing the precision of $\bar{M}$. When $p>2$, equations (14.1)–(14.3) may still be used, but no tables are available for the determination of fiducial limits. As an approximation, a value of t with fewer degrees of freedom than Σf_i, but more than for the s_i^2 with the smallest number of degrees of freedom, should be used in equations (14.7). A closer approximation is illustrated in § 14.2.

14.2   Examples of weighted means

Suppose that three assays of a certain test preparation, using the same experimental technique and response measurement but not necessarily of the same design, have given estimates of log potency :

$$M_1 = 1·665 \pm 0·270,$$
$$M_2 = 2·430 \pm 0·389, \qquad (14.8)$$
$$M_3 = 2·019 \pm 0·284.$$

The variances of the estimates are then

$$V_1 = 0·07290,$$
$$V_2 = 0·15132,$$
$$V_3 = 0·08066,$$

and the weights, the reciprocals of the variances, are

$$\omega_1 = 13·72,$$
$$\omega_2 = 6·61,$$
$$\omega_3 = 12·40.$$

Hence, by equation (14.2),

$$\bar{M} = \frac{13·72 \times 1·665 + 6·61 \times 2·430 + 12·40 \times 2·019}{13·72 + 6·61 + 12·40}$$

$$= \frac{63·9417}{32·73}$$

$$= 1·954.$$

If the standard errors for the M_i have been calculated from true variances, the homogeneity of the three estimates may be examined by means of equation (14.5), or, numerically,

$$\chi^2_{[2]} = 127·613 - \frac{(63·9417)^2}{32·73}$$

$$= 2·70.$$

Appendix Table IV shows this to be well within the reasonable limits of sampling variation for χ^2, so that the M_i are in satisfactory agreement. Now

$$V(\bar{M}) = 1/32·73$$
$$= 0·03055 ;$$

therefore, the standard error of $\bar{M}$ is 0·175, and, by equations (14.4), the 95 per cent. fiducial limits for $\bar{M}$ are 1·611, 2·297.

If the variances per response were not known exactly, but the estimates, s_i^2, were based on 24, 12, 20 degrees of freedom for the three assays, a pooled $\bar{s}^2$ with 56 degrees of freedom would be used unless evidence of variance heterogeneity appeared. On the supposition that the standard errors quoted for the M_i in equations (14.8) have been calculated from this $\bar{s}^2$, the calculations required would be almost the same as above. Instead of the χ^2, $F = 1\cdot35$ would be tested as a variance ratio, with (2, 56) degrees of freedom ; it is obviously not significant. The weighted mean log potency, $\bar{M}$, is still $1\cdot954$, but, in equations (14 7), $t = 2\cdot003$ must be inserted to give the fiducial limits, $1\cdot603$, $2\cdot305$.

If only M_1 and M_2 were available, and their values of s_i^2, based on 24 and 12 degrees of freedom, were no longer to be assumed homogeneous and pooled, the test of agreement of the estimates would be obtained from formula (2.11), by calculating

$$d = \frac{2\cdot430 - 1\cdot665}{(0\cdot15132 + 0\cdot07290)^{\frac{1}{2}}}$$
$$= 1\cdot62.$$

(The standard errors in equations (14.8) are now assumed to be based on separate s_i^2, not on $\bar{s}^2$.) This is to be compared with a tabular value for (24, 12) degrees of freedom and an angle θ, given by

$$\tan^2 \theta = \frac{0\cdot07290}{0\cdot15132}$$
$$= 0\cdot482 ;$$

thus $\theta = 35°$, and the 5 per cent. value for d is $2\cdot132$ (Appendix Table III). Clearly the difference between M_1 and M_2 is not significant. The weighted mean is

$$\bar{M} = \frac{13\cdot72 \times 1\cdot665 + 6\cdot61 \times 2\cdot430}{13\cdot72 + 6\cdot61}$$
$$= \frac{38\cdot9061}{20\cdot33}$$
$$= 1\cdot914,$$

with variance

$$V(\bar{M}) = 1/20\cdot33$$
$$= (0\cdot222)^2$$

by equation (14.3) or equation (2.14). The d-deviate required for the fiducial limits has (24, 12) degrees of freedom and

$$\tan^2 \theta = \frac{0\cdot15132}{0\cdot07290},$$

whence $\theta = 55°$. The deviate for a 5 per cent. probability is 2·094, and the limits are therefore 1·449, 2·379.

Under the same conditions of heterogeneity of the s_i^2, no complete solution to the problem of combining three or more values of M can be given. If the three M_i in equations (14.8) had heterogeneous s_i^2, $\bar{M}$ and $V(\bar{M})$ would be computed by equations (14.2) and (14.3), using values of $V(M_i)$ based upon s_i^2 instead of upon a pooled variance. The theory of the Behrens distribution, and of the uses to which it is put in § 2.6, could be generalized from 2 to p independent variance estimates, but tables of deviates like Appendix Table III would have to be very extensive and are unlikely to be computed in the near future. In the absence of these tables, the best that can be done is to state upper and lower bounds to the deviate that should replace t in equations (14.7). Clearly it cannot be less than the t-deviate for Σf_i degrees of freedom, or in the numerical example 2·003. Similarly, the deviate required cannot exceed the largest d-deviate obtained by applying the method of the last paragraph to all possible pairs of estimates, though, if the pair for which d is largest happens to account for most of $\Sigma \omega_i$, the required deviate may be almost as great as this d. If now the standard errors in equations (14.8) are assumed to have been computed from the separate s_i^2, the d-deviate for M_1 and M_2 is 2·094, as found in the last paragraph; similarly, for M_1 and M_3 the deviate is 2·067 and for M_2 and M_3 it is 2·110. Consequently, equations (14.7) must be applied to the estimate

$$\bar{M} = 1·954 \pm 0·175$$

with a numerical value between 2·003 and 2·110 inserted for t. Often this argument is sufficiently exact for practical purposes. Here it indicates that at worst the limits are 1·59 and 2·32, but, since M_1 and M_3 carry most of the weight and have a smaller d-deviate, the range might safely be narrowed a little.

14.3 The combination of parallel line assays

The suggestions made in § 14.1 are far from satisfactory, since they depend upon g being negligible. Experience of parallel line assays indicates that very often g is too large to be ignored, and methods for combining estimates not subject to this restriction are therefore needed. The procedure suggested in this section is subject only to the condition that σ^2, the true variance per response, is the same for all the p assays, so that, as a preliminary to the computation of a combined estimate, $\bar{s}^2$, a pooled estimate of σ^2 may be formed. Thus the procedure cannot be used for assays in which different species of animal have been used as subjects, or different measurements have been taken as responses, or experimental techniques have been fundamentally different, since σ^2 could not then be regarded as constant. This is a severe restriction, but a method for the combination of estimates from assays using the same experimental technique (though not necessarily the same assay design) is valuable. In theory, homogeneity of the variance estimates for the several assays is essential ; in practice, general experience indicates that considerable heterogeneity may be permitted without serious effect on the conclusions. This question has not been thoroughly investigated, but no great harm seems likely to result from the pooling of estimates of σ^2 unless the several values of s^2 differ by factors of 10 or more.

Whatever the design of an assay, the log potency, M_i, in assay i may be written

$$M_i = \frac{1}{b_i} (H_i - b_i G_i), \tag{14.9}$$

where

$$G_i = \bar{x}_T - \bar{x}_S, \tag{14.10}$$

and

$$H_i = \bar{y}_T - \bar{y}_S. \tag{14.11}$$

Equation (14.9) is equivalent to equation (4.11). If R_0, the assumed potency used in determining doses for the test preparation, has been the same for all assays of a series, so that $(\bar{x}_T - \bar{x}_S)$ is constant, the equation might more conveniently be written

$$M_i = -G + \frac{H_i}{b_i}. \tag{14.12}$$

In some series, however, improving knowledge about ρ will lead to changes in R_0 for successive assays, and discussion of the more general problem is therefore desirable. An average log potency may be taken as

$$\bar{M} = \frac{\Sigma \omega_i (H_i - b_i G_i)}{\Sigma \omega_i b_i}, \tag{14.13}$$

where the weights, ω_i, are arbitrary quantities independent of the observations. Minor variations in weighting seldom affect the precision of a weighted mean to any important extent, especially if the weights are fairly near to the optimal. Some rule for selecting the ω_i is required, with the proviso that a complicated expression will almost certainly prove mathematically intractable.

As in § 13.1, the best procedure that is also amenable to a reasonably simple analysis appears to be to use as a criterion for selecting the ω_i an approximate minimization of the variance of $\bar{M}$. Even though some of the b_i are not large relative to their standard errors, in any useful compound of the assays

$$\bar{g} = \frac{t^2 \bar{s}^2 \Sigma \{ \omega_i^2 V(b_i) \}}{(\Sigma \omega_i b_i)^2} \qquad (14.14)$$

is likely to be small enough for $V(\bar{M})$ to be a good guide to the reliability of $\bar{M}$. With the suppositions that have been made, the numerator and denominator of $\bar{M}$ satisfy the conditions for Fieller's theorem. The variance formula, equation (2.10), may be written

$$V(\bar{M}) = \frac{1}{(\Sigma \omega_i b_i)^2} \left[\Sigma \{ \omega_i^2 V(H_i) \} - 2\Sigma \{ \omega_i^2 (\bar{M} + G_i) C(H_i, b_i) \} \right.$$
$$\left. + \Sigma \{ \omega_i^2 (\bar{M} + G_i)^2 V(b_i) \} \right], \qquad (14.15)$$

where $V(H_i)$, $V(b_i)$ are the variances of H_i and b_i and $C(H_i, b_i)$ is the covariance of these quantities. Most good assays will make the second and third terms on the right-hand side of equation (14.15) small relative to the first, so that

$$V(\bar{M}) \doteqdot \frac{\Sigma \omega_i^2 V(H_i)}{(\Sigma \omega_i b_i)^2} . \qquad (14.16)$$

Even if these terms are not small, the use of weights chosen to minimize the expression in equation (14.16) will not be wrong, but will merely fail to give the most precise estimate of potency.

The condition that this approximation to $V(\bar{M})$ shall take its minimum value is

$$\omega_i \propto \frac{b_i}{V(H_i)} . \qquad (14.17)$$

The numerator, b_i, is, unfortunately, dependent upon the data. In a series of assays of the same kind, however, it is likely to show only random variations, or genuine variations (attributable to minor changes in conditions) that are relatively small. Rejection of the factor b_i simplifies the statistical theory, and will have no material effect on the estimate unless the assays differ widely in their regression coefficients ; indeed, this step has the positive advantage of not giving extra weight to an assay which chances to have a large value of b_i for reasons unconnected with intrinsic precision. The denominator, $V(H_i)$, is the product of $\bar{s}^2$ and some factor determined merely by the configuration of the assay. In many simple assays, such as that in § 4.2,

$$V(H_i) = \bar{s}^2 \left(\frac{1}{N_S} + \frac{1}{N_T} \right)_i , \tag{14.18}$$

where N_S and N_T are the numbers of subjects for the standard and test preparations and the suffix i identifies the particular assay ; this remains true for a multiple assay from which information on a particular test preparation is to be abstracted, but may need to be modified for more complex assay designs such as the incomplete block designs of Chapter 9. Since $\bar{s}^2$ is a constant, the general rule is to take

$$\omega_i = \frac{\bar{s}^2}{V(H_i)} , \tag{14.19}$$

which for the simpler designs will reduce to

$$\omega_i = \left(\frac{N_S N_T}{N_S + N_T} \right)_i . \tag{14.20}$$

The fiducial limits of $\bar{M}$ can then be computed by the application of Fieller's theorem to the ratio in equation (14.13), with the aid of

$$V\{\Sigma\omega (H - bG)\} = \Sigma\omega^2 V(H) - 2\Sigma\omega^2 GC(H, b)$$
$$+ \Sigma\omega^2 G^2 V(b), \tag{14.21}$$

$$V\{\Sigma\omega b\} = \Sigma\omega^2 V(b), \tag{14.22}$$

$$C\{\Sigma\omega (H - bG), \Sigma\omega b\} = \Sigma\omega^2 C(H, b) - \Sigma\omega^2 GV(b). \tag{14.23}$$

In the simpler types of assay, for which H_i and b_i are based on orthogonal contrasts, $V(H_i)$ is given by equation (14.18) and

$$V(b_i) = \frac{\bar{s}^2}{(S_{xx})_i} ; \tag{14.24}$$

equations (14.21)–(14.23) then become

$$V\{\Sigma\omega\,(H-bG)\} = \bar{s}^2\left\{\Sigma\omega + \Sigma\left(\frac{\omega^2 G^2}{S_{xx}}\right)\right\}, \qquad (14.25)$$

$$V\{\Sigma\omega b\} = \bar{s}^2\Sigma\left(\frac{\omega^2}{S_{xx}}\right), \qquad (14.26)$$

$$C\{\Sigma\omega\,(H-bG),\ \Sigma\omega b\} = -\bar{s}^2\,\Sigma\left(\frac{\omega^2 G}{S_{xx}}\right). \qquad (14.27)$$

Equation (14.15) takes the simple form

$$V(\bar{M}) = \bar{s}^2\left[\Sigma\omega + \Sigma\left\{\frac{\omega^2\,(\bar{M}+G)^2}{S_{xx}}\right\}\right] \div (\Sigma\omega b)^2, \quad (14.28)$$

and for a theoretically preferable determination of limits Fieller's theorem may easily be applied. If the assays are all of identical design except for differences in the total number of subjects, $(N_S + N_T)$, the formulæ may be further simplified.

The method of weighting advocated above is very similar to that proposed by Fieller (1944), who, however, was concerned with a more restricted class of designs (4-point twin cross-overs). He determined his weights so as to minimize $V(b)$, where b is the weighted mean regression coefficient

$$b = \frac{\Sigma\omega b}{\Sigma\omega}, \qquad (14.29)$$

and therefore took

$$\omega_i = \frac{\bar{s}^2}{V(b_i)}. \qquad (14.30)$$

The definition of ω_i in equation (14.19) seems preferable, because in general it will lead more nearly to the minimization of $V(\bar{M})$. In many simple instances, and in particular for the assays discussed by Fieller (cf. § 14.6), the alternative formulæ for ω_i differ only by a constant factor and therefore lead to the same conclusions.

If the true variance per response, σ_i^2, were known for each assay, the necessity for pooling information on $\bar{s}^2$ would disappear. The same line of argument would be used, but the σ_i^2 would be incorporated into the weights to give

$$\omega_i = \frac{1}{V(H_i)}. \qquad (14.31)$$

Equations (14.21)–(14.23) would remain applicable, and equations (14.24)–(14.28) would require little modification. Even though the σ_i^2 are unknown, if the s_i^2 are heterogeneous and each is based on a large number of degrees of freedom (say 30 or more), the same procedure might be used. For heterogeneous values of s_i^2 based on small numbers of degrees of freedom, no exact method is possible except when only two assays are involved and the conditions for the second analogue of Fieller's theorem are fulfilled (*cf.* § 9.5).

When the assays to be combined are entirely different in type, as for example line test and percentage ash assays for vitamin D, the units of measurement for H_i and b_i will be different in different assays, and combination in the manner described here seems inappropriate. Irwin's (1950) suggestions for dealing with this problem are closely related to the method of this section. He defined a weighted mean as in equation (14.13), and noted that, whatever the weights may be, the expression

$$\Sigma \omega_i \left(H_i - b_i G_i - b_i \log \rho \right) \qquad (14.32)$$

has expectation zero ; he then proposed to choose the ω_i so as to minimize the variance of this expression, but considered that the difference of units of measurement made inevitable a choice of weights inversely proportional to the standard errors of $(H_i - b_i G_i - b_i \log \rho)$. This seems rather to beg the question, for there is no obvious sense in which it leads to the ' best ' composite estimate of ρ. It overcomes the difficulty of deciding what is meant by the weighted totals in the numerator and denominator of $\bar{M}$, but adopts the arbitrary convention that the $(H_i - b_i G_i)$ and the b_i are to be regarded as simply additive after division by the standard errors of $(H_i - b_i G_i - b_i \log \rho)$. A more satisfactory alternative will not easily be found.

14.4 Replication within blocks

A question that may conveniently be examined at this stage is that of the form of analysis to be adopted when doses are replicated within all or some of the blocks of subjects. For example, if litters of eight subjects were available for use in a 4-point assay such as that in § 4.13, the natural course would be to assign two subjects from each litter to each dose. How should this affect the analysis of the data and the assessment of potency ? For the laboratory animals in general use, litters large enough to allow more than two subjects per dose will be uncommon, but blocks based upon some other classification of subjects might easily be larger.

In an assay that employs litter-mate control and has one subject per dose from each litter, the component of the analysis of variance commonly termed 'Error' (*cf.* Table 4.6) is in reality composed of 'Doses × Litters' interactions. When replication within blocks is adopted, the analysis of variance will have a component for intra-litter error independent of (orthogonal to) these interactions. If the experimenter wished only to test the significance of the separate dose contrasts, he would be concerned with whether a contrast was large in comparison with its variations from litter to litter ; as is right and customary in the analysis of experiments, he would use the interaction with litters for his estimate of error. Most workers in biological assay, including the present writer, have assumed the same estimate of error variance to be appropriate when the relative potency is estimated : examination of the mathematical model of the experiment has now shown this to be entirely false.

The right procedure might have been guessed from an alternative approach to the problem. Each litter can be regarded as constituting a self-contained assay. When litters are of a size to give only two subjects per dose, the idea of analysing for each separately is unattractive because the estimates would be of very low precision. Nevertheless, they could be formed, and, if they were, the intra-litter variance would almost certainly be used without further thought. Provided that the intra-litter variances from the several litters could be pooled, the method of combining independent estimates of potency (§ 14.3) could be used, and would take the simple form applicable when G_i is the same for all assays and the H_i and b_i contrasts are orthogonal (at least in fully symmetrical assays). The interactions between dose differences and litters play no part in the assessment of error, and are relevant only to tests of the agreement between litters in respect of the magnitudes of separate contrasts.

This argument is easily justified and clarified by study of the structure of the analysis of variance. For simplicity, consider a 6-point assay. Suppose that K litters each contain $6r$ subjects, so that every litter provides r subjects per dose. The natural mathematical model to take will be one in which the response to any specified dose is the sum of four components ; these represent the responsiveness of the litter, the general level of potency of the preparation, a regression coefficient (characterizing the sensitivity of a litter) multiplied by the deviation of log dose from an arbitrary zero, and a random error. Thus a regression coefficient calculated from the data for the ith litter alone would be an estimate of β_i, where β_i may be supposed to arise in a random selection of litters from a population in which the true coefficients have mean $\bar{\beta}$ and variance ψ^2 between litters. Of course, $\psi^2 = 0$ (and consequently $\beta_i =$ constant) is a permissible special case of this specification, but the more general situation needs to be discussed here. The condition of similarity (§ 3.3) requires that ρ be constant over all litters ; the difference in expected response between doses of the two preparations having equal dose metameters must therefore be $\beta_i \log \rho$. This establishes a relationship between two of the components of the responses ; with the symbols and conventions of Chapter 5, the doses and expected responses for the ith litter, expressed as deviations from the mean for the litter, are :—

Dose	x	Expected response
S_1	-1	$-\beta_i (\tfrac{1}{2} \log \rho + 1)$
S_2	0	$-\tfrac{1}{2}\beta_i \log \rho$
S_3	1	$-\beta_i (\tfrac{1}{2} \log \rho - 1)$
T_1	-1	$\beta_i (\tfrac{1}{2} \log \rho - 1)$
T_2	0	$\tfrac{1}{2}\beta_i \log \rho$
T_3	1	$\beta_i (\tfrac{1}{2} \log \rho + 1)$

The difference between any observed response and its expectation according to this model will be ε, a random error usually supposed normally distributed with mean zero and variance σ^2 ; as implied above, σ^2 will be assumed to be the same for all litters.

The model is similar to the one that would be used if, say, the experiment were intended only for examining the significance of differences between six different diets in respect of weight changes of animals. The only modification is the restriction in the parametric representation of expected responses brought about by the condition of similarity and the logical relationship between doses. The formation of the expectations of the mean squares in the analysis of variance is a familiar problem in the study of experimental designs (*e.g.* Fisher, 1958, § 40 ; Snedecor, 1956, Chapter 11), and Table 14.1 summarizes these expectations for the present assay. The first point that emerges is that, unless all the regression coefficients are equal, the five constituents of the Doses × Litters interaction are not homogeneous ; in general, the mean squares for Preparations × Litters and Regression × Litters will have expectations that are unequal and greater than those for the other three items. This in itself is interesting, since the common practice is to pool the interactions, but the next stage is still more remarkable.

TABLE 14.1—Expectations of mean squares in the analysis of variance for a 6-point assay with K litters of $6r$ subjects each

Nature of variation	d.f.	Expected mean square
Litters	$K - 1$	—
Preparations (L_p) ...	1	$\sigma^2 + \frac{3}{2}r\psi^2(\log\rho)^2 + \frac{3}{2}Kr\bar{\beta}^2(\log\rho)^2$
Regression (L_1) ...	1	$\sigma^2 + 4r\psi^2 + 4Kr\bar{\beta}^2$
Parallelism (L_1') ...	1	σ^2
Quadratic (L_2) ...	1	σ^2
Difference of quadratics (L_2')	1	σ^2
$L_p \times$ Litters	$K - 1$	$\sigma^2 + \frac{3}{2}r\psi^2(\log\rho)^2$
$L_1 \times$ Litters	$K - 1$	$\sigma^2 + 4r\psi^2$
$L_1' \times$ Litters	$K - 1$	σ^2
$L_2 \times$ Litters	$K - 1$	σ^2
$L_2' \times$ Litters	$K - 1$	σ^2
Error	$6K(r - 1)$	σ^2
Total	$6Kr - 1$	—

A test of significance of the difference between mean responses to the two preparations is an adjunct to the testing of validity (§ 4.7), and may be both interesting and important if corresponding doses have been chosen on the basis of some guessed or theoretical potency. For this test, the mean squares for L_p and $L_p \times$ Litters should be compared by the variance ratio distribution (Appendix Table II). Similarly, a comparison of the mean squares for L_1 and $L_1 \times$ Litters would give a test of significance of the deviation from zero of the mean regression coefficient ; this test is of little interest, since no assay would be undertaken without strong prior evidence of significance. The tests of significance usually required, however, are the validity tests of the squares for L_1', L_2, and (of less importance) L_2' ; these might be compared each with the corresponding interaction mean square, or all with a pooled mean square formed from the three interactions and the intra-litter error. In the model that is the basis of Table 14.1, this pooling is legitimate, but the homogeneity of the four components pooled would be disturbed if the model were modified to allow for, say, non-parallelism or non-linearity : since the need for such a modification would demonstrate either statistical or fundamental invalidity, the tests may legitimately be made against the pooled error with $3(2Kr - K - 1)$ degrees of freedom.

For an assay that is regarded as valid, interest attaches not to L_p and L_1 separately, but to their ratio, which is linearly related to M. In fact, if the dose scales have been so chosen that the values of x given above are actual log doses, the argument of § 5.2 shows that

$$M = \frac{4L_p}{3L_1}. \tag{14.33}$$

This and its limits need to be multiplied by d, in order to convert to logarithms to base 10, but that is a final stage independent of the present discussion. The fiducial limits of M will be found by Fieller's theorem, which depends upon consideration of the quantity

$$\frac{4L_p}{3} - L_1 \log \rho. \tag{14.34}$$

Now, from the model of the experiment,

$$L_1 = 4r\,(\beta_1 + \beta_2 + \ldots + \beta_K) + \text{sums and differences of } 4Kr \text{ values of } \varepsilon, \tag{14.35}$$

and

$$L_p = 3r\,(\log \rho)(\beta_1 + \beta_2 + \ldots \beta_K) + \text{sums and differences of } 6Kr \text{ values of } \varepsilon, \tag{14.36}$$

from which

$$E(L_1) = 4Kr\bar{\beta} \tag{14.37}$$

and

$$E(L_p) = 3Kr\bar{\beta} \log \rho. \tag{14.38}$$

Hence

$$V(L_1) = 4Kr\sigma^2 + 16Kr^2\psi^2 \tag{14.39}$$

and

$$V(L_p) = 6Kr\sigma^2 + 9Kr^2\psi^2 (\log \rho)^2. \tag{14.40}$$

Moreover, although the functions of the random errors, ε, that occur in L_p and L_1 are orthogonal, the first terms in equations (14.35) and (14.36) are proportional. Consequently, L_p and L_1 have a covariance of amount

$$C(L_p, L_1) = 12Kr^2\psi^2 \log \rho. \tag{14.41}$$

The variance of the expression (14.34) is therefore

$$\begin{aligned} V\left(\frac{4L_p}{3} - L_1 \log \rho\right) &= \frac{32}{3} Kr\sigma^2 + 16Kr^2\psi^2 (\log \rho)^2 - 32Kr^2\psi^2 (\log \rho)^2 \\ &\quad + 4Kr\sigma^2 (\log \rho)^2 + 16Kr^2\psi^2 (\log \rho)^2 \\ &= \frac{4}{3} Kr\sigma^2\{8 + 3 (\log \rho)^2\}, \end{aligned} \tag{14.42}$$

which is a function of σ^2 only, independent of ψ^2. Though variations in β_i from litter to litter increase the variances of L_p and L_1 separately, the variance of the expression (14.34), and therefore also the fiducial limits of M, are unaffected by these variations. If σ^2 is replaced by s^2, an estimate from the analysis of variance, the method of derivation of Fieller's theorem (Fieller, 1940, 1944) shows that the fiducial limits to M are the roots of the equation obtained by equating the square of the expression (14.34) to t^2 times its variance. Writing μ for $\log \rho$, the equation becomes

$$\left(\frac{4L_p}{3} - \mu L_1\right)^2 = \frac{4}{3} Krt^2s^2 (8 + 3\mu^2). \tag{14.43}$$

The roots of this equation are easily shown to lead to equation (5.28) for the fiducial limits of ρ, with $N = 6Kr$. The value of s^2 used might be the intra-litter estimate with $6K(r-1)$ degrees of freedom, or, as recommended above, the pooled estimate with $3(2Kr - K - 1)$ degrees of freedom. The choice should be made on grounds of general policy before the experiment is done, and not simply as the smaller of the two alternatives.

Table 14.1 indicates that information on ρ, additional to that obtained in the ordinary manner from the ratio of the L_p and L_1 totals, is contained in the mean square for $L_p \times$ Litters. In fact, an estimate could be constructed from comparison of the mean squares for $L_p \times$ Litters, $L_1 \times$ Litters, and intra-litter error, but the precision of this seems likely to be too low to make the development of the appropriate complicated theory worthwhile.

Though the theory has been developed only for the particular case of a 6-point assay, it may easily be seen to be perfectly general. The same result will hold for any parallel line or slope ratio assay in which the blocks are large enough to provide two or more subjects for each dose ; even the use of blocks of different sizes, as when some litters of eight subjects and others of four are available for a 4-point assay, does not alter it. In all these assays, the fiducial limits to the relative potency should be based upon an estimate of the intra-litter variance (which may include such Doses × Litter interactions as have the same expected mean squares) and not on the mean square from interactions of the preparations and regression contrasts with litters. This is in direct contradiction of statements made by Wood at a meeting of the Biometric Society in 1950, with which I then expressed full agreement (Gridgeman, 1950) ; we have since corrected ourselves (Finney and Wood, 1951).

What are the implications of this when $r = 1$, that is to say when the blocks are large enough only for one subject per dose to be taken from each ? The analysis then provides no direct estimate of intra-block variance, and the usual practice is to describe as ' error ' the pooled Doses × Litters interactions. Provided that ψ^2, the inter-block variance of the regression coefficients, is zero or negligible, this will be satisfactory, but if ψ^2 is large it will lead to over-estimation of variance and thus to fiducial limits that are too widely spaced. The difficulty could be overcome by eliminating the $L_p \times$ Litters and $L_1 \times$ Litters components from the estimate of error, but this would often leave too few degrees of freedom for a satisfactory estimate. In practice, ψ^2 is likely to be small in many assays, but the possibility must be borne in mind that the familiar methods of analysis for assays such as the oestrone assay in Table 4.5

or the penicillin assay in Table 5.5 may underestimate the precision of the figure obtained for relative potency. The consequences for incomplete block designs will be similar in principle but more complicated in arithmetic; they will not be discussed here, but are likely to be reasonably straightforward for confounded designs such as those of § 9.9, very awkward for balanced incomplete blocks.

In their 4-point penicillin assays, Knudsen and Randall (1943) found greater inter-plate variance for L_1 than for L_p, and concluded that the numerator and denominator of M must be assigned different variances for calculating limits. As shown in § 6.7, failure to randomize does not satisfactorily explain the situation. An alternative worth considering is that the plates differed in values of β, making ψ^2 appreciably greater than zero, so that the expected mean squares for $L_p \times$ Plates and $L_1 \times$ Plates would differ from one another and from that for $L_1' \times$ Plates. The correct procedure then would not be that adopted by Knudsen and Randall, but rather to use the mean square from $L_1' \times$ Plates as s^2.

Bliss (1952a, b) has strongly criticized the model suggested here, but his objection appears to be only that in assays he has examined he found no evidence of a non-zero ψ^2. The present model includes the simpler as a special case that is doubtless the most important in practice. However, Bliss's contention that to estimate σ^2 by pooling interactions of L_p and L_1 as well as of other contrasts will make appropriate allowance for non-linearity and even for imperfect parallelism seems to lack justification.

14.5 Two assays of vitamin D_3

Table 14.2 contains data from two assays of vitamin D_3 in the same test preparation, each using the line test scores as responses; the scores were recorded to the nearest half-unit, and have been multiplied by two for arithmetical convenience. These were 4-point assays, using litter-mate control; eight rats from each of six litters were divided into four pairs, one for each dose. In the first assay, the doses for the test preparation were chosen on the basis of an assumed potency of 4/3 i.u. per mg., and in the second this was changed to 16/15 i.u. per mg. The dose ratio, D, was 2 in both.

TABLE 14.2—Line test scores for two assays of vitamin D₃ in a test preparation

The scores are multiplied by 2

(a) Assay 1

Litter	Standard preparation		Test preparation		Total
	0·4 i.u.	0·8 i.u.	0·3 mg.	0·6 mg.	
I	3 4 } 7	4 6 } 10	4 2 } 6	4 5 } 9	32
II	2 4 } 6	4 5 } 9	5 5 } 10	5 7 } 12	37
III	3 2 } 5	3 4 } 7	3 4 } 7	4 4 } 8	27
IV	4 4 } 8	5 7 } 12	2 3 } 5	4 5 } 9	34
V	4 5 } 9	6 7 } 13	4 5 } 9	5 5 } 10	41
VI	4 6 } 10	5 7 } 12	4 4 } 8	6 7 } 13	43
Total	45	63	45	61	214

(b) Assay 2

Litter	Standard preparation		Test preparation		Total
	0·4 i.u.	0·8 i.u.	0·375 mg.	0·75 mg.	
I	3 3 } 6	4 7 } 11	4 6 } 10	5 7 } 12	39
II	2 2 } 4	4 4 } 8	4 5 } 9	5 6 } 11	32
III	2 3 } 5	5 5 } 10	4 4 } 8	5 5 } 10	33
IV	3 3 } 6	4 5 } 9	4 5 } 9	5 7 } 12	36
V	3 3 } 6	4 4 } 8	3 2 } 5	6 5 } 11	30
VI	3 4 } 7	4 5 } 9	3 6 } 9	4 7 } 11	36
Total	34	55	50	67	206

The analyses of variance follow the standard pattern, except that the use of pairs of litter-mates on each dose, made possible by the availability of large litters, allows direct estimation of an intra-litter variance, as described in § 14.4. Thus, for the first assay,

$$L_p = - 45 - 63 + 45 + 61$$
$$= - 2,$$

and the square for preparations is therefore

$$\frac{(- 2)^2}{48} = 0 \cdot 0833.$$

A component for the interaction of preparations and litters is obtained by forming the L_p contrast for each litter and computing in the usual manner:

$$[(- 2)^2 + (7)^2 + (3)^2 + (- 6)^2 + (- 3)^2 + (- 1)^2$$
$$- 8 \times 0 \cdot 0833] \div 8 = 13 \cdot 4167.$$

The other litter interactions are similarly formed. Just as the sum of the components for preparations, regression, and parallelism is checked by agreement with the sum of squares of deviations between doses, so the sum of the litter interactions is checked by agreement with the complete Doses × Litters component:

$$[(7)^2 + (6)^2 + (5)^2 + (8)^2 + \ldots + (10)^2 + (13)^2$$
$$- 2 \times 954 \cdot 0833] \div 2 - 21 \cdot 9167$$
$$- (0 \cdot 0833 + 24 \cdot 0833 + 0 \cdot 0834) = 17 \cdot 7500.$$

As a further check, the error (within litters) may be formed independently, from differences between pairs of responses:

$$[(4 - 3)^2 + (4 - 2)^2 + (2 - 3)^2 + \ldots + (7 - 6)^2] \div 2 = 20 \cdot 0000.$$

The two analyses of variance appear in Table 14.3.

The analysis of assays of this type has been discussed in § 14.4, where the conclusion was reached that the estimate of error variance to be used in the computation of fiducial limits should be taken from the intra-litter sum of squares augmented by interactions of dose contrasts other than L_p and L_1 with litters. Thus for each assay a value of s^2 with 29 degrees of freedom is obtained. Comparison of $L_p \times$ Litters and $L_1 \times$ Litters with this error does not give any clear indication of a variation in the regression coefficient from litter to litter. The large mean square for $L_p \times$ Litters in Assay 1 is worrying, but the smallness of the $L_1 \times$ Litters mean square in the same analysis suggests that chance is responsible. Some suspicion of statistical invalidity is aroused by this odd behaviour,

TABLE 14.3—Analyses of variance for the data of Table 14.2
(a) Assay 1

Adjustment for mean		954·0833	Mean square
Nature of variation	d.f.	Sum of squares	
Litters	5	21·9167	4·3833
Preparations	1	0·0833	0·0833
Regression	1	24·0833	24·0833
Parallelism	1	0·0834	0·0834
$L_p \times$ Litters	5	13·4167	2·6833
$L_1 \times$ Litters	5	1·9167	0·3833
$L_1' \times$ Litters	5	2·4166	0·7730
Error (intra-litter) ...	24	20·0000	
Total	47	83·9167	

(b) Assay 2

Adjustment for mean		⁻ 884·0833	Mean square
Nature of variation	d.f.	Sum of squares	
Litters	5	6·6667	1·3333
Preparations	1	16·3333	16·3333
Regression	1	30·0833	30·0833
Parallelism	1	0·3334	0·3334
$L_p \times$ Litters	5	2·9167	0·5833
$L_1 \times$ Litters	5	1·1667	0·2333
$L_1' \times$ Litters	5	4·4166	0·9799
Error (intra-litter) ...	24	24·0000	
Total	47	85·9167	

but, for the present purpose of illustrating the computations for the combination of data, it may be ignored. Assay 2 has a regrettably large mean square for preparations, indicating that the

change in the assumed potency made for this assay was for the
worse. However, no signs of invalidity such as non-parallelism
appear, and the estimation of potency may proceed.

Before combining the results of the two assays, separate computations will be shown for each. In order to apply the formulæ
of § 14.3, $(\bar{x}_T - \bar{x}_S)$ must be expressed on the same scale of logarithms
as is to be used in the calculations ; the ratio of high dose to low
is 2 in both assays, and therefore logarithms to base $2^{\frac{1}{2}}$ will be used,
so that G_i is obtained by division of the common logarithm of the
ratio of corresponding doses, $\log_{10}(3/4)$ or $\log_{10}(15/16)$, by $\frac{1}{2} \log_{10}2$.
Preliminary steps in the computations may be summarized as in
Table 14.4, these having been obtained by the procedures usual for
4-point assays.

TABLE 14.4—Summary of first stages in potency estimation for the assays
of Table 14.2

	Assay 1	Assay 2
$\bar{x}_T - \bar{x}_S$	− 0·8301	− 0·1862
$\bar{y}_T - \bar{y}_S$	− 0·08333	1·16667
b	0·70833	0·79167
$M + (\bar{x}_T - \bar{x}_S)$	− 0·1176	1·4737
M	0·7125	1·6599
s^2 (29 d.f.)	0·7730	0·9799
t	2·045	2·045
g	0·1342	0·1362

From Table 14.4, for the first assay

$$M_L, M_U = 0\cdot8301 - \left[0\cdot1176 \pm \frac{2\cdot045}{0\cdot70833} \left\{ \left(\frac{0\cdot8658}{12} + \frac{(0\cdot1176)^2}{48} \right) \times 0\cdot7730 \right\}^{\frac{1}{2}} \right] \div 0\cdot8658$$

$$= 0\cdot8301 - [0\cdot1176 \pm 0\cdot6832] \div 0\cdot8658$$

$$= - 0\cdot0948, \ 1\cdot4834.$$

Similarly for the second assay
$$M_L, M_U = 0\cdot8787, 2\cdot9058.$$
Multiplication by $0\cdot15052$ converts all M values to logarithms to base 10, whence the potency estimates are as shown in Table 14.5. Each R lies just outside the fiducial range for the other ; this does not imply that they are significantly different, since the minimum significant difference between two values of M will exceed the semi-fiducial range of either.

From the values already quoted, s_1^2 and s_2^2 are seen to be not significantly different. Hence the pooled estimate of variance, with 58 degrees of freedom, may be used in combining the evidence of the two assays :
$$\bar{s}^2 = \frac{22\cdot4166 + 28\cdot4166}{58}$$
$$= 0\cdot8764.$$
The designs are fully symmetrical, and equation (14.20) gives
$$\omega_1 = \omega_2 = \frac{24 \times 24}{48}$$
$$= 12.$$
Some arithmetic might be saved here by taking both weights as unity, but this would slightly alter equation (14.25), and the method of § 14.3 will here be retained exactly.

The numerical values for the separate assays lead to
$$H_1 - b_1 G_1 = -0\cdot08333 + 0\cdot70833 \times 0\cdot8301$$
$$= 0\cdot5047,$$
$$H_2 - b_2 G_2 = 1\cdot3141.$$
By equation (14.13),
$$\bar{M} = \frac{12 \times 0\cdot5047 + 12 \times 1\cdot3141}{12 \times 0\cdot70833 + 12 \times 0\cdot79167}$$
$$= 1\cdot2125.$$
Since $S_{xx} = 48$ for each assay, equations (14.25)–(14.27) give
$$V\{\Sigma\omega\,(H - bG)\} = \bar{s}^2\,(24 + 3G_1^2 + 3G_2^2)$$
$$= 26\cdot1712\bar{s}^2,$$
$$V\{\Sigma\omega b\} = 6\cdot0000\bar{s}^2,$$
$$C\{\Sigma\omega\,(H - bG), \Sigma\omega b\} = -\bar{s}^2\,(3G_1 + 3G_2)$$
$$= 3\cdot0489\bar{s}^2,$$

In the usual manner

$$g = \frac{(2 \cdot 002)^2 \times 6\bar{s}^2}{(18 \cdot 0000)^2}$$
$$= 0 \cdot 0650,$$

and Fieller's theorem gives

$$\bar{M}_L, \bar{M}_U = [\, 1 \cdot 2125 - \frac{0 \cdot 0650 \times 3 \cdot 0489}{6 \cdot 0000} \pm \frac{2 \cdot 002}{18 \cdot 000} \{ \bar{s}^2 \times (26 \cdot 1712$$
$$- 2 \times 1 \cdot 2125 \times 3 \cdot 0489 + (1 \cdot 2125)^2 \times 6 \cdot 0000$$
$$- 0 \cdot 0650 \times 24 \cdot 6219) \}^{\frac{1}{2}}] \div 0 \cdot 9350$$
$$= [1 \cdot 2125 - 0 \cdot 0330 \pm 0 \cdot 5309] \div 0 \cdot 9350$$
$$= 0 \cdot 6937, \ 1 \cdot 8293.$$

The estimated potency is now evaluated as 1·52 i.u. per mg., with fiducial limits at 1·27 i.u. per mg. and 1·88 i.u. per mg. When the two assays were analysed separately, the fiducial ranges were found to be 54 per cent. and 78 per cent. of the respective estimates ; the combination of evidence has reduced the range to 40 per cent. of the estimate.   As might be expected, the combination of two assays of approximately equal precision reduces the fiducial range by a factor of about $\sqrt{2}$ (rather more, because of the reduction in g).

TABLE 14.5—Comparison of estimates and fiducial limits in two assays of vitamin D_3

	Assay 1	Assay 2	Combined
Estimated potency of test preparation (i.u. per mg.)	1·28	1·78	1·52
Limits (i.u. per mg.) ...	0·97–1·67	1·36–2·74	1·27–1·88
Limits as % of estimate	76–130	76–154	84–124

14.6   A series of cross-over assays

The arithmetic becomes less laborious when G_i is constant. In the paper from which the example in § 10.3 was taken, Smith et al. (1944) report briefly three more cross-over assays of the same sample of insulin ; all were identical in design and doses, and only the first had the complication of a lost subject. The quantities required in combining the information from the four assays are summarized in Table 14.6, using the notation of Chapter 10 and the present chapter instead of that adopted by the original authors. The exact analysis for the first assay has been discussed in § 10.8, and entries in Table 14.6 are either from that section or adapted from Tables V and VI of Smith's paper.

TABLE 14.6—Summary of four assays of a test preparation of insulin

Assay no.	Error		$H = \bar{y}_T - \bar{y}_S$	b	$V(H)$	$V(b)$	$C(H, b)$
	d.f.	Sum of squares					
1	7	70·67	0·833	3·500	$3s^2/16$	$3s^2/64$	$- s^2/96$
2	8	151·87	− 3·942	3·262	$s^2/6$	$s^2/24$	0
3	8	267·32	− 0·432	5·584	$s^2/6$	$s^2/24$	0
4	8	325·40	2·150	5·759	$s^2/6$	$s^2/24$	0

At first sight, the error mean squares for the four assays seem to differ quite widely, but equation (3.39) gives

$$\chi^2_{[3]} = 3 \cdot 90,$$

a value in good agreement with a hypothesis of homogeneity. The pooled variance estimate is

$$\bar{s}^2 = \frac{815 \cdot 26}{31}$$
$$= 26 \cdot 299$$

with 31 degrees of freedom. From the $V(H)$ column in Table 14.6, the weights to be assigned to the assays ought to be taken as 16/3 for the first, 6 for each of the others. For arithmetical convenience, take weights in proportion to these :

$$\omega_1 = 8,$$
$$\omega_2 = \omega_3 = \omega_4 = 9.$$

This series of assays introduces the complication of non-orthogonality of H_i and b_i, on account of the missing subject in Assay 1, but is simplified in another direction because the G_i are zero. By equation (14.13),

$$\bar{M} = -\frac{13 \cdot 352}{159 \cdot 445}$$
$$= -0 \cdot 0837.$$

Equations (14.21) (14.23) give

$$V(\Sigma\omega H) = \bar{s}^2 \left(64 \times \frac{3}{16} + 81 \times 3 \times \frac{1}{6} \right)$$
$$= \frac{105\bar{s}^2}{2},$$

$$V(\Sigma\omega b) = \bar{s}^2 \left(64 \times \frac{3}{64} + 81 \times 3 \times \frac{1}{24} \right)$$
$$= \frac{105\bar{s}^2}{8},$$

and

$$C(\Sigma\omega H, \Sigma\omega b) = -\frac{64\bar{s}^2}{96}$$
$$= -\frac{2\bar{s}^2}{3}.$$

Hence

$$g = \frac{(2 \cdot 039)^2 \times 105 \times 26 \cdot 299}{(159 \cdot 445)^2 \times 8}$$
$$= 0 \cdot 0564,$$

and the fiducial limits to $\bar{M}$ are

$$M_L, M_U = \left[-0 \cdot 0837 + \frac{0 \cdot 0564 \times 16}{315} \pm \frac{2 \cdot 039}{159 \cdot 445} \{ 26 \cdot 299 \times (52 \cdot 5000 \right.$$
$$- 2 \times 0 \cdot 0837 \times 0 \cdot 6667 + (0 \cdot 0837)^2 \times 13 \cdot 1250$$
$$- 0 \cdot 0564 \times 52 \cdot 4661) \}^{\frac{1}{2}}] \div 0 \cdot 9436$$
$$= -0 \cdot 5747, \ 0 \cdot 4035.$$

The assumed potency was 22 units per mg., and the dose ratio was 2. Multiplication of the M values by $0 \cdot 15052$ and evaluation of the antilogarithms gives a potency estimate of $21 \cdot 4$ units per mg., with limits at $18 \cdot 0$ units per mg. and $25 \cdot 3$ units per mg.

14.7 The combination of slope ratio assays

A method similar to that of § 14.3 may be applied to slope ratio assays. Only the simplest form will be discussed here. Suppose that a pooled variance estimate, $\bar{s}^2$, can be used, and that the choice of doses for all assays of the series was based on the same assumed potency, R_0. For any one assay,

$$R = \frac{R_0 b_T}{b_S} \, .$$ (14.44)

An average potency, $\bar{R}$, may be defined with the aid of arbitrary weights as

$$\bar{R} = \frac{R_0 \Sigma \omega b_T}{\Sigma \omega b_S} \, .$$ (14.45)

The formula for the approximate variance of $\bar{R}$, analogous to equation (7.21), is

$$V(\bar{R}) = \frac{R_0^2 \bar{s}^2}{(\Sigma \omega b_S)^2} \left\{ \Sigma \omega^2 \, v_{22} - \frac{2\bar{R} v_{12}}{R_0} + \frac{\bar{R}^2 v_{11}}{R_0^2} \right\},$$ (14.46)

where v_{11}, v_{12}, v_{22} are the usual multipliers of s^2 required to give the variances and covariance of b_S, b_T.

Now $V(\bar{R})$ will be minimized by a choice of weights that gives

$$\omega \propto \frac{b_S}{v_{22} - \dfrac{2\bar{R} v_{12}}{R_0} + \dfrac{\bar{R}^2 v_{11}}{R_0^2}} \, .$$ (14.47)

If the choice of doses has been good, $\bar{R}$ will be approximately equal to R_0, and in ω they may be taken as equal ; retention of $\bar{R}$ in a formula for the weight would create difficulties because of its dependence on the data. Moreover, the factor b_S must be dropped, just as was b in § 14.3. Hence the weight may be defined as

$$\omega = \frac{1}{v_{22} - 2v_{12} + v_{11}} \, ,$$ (14.48)

a formula which depends only on the design of the assay and not on the data. If all the assays have the same design, though they differ in their total numbers of subjects, N,

$$\omega = N$$ (14.49)

may be taken. If all are $(2k + 1)$-point symmetrical designs, but not necessarily having the same N or k, equation (7.28) may be used to show that

$$\omega = \frac{N(k + 1)}{k} \, ,$$ (14.50)

apart from a constant factor. When the weights have been decided, Fieller's theorem may be applied to the determination of fiducial limits to $\bar{R}$, as defined by equation (14.45), in the usual manner.

CHAPTER 15

VALIDITY AND THE CHOICE OF METAMETERS

15.1 Fundamental validity

A number of questions relating to the validity of assays, and especially to statistical validity, must now be examined in greater detail than before. Some of the ideas of this chapter have been presented earlier, especially in Chapters 3, 4, and 6, but their reconsideration at this stage should enable the reader to appreciate more fully their importance to the whole practice of assay. This chapter relates only to analytical dilution assays, since the whole problem of what is being estimated, and consequently what is the validity of the estimate, is much less clearly defined for purely comparative assays. The discussion in §§ 15.1 to 15.5 owes much to an important paper by Jerne and Wood (1949). Papers by Gaddum (1950), Miles (1952) and Schild (1950) should also be read, with particular attention to Miles's remarks on heterogeneous materials.

The fundamental condition for assay validity is that expressed by the condition of similarity (§ 3.3), namely that the dose-response curves for the standard and test preparations are identical except for replacement of z by ρz (where z measures the actual amount of the dose). If the condition of similarity is not satisfied, the test preparation cannot be regarded simply as a dilution of the standard preparation in an inert diluent, and the assay is therefore fundamentally invalid. If the true response curves could be determined exactly, an exact check on this condition could be applied. Even a small discrepancy between the forms of the two curves would suffice to disprove it, and, however valuable the dose-response relationships might then be as expressions of the reactions of the subjects to the two preparations, they could not legitimately be used as a basis for an analytical dilution assay. A point sometimes forgotten is that similarity requires identity of form in the response curves over the complete range of doses, not merely over some restricted portion for which they are linear.

In particular, if the standard preparation shows a response curve which asymptotically approaches a limiting value, the test preparation must have the same asymptote.

In practice, of course, the response curves cannot be known exactly, and must be estimated from experimental data. The curves estimated for the two preparations may fail to be identical in form for one of two reasons :

(i) Errors of estimation, arising from the natural variability of responses, obscure the true relationship ;

(ii) The true curves do not conform to the condition of similarity.

The first of these reasons is complicated by the fact that, in order to enable an estimate to be formed, a mathematical model for the response curve must be known or assumed ; for example, it might be assumed to be a straight line, a cubic polynomial, or a logistic function of the logarithm of dose. The process of estimation then involves determination of the best values for a specific set of parameters. Apparent deviation from similarity may result from use of a model that is adequate only over a limited range of doses. For example, an attempt might be made to represent the regression of response on log dose by a straight line, when in reality the relationship is logistic but effectively linear over a moderate range of doses. If the doses used for the standard preparation lie within the linear portion of the curve, but those chosen for the rest preparation happen to be a little too high, the best fitting straight line for the test preparation will tend to have a lesser slope than the corresponding line for the standard preparation. When a test of parallelism is applied as a test of similarity, a significant deviation may be found, yet the true curves might conform perfectly to the condition of similarity. This is an additional reason for the use of symmetrical assay designs, with doses of the test preparation guessed as well as possible to be equivalent to corresponding doses of the standard (§§ 6.8, 8.2), since the two response curves are thereby examined over equivalent portions. In a parallel line assay, any deviation from parallelism must then be the result of chance fluctuations in the size of the responses, and a significance test is directly a test for the condition of similarity.

No statistical test of significance can give an absolute decision on this question, but it can lead to objective and standardized evaluation of the evidence. If the experimenter were very anxious not to reject as invalid any assays that are really valid, he might use a test of deviation from parallelism at a probability of 0·01. He would then fail to reject assays which deviated only slightly and he would still reject 1 in 100 of perfectly good assays. If, on the other hand, he were anxious to reject all suspicious data, he might choose a probability level of, say, 0·1 for his significance test. He would reject 1 in 10 of good assays and would still fail to reject assays deviating from similarity so slightly as not to be detectable without more extensive evidence (*cf.* § 4.10). The responsibility rests with the experimenter : on the basis of his past experience with like material and the evidence of the present data, he must decide whether or not he believes the assay to be valid. Statistical analysis cannot enable him to evade his responsibility, but can ensure that all relevant evidence is presented in a clear, objective manner.

For simplicity of discussion, a representation of the dose-response relationship by a linear regression on log dose will be assumed ; analogous arguments could be given for a power dose metameter (§ 7.1). On the hypothesis of similarity, if the design is symmetrical and the difference between mean responses to the two preparations is not significant, the data for both preparations should relate to the same portion of the response curve. Any significant deviation from parallelism is then likely to be the result of fundamental invalidity, such as would require the rejection of the whole assay. The experimenter who accepts an assay in the face of this evidence must realize that he is asserting the observed deviation from parallelism to be in reality the result of chance, in spite of the low probability : in other words, he claims that the 1 in 20 or the 1 in 100 chance has occurred. Deviations from linearity, on the other hand, may merely be signs that the statistical analysis is invalid because the wrong metameters are being used. A significant difference between preparations does not of itself call for rejection of the assay, but is a danger signal. Just as a valid assay might appear to give non-parallel response curves on account of unsatisfactory choice of doses, so an invalid assay might appear to give two parallel lines if tested over particular ranges of dose giving different levels of response. Consequently, if a significant difference between preparations is found, the evidence on non-linearity should be examined with especial care ; the need for this is one strong reason for preferring assays with at least three points on each line.

15.2 The validity of 4-point assays

Many experimenters argue that, in a 4-point assay, the contrast for parallelism may also be regarded as providing a test of significance for deviations from linearity. Unfortunately, however, the need for distinguishing the two types of invalidity is greatest in circumstances which make the contrast most susceptible to disturbances from both (*i.e.* when a poor choice of doses has produced a large contrast for ' Preparations '). In an assay with three or more doses of each preparation, the occurrence of a significant difference between preparations, accompanied by either significant non-linearity or significant deviation from parallelism, would be a strong indication that the assay was statistically or fundamentally invalid. Simultaneous non-parallelism of the best fitting straight lines and non-linearity are in theory not inconsistent with the condition of similarity, since they might be due to a non-linear regression with a poor choice of doses (Fig. 4.4) ; nevertheless, they open the way to grave dangers, and an assay in which they occur should be treated with great reserve. When three or more doses of each preparation have been tested, the experimenter has some chance of distinguishing these various possibilities, and is moderately safe from the danger that two different sources of invalidity may compensate for one another in their effects on a particular test criterion. Without *a priori* knowledge that the effective stimuli in the standard and test preparations are qualitatively identical, the employment of 4-point designs is sheer obscurantism. The many merits of the 4-point scheme can be enjoyed only when experiments have shown that, for the group of materials under study, there is little danger of invalidity, at least of the fundamental kind that controverts the condition of similarity.

15.3 Statistical validity

The method adopted for the evaluation of data from an analytical dilution assay (or, indeed, of data from a comparative assay) almost inevitably requires for its strict validity a number of assumptions additional to the condition of similarity. Whether failure of the data to satisfy these assumptions perfectly affects the validity of conclusions to an extent that is of practical importance remains to be seen. The question of truth or falsity of certain assumptions which are theoretically requisite for the applicability of statistical techniques has been widely discussed in connexion with biological assay ; the paper of Jerne and Wood (1949) is especially valuable. The difficulties are not peculiar to biological assay, however, and similar theoretical problems arise over most of the statistical techniques commonly applied to biological data. Except for certain non-parametric techniques, most statistical analyses involve assumptions about the nature of distributions ; an experimenter is seldom, if ever, certain that these assumptions are correct, and he ought therefore to consider how far deviations from the assumptions destroy the *practical* validity of methods based upon them.* Use of non-parametric techniques might seem to be the obvious way of avoiding this difficulty, but these neglect completely all knowledge of the forms of distributions. In practice, the experimenter may have good reason to believe that a distribution is unimodal and roughly symmetrical, with finite moments, yet may not be able to describe it more exactly ; a non-parametric analysis then fails to utilize this rather vague information. The problem is moral and philosophical as well as mathematical and statistical : the emphasis here given to its relevance in biological assay must not be regarded as implying unique importance in that field.

Analysis of an assay in the usual form involves expression of the relationship between dose and response in terms of a linear regression. The assumptions used in the simple type of assay, in which several doses of each preparation are tested on a homogeneous set of subjects, will now be listed. The specification

---

* For example, employment of the *t* test for examining the significance of a difference between two means assumes that the variations of each set of observations about their true means are normally distributed, and that the standard deviations of the two distributions are equal. The test is often used when one of these conditions is manifestly untrue (as when the observations are essentially positive measurements and therefore cannot be normally distributed), with a confident belief that conclusions based upon it will be near enough to the truth for practical purposes. To give logical justification for this confidence is difficult: it rests in part upon the central limit theorem, in part upon empirical investigation and experience, and in part—let us be thoroughly honest—upon ignorance of any satisfactory alternative course of action. Most applications of statistical theory to ' real ' data involve an assumption that a particular mathematical model adequately represents the factors determining the data. The logic and validity of this step deserve more consideration from statisticians than they have received in the past.

would need to be a little more complicated in order to allow for litter-mate or other block restrictions, or if it were possible to make several tests on the same subject, but the necessary alterations would concern points of detail, not principles. If z and u are the dose and response as actually measured, the implicit assumptions are :

(i) Errors of measurement in the magnitude of the dose, z, are negligible. For the test preparation, of course, the factor ρ is unknown, and only the ratios between values of z are assumed to be exactly known.

(ii) For any specified z, individual values of the response, u, are random observations from a frequency distribution
$$f(u) \, du, \qquad (15.1)$$
in which z plays the part of a parameter.

(iii) There exists at least one pair of transformations
$$\left. \begin{array}{l} x = x(z), \\ y = y(u), \end{array} \right\} \qquad (15.2)$$
uniquely defining x and y as functions of z and u respectively, such that y has a linear regression on x :
$$Y = E(y) = \int_{-\infty}^{\infty} yf(u) \, du$$
$$= a + \beta x \qquad (15.3)$$
(x and y are known as the dose and response metameters).

(iv) The explicit formulation of such a pair of transformations, which also satisfy assumptions (v) and (vi), is either known completely or known in terms of a finite number of additional parameters. There is no *a priori* reason why some parameters should not occur in both transformations, but the dose transformation does not involve the response, and *vice versa*.

(v) The response metameter, y, is normally distributed about its expectation for any particular z.

(vi) The variance of y for any stated dose,
$$V(y) = E\{(y - a - \beta x)^2\}, \qquad (15.4)$$
is either :—

(a) constant,

or (b) a known function of Y, the expectation of y,

or (c) expressible as a function of Y with the aid of a finite number of additional parameters.

(vii) All the standard theory of mathematical statistics is accepted as applicable to entities which satisfy the strict conditions laid down in the relevant theorems.

(viii) If due attention is paid to the inexactness of correspondence between ideal entities of mathematics and measurements of material bodies, inferences of practical value may be drawn from the application of techniques developed in mathematical statistics to the data of biological experimentation and observation.

All these assumptions are at present intended as exact statements of fact. How far they must be modified, because a scientific measurement is not the same thing as a mathematical concept, remains to be discussed.

15.4 Comments on the conditions of statistical validity

The following comments may be made on the assumptions listed in § 15.3 :—

(i) This is needed because regressions are to be calculated on the assumption that the dose measurement is free from error. The condition might be relaxed so as to allow for a specified distribution of errors of measurement of z, but these will usually be so small in comparison with the errors of response measurements that they can be ignored. Any such relaxation would require a modification in the regression theory. ' There are a few assays in which the error of measuring the dose is unavoidably large ; for example, when the dose is measured as numbers of bacteria injected, the magnitude of each dose is dependent upon a plate count of bacteria and is thus subject to considerable error. The magnitude of the error in x should then be estimated separately if possible and the computations modified accordingly ' (Jerne and Wood, 1949).

(ii) Randomness can be ensured only by a suitable randomization procedure in the assignment of subjects to doses: Any departure from strict randomization here may result in the two preparations, or different doses of either preparation, being tested on non-comparable subjects (§§ 4.21, 6.7).

(iii) and (iv) Even if the exact mathematical specification of the frequency distribution of responses were known, transformation of z into x and u into y so as to satisfy (iii) may be impossible. Alternatively, a number of pairs of transformations exactly satisfying the requirements may exist. Moreover, if such transformations exist, and perhaps even if they do not, other transformations not exactly correct but adequate within the limits of experimental error can easily be devised. For example, if

$$\left. \begin{array}{l} x = \log z, \\ y = u, \end{array} \right\} \qquad (15.5)$$

give a linear regression, or at least no serious deviation from linearity according to the evidence of the data, then alternatives such as

$$\left. \begin{array}{l} x = \log z, \\ y = u^{0 \cdot 9}, \end{array} \right\} \qquad (15.6)$$

or

$$\left. \begin{array}{l} x = \log (z - 0 \cdot 1), \\ y = (u - 1 \cdot 1)^{1 \cdot 05}, \end{array} \right\} \qquad (15.7)$$

or

$$\left. \begin{array}{l} x = 3 \log z + z^{0 \cdot 01}, \\ y = 7 u^{0 \cdot 95} + 4 u^{0 \cdot 15} - \log u, \end{array} \right\} \qquad (15.8)$$

are likely to accord with any reasonable amount of data just as satisfactorily.

Theoretical reasons for adopting a particular pair of transformations are rarely found ; usually empirical evidence is all that is available, though of course experience from previous similar work will be taken into account. No technique is available for finding the 'best' set of transformations, unless a restriction of choice to a given type is made. For example, additional parameters might be introduced, so that the metameters were determined as

$$\left. \begin{array}{l} x = z^i, \\ y = (u - u_0)^\varepsilon \end{array} \right\} \qquad (15.9)$$

where i, u_0, ε are also to be estimated from the data. Such a procedure would be quite impratcticable or routine use, and, unless the data were very extensive, would be unlikely to give estimates of all the parameters with reasonable precision.

The usual practice is to assume that some very simple choice of metameters will suffice, for example

$$\left.\begin{array}{l} x = z, \\ y = u \end{array}\right\} \tag{15.10}$$

in slope ratio assays, and

$$\left.\begin{array}{l} x = \log z, \\ y = u \end{array}\right\} \tag{15.5}$$

in parallel line assays, with occasional uses of others such as

$$\left.\begin{array}{l} x = \log z, \\ y = \log u \end{array}\right\} \tag{15.11}$$

for special purposes (*cf.* § 16.2). This may seem so crude as to be quite unjustifiable, but in fact it is often good enough. In the absence of theoretical reasons for choosing a particular metametric transformation, nothing is gained by the choice of a complicated rule instead of a simple one that accords just as well with the data. If the experimenter has any doubts about the adequacy of the metameters that he proposes to use, he must design his assay so as to permit the making of the appropriate validity tests ; in a well-conducted assay, if these tests disclose no signs of invalidity, the conclusions drawn are unlikely to be seriously wrong because of a wrong choice of metameters (§ 15.6).

(v) Strictly interpreted, this is clearly a severe restriction on metameter transformations. The central limit theorem (Cramér, 1946, § 17.4; Kendall & Stuart, 1963), however, states that, for a wide class of frequency distributions, the distribution of a linear function of independent observations is more closely approximated by a normal distribution than is that of individual observations. Many sampling studies and experiments have shown a rapid tendency to normality of distribution resulting from combination of even very few observations from distributions that are themselves far from normal. Now $(\bar{y}_T - \bar{y}_S)$ and b, or b_T and b_S, the two quantities whose ratio leads to the potency estimate in parallel line and slope ratio assays respectively, are linear functions of the observations. Provided that there are twenty or more responses in all (and few assays will be attempted with less), the ill consequences of non-normality seem unlikely to be serious. This is indeed fortunate, for no test of the significance of deviations from normality sufficiently sensitive to be of practical value is likely ever to be devised for typical data from biological assays, namely, small numbers of observations spread over several dose groups. Admittedly, the general tendency to normality stated by the central limit theorem may be to some extent upset for regression coefficients by the unequal weighting of the several responses.

Though the central limit theorem gives a reasonable assurance that the distributions of means of responses are approximately normal, it does not ensure that the variances assessed in the ordinary manner behave as would variance estimates from a truly normal distribution. Geary (1947) has shown that tests of significance based upon the t distribution can be seriously misleading if the data are not normally distributed ; Jerne and Wood (1949) have pointed out that, if in reality the distribution is skew, " fiducial limits " to a potency estimate calculated as though the measured responses were normally distributed may be very different from the correct values. In the absence of detailed information about the nature of any non-normality, nothing can be done about this. The danger to the statistical validity of assays from this source must not be forgotten, but should not be exaggerated : the analyses discussed in § 15.6 indicate that gross non-normality may often fail to affect the fiducial limits to an appreciable extent, unless accompanied by other even more obvious signs of invalidity.

(vi) (a) For quantitative responses, in the absence of strong contrary evidence, the response metameter is usually assumed to have a homoscedastic regression. The assumption is unlikely to be exactly true, but may be effectively true over a limited range of expected responses. In a symmetrical design with a good choice of doses, even though the assumption be false it will lead to results almost exactly the same as those for a properly weighted analysis. Indeed, if the assumptions relating to linearity and similarity are exactly true, the assumption of constant variance will never invalidate the estimation of potency. The only harm that can result is that the data are not used in the most efficient manner possible ; by making allowance for dependence of the variance on Y, an estimate having higher precision might be obtained.

(b) As will be seen from Chapter 17, a dependence of variance on Y is generally assumed in assays based on quantal responses. Such a dependence is also occasionally appropriate for quantitative assays, and may legitimately be used as described in § 16.3 if the approximate form of the dependence is known. For example

$$V(y) = KY, \qquad (15.12)$$

or

$$V(y) = KY^2 \qquad (15.13)$$

might be taken. If the change in $V(y)$ as Y changes is very noticeable, a rough guess at the form of dependence is likely to be better than ignoring it completely, and a simple relationship like those just suggested might be postulated.

(c) When several responses have been measured for each dose, so giving the results of tests at that dose on a number of different subjects, or on the same subject at different times, valuable empirical evidence on the form of any relationship between $V(y)$ and Y will be available. If a general formula involving additional parameters, for example

$$V(y) = KY^i \qquad (15.14)$$

or

$$V(y) = HY + KY^2, \qquad (15.15)$$

could be postulated, estimates of these parameters might be formed from the data. An exact statistical theory would be complicated, but an approximate analysis would probably be fairly satisfactory. This third possibility does not seem of great practical importance.

Fieller (1947) has expressed the opinion that to take account of heteroscedasticity, by a transformation for equalizing variances or otherwise, is of primary importance in the analysis of assays. Undoubtedly any criterion for the heterogeneity of variance will be sensitive to certain types of change in the response metameter, as is exemplified by assays discussed in § 15.6. In general, however, the effects of failure to allow perfectly for the relationship between $V(y)$ and Y are of the second order : provided that the main assumptions of the analysis are correct, they will not affect the validity of the estimation of ρ unless the variance used is grossly wrong. They may affect the precision of that estimate, for use of the wrong expression for $V(y)$ is equivalent to attaching a wrong weight to different responses in the assay, and so not making the best possible use of the data. Experience of the weighting of data suggests that the loss is likely to be trivial as long as approximately the right relative values are given to the variances (Tukey, 1948). On the other hand, application of a stringent criterion for homoscedasticity would lead to rejection of analyses based on certain metameters when in fact the analyses would give potency estimates satisfactorily close to the estimate based upon an apparently better metameter (cf. § 15.6).

(vii) If this were not believed, the subject of mathematical statistics would not exist !

(viii) If this were not believed, books on statistical science would not be written !

If all the assumptions stated were exactly satisfied, the standard process of calculation, of which many examples have been given in other chapters, would lead to fiducial limits, in the sense of the orthodox theory of statistical estimation. That is to say, R_L is the lowest value for the unknown parameter ρ which is not contradicted by a significance test based on the observed responses, and R_U is the highest value for ρ which is not contradicted by a significance test (§ 2.4). Both significance tests use single-tail probabilities, in this book conventionally of $2\frac{1}{2}$ per cent., so that, in asserting that the true ρ lies between R_L and R_U, the fiducial probability of being correct is 0·95.

15.5   The objectivity of statistical analysis

The experimenter will rarely, if ever, have the knowledge implied by the conditions of statistical validity listed in § 15.3. Without these conditions, statistical analysis of his assay cannot be exactly correct, and he might therefore seem to be debarred from the use of statistical science. Criticisms of this kind are not confined to biological assay, but can be levelled at almost any application of statistical methods to biological data that employs representation of variation by a normal or other theoretical distribution. Few would refuse to use theorems of pure geometry in the applied science of surveying, on the grounds that the ' straight lines ' there encountered do not have the ideal properties required by Euclid's definition. Nor should statistical methods be dismissed from the evaluation of scientific data because the entities observed are not precisely the same as those used in theories of mathematical statistics (*cf.* § 2.9). A better procedure (which perhaps may not find an easy philosophical justification) is to devise a theory with which the observations will generally be in reasonable agreement, and then to examine the results of every experiment, or every series of observational results, for evidence of deviations from the approximation so great as to invalidate a statistical analysis.

Any assay involves four classes of parameter :—

(i) the relative potency, ρ ;

(ii) the parameters α, β of the linear regression, as defined in (iii) of § 15.3 ;

(iii) parameters defining the metametric transformations ;

(iv) parameters occurring in the expression of $V(y)$ as a function of Y.

Data from one assay of moderate size cannot give adequate information for the estimation of all these, especially as even the algebraic models containing the last two classes of parameter are unlikely to be known. Conclusions drawn from a single assay of a new type are necessarily tentative, as they will be based upon very simple assumptions about parameters, such as are expressed by

$$\left.\begin{aligned} x &= \log z \\ y &= u \\ V(y) &= \text{constant.} \end{aligned}\right\} \tag{15.16}$$

and

The situation is altered when data from a number of similar assays have accumulated, or when a planned investigation of the regression relationship (§ 3.5) has preceded any assays. The adequacy of the assumptions can then be examined in relation to all the evidence, and modifications introduced if these are found necessary. As the volume of data grows, so do more sensitive tests of linearity, normality, homoscedasticity, and the rest become possible, and the technique of analysis may be adapted to take account of the findings in these tests. Thus the difficulties are evaded by admitting the impracticability, or even impossibility, of determining for every assay separately the ideal dose and response metameters. Instead, the evidence of preliminary investigations, and the experience gained from past assays of the same type, are used to guide the choice of metameters for adoption in the future. These future assays are then so planned as to make them provide : —

(i) Tests of fundamental validity, which are essentially tests of deviation from the condition of similarity ;

(ii) Tests of statistical validity, in terms of the metameters adopted. The chief of these is the test of linearity of regression, since the central limit theorem gives reasonable confidence that only very serious non-normality will upset the conclusions, and non-constancy of variance is seldom of first order importance. Of course, the data must be examined for evidence of serious non-normality or hetero-scedasticity.

The design of an assay must permit both sets of tests to have reasonable sensitivity. In each assay performed, the appropriate tests are made, and, in the absence of strong evidence against either fundamental or statistical validity, the assay is accepted as valid : the calculations are completed just as though all the assumptions were known to be exactly satisfied. Invalidity in respect of the test for similarity must lead to rejection of an assay, except in so far as any apparent invalidity may be explicable as an alternative manifestation of statistical invalidity. If an assay shows only statistical invalidity, the analysis may be modified using other metameters, or a decision between acceptance and rejection may be deferred until further information on the metameters has accumulated.

In this way the objectivity of statistical analysis is restored. Before the assay is performed, there should be strong reasons for belief in its fundamental validity. The metameters have been decided in advance, so that the whim of the statistician does not influence the conclusions. The validity tests should then be regarded as confirmation that no abnormal behaviour of the subjects, or other disturbance from unknown causes, has upset either the fundamental or the statistical validity of the assay, and not as a demonstration of the validity of a set of assumptions peculiar to one assay. The fiducial limits eventually stated may not be exactly the same as would be obtained if the exact transformations appropriate to the data were known, but, as the experimenter has no hope of ever possessing this knowledge, that is no cause for despair. For example, one set of data might give $R = 1.12$ with limits at 0.95, 1.32 if the responses as measured were assumed to have a linear regression on log dose, and $R = 1.08$ with limits at 0.92, 1.27 if the logarithm of the response and log dose were used. The existence of two or more different estimates of a parameter from a particular set of data, depending upon the estimation procedure chosen, is not in itself unusual ; if the limits are interpreted as conventional guides to the reliability of the estimates, rather than as satisfying the theory of fiducial inference in the strictest mathematical sense, the occurrence of slightly different values according to the form of analysis ceases to be objectionable. When a scheme of analysis is decided objectively, and not after inspection of the data from a particular assay, the subjective judgment of the statistician no longer determines the conclusions. The final statement that, say, ρ lies between 0.95 and 1.32 may not be the best possible statement of this character that might be made from the assay, but it possesses the advantage of being objectively determinable, and the analyst may be sure that a large proportion of such statements will be correct. This attitude is no more unjustifiable than in any branch of biometry in which some form of distribution is arbitrarily assumed. As a guide to the practical action based on the assay, the limits should be trustworthy and objective, even though to attach exact probability concepts to them may be difficult. Empirical investigation suggests that variation in the choice of metameters will not affect the fiducial limits to an extent that would influence the action to be taken on the results of an assay, unless the choice is so extreme as to make statistical invalidity, in one or more of its forms, unmistakably clear (§ 15.6).

In any experimental programme of assays for a particular substance or group of substances, unless the choice of metameters is considered to be firmly established, continuous records of the evidence of validity tests should be kept (by control charts or otherwise), and a change should be made in the standard form of statistical analysis if the accumulated evidence makes this seem desirable (§ 5.10).   Until evidence to the contrary is apparent, the simpler of two alternative metametric transformations may be preferred.   For example, in a description of a new technique for penicillin assay, Pratt and Dufrenoy (1947) stated that the regression of the logarithm of the diameter of the zone of inhibition on log dose was linear ; the data they published agree equally well with the hypothesis of a linear regression for the diameter itself, and, in view of general experience for penicillin assays, this simpler ' metameter ' might reasonably be preferred.   Of course, if the authors already had, or have subsequently obtained, data pointing more strongly to the logarithmic metameter, a change would have to be made.

15.6   The comparison of alternative metametric transformations

After the publication of a paper (Finney, 1947e) which contained an earlier version of the covariance analysis discussed in §§ 12.2–12.4, Dr. N. K. Jerne pointed out to me that the statements of potency and its fiducial limits might be misleading.   The basis of his criticism was that the conditions of statistical validity were not fulfilled, in that the variance was not homogeneous.   The charge was entirely justified, as inspection of Table 12.1 will confirm : the two very high responses, 144 and 130, suggest a positive skewness of the response distribution, and the variance within dose groups is undoubtedly considerably higher for the two highest doses than for the two lowest.   Nevertheless, the use of the measured responses as their own metameters, which has been retained in Chapter 12, was not undertaken without thought.   In the belief that the deviations from theoretical requirements were not great enough to impair the conclusions seriously, and in the certainty that the data from the one assay were inadequate for indicating the right metameter, $y = u$ was adopted.   At that time, these reasons were less clearly formulated than they are now, but general statistical experience supported the view that to allow for the heteroscedasticity and possible skewness would add much to the labour without appreciably affecting the conclusions.

In an attempt to investigate the effect of metametric transformation on data such as these, a series of analyses was later performed (Finney, 1949c). At the same time, data from another parallel line assay, the testosterone propionate assay in Table 5.1, were also examined. Each set of data was analysed for a metameter

$$y = u^i, \qquad (15.17)$$

where i was given values between $+3$ and -3*. A little algebra proves that the limit of the potency estimate as i tends to zero is obtainable by using the metameter

$$y = \log u \; ; \qquad (15.18)$$

the base of logarithms is immaterial, as all the results to be presented are independent of linear transformations of y. The method of analysis was exactly that of § 5.1.

For neither assay are the data adequate to provide tests of deviations from normality. The transformations tried will intensify any positive skewness when $i > 1 \cdot 0$, and they include extremes of skewness more marked than any that would ordinarily be encountered in practical consideration of alternative response metameters. When $i < 0$, a negative skewness appears and becomes steadily more pronounced as i is decreased. The range of metameters studied includes a region in which no skewness is apparent, and that negative virtue is about the nearest to a criterion of normality that may be expected on so few data.

In Tables 15.1 and 15.2 are summarized validity tests for the two assays as obtained with various values of i. The first of these, a test of homoscedasticity, has been made by calculating Fisher's z for the ratio of the pooled error mean squares in the highest dose groups of the standard and test preparations to that in the lowest dose groups ; for the two assays, this statistic has (6, 6) and (8, 8) degrees of freedom respectively. Values of z for 10 per cent., 5 per cent. and 1 per cent. probability levels, on the null hypothesis that the true variances at the extremes of doses are equal, are shown at the bottom of the columns. For any value of i outside the range $0 \cdot 7 > i > -1 \cdot 5$ for the prolactin assay, or $0 \cdot 9 > i > -0 \cdot 2$ for

---

* The adjustments for variation in initial body-weight discussed in § 12.4 were not used for the prolactin assay : they would have increased the arithmetical labour without being of any special interest for the present inquiry.

the testosterone propionate, the evidence against homoscedasticity would be judged significant ; for values of i very little more extreme, the evidence would be overwhelming. This validity test is more sensitive to changes of metameter of the type under discussion than are the others shown in Tables 15.1, 15.2, and it may often be unduly sensitive. In well-planned symmetrical assays of ordinary size, modification of the statistical analysis on account of heteroscedasticity is seldom needed, unless the evidence against a constant variance is significant at the 1 per cent. level.

TABLE 15.1—Summary of validity tests for the prolactin assay

Metameter index	Fisher's	Values of t for		
i	z	Preparations	Linearity	Parallelism
3·0	2·38	0·80	0·54	− 0·41
2·5	2·01	0·88	0·44	− 0·37
2·0	1·64	0·99	0·30	− 0·32
1·5	1·28	1·11	0·12	− 0·24
1·0	0·93	1·24	− 0·10	− 0·12
0·5	0·58	1·38	− 0·35	0·03
0·0	0·24	1·50	− 0·63	0·23
− 0·5	− 0·09	1·60	− 0·91	0·46
− 1·0	− 0·41	1·67	− 1·15	0·70
− 1·5	− 0·73	1·69	− 1·32	0·93
− 2·0	− 1·05	1·69	− 1·47	1·12
− 2·5	− 1·37	1·67	− 1·54	1·28
− 3·0	− 1·70	1·64	− 1·56	1·41
10%	0·56	1·73		
5%	0·73	2·10		
1%	1·07	2·88		

TABLE 15.2—Summary of validity tests for the testosterone propionate assay

Metameter index i	Fisher's z	Values of t for Preparations	Linearity	Parallelism
3·0	2·91	1·33	2·32	1·34
2·5	2·37	1·40	2·07	1·37
2·0	1·83	1·46	1·64	1·38
1·5	1·29	1·48	0·98	1·36
1·0	0·74	1·42	0·08	1·31
0·5	0·18	1·26	− 0·94	1·21
0·0	− 0·38	0·99	− 1·89	1·08
− 0·5	− 0·95	0·67	− 2·55	0·95
− 1·0	− 1·53	0·36	− 2·86	0·85
− 1·5	− 2·11	0·10	− 2·90	0·80
− 2·0	− 2·70	− 0·11	− 2·78	0·77
− 2·5	− 3·29	− 0·27	− 2·57	0·78
− 3·0	− 3·88	− 0·39	− 2·34	0·79
10%	0·48		1·71	
5%	0·62		2·06	
1%	0·90		2·80	

The other tests summarized in Tables 15.1, 15.2 are those for the difference between preparations in respect of their mean responses, the deviations from linearity, and the deviations from parallelism of the two regression lines. Instead of their usual analysis of variance form, these have been made directly on the contrasts L_p, L_2, L_1', by finding the ratio of each contrast to a standard error based upon pooled variances from all doses. The ratios are t-ratios with 18 or 24 degrees of freedom, and the values for 10 per cent., 5 per cent. and 1 per cent. probability are shown at the foot of each table. The only test to give a result beyond even the 10 per cent. significance level is the linearity test in the second assay ; this shows strong indications of non-linearity except when $2.5 > i > -0.1$. A further column for the contrast L_2' might have been included, but this would be of little interest because, over the range of values of i studied, its t is always less than unity. A point of interest is that the value of t for any one of these validity tests is not necessarily a monotonic function of i.

These tables show that different statisticians might choose very different response metameters without any of them finding reason to doubt the statistical validity of his analysis. For the prolactin assay, any value of i between 3.0 and -3.0 is admissible as judged by the tests of L_p, L_2, L_1', and even the condition of homoscedasticity

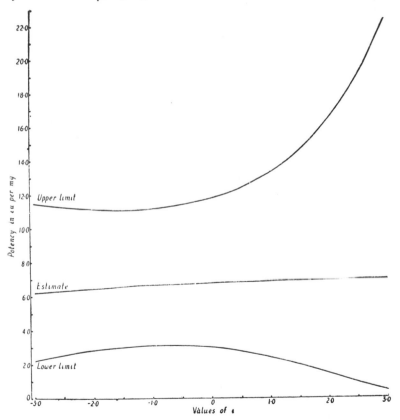

Fig. 15.1—Potency estimates and fiducial limits for the assay of prolactin, Table 15.3

admits metameters as different as $u^{0.7}$ and $u^{-1.5}$. The testosterone data are not satisfied by quite so wide a range, and, if the homoscedasticity and linearity tests are considered simultaneously, a value of i between 1·0 and 0·0 seems indicated. In order to see how the potency estimates are affected by the choice of i, the potency of the test preparation relative to the standard has been calculated for various values of i. Table 15.3 summarizes the results, and shows also the fiducial limits and the value of g for each i. The estimate and its limits are represented graphically as functions of i in Figs. 15.1, 15.2.

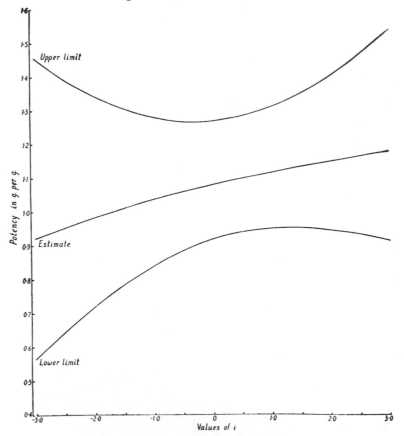

Fig. 15.2—Potency estimates and fiducial limits for the assay of testosterone propionate, Table 15.3

TABLE 15.3—Summary of potency estimates and fiducial limits in the prolactin and testosterone propionate assays

Metameter index	Assay of prolactin			Assay of testosterone propionate		
	g	Potency (i.u. per mg.)	95% limits	g	Potency (g. per g.)	95% limits
3·0	0·71	6·96	0·37–22·5	0·050	1·18	0·91–1·54
2·5	0·60	6·92	0·85–18·9	0·038	1·16	0·93–1·47
2·0	0·49	6·88	1·39–16·4	0·030	1·15	0·94–1·41
1·5	0·40	6·84	1·91–14·6	0·023	1·13	0·95–1·36
1·0	0·33	6·80	2·36–13·3	0·020	1·12	0·95–1·32
0·5	0·28	6·76	2·72–12·4	0·019	1·10	0·94–1·29
0·0	0·24	6·71	2·97–11·8	0·020	1·08	0·92–1·27
−0·5	0·22	6·66	3·09–11·4	0·025	1·06	0·89–1·27
−1·0	0·22	6·58	3·08–11·2	0·034	1·04	0·84–1·28
−1·5	0·22	6·53	3·01–11·1	0·048	1·01	0·78–1·31
−2·0	0·24	6·42	2·81–11·2	0·071	0·98	0·72–1·34
−2·5	0·26	6·32	2·55–11·3	0·104	0·95	0·65–1·39
−3·0	0·30	6·19	2·22–11·5	0·148	0·92	0·56–1·46

For the prolactin assay, g is large ; it always exceeds 0·2, has a minimum near $i = -1·0$, and probably exceeds unity at values of i a little more extreme than those studied. Clearly the imprecision of the regression coefficient is an important factor in the assessment of the fiducial limits. For the testosterone assay, g has a minimum near $i = 0·5$, and for $3·0 > i > -1·5$ it is small enough to be neglected ; outside these limits it also appears to become large.

The potency estimate is altered surprisingly little by small changes in i. Even without any formal validity tests, no statistician shown the data for either assay would contemplate using a response metameter of the form of equation (15.17) with $i > 2·0$ or $i < -1·0$, and over this extreme range the potency estimate changes only by 5 per cent. or 10 per cent. In the absence of prior evidence to the contrary, his choice would almost certainly be made between $i = 1$ and $i = 0$, so that his subjective judgment would affect the estimate only by 2 per cent. or 4 per cent.

The fiducial limits are more sensitive to metameter changes. For the prolactin assay, the fiducial range is narrowest at about $i = -1·0$, and is appreciably widened (primarily because of the increase in g) if $i > 0·5$ or $i < -2·0$. For the testosterone assay, the range is narrowest at about $i = 0·0$, and begins to widen seriously for $i > 1·5$ or $i < -1·0$. Narrowness of the fiducial range is, of course, no criterion for the right choice of a response metameter, especially as the method of calculating the limits assumes validity. If the mathematical model and the experimental data corresponded perfectly, exact probability statements could be made about the fiducial limits, but that is an ideal impossible of achievement. In practice, all that is required of fiducial limits is that, when computed according to standard rules, they shall give an indication of a range within which the true value almost certainly lies. The user of a biological assay will wish to base some course of action on its results, but he would be unwise to base critical decisions on whether the potency he requires is just within or just beyond the calculated limits. For most of his questions, the limits will give a clear answer : cases of doubt should be resolved by further experimentation, not by undue reliance upon the truth of an abstract model.

The main conclusion to be drawn from Table 15.3 and Figs. 15.1, 15.2 is that, over quite a wide range of values of i, neither the potency estimate nor its fiducial limits (calculated by the standard procedure) are affected by a change of metameter to an extent that would seriously affect decisions which had to be based upon the assay results. A conclusion that the test preparation of prolactin was estimated to contain 6·8 i.u. per mg., and that the true value was almost sure to lie between 2·5 i.u. per mg. and 13 i.u. per mg., or that 1 g. of the test preparation of testosterone propionate was estimated to be equivalent to 1·1 g. of the standard, and that the true value was almost sure to lie between 0·9 g. per g. and 1·3 g. per g., is probably all that the data justify by any analysis ; all reasonable choices of metameter agree in those conclusions.

TABLE 15.4—Summary of validity tests for the riboflavin assay

Metameter index i	Fisher's z	Values of t for Blanks	Values of t for Intersection
3·0	2·78	8·43	− 5·49
2·5	2·10	7·70	− 4·90
2·0	1·43	6·09	− 4·03
1·5	0·76	3·39	− 2·88
1·0	0·09	− 0·39	− 1·54
0·5	− 0·58	− 4·63	− 0·27
0·0	− 1·25	− 8·19	0·63
− 0·5	− 1·92	− 10·25	1·04
− 1·0	− 2·58	− 10·88	1·08
− 1·5	− 3·22	− 10·63	0·93
− 2·0	− 3·86	− 9·95	0·74
− 2·5	− 4·52	− 9·13	0·56
− 3·0	− 5·16	− 8·32	0·41
10%	0·83, − 0·60	1·75	
5%	1·10, − 0·78	2·13	
1%	1·66, − 1·14	2·95	

A similar series of analyses, based on equation (15.17), has been made for the riboflavin assay in Table 7.5. For each value of i the statistical analysis followed the plan of § 7.10. Table 15.4 summarizes the validity tests. As a test of homoscedasticity, Fisher's z for the ratio of the error mean squares in the two high dose groups to that in the blanks was calculated ; it has (6, 3) degrees of freedom. The upper and lower 10 per cent., 5 per cent. and 1 per cent. probability levels are shown at the foot of the column. For any value of i outside the range $1 \cdot 8 > i > 0 \cdot 3$, analysis would show heteroscedasticity. The tests for blanks and intersection have

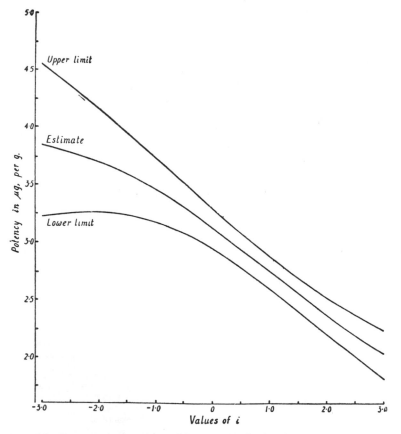

Fig. 15.3—Potency estimates and fiducial limits for the assay of riboflavin, Table 15.5

been made by regarding the ratios of L_B and L_I to their standard errors as t-deviates. Clearly the blanks contrast is very sensitive to changes in i ; values of i in a narrow range about 1·0 are acceptable, but anything more extreme gives a mean response for the blanks far from the regression lines indicated by the non-zero doses. The intersection contrast is less sensitive, and attains significance only for $i > 1·2$.

For this assay, tests of homoscedasticity and of blanks strongly indicate that only a metameter with i near to unity can reasonably be used. Nevertheless, estimates of potency have been calculated for the whole range of values of i ; these with their fiducial limits are summarized in Table 15.5 and are shown graphically in Fig. 15.3. An additional column of the table shows g, which is practically

TABLE 15.5—Summary of potency estimates and fiducial limits in the riboflavin assay

Metameter index		Potency	95% limits
i	g	(μg. per g.)	
3·0	0·004	2·03	1·81–2·24
2·5	0·003	2·19	2·00–2·38
2·0	0·003	2·36	2·19–2·53
1·5	0·002	2·55	2·39–2·71
1·0	0·002	2·74	2·59–2·89
0·5	0·002	2·93	2·77–3·09
0·0	0·003	3·12	2·94–3·30
− 0·5	0·004	3·29	3·07–3·52
− 1·0	0·006	3·45	3·17–3·74
− 1·5	0·010	3·58	3·23–3·95
− 2·0	0·015	3·69	3·26–4·16
− 2·5	0·023	3·77	3·25–4·36
− 3·0	0·032	3·84	3·22–4·56

negligible for all i in the range studied and has a minimum near $i = 1 \cdot 0$. The change in R as i changes is much more marked than for the prolactin and testosterone propionate assays, and between $i = 1 \cdot 5$ and $i = 0 \cdot 5$ amounts to about 14 per cent. All considerations combine, however, to indicate $i = 1 \cdot 0$ as ideal ; even the fiducial range is there at its narrowest. Thus this investigation serves to confirm the conclusions reached in § 7.10.

It is not suggested that calculations of this kind should be undertaken as part of the statistical analysis of every biological assay ! The investigations here reported were undertaken as a corollary to the work of Jerne and Wood (1949), and as a warning to users of bio-assay against uncritical acceptance of a standard pattern of computation without thought of the assumptions involved. The theoretical implications of a particular choice of metameter must not be forgotten, however little any alternative might alter the inferences from the data.

The metameters obtained from equation (15.17) belong to a very restricted class, though they are probably sufficiently diverse to illustrate the most interesting effects. A larger set of possibilities would be comprised within the formulation used by Kapteyn (1903)

$$y = (u - u_0)^i, \tag{15.19}$$

where both i and u_0 may be chosen so that the transformed data satisfy the basic assumptions of the assay and its analysis. Another alternative would be a metameter that recognized the existence of both an upper and a lower limit to possible values of y, and the consequent sigmoidal regression of u on x (cf. equations (3.18)).

CHAPTER 16

THE 'GENERAL' METHOD

16.1 Curvature and heteroscedasticity

The methods of analysis and the examples of assay data discussed in Chapters 4 to 14 have all related to a homoscedastic linear regression of response on either dose or log dose. Important as these two types of dose-response relationship are, they are not the only possibilities that must be considered in the study of biological assays. The examples in § 15.6 illustrated the fact that small changes in the metametric transformations need not seriously affect either the estimate of potency or its fiducial limits. Data from some assays, however, exhibit undoubted curvature or heteroscedasticity of the dose-response relationship on either of the simple metameter systems mentioned, and for these some alternative must be found.

The conclusion reached in Chapter 15 was that data from one assay could not be expected to determine their own metameters. Preliminary investigations and past experience of similar assays must be used to indicate transformations likely to be sufficiently good ; for future assays, these transformations would be postulated, but the design of the assay should permit the making of tests for the detection of serious discrepancies. A further problem concerns the variance of responses. After dose and response metameters that linearize the regression have been found, an assumption of constancy for the variance of individual values of y about the regression line is temptingly convenient and greatly simplifies subsequent calculations. Even if untrue, it will not seriously bias the potency estimate from a symmetrical assay with well-chosen doses, though it may invalidate the assessment of fiducial limits. In order that the mathematical model may correspond more closely to biological reality, a dependence of the variance of y upon Y, the expected response, may sometimes have to be considered. An important case is that of responses having constant variance on the original scale of measurement, u : the variance of any non-linear transform of u must then be dependent upon U (or upon Y). The general method of fitting the regression equation (§ 3.13) may be used to give the maximum likelihood estimate of potency, provided that the functional dependence of $V(y)$ on Y can be expressed. In practice, of course, the experimenter rarely knows that any one formulation of this dependence is preferable to all alternatives, though preliminary investigations for the standard preparation ought to have given some indication. A reasonable approximation, however, will be good enough for most purposes.

The theory on which the calculations are based has been developed in Chapter 3. The purpose of the present chapter is to illustrate the arithmetical processes, and to compare, for this example, the conclusions drawn from two different assumptions about the scedasticity.

16.2 Unweighted analysis of an assay of *dl*-tryptophan

In the microbiological assay of many amino-acids, the regression of response on dose is found to be linearized by logarithmic transformation of both variates (Wood, 1946*b*, 1947*a*). The data in Table 16.1 were obtained in an assay of *dl*-tryptophan, using *Lactobacillus arabinosus* as the test subject. Previous experience had suggested that the double logarithmic transformation would be appropriate, and therefore metameters were defined by

$$x = \log z, \\ y = \log u. \qquad (16.1)$$

Table 16.2 is a metametric version of Table 16.1. For arithmetical convenience, 2 has been added to the dose metameters for the test preparation, a modification equivalent to expressing the doses in units of 0·01 ml.

The design of this assay is obviously open to criticism. Of the total number of responses measured, only one-third relate to the test preparation, instead of one-half. The design is not symmetrical, and no attempt has been made to have doses of the test preparation corresponding to those of the standard. If the experimenter expected to need a logarithmic dose metameter, he ought to have chosen doses in geometric rather than arithmetic progression. The ill consequences of these flaws in design will be discussed later (§ 16.4) : for the present, the chief concern is with the analysis of the data as they stand.

TABLE 16.1—Responses in an assay of *dl*-tryptophan
(ml. N/10 NaOH)

Dose of standard preparation (µg. per tube)								
2·0	4·0	6·0	8·0	10·0	12·0	14·0	16·0	18·0
2·2	3·7	5·6	7·1	8·5	9·8	11·3	12·2	13·2
2·2	3·8	5·6	7·3	8·5	9·8	11·3	12·2	13·6
2·2	4·0	5·6	7·6	8·7	—	11·4	12·4	—

Dose of test preparation (ml. per tube)						
0·05	0·10	0·15	0·20	0·30	0·40	0·50
1·2	1·8	2·8	3·4	5·3	6·7	8·2
1·3	2·0	3·0	3·6	5·6	7·0	8·4

TABLE 16.2—Metametric transformation of the data in Table 16.1

Dose metameter for standard preparation								
0·301	0·602	0·778	0·903	1·000	1·079	1·146	1·204	1·255
0·342	0·568	0·748	0·851	0·929	0·991	1·053	1·086	1·121
0·342	0·580	0·748	0·863	0·929	0·991	1·053	1·086	1·134
0·342	0·602	0·748	0·881	0·940	—	1·057	1·093	—

Dose metameter for test preparation						
0·699	1·000	1·176	1·301	1·477	1·602	1·699
0·079	0·255	0·447	0·531	0·724	0·826	0·914
0·114	0·301	0·477	0·556	0·748	0·845	0·924

In this section, an unweighted analysis that takes no account of any heteroscedasticity in the regression of y on x will be summarized. When the response metameters in Table 16.2 are plotted against the dose metameters (Fig. 16.1), the regressions

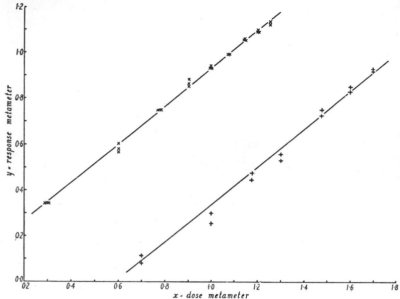

Fig. 16.1—Linear dose-response regressions for the assay of *dl*-tryptophan, Tables 16.1 and 16.2

     × : Response metameters for standard preparation
     + : Response metameters for test preparation
         The straight lines are those mentioned in § 16.2 as having been drawn by eye, but are very close to the lines represented by equations (16.14).

appear to be nearly linear over the range of doses. Parallel lines have been drawn by eye in Fig. 16.1 ; these lines, which will be used in the computations of § 16.3, indicate that (on the x-scales used) M is about -0.72. Inspection of Fig. 16.1 leads to an impression that the variance of y is greater at low doses than at high, but this will be ignored for the present.

The calculations for an unweighted linear regression analysis of Table 16.2 are of the same type as those used for Table 4.1, though the unequal spacing of the dose metameter makes them even more laborious.· For reasons that will be clear later, separate analyses of variance have been made for the two preparations, these being later combined into a single analysis of variance on conventional lines.   Table 16.3 shows the separate analyses, the

TABLE 16.3—Separate unweighted analyses of variance for the two preparations in Table 16.2

(*a*) Standard preparation

Adjustment for mean		17·771283	Mean square
Nature of variation	d.f.	Sum of squares	
Regression	1	1·525842	
Linearity	7	0·002327	0·000332
Between doses	8	1·528169	
Within doses	16	0·001260	0·000079
Total	24	1·529429	

(*b*) Test preparation

Adjustment for mean		4·280220	Mean square
Nature of variation	d.f.	Sum of squares	
Regression	1	1·071422	
Linearity	5	0·007858	0·001572
Between doses	6	1·079280	
Within doses	7	0·002951	0·000422
Total	13	1·082231	

formation of which should give no difficulty. For each preparation, the total sum of squares is divided into components between and within doses. The data for the standard preparation give

$$S_{xx} = 2 \cdot 192386,$$
$$S_{xy} = 1 \cdot 828998 ;$$

the square for regression is therefore

$$\frac{S_{xy}^2}{S_{xx}} = 1 \cdot 525842,$$

which, subtracted from the sum of squares between doses, leaves the component for linearity.

A disquieting feature of both analyses in Table 16.3 is the size of the mean square for deviations from linearity, which for the standard preparation is significantly greater than that within doses and for the test preparation is almost significant. Inspection of Fig. 16.1 discloses no consistent trend of deviations, such as would occur if the regression were in reality curved. Inadequate randomization is an alternative possible explanation, a danger to which attention has already been drawn in §§ 4.21, 4.22, 6.7, 7.5 : the tubes for any one dose may have been filled consecutively, incubated in adjacent positions, or in some other manner subjected to conditions producing a correlation of responses. If the order of the doses was properly randomized at every stage, so that they were not prepared in an ascending or descending sequence, the mean square for deviations from linearity may be used as s^2 in the subsequent analysis ; if this assumption is incorrect, the data are of questionable value, as a cardinal principle of unbiased experimentation is violated by a failure to include any element of randomization.

The mean squares for error and linearity in the test preparation section of Table 16.3 are considerably larger than the corresponding mean squares for the standard preparation. This is a consequence of the neglect of the dependence of $V(y)$ on Y : in reality, the variance of individual values of y about their regression line decreases as Y increases, and the general level of response is lower for the test preparation, than for the standard.

The two analyses in Table 16.3 may now be combined into a complete analysis of variance, Table 16.4. For the regression component,

$$\Sigma S_{xx} = 2 \cdot 192386 + 1 \cdot 490534 = 3 \cdot 682920,$$

and
$$\Sigma S_{xy} = 1{\cdot}828998 + 1{\cdot}263721 = 3{\cdot}092719,$$
whence the square for regression is
$$(3{\cdot}092719)^2/3{\cdot}682920 = 2{\cdot}597100.$$
The difference between this and the sum of the corresponding squares for the preparations separately is the component for parallelism.

TABLE 16.4—Complete unweighted analysis of variance for the data of Table 16.2

Adjustment for mean		21·295763	Mean square
Nature of variation	d.f.	Sum of squares	
Preparations	1	0·755740	
Regression	1	2·597100	
Parallelism	1	0·000164	0·000164
Linearity	12	0·010185	0·0008488
Between doses	15	3·363189	
Within doses	23	0·004211	0·0001831
Total	38	3·367400	

Table 16.4 shows no evidence of lack of parallelism, but emphasizes the need to use the mean square for deviations from linearity,
$$s^2 = 0{\cdot}0008488$$
as the estimated variance per response. On account of the unsatisfactory choice of doses, the difference between preparations is highly significant, but, if the linearity of the regression be accepted, this does not cause any worry. Now
$$b = \frac{3{\cdot}092719}{3{\cdot}682920}$$
$$= 0{\cdot}83975$$

and therefore, from values of $\bar{x}$ and $\bar{y}$ calculated in the usual manner,
$$M = 0.89880 - 1.27914 - (0.84312 - 0.55293)/0.83975$$
$$= -0.7259.$$
Also
$$g = \frac{(2.179)^2 \times 0.0008488}{(0.8397)^2 \times 3.6829}$$
$$= 0.0016,$$
which could safely be ignored. Fieller's theorem gives
$$M_L, M_U = -0.7558, -0.6983.$$
The dose metameter in Table 6.2 was the logarithm of the dose in Table 6.1, and therefore the antilogarithm of a value of M is a potency in μg. tryptophan per 0.01 ml. of the test preparation. Hence the relative potency is estimated as 18.80 μg. dl-tryptophan per ml., with fiducial limits at 17.55 μg. per ml. and 20.03 μg. per ml.

16.3 Weighted analysis of the assay of dl-tryptophan

Inspection of Table 16.1 suggests that the variance of u, the measured response, is nearly constant, whereas Table 16.2 and Fig. 16.1 show clearly that the variance of log u decreases with increasing U. Instead of the unweighted analysis in § 16.2, the general method described in § 3.13 therefore seems appropriate. Suppose that
$$V(u) = \sigma^2, \tag{16.2}$$
a constant, is the variance of u about its expectation, U. The transformation used for the response metameter may be written
$$Y = f^{-1}(U) = \log U; \tag{16.3}$$
in discussions of the theory, natural logarithms are more convenient than logarithms to base 10, and therefore
$$U = e^Y. \tag{16.4}$$
Since
$$f'(U) = U, \tag{16.5}$$
equations (3.53) and (3.57) give
$$w = U^2 \tag{16.6}$$
and
$$y = Y - 1 + \frac{u}{U} \tag{16.7}$$

for the weighting coefficient and working response respectively. In computation, logarithms to base 10 will be preferred ; if equation (16.3) is so interpreted, and

$$\varepsilon = \log_{10}e = 2\cdot30259 \ . \ . \ . \ , \tag{16.8}$$

then

$$w = \varepsilon^2 U^2 = 5\cdot30190 \ U^2 \tag{16.9}$$

and

$$y = Y - 0\cdot43429 + 0\cdot43429 \left(\frac{u}{U}\right). \tag{16.10}$$

The weighting coefficient could be taken as U^2, provided that the constant factor ε^2 were introduced later, as a multiplier of the total weight and of all sums of squares and products, before the calculation of any variances or fiducial limits. This would save some arithmetic, and is the practice that would generally be followed. For ease of comparison with § 16.2, however, equation (16.9) is used here.

These formulæ, and their use in an iterative process, can now be illustrated. The first step is the estimation of σ^2, the supposedly constant variance of the actual responses.* Sums of squares within dose groups in Table 16·1 amount to

$$S_{uu} = 0\cdot31333, \text{ with 16 degrees of freedom,}$$

for the standard and

$$S_{uu} = 0\cdot17500, \text{ with 7 degrees of freedom,}$$

for the test preparation. Neither preparation shows any dependence of variance on U, and the two mean squares are nearly equal (by contrast with the intra-dose mean squares in the two analyses of variance in Table 16.3). A pooled estimate is

$$s^2 = \frac{0\cdot48833}{23}$$

$$= 0\cdot02123, \text{ with 23 degrees of freedom.} \tag{16.11}$$

The main computing table is shown as Table 16.5. At first sight it appears complicated, but its construction is very similar to that long familiar for assays based on quantal responses and using the probit transformation (*cf.* §§ 18.1, 18.2). Systematic

* This is a mean of squares of deviations of u, not of y. Although subsequent calculations are made with the aid of y, they are brought to the u-scale by the weighting coefficient, so that weighted sums of squares of y are in the same units as σ^2 and its estimate.

completion of the table minimizes its difficulties. The columns should be filled in order :—

(i) Insert x, the logarithmic dose metameter, from Table 16.2.

(ii) Insert n, the number of responses measured for each dose.

(iii) Insert the mean value of u, the measured response for each dose, as obtained directly from Table 16.1. The standard errors of these means, $s/\sqrt{n}$, are of the order of 0·1, and therefore at most two places of decimals are needed.

(iv) On a diagram such as Fig. 16.1, representing log u plotted against x, draw two regression lines by eye, constraining these to be parallel and, because of the increase in the weighting coefficient as U increases, regarding deviations from the line as less serious for small values of x than for large values. Then, either directly from the diagram or with the aid of a regression coefficient measured on the diagram, enter Y, the expected value for log u, at each dose. In Fig. 16.1, the regression coefficient was measured as 0·82, and successive values of Y were constructed from this.

(v) Insert $U =$ antilog Y for each dose.

(vi) Calculate nw from equation (16.9) ; three or four digits in weights are adequate for most purposes, and nw is here taken to the nearest integer.

(vii) Form $(u - U)$, multiply by 0·43429, divide by U, and add the quotient to Y ; by equation (16.10), the result is y, the working response. The variance of any y is approximately σ^2/nw, where σ^2 is the variance per response on the original u scale. Thus even with nw at its maximum of 2,400 and σ^2 estimated by s^2 in equation (16.11), the standard error of y would be of the order of 0·003. Consequently, three decimals in y are as many as the data warrant.

(viii), (ix) Enter the individual products nwx, nwy, retaining the full number of decimals in order to assist checking.

(x) Reserve a final column for new calculations of expected response metameters.

TABLE 16.5—Computations for the weighted analysis of the assay of *dl*-tryptophan

x	n	u	Y	U	nw	y	nwx	nwy	Ys, YT
Standard preparation									
0·301	3	2·20	0·352	2·249	80	0·343	24·080	27·440	0·354
0·602	3	3·83	0·599	3·972	251	0·583	151·102	146·333	0·601
0·778	3	5·60	0·743	5·534	487	0·748	378·886	364·276	0·745
0·903	3	7·33	0·846	7·015	783	0·866	707·049	678·078	0·848
1·000	3	8·57	0·925	8·414	1,126	0·933	1,126·000	1,050·558	0·927
1·079	2	9·80	0·990	9·772	1,013	0·991	1,093·027	1,003·883	0·992
1·146	3	11·33	1·045	11·092	1,957	1·054	2,242·722	2,062·678	1·047
1·204	3	12·27	1·092	12·359	2,430	1·089	2,925·720	2,646·270	1·094
1·255	2	13·40	1·134	13·614	1,965	1·127	2,466·075	2,214·555	1·136
					10,092		11,114·661	10,194·071	
Test preparation									
0·699	2	1·25	0·091	1·233	16	0·097	11·184	1·552	0·091
1·000	2	1·90	0·338	2·178	50	0·283	50·000	14·150	0·338
1·176	2	2·90	0·482	3·034	98	0·463	115·248	45·374	0·482
1·301	2	3·50	0·585	3·846	157	0·546	204·257	85·722	0·584
1·477	2	5·45	0·729	5·358	304	0·736	449·008	223·744	0·729
1·602	2	6·85	0·831	6·777	487	0·836	780·174	407·132	0·831
1·699	2	8·30	0·911	8·147	704	0·919	1,196·096	646·976	0·911
					1,816		2,805·967	1,424·650	

	S_{xx}	S_{xy}	S_{yy}
Standard preparation :	12,524·4766	11,455·0154	10,481·0908
	12,240·9522	11,227·0752	10,297·1744
	283·5244	227·9402	183·9164
Test preparation :	4,404·2783	2,262·0266	1,171·5762
	4,335·6007	2,201·2780	1,117·6364
	68·6776	60·7486	53·9398
Total :	352·2020	288·6888	237·8562

(xi) **Form** totals of nw, nwx, and nwy columns for each preparation.

(xii) Apply equations (3.62), (3.63), to give weighted sums of squares and products of deviations for each preparation, as shown at the foot of the table, and add pairs of corresponding components.

These calculations constitute one cycle of the iteration. Before the potency estimate is obtained, the possible need for further cycles must be considered. The weighted means, by equations (3.60), (3.61), are

$$\bar{x}_S = 1 \cdot 1013, \ \bar{x}_T = 1 \cdot 5451, \\ \bar{y}_S = 1 \cdot 0101, \ \bar{y}_T = 0 \cdot 7845. \quad (16.12)$$

Also

$$b = \frac{288 \cdot 6888}{352 \cdot 2020}$$
$$= 0 \cdot 8197, \quad (16.13)$$

a value very close to that used in the first cycle, 0·82. In the usual manner, the two regression equations fitted are evaluated as

$$Y_S = 0 \cdot 1074 + 0 \cdot 8197x, \\ Y_T = -0 \cdot 4820 + 0 \cdot 8197x. \quad (16.14)$$

The final column in Table 16.5 has been filled by calculating the value of Y_S or Y_T appropriate to each dose ; the entries for the standard preparation are 0·002 higher than those on which the first cycle was based, and for the test preparation the differences are almost zero. Had this new column differed to any appreciable extent from the Y column, a second cycle of iteration would have been performed with the values of Y_S, Y_T replacing Y. The process would have been repeated until the difference became negligible. Here no further iteration is needed.

The S_{yy} values at the foot of Table 16.5 are weighted sums of squares between doses, with 8 degrees of freedom for the standard and 6 degrees of freedom for the test preparation. The method of determining weights (provided that the factor ε^2 is not omitted), gives these as comparable with the sum of squares within doses calculated from Table 16.1 earlier in this section ; as usual, the quantity $(S_{xy})^2/S_{xx}$ is the portion of the sum of squares between doses attributable to the linear regression of y on x. Table 16.6

may be compared with Table 16.3; no total sums of squares are shown in it since they are never wanted and need not be calculated.

TABLE 16.6—Separate weighted analyses of variance for the two preparations in Tables 16.1 and 16.2

(*a*) Standard preparation

Nature of variation	d.f.	Sum of squares	Mean square
Regression	1	183·2531	
Linearity	7	0·6633	0·0948
Between doses	8	183·9164	
Within doses	16	0·3133	0·0196

(*b*) Test preparation

Nature of variation	d.f.	Sum of squares	Mean square
Regression	1	53·7350	
Linearity	5	0·2048	0·0410
Between doses	6	53·9398	
Within doses	7	0·1750	0·0250

Again the deviations from linearity, at least for the standard preparation, are too great to be explained by intra-dose variation, and, on the assumption that the variation between doses is validly estimated (after a proper randomization), a pooled mean square for deviations from linearity must be taken as s^2, the estimate of σ^2, instead of that in equation (16.11); the mean squares for the two preparations separately differ appreciably, but, as a consequence of the weighting of the data, the difference is much less marked than in Table 16.3*. In the combined analysis of variance, Table 16.7,

---

* In theory, further complications arise because the number of tubes per dose is not the same for both preparations. A rigorous analysis would require separate consideration of intra-dose and inter-dose variations; this will not be attempted here, as it cannot be of much importance for these data.

the component for a single regression coefficient is, as usual,

$$\frac{(\Sigma S_{xy})^2}{\Sigma S_{xx}} = 236 \cdot 6290,$$

and that for deviations from parallelism is obtained by subtraction of this quantity from the sum of the corresponding components in Table 16.6. The component for preparations is similarly found as

$$\Sigma \left\{ \frac{(Snwy)^2}{Snw} \right\} - \frac{(\Sigma Snwy)^2}{\Sigma Snw} = 10,297 \cdot 1744 + 1,117 \cdot 6364$$

$$- 11,336 \cdot 4694$$

$$= 78 \cdot 3414.$$

TABLE 16.7—Complete weighted analysis of variance for the data of Tables 16.1 and 16.2

Nature of variation	d.f.	Sum of squares	Mean square
Preparations	1	78·3414	
Regression	1	236.6290	
Parallelism	1	0·3591	0·3591
Linearity	12	0·8681	0·07234
Between doses	15	316.1976	
Within doses	23	0·4883	0·02123

The relatively greater weight given to high responses in this analysis, as compared with Table 16.4, has the result of making the square for the deviations from parallelism just significantly greater than the liearity mean square

$$s^2 = 0 \cdot 07234; \tag{16.15}$$

the regression line for the test preparation is steeper than that for the standard. Taken in conjunction with the large difference between preparations, this casts considerable doubt upon the validity of the assay. On internal evidence, the condition of similarity seems not to be satisfied, although some slight non-linearity at high levels of response may be responsible. For the sake of illustrating the method, however, the calculations are concluded as though the assay were valid.

From the means and regression coefficient, equations (16.12) and (16.13),

$$M = -0.4438 - \frac{0.2256}{0.8197}$$

$$= -0.7190.$$

Also, by adaptation of equations (3.66), (3.67)

$$V(\bar{y}_S - \bar{y}_T) = s^2 \Sigma \frac{1}{Snw} \qquad (16.16)$$

and

$$V(b) = s^2 / \Sigma S_{xx}. \qquad (16.17)$$

The variance per unit weight must be taken from equation (16.15), and not from equation (16.11). Hence

$$g = \frac{(2.179)^2 \times 0.07234}{(0.8197)^2 \times 352.2020}$$

$$= 0.0015.$$

Fieller's theorem gives the limits to M as

$$M_L, M_U = -0.4438 - \left[0.2752 \right.$$

$$\pm \frac{2.179}{0.8197} \left\{ 0.07234 \times \left(0.9985 \times \left(\frac{1}{10,092} + \frac{1}{1,816} \right) \right. \right.$$

$$\left. \left. + \frac{(0.2752)^2}{352.2020} \right) \right\}^{\frac{1}{2}} \right] \div 0.9985$$

$$= -0.4438 - [0.2752 \pm 0.0210] \div 0.9985$$

$$= -0.7404, \, -0.6984.$$

The potency of the test preparation is therefore estimated to be 19·10μg. tryptophan per ml., with fiducial limits at 18·18μg. per ml. and 20·03μg. per ml. These limits are 95·2 per cent. and 104·9 per cent. of the estimate, as compared with limits at 93·4 per cent. and 106·5 per cent. of the estimate in the unweighted analysis.

The computations of this section, though obviously much more laborious than those of § 16.2, have not made much difference to the estimate of potency, but the more rational interpretation of the relationship of variance to response has improved the precision. This illustrates the general rule that, almost certainly in a valid assay and often even when (as here) validity is in doubt, a wrong choice of weighting will seldom give a misleading estimate of potency. Of course,

$$V(u) = \text{constant}$$

is not necessarily true in any exact sense, but it is certainly much nearer the truth than the assertion

$$V(\log u) = \text{constant}$$

implicit in § 16.2 ; further refinement would have little effect, even if the data were sufficient to suggest any.

When the dependence of $V(y)$ upon Y is as pronounced as in the tryptophan assay, an analysis that takes no account of differential weighting is bound to involve serious loss of precision. The analysis in § 16.3 gives correctly weighted estimates of the parameters, and consequently leads to a more precise estimate of potency. Experimenters must recognise that the obtaining of the most precise conclusions from data such as these may be possible only at the price of laborious computation. Here the weighted analysis has also disclosed evidence of invalidity. That discovery must not be regarded as a flaw in the analysis : if the assay is invalid, this needs to be known and ought not to be concealed by imperfect analysis. In the present instance, the non-parallelism may indicate fundamental invalidity ; alternatively, it may be due only to an unsuccessful choice of doses having brought the highest doses of the standard or the lowest doses of the test preparation outside the region of linearity, although Fig. 16.1 gives little support to this view.

16.4 Criticism of the design of the tryptophan assay

Though not directly relevant to the subject of this chapter, some discussion of the design of the assay of *dl*-tryptophan seems desirable. Criticism tends to be unfair, however, because the critic cannot put himself in the state of knowledge and state of mind of the experimenter at the time the assay was planned. Probably the assay was intended to be exploratory, rather than to be just one member of a routine series. The experimenter may have known little about the range of linearity of his regression ;

indeed, he may not have been aware that the double logarithmic transformation would linearize his regression, since Wood's first proposals for this were about contemporary with the assay. Consequently, he may deliberately have used a wide range of doses, in the expectation that he would have to discard some from his analysis.

In these circumstances, any analysis of the kind described in this chapter may be regarded as ' making the best of a bad job ', and any criticism of the design should be regarded as guidance for future similar assays, rather than as condemnation of the practice in the past. With this in mind, application of the arguments in Chapter 6 is valuable : these indicate that the design was far from optimal, and that the narrow limits of error might have been made much narrower by a better choice. The following points should be noted :—

(i) Allocation of unequal numbers of subjects (tubes) to preparations has had its usual bad consequences, especially in respect of $V(\bar{y}_S - \bar{y}_T)$.

(ii) The dose range for the test preparation was unfortunately chosen. Had the range for the standard been known in advance to be satisfactory, a better guess at the relative potency would have made the experimenter choose higher doses for the test preparation.

(iii) The change in dose range should also reduce $(M - \bar{x}_S + \bar{x}_T)$, by making the mean responses to the preparations almost equal. In § 16.3, this quantity made a large contribution to the width of the fiducial range for M, and, even without a really good preliminary estimate of potency, considerable improvement ought to have been possible.

(iv) The evidence of non-linearity and non-parallelism reported in § 16.3 seems more likely to be the result of flaws in randomization than a sign of either fundamental invalidity or a dose range too wide for linearity. If this be true, stricter attention to the randomization procedures should make the intra-dose mean square an estimate of σ^2, the variance per response. The result might not be as low as the value 0·021 in Table 16.7, but it ought to be less than the value 0·072 that was used in § 16.3.

(v) If action were taken under (iv), a further improvement would be to reduce the number of doses tested, so as to give a 6-point or perhaps an 8-point symmetrical design. Regular spacing of doses on the logarithmic scale, over a range as wide as for the standard preparation, is desirable. In this way ΣS_{xx} would be increased, g decreased, and possibly even Snw increased. The degrees of freedom for the intra-dose s^2 would be increased, at the expense of the degrees of freedom for deviations from linearity, so that the change here recommended would not be ideal if for any reason imperfect randomization were inevitable.

The changes suggested in (i), (ii), (iii) would narrow the fiducial range to an extent that can be roughly estimated. Equal division of subjects, and a dose range for the test preparation corresponding closely to that for the standard, would give Snw and S_{xx} for each preparation about 78 per cent. of that found in § 16.3 for the standard. Hence ΣS_{xx} would be increased to about 440, g would be decreased to about 0·001, and the semi-fiducial range for M would become of the order of

$$\frac{2 \cdot 18}{0 \cdot 82 \times 0 \cdot 999} \times \left\{ 0 \cdot 072 \times 0 \cdot 999 \times \frac{2}{7,870} \right\}^{\frac{1}{2}} = 0 \cdot 0114,$$

instead of the previous 0·0210 ; in this calculation, $(M - \bar{x}_S + \bar{x}_T)$ has been assumed negligible. These changes alone almost cut the fiducial range by half, and so improve the precision of R to the same extent as would a fourfold increase in subjects on the old design. Inadequate knowledge on which to base the choice of doses would reduce the gain in precision ; the considerations advanced in (iv) and (v), however, ought at least to compensate, and might themselves give still bigger advantages, as well as making computation much simpler.

CHAPTER 17

QUANTAL RESPONSES AND THE TOLERANCE DISTRIBUTION

17.1 The use of quantal responses

The third of the three types of dilution assay listed in § 2.1 is that based upon quantal responses. For some stimulus-subject systems, quantitative measurement of a response attributable to the action of the stimulus is impossible or impracticable, and all that can be done is to record whether or not the subject manifests a certain reaction. The quantal response so used is often death, but may be any other easily recognizable change in the subject. For example, insecticides may be assayed by assigning batches of insects to doses of the standard and test preparations and analysing the relationship between death rate and dose. Other examples are the assay of fungicides by means of spore germination rates, the assay of insulin by the mouse convulsion method, the assay of oestrogenic hormones by techniques dependent upon the induction of oestrus in test subjects, and the assay of vitamins by their success in curing deficiency symptoms. Many of the quantal responses used for assays involve an irreversible change in the subjects that respond, so that each can be used once only : an insect that has died after spraying, or a spore that has germinated, cannot be used again. Even subjects that have failed to respond may have been so affected by the stimulus that thereafter they react differently from others not previously exposed to the stimulus. Some responses, however, may have no permanent effect on the subjects, and, as usual, increased precision is then to be expected from a design that allows several tests to be made on each subject. For the present, attention will be restricted to assays in which each subject is used once.

In certain important respects, quantal response assays are closely related to direct assays. The *tolerance* of any one subject is defined as that dose which would be just sufficient to produce the characteristic response ; to any lesser dose the subject will fail to respond, to any greater dose it will respond. This tolerance may be a fixed quantity for any one subject, or it may vary with time, but the experimenter can discuss only the value that it has at the instant of his test. In a direct assay, the tolerance is measured for each subject, and the estimation of potency is a comparison of mean tolerances. In a quantal response assay, all that can be done with one subject is to apply a selected dose, to observe whether or not the response occurs, and so to record whether the tolerance was less or greater than the dose ; the object, however, is still to make inferences about mean tolerances. The practical difficulties in the way of measuring the amount of a pyrethrin spray needed to kill an insect, or the amount of insulin needed to produce convulsions in a mouse, are obvious, yet assays based on these responses are similar in purpose to the ' cat ' method for digitalis assay (§§ 2.2, 2.3). Information on whether the tolerance of each of a set of subjects is greater or less than a specified dose (not necessarily the same dose for every subject) is clearly less valuable than information on direct measurements of tolerance for the same number of subjects ; nevertheless, even the quantal information can be used for the estimation of the mean of the tolerance distribution.

In spite of this logical similarity to direct assays, the design and statistical analysis of assays based on quantal responses are more like the design and analysis for quantitative responses. The usual scheme is to choose a set of doses of each preparation, and to test a batch of subjects at each dose. The number of subjects needed will in general be rather greater than for an assay using quantitative measurements, in order to allow for the loss of information on the tolerance of each. The estimation of potency is made by use of the relationship between the percentage responding and the dose, the procedure being analogous to the use of the relationship between mean response and dose for quantitative responses.

The percentage response is not likely to have a linear regression on any simple dose metameter, although approximate methods of analysis which ignore this non-linearity may sometimes be adequate. Theoretically preferable are methods that take account of the form of the tolerance distribution, in a manner consistent with the practice for direct assays. The assumption of a normal distribution of log tolerances leads to the probit transformation (Finney, 1952), which achieves the linearization of the regression by metametric transformation of the percentage responses. Other mathematical models are possible, however, and the general theory discussed in this chapter is applicable to many alternatives.

17.2 The minimal effective dose

The early users of quantal response techniques based their estimations of potency on assessments of *minimal lethal doses*, or, more generally, *minimal effective doses* for each preparation. Whether the minimal lethal dose was intended to be the smallest dose sufficient to kill at least one subject or the smallest dose sufficient to kill every subject was never very clear. In an important paper that was largely responsible for the rejection of the concept of minimal effective doses from assay investigations, Trevan (1927) demonstrated the unsatisfactory nature of the phrase. Trevan wrote, ' The common use of this expression in the literature of the subject would logically involve the assumptions that there is a dose, for any given poison, which is only just sufficient to kill all or most of the animals of a given species, and that doses very little smaller would not kill any animals of that species. Any worker, however, accustomed to estimations of toxicity, knows that these assumptions do not represent the truth '. In fact, the assumptions imply a belief that all subjects have the same tolerance ; as soon as the existence of a distribution of tolerances is admitted, consideration of the properties of that distribution is imperative (but see § 17.10).

17.3 The median effective dose

In the paper to which reference has already been made, Trevan advocated the characterization of the potency of a material by means of its *median lethal dose* (for a poison) or, more generally, by its *median effective dose*. These quantities are often indicated by LD50, or ED50, to symbolize the dose producing a response in 50 per cent. of trials (so, by extension, ED90 is used for the dose that produces a response in 90 per cent. of trials). If the tolerance distribution is symmetrical, the median effective dose will coincide with the mean of the distribution. As will be shown later, the estimation of a dose that produces a 50 per cent. response is much more satisfactory than that of a dose producing a 5 per cent. or

95 per cent. response, and greater precision can be obtained for a fixed number of subjects. The condition of similarity requires that the distributions of tolerances for the two preparations shall be identical except for a factor ρ relating their scales : the relative potency may therefore be estimated as the ratio of any corresponding pair of doses. In particular, the ratio of either the median or the mean effective doses is an estimate of ρ, whatever the form of the distribution ; if a logarithmic dose metameter is used, the difference between any pair of corresponding statistics defining the locations of the distributions (*e.g.* median, mean, mode, ED90) on the metametric scale will be an estimate of log ρ.

The methods recommended here for estimating a median effective dose employ computational procedures for the estimation of the parameters of the tolerance distribution, under certain assumptions about its mathematical form. The particular choice of mathematical form adopted is less important than might at first appear, though its expression in terms of a logarithmic dose metameter is usually convenient. The calculations are applicable to all data, without restriction on the allocation of subjects to doses, so that the experimenter is free to base that allocation on considerations of precision. These methods are like those for quantitative responses described in earlier chapters, in that they permit the assessment of precision from the internal evidence of an assay, they assist the discussion of improvements in precision, and they encourage the exploitation of modern ideas on experimental design.

The theory of these methods of estimation will be developed in this chapter ; all practical application is deferred until Chapter 18. This theory is closely related to that for quantitative responses in Chapter 3 (especially § 3.13). Those to whom mathematical theory is unwelcome should not need to study § 17.5 in detail, as Chapter 18 contains full working instructions based upon the formulæ given here ; § 17.4 should be read, however, for the sake of its analogy with § 3.7.

Many other methods of estimating the median effective dose from records of quantal responses have been proposed. Some are temptingly simple in calculation, and apparently avoid all reference to the tolerance distribution ; in fact, most of them contain an implicit assumption that the tolerance distribution is symmetrical, either for the measured dose or for a logarithmic dose metameter. Moreover, to design an experiment in such a way as to permit their use may require an uneconomic allocation of subjects to doses. Such methods are undoubtedly helpful in certain circumstances, and nothing in this book is intended to imply a complete condemnation of them, but their general adoption purely on the score of simplicity is to be deprecated. For this reason, their description is deferred until Chapter 20, at which stage they can be seen in proper perspective in relation to the methods of the present chapter.

17.4 The equivalent deviate transformation

For quantitative responses, a linear regression of response metameter on dose metameter, involving two unknown parameters, has been found adequate as a mathematical model of many dose-response relationships, at least over the range important in biological assay. For direct assays, a normal distribution of log tolerances was suggested in § 2.9 ; this also involves two parameters. An assumption analogous to the first, and including the second as a particular case, is that of representing the distribution of individual log tolerances in terms of two parameters, one of location and the other of scale. If

$$x = \log z \qquad (17.1)$$

is the dose metameter, this type of distribution may be written

$$dP = \beta f(a + \beta x)\, dx, \qquad (17.2)$$

where $f(\theta)\, d\theta$ is a distribution function* containing no unknown parameters, and therefore

$$\int_{-\infty}^{\infty} f(\theta)\, d\theta = 1. \qquad (17.3)$$

Either or both tails of the distribution may have finite limits, but for convenience these may be regarded as contained within infinite limits without affecting the general theory ; the limits of the distribution are assumed to be independent of the parameters. The normal tolerance distribution

$$dP = \frac{1}{\sigma\sqrt{2\pi}} \cdot \exp\left\{ -\frac{(x - \mu)^2}{2\sigma^2} \right\} \cdot dx \qquad (17.4)$$

---

* In this chapter, θ is used as a ' dummy ' variate without any special meaning, merely for expressing functional forms and relationships.

is an example of the general two-parameter distribution (17.2), having its mean

$$\mu = -\frac{\alpha}{\beta} \qquad (17.5)$$

and its standard deviation

$$\sigma = \frac{1}{\beta}. \qquad (17.6)$$

The probability that a dose whose measure on the metametric scale is x will cause the characteristic response in a subject chosen at random is the probability that the tolerance of the subject is less than x, or

$$P = \int_{-\infty}^{x} \beta f(\alpha + \beta x)\, dx. \qquad (17.7)$$

For any specified distribution function, $f(\theta)\, d\theta$, define Y, the *equivalent deviate* of P, by the equation

$$P = \int_{-\infty}^{Y} f(\theta)\, d\theta. \qquad (17.8)$$

A value of either P or Y determines the other uniquely, and the relationship between them can be put into the form of a numerical table which gives a metametric transformation of the response rate, P. From equations (17.7), (17.8),

$$Y = \alpha + \beta x, \qquad (17.9)$$

an equation which completely specifies the tolerance distribution provided that the function $f(\theta)$ has been agreed.

Consequently, the procedure for estimating the parameters α and β may be regarded as finding a linear relationship between x and the Y-transform of the probability of response ; this probability is itself estimated by p, the proportion of subjects observed to respond to a particular dose, and from these empirical values an equation

$$Y = a + bx \qquad (17.10)$$

may be calculated as an estimate of (17.9). As might be expected, the computations needed are very similar to those for a linear regression, though an iterative process like that of § 3.13 will usually be needed. With a, b as estimates of α, β, any other quantity relating to the tolerance distribution, such as the mean tolerance or the median effective dose, may easily be estimated. The particular forms of distribution considered in this chapter are symmetrical, so that the mean and median coincide, but that need not always be so. For the normal tolerance distribution, (17.4), equation (17.8) gives Y as the *normal equivalent deviate* of P (Gaddum, 1933), as discussed below in § 17.8.

In an assay, each preparation tested will have corresponding to it an equation like (17.9). From the considerations advanced in § 2.9 as pertaining generally to dilution assays, or from the condition of similarity (§ 3.3), the values of β must be identical. Hence the regression lines must be parallel, except for deviations attributable to sampling variation, and the log relative potency will be estimated by the horizontal distance between two parallel lines. In fact, equation (4.10) will apply, though the estimation of the lines and the assessment of precision introduce new features. In this chapter, only the estimation of equation (17.9) for a single preparation will be discussed, as the extension of that theory needed for assay purposes is very simple and can properly appear with the instructions for assay computations (§ 18.1).

17.5 Estimation of the two parameters

Suppose that n subjects receive a dose whose logarithm is x, under conditions that make the reactions of each subject independent of all others, and r respond. The probability of this result, relative to all possible results with n subjects, is given by the binomial distribution, and is

$$P(r) = \binom{n}{r} P^r Q^{n-r}, \qquad (17.11)$$

where

$$\binom{n}{r} = \frac{n!}{r!\,(n-r)!} \qquad (17.12)$$

and $P\;(= 1 - Q)$ is defined by equation (17.7) as a function of x involving the parameters α, β. From data such as these, obtained at two or more levels of dose, estimates of α, β may be formed ; the method of maximum likelihood is one of several mathematical techniques that may be adopted in order to develop a computational procedure (§§ 3.12, 20.3).

Experimentation leading to direct observation of p, an empirical value of P for a selected x, is not always possible. For example, the population may contain an unknown proportion of subjects which will respond whatever dose is given (Finney, 1944a), or the total number of individuals receiving a particular dose may have to be estimated from a parallel sample instead of being counted (Wadley, 1949a). A generalization of the theory that includes problems of this kind has been obtained (Finney, 1949b), and will be summarized here. Suppose that the tolerance distribution for individuals is that given above as (17.2), so that the probability of response at dose x, *due to the action of that dose alone*, is P. Suppose further that an experiment is performed in which r, the number of subjects responding in a group of n, can be observed for a series of values of the dose, x, and that, *under the conditions of experiment*, the probability of exactly r responses at a particular x is

$$P(r) = F(J + KQ) ; \qquad (17.13)$$

here J and K are additional parameters and $F(\theta)$ is a known function.

As an example of the use of this formula, suppose that a proportion C_1 of the population will respond even to zero dose and that a proportion C_2 is unable to respond however large the dose ; the probability that a subject selected at random will respond when it receives a dose x is then

$$P^* = (1 - C_2) - Q (1 - C_1 - C_2). \qquad (17.14)$$

The number of responses in a batch of n subjects exposed to a dose x will have a binomial distribution based upon P^* instead of on P :

$$P(r) = \binom{n}{r} (P^*)^r (Q^*)^{(n-r)}, \qquad (17.15)$$

which has the form of equation (17.13). Unless C_1 and C_2 are known, direct estimation of P from tests at a particular x is impossible, and the whole data must be used in order to estimate also the additional parameters. If C_2 is known to be zero and the distribution of tolerances is normal, the problem reduces to that of taking account of ' natural mortality ' in probit analysis (Finney, 1944a ; 1952, Chapter 6 ; see § 21.3 below).

The logarithm of the likelihood of the results obtained for a series of doses is, except for a constant,

$$L = S \{\log P(r)\} = S \{\log F (J + KQ)\}. \qquad (17.16)$$

The maximum likelihood estimates of α, β, J, K will be obtained by equating to zero the partial differential coefficients of L with respect to each of these parameters ; if the conditions of the problem specify J or K exactly, the corresponding equation will be omitted. From equations (17.7)–(17.9),

$$\frac{\partial Q}{\partial \alpha} = - f (\alpha + \beta x) = - Z, \text{ say,}$$

and

$$\frac{\partial Q}{\partial \beta} = - xZ, \qquad (17.17)$$

where Z is the ordinate to the standardized tolerance distribution, $f (\theta) \, d\theta$, corresponding to the deviate Y. Consequently, the maximum likelihood equations are

$$\frac{\partial L}{\partial \alpha} \equiv - K S\left(\frac{ZF'}{F}\right) = 0,$$

$$\frac{\partial L}{\partial \beta} \equiv - K S\left(\frac{xZF'}{F}\right) = 0,$$

$$\frac{\partial L}{\partial J} \equiv S\left(\frac{F'}{F}\right) = 0, \qquad (17.18)$$

$$\frac{\partial L}{\partial K} \equiv S\left(\frac{QF'}{F}\right) = 0,$$

where

$$F' (\theta) = \frac{\partial}{\partial \theta} \left\{ F (\theta) \right\}. \qquad (17.19)$$

In general, equations (17.18) do not reduce to any simple form capable of explicit solution. The most satisfactory method of solving them is by an iterative process, analogous to that described in § 3.13 ; provisional values for the four parameters are obtained from a diagram, a rough calculation, or even a guess, and adjustments to these are calculated from first order Taylor-Maclaurin expansions of the first differential coefficients. The improved values are used as a basis for a second cycle of calculation, and iteration continues as long as is necessary for adequate convergence to the solutions.

Suppose that a_1, b_1, j_1, k_1, are the first values, with which the iteration is to be begun. Define the *empirical rate of response* to any one dose tested as p $(= 1 - q)$, the maximum likelihood estimate of P using only the data from that dose and taking $J = j_1$, $K = k_1$; hence q is the solution of*

$$F'(j_1 + k_1 q) = 0. \tag{17.20}$$

As shown by Finney (1949b), values of δa_1, δb_1, δj_1, and δk_1, adjustments to the provisional estimates of the parameters, are obtainable as the constant term and the three partial regression coefficients in the weighted linear regression of $(Q - q)/Z$ on x, λ_1, λ_2 ; the *auxiliary variates*, λ_1 and λ_2, are defined by

$$\lambda_1 = -\frac{1}{KZ}, \tag{17.21}$$

$$\lambda_2 = -\frac{Q}{KZ}, \tag{17.22}$$

and the weight to be associated with each $(Q - q)/Z$ is

$$W = -E\left\{\frac{K^2 Z^2 F''}{F}\right\}. \tag{17.23}$$

The development is similar to that in § 3.13, and a final simplification is achieved by introducing a *working equivalent deviate*, y, defined as

$$y = Y + \frac{Q - q}{Z}, \tag{17.24}$$

analogous to equation (3.57), the right-hand side being evaluated with the aid of the first approximation to the estimates (*cf.* Fisher, 1935). The result may then be expressed

$$a_2 = \bar{y} - b_2 \bar{x} - \delta j_1 \bar{\lambda}_1 - \delta k_1 \bar{\lambda}_2, \tag{17.25}$$

and

$$\left. \begin{array}{l} b_2 S_{xx} + \delta j_1 S_{x\lambda_1} + \delta k_1 S_{x\lambda_2} = S_{xy}, \\ b_2 S_{x\lambda_1} + \delta j_1 S_{\lambda_1\lambda_1} + \delta k_1 S_{\lambda_1\lambda_2} = S_{\lambda_1 y}, \\ b_2 S_{x\lambda_2} + \delta j_1 S_{\lambda_1\lambda_2} + \delta k_1 S_{\lambda_2\lambda_2} = S_{\lambda_2 y}. \end{array} \right\} \tag{17.26}$$

---

* If j_1, k_1 differ very much from the true (unknown) values of J, K that operated for a particular batch of subjects, the value of q may chance to be negative or to exceed unity. In reality, q is introduced only as an aid to the solution of equations (17.18), and the name given to p should not deter the user from employing such an apparently anomalous value in all the formulæ that follow.

where a_2 and b_2 have been written for the revised values of the parameters, $(a_1 + \delta a_1)$, $(b_1 + \delta b_1)$. The means and the sums of squares and products are weighted, so that, for example,

$$\bar{y} = \frac{SWy}{SW} \tag{17.27}$$

and

$$S_{xy} = SW (x - \bar{x})(y - \bar{y}) \tag{17.28}$$
$$= SWxy - \frac{(SWx)(SWy)}{SW} .$$

Thus b_2, δj_1, δk_1 are the linear regression coefficients in a weighted regression equation of y on x, λ_1, λ_2, and a_2 is the constant term in this equation.

Provided that no doses are included for which P is known absolutely, instead of merely estimated, equations (17.26) are complete as shown. Often, however, ' control ' batches of subjects are tested in the absence of the stimulus, and so have $x \longrightarrow -\infty$. For these controls, $Q = 1$ is known ; therefore they make no contribution to information on α and β, though q, derived from equation (17.20), need not be unity. The controls do give information on J and K. Examination of the method of derivation of equations (17.26) shows that $(- F''/F)$, evaluated for $Q = 1$, must be added to $S_{\lambda_1\lambda_1}$, $S_{\lambda_1\lambda_2}$, and $S_{\lambda_2\lambda_2}$, and that $k_1 (1 - q) F''/F$ must be added to $S_{\lambda_1 y}$ and $S_{\lambda_2 y}$, the other coefficients of the equations remaining unchanged. Occasionally, a maximal dose $(x \longrightarrow +\infty)$ may be applied, for which the conditions of the problem require $Q = 0$ exactly. From equation (17.13), it is clear that subjects so tested can give information only on J, which is therefore in some way a measure of that part of the population of subjects immune to the stimulus. Only two coefficients of equations (17.26) are affected : $(- F''/F)$ must be added to $S_{\lambda_1\lambda_1}$ and $(- k_1 q F''/F)$ must be added to $S_{\lambda_1 y}$, these being evaluated with $Q = 0$.

The second cycle of calculation will have $a_2, b_2, j_2, (= j_1 + \delta j_1)$, $k_2 (= k_1 + \delta k_1)$ in place of a_1, b_1, j_1, k_1, and iteration continues until two successive cycles agree closely. Each cycle has its own set of empirical response rates, defined by equation (17.20) with the appropriate j, k. In the limit, δj and δk become zero, so that b is simply the weighted regression coefficient of the final set of working equivalent deviates on x. For practical purposes, the iteration seldom needs to be carried to many cycles, and the last adjustments to j and k are almost always negligible; indeed, if care is exercised in the choice of the provisional values with which to initiate the computations, one or at most two cycles of the iterative process will usually suffice (§ 18.3).

Though the general theory based on equation (17.13) involves the estimation of four parameters, most biological assays require only the simpler two-parameter expression for $P(r)$ in equation (17.11). This may be regarded as a particular case of equation (17.13) with both J and K known, in fact with $J = 0$, $K = 1$. As might be expected, equation (17.20) then reduces to

$$p = r/n, \qquad (17.29)$$

so that the quantity called the empirical response rate is now the actual proportion of responses observed. Equation (17.23) becomes

$$W = \frac{nZ^2}{PQ}, \qquad (17.30)$$

which may be regarded as made up of a *weighting coefficient*, w, multiplied by the number of subjects at a dose, where

$$w = \frac{Z^2}{PQ}. \qquad (17.31)$$

The auxiliary variates λ_1, λ_2 are not required. Each cycle of iteration consists merely in calculating W, y from the previous cycle and forming the weighted linear regression of y on x.

Application of this method to actual data requires that some assumption be made about the form of the function $f(\theta)$. No further progress can be made in purely general terms : the distribution (17.2) must now be replaced by the normal distribution, (17.4), or by some alternative specific distributional form. In §§ 17.8–17.13, several of these will be discussed ; before that, however, something must be said about validity tests and about variances of the estimates of parameters. Only the two-parameter equation, (17.11), will be considered, but formulæ applicable to any particular form of equation (17.13) can easily be found for each distribution.

Suffices indicating the cycle of iteration were needed for the argument of this section, but will not be used in future. No confusion should be caused by their omission, because in the calculations of any one cycle all steps employ only the approximations obtained in the immediately preceding cycle.

17.6 The test of homogeneity

If an experiment has tested subjects at each of v doses, a χ^2 test will be needed for assessment of the significance of evidence against the model represented by equations (17.7) and (17.13). The expected number of responses amongst a batch of n subjects at dose x may be calculated from the estimates of the parameters, a, b, j, k, and is

$$E(r) = \sum_{r=0}^{n} rF(j + kQ) ; \qquad (17.32)$$

n, of course, need not be the same for every dose. Then

$$\chi^2_{[v-4]} = S\left[\frac{n\{r - E(r)\}^2}{E(r)\{n - E(r)\}} \right], \qquad (17.33)$$

in which the summation extends over every dose, may be tested as a χ^2 with $(v - 4)$ degrees of freedom (Appendix Table IV ; Fisher and Yates, 1963, Table IV). If the iteration were carried through to its limits, this could alternatively be calculated as

$$\chi^2_{[v-4]} = S_{yy} - \frac{(S_{xy})^2}{S_{xx}},$$

but a better approximation at an earlier stage of the iteration is

$$\chi^2_{[v-4]} = S_{yy} - bS_{xy} - \delta j S_{\lambda_1 y} - \delta k S_{\lambda_2 y}. \qquad (17.34)$$

In these last two expressions for χ^2, S_{yy} must be understood to be the ordinary weighted sum of squares of deviations increased by contributions $n\{r - E(r)\}^2/E(r)\{n - E(r)\}$ from the controls (for which $x \longrightarrow -\infty$) and any batch of subjects tested at a maximal dose $(x \longrightarrow +\infty)$. Equation (17.34) is strictly valid only in the limit of the iteration (and for large samples), but for most purposes it is close enough to the truth at the last cycle calculated ; since it is so easily evaluated, it will be used unless a result on the border-line of significance indicates a need for more detailed computation. If either J or K is known, the degrees of freedom for χ^2 are $(v - 3)$, and if both are known they are $(v - 2)$.

Reference of χ^2 as calculated from equation (17.33) or equation (17.34) to the tabulated distribution (Appendix Table IV) presupposes that none of the expected frequencies is very small. If $E(r)$ or $\{n - E(r)\}$ is less than 5 for any dose, χ^2 should be computed by equation (17.33) after combining observed and expected frequencies for this and the next dose ; the number of degrees of freedom is then reduced by 1. This has been discussed elsewhere (Finney, 1952, § 18). The effect of small expectations is to increase the dispersion of χ^2 values calculated from equation (17.34) without modification, so that data having no heterogeneity show very large or very small values too frequently. A large χ^2 should always be examined closely, in order to see whether excessive contributions come from classes with small expectations, so that a spurious appearance of significance is produced ; a small χ^2, on the other hand, is safe, in the sense that small expectations are unlikely to cause the concealment of a genuinely significant deviation from chance.

A significantly large value of χ^2 would indicate the failure of the forms assumed for the tolerance distribution and for $F(\theta)$ to give $P(r)$ at all levels of dose. This is a test of statistical validity (§ 15.3), corresponding closely to the test of deviations from linearity in an assay based upon quantitative responses. If *a priori* the experimenter believes in the validity of the statistical model, and this χ^2 is not significant, he may regard it as confirmation of his right to proceed with calculations of a standard type (§ 15.5). The action to be taken when χ^2 is significant will be discussed later (§ 18.1).

17.7   The variances of estimates

If the data show no heterogeneity (*i.e.* χ^2 is non-significant), the variances of the estimates of the parameters may be found by formulæ that are generalizations of the formulæ for unweighted regressions. The variance of $\bar{y}$ is

$$V(\bar{y}) = \frac{1}{SW}, \tag{17.35}$$

and the variances and covariances of b, j, k are the elements of the inverse matrix, V, where

$$V^{-1} = \begin{pmatrix} S_{xx} & S_{x\lambda_1} & S_{x\lambda_2} \\ S_{x\lambda_1} & S_{\lambda_1\lambda_1} & S_{\lambda_1\lambda_2} \\ S_{x\lambda_2} & S_{\lambda_1\lambda_2} & S_{\lambda_2\lambda_2} \end{pmatrix} ; \tag{17.36}$$

V will generally be calculated as a stage in the solution of equations (17.26), in the manner illustrated in § 4.19. The mean, $\bar{y}$, is uncorrelated with b, j, k, and the variance of a is easily formed from consideration of equation (17.25) as a linear function of $\bar{y}$, b, δj, δk. The variances and covariances of other combinations of the parameters can be similarly constructed, and Fieller's theorem can be applied to their ratios. When J and K are known, and the numbers of responses conform to equation (17.11), equation (17.36) reduces to

$$V(b) = \frac{1}{S_{xx}} \cdot \tag{17.37}$$

Equations (17.35), (17.37) are the same as for an ordinary linear regression, except that the observations are differentially weighted and the variance per observation, s^2, is replaced by unity. The variances are essentially expected variances, not empirical estimates of variances, and any use of them in the determination of fiducial limits will employ the normal distribution instead of the t distribution.*

17.8 Normal distribution

In § 2.9, the assumption that the distribution of log tolerances is normal has been recommended as a working hypothesis for direct assays. The argument in favour of this is neither stronger nor less strong than in any other branch of biometry. The true distribution may not be normal, but, in the absence of evidence favouring a specific alternative, the fact that the normal accords fairly well with observation and is mathematically tractable makes the hypothesis of normality very appealing; the central limit theorem (Cramér, 1946, § 17.4; Kendall & Stuart, 1963) gives reason for hoping that conclusions based on the normal assumption will be close to the truth when means of several observations are involved.

If a normal distribution is assumed for direct assays (*cf.* § 2.9), the same choice suggests itself for assays based on quantal responses. If the log tolerances of cats used in the assay of digitalis by a direct

---

* Though this is usually assumed, it cannot be stated as rigorously true. The number of degrees of freedom for the variances might perhaps be taken as the difference between the total number of subjects and the number of doses (*i.e.* as the number of degrees of freedom within doses), but in almost all assays this will be sufficiently large for the t distribution to be very nearly normal.

technique can be regarded as normally distributed, then a hypothesis of normality for the log tolerances of frogs in an indirect assay of strophanthus, or for the log tolerance of aphids in an indirect assay of derris, seems at least worth trial, and, in the absence of controverting evidence, may well be adopted. Positive evidence for normality is unlikely to exist, but considerations such as those of § 2.9 and § 15.4 justify this step. To adopt different hypotheses about the tolerance distribution according to whether assays are direct or quantal would be irrational unless either the quantal assays are in some essential respects different or expediency carries greater weight than consistency.

The normal distribution (17.4) may be written

$$dP = \frac{\beta}{\sqrt{2\pi}} e^{-\frac{1}{2}(\alpha + \beta x)^2} dx. \tag{17.38}$$

Hence, by the first of equations (17.17),

$$Z = \frac{1}{\sqrt{2\pi}} e^{-\frac{1}{2}Y^2}. \tag{17.39}$$

From equations (17.24) and (17.31), y and w are calculated (Appendix Tables VI and VII), and the iterative process is begun. The idea of using the normal deviate in order to represent quantal response data by a linear regression has a long history (Finney, 1952, § 14). It appears to have originated with Fechner (1860), and, with improvements by other workers, it was used by psychometrists for seventy years before it was either re-discovered or adapted for the study of dose-reponse relationships in biology. Its first use for biological assay was by Gaddum (1933), who developed his method of normal equivalent deviates in a manner very similar to that used later by Bliss (1935a, b ; 1938) for probits. Bliss, however, was the first to present the full maximum likelihood method. He introduced the *probit* of P, the normal equivalent deviate increased by 5 (Bliss, 1934a, b), with the object of making the occurrence of negative values very rare. Thus the metametric transformation is taken to be

$$P = \int_{-\infty}^{Y-5} \frac{1}{\sqrt{2\pi}} e^{-\frac{1}{2}\theta^2} d\theta. \tag{17.40}$$

The advantage of this is slight, for the avoidance of negative values is bought at the price of more cumbrous tables, but the use of probits is now customary in biological assay and will be adopted here. The scheme of iterative calculation for the probit transformation, based on the method of § 17.5, is described and illustrated in Chapter 18. Finney (1952) has discussed the probit transformation and many of its applications in considerable detail; the theory presented in §§ 17.5–17.7 is a generalization of that developed, in Appendix II and elsewhere, in this earlier book.

17.9 Rectangular distribution

The simplest of all assumptions that might be made about the tolerance distribution is that the regression of proportion responding on x is linear: the tolerance distribution is rectangular, and is expressed by

$$f(\theta) = \begin{cases} 1 & 0 \leqslant \theta \leqslant 1 \\ 0 & \theta < 0, \theta > 1 \end{cases} \tag{17.41}$$

in the notation of § 17.4. Then

$$P = Y, \tag{17.42}$$

and equations (17.31) and (17.24) reduce to the simple forms

$$w = \frac{1}{PQ} \tag{17.43}$$

and

$$y = p. \tag{17.44}$$

The working equivalent deviate is identical with the empirical response rate, and the analysis consists in fitting a linear regression of p on x. This is not an unweighted regression, such as was often used in early attempts to analyse quantal response data, but uses a weighting coefficient dependent upon P, the expected response rate.

The assumption of a rectangular distribution will not bear close examination. The exact limitation of range implies the existence of a dose $-a/\beta$ below which no subject would respond, and a dose $(1 - a)/\beta$ above which all subjects would respond. In the estimation of these limits, excessive importance is attached to data for doses that happen to give very small or very large response rates. Nevertheless, for data from a well-designed assay using reasonably large numbers of subjects and no very extreme doses, conclusions based on this assumption are likely to agree with those from more logical alternatives.

17.10   Logistic distribution

Berkson (1944) has discussed the use of a logistic function as an alternative to the normal sigmoid for the representation of the regression of a quantal response rate on dose. He stated that ' In view of the wide use of the normal curve to represent the distribution of biologic traits and also because of direct experimental evidence of the normal distribution of susceptibility, it is to be conceded that the integral of the normal curve recommends itself.' Nevertheless, he held the opinion that ' However, the logistic function is very near to the integrated normal curve, it applies to a wide range of physicochemical phenomena and therefore may have a better theoretic basis than the integrated normal curve. Moreover, there are reasons for believing it to be easier to handle statistically.' The argument that the theoretical basis of the logistic curve may be more appropriate to assays than that of the normal distribution is here a little obscure and needs expansion. When the reason for unlike behaviour of similarly treated subjects is primarily their intrinsic differences in susceptibility, the specification in terms of a frequency distribution of individual tolerances is natural, and, as explained in § 17.8, the assumption of a normal distribution of log tolerances seems the most reasonable procedure in the absence of evidence for any alternative. Use of the logistic instead would imply the assumption of a tolerance distribution defined by equation (17.48), a distribution that seems much less likely to correspond to reality.

On the other hand, not all assays are of this kind, and stimulus-subject reactions of a very different nature may be used. Bliss and Packard (1941) reported an examination of the relationship between the mutation rate of *Drosophila melanogaster* and the dose of roentgen rays with which the eggs were irradiated. The probability of a mutation increases with increasing dosage, but presumably because of an increased chance that the appropriate gene-locus is ' hit ' rather than because of variations in the susceptibility to mutation of individual flies. The titration of sera by means of their effectiveness in producing haemolysis of red blood cells is another situation in which the physicochemical model of the reaction, rather than a tolerance distribution, is the most reasonable starting point for the specification of the problem. If reactions such as these are made the basis of biological assays, the logistic or auto-catalytic function

$$P = \frac{1}{1 + e^{-(\alpha + \beta x)}} \tag{17.45}$$

may well be more appropriate. Indeed, equation (17.45) has been developed theoretically for the representation of phenomena such as haemolysis and population growth. Proposals to use equation (17.45) in bio-assay have aroused considerable interest, and some controversy (which may be resolved by the recognition that this and the probit method have each their importance, the choice between them depending upon the nature of the biological reactions in use).

The metametric transformation advocated by Berkson, on the basis of equation (17.45), may be written

$$P = \frac{e^Y}{1 + e^Y}, \tag{17.46}$$

or

$$Y = \log_e (P/Q) ; \tag{17.47}$$

he termed Y the *logit* of P. Essentially the same transformation, differing only in a factor of 2, was proposed by Fisher and Yates in the first edition of their *Statistical Tables* (6th edition, 1963), and independently by Wilson and Worcester (1943a, b, d). As stated above, the logistic transformation may be required for assays in which no question of a frequency distribution of individual tolerances arises. Nevertheless, it can also be generated by a tolerance distribution, in the ordinary manner. Even in circumstances where the concept of tolerance is biologically inappropriate, the mathematical structure of the analysis is the same, and expression of the methods and formulæ in terms of the tolerance distribution enables the computational terminology to be kept unaltered.

For a tolerance distribution corresponding to

$$f(\theta) = \tfrac{1}{2} \operatorname{sech}^2 \theta \tag{17.48}$$

the general method of § 17.4 leads to

$$P = \tfrac{1}{2} (1 + \tanh Y)$$
$$= \frac{e^{2Y}}{1 + e^{2Y}}, \tag{17.49}$$

which is the metametric transformation for the Wilson-Worcester form of the logistic transformation. From equation (17.49),

$$Y = \tanh^{-1}(2P - 1)$$
$$= \tfrac{1}{2}\log_e(P/Q). \tag{17.50}$$

Since

$$Z = \tfrac{1}{2}\operatorname{sech}^2 Y = 2PQ,$$

the weighting coefficient is

$$w = 4PQ \tag{17.51}$$

and the working equivalent deviate

$$y = Y + \frac{1}{2P} - \frac{q}{2PQ}. \tag{17.52}$$

Worcester and Wilson (1943) have given tables to assist calculation of the estimate of the median effective dose for data relating to three equally spaced doses with the same number of subjects at each. Their scheme is ingenious, but lacks the flexibility needed for general assay use and does not fit the general pattern of analysis for two preparations simultaneously. Fisher and Yates indicated how the maximum likelihood estimates could be obtained by a procedure equivalent to that now recommended.

Berkson's remarks about the closeness of approximation of the logistic curve to the integrated normal, and the greater ease of computing with the logistic will be considered further in § 17.15.

17.11   Angle distribution

In the analysis of experimental data expressed as percentages, the transformation of an observed proportion, p, to an angle φ given by

$$p = \sin^2 \varphi$$

is often used because of its property of making $V(\varphi)$ independent of $E(\varphi)$. Knudsen and Curtis (1947) have proposed to take advantage of this for the analysis of assays. Suppose that the tolerance distribution is defined by

$$f(\theta) = \begin{cases} \sin 2\theta & 0 \leqslant \theta \leqslant \dfrac{\pi}{2} \\[2mm] 0 & \theta < 0, \quad \theta > \dfrac{\pi}{2} \end{cases} . \tag{17.53}$$

Then
$$P = \sin^2 Y \qquad (17.54)$$
gives the metametric transformation, and, since
$$Z = \sin 2Y,$$
equation (17.31) becomes
$$w = 4. \qquad (17.55)$$
The working equivalent deviate is
$$y = Y + \tfrac{1}{2} \cot Y - q \csc 2Y. \qquad (17.56)$$
There is no reason to suppose that the distribution represented by (17.53) is in truth the tolerance distribution for any of the dose-response relationships encountered in biological assay. It may prove to be a reasonable approximation, however, provided that the data avoid extremes of dose at which the finite limits to the distribution, $-\alpha/\beta$ and $\left(\dfrac{\pi}{2} - \alpha\right)/\beta$, become important. The constancy of the weighting coefficient is a considerable practical advantage in computing, as will be seen from the example in § 18.6.

17.12 Cauchy distribution

In a study of the statistical analysis of quantal responses in psychometry, Urban (1909, 1910) proposed
$$f(\theta) = \frac{1}{\pi(1 + \theta^2)} \qquad (17.57)$$
as an alternative to the normal distribution. This distribution, known to mathematicians as the Cauchy distribution, appears to have no special merits and some serious disadvantages. Nevertheless, the usual iterative scheme, based upon a metameter defined by
$$P = \tfrac{1}{2} + \frac{1}{\pi} \tan^{-1} Y, \qquad (17.58)$$
would allow the parameters to be estimated.

17.13 Wilson-Worcester distribution

Wilson and Worcester (1943c) discussed the general problem of a two-parameter tolerance distribution, and proposed to estimate the parameters by a method essentially the same as that of § 17.5.

As possible forms of distribution, they suggested the normal, rectangular, logistic, and angle types, and also one for which

$$f(\theta) = \tfrac{1}{2}(1 + \theta^2)^{-\frac{3}{2}}.$$ (17.59)

The corresponding metameter is defined by

$$P = \tfrac{1}{2}\left\{ 1 + \frac{Y}{(1 + Y^2)^{\frac{1}{2}}} \right\}.$$ (17.60)

This also appears to have no special merits, nor indeed do Wilson and Worcester attach any importance to it except as one of the family of two-parameter specifications.

17.14   Comparisons between transformations

In §§ 17.8–17.13, formulæ relating to various alternative transformations and tolerance distributions have been presented. The suggestion was made that the normal and the logistic distributions are each appropriate to some types of data. The others have little theoretical interest, but the angle distribution has the great practical convenience of a constant weighting coefficient ; unless conclusions based upon it are likely to be seriously misleading, its use may be an irresistible temptation to many.

How far does the choice of transformation influence conclusions ? A first step in answering this question is to examine the similarity between the transformations themselves (*cf.* Miller, 1950). Fig. 17.1 shows the relationship between x and P for four tolerance distributions which have been standardized so as to have zero mean and unit variance ; the Cauchy and Wilson-Worcester transformations cannot be standardized in this way, as they have infinite variances. For the normal, rectangular, logistic, and angle distributions, the relationships between x and P are seen to be very similar over a wide range, and between response rates of 0·05 and 0·95 only very intensive experimentation could discriminate between them. Indeed, all but the rectangular are very nearly the same between 0·02 and 0·98 ; in practice, the rectangular has little to recommend it, for it is unlikely to have any theoretical merits and, unless the correct weighting procedure be abandoned, it does not lead to much saving in computation. Fig. 17.2 presents these comparisons in slightly different form. When the probit of P is plotted against x, a straight line will be obtained only if the tolerance distribution is normal. Fig. 17.2 shows this line, and also the

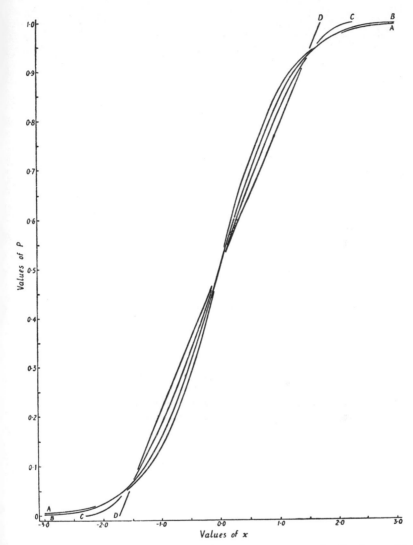

Fig. 17.1—Relationship between x and P for tolerance distributions with zero mean and unit variance

Curve A : Logistic   Curve C : Angle
Curve B : Normal   Curve D : Rectangular

curves given by this process if the distribution is in reality one of the other three.   Inspection of this diagram shows clearly the

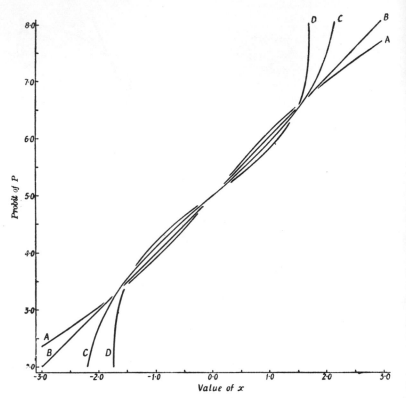

Fig. 17.2—Relationship between x and the probit of P for tolerance
distributions with zero mean and unit variance

Curve A : Logistic   Curve C : Angle
Curve B : Normal   Curve D : Rectangular

difficulty of detecting non-normality of distribution by a search
for curvature in the probit diagram.   Even if the true distribution
were rectangular, curvature could not be detected between responses
of 0·05 and 0·95 without the use of considerably larger numbers of
subjects than an assay generally employs ; the logistic distribution
is scarcely distinguishable from the normal between response rates
of 0·01 and 0·99.

In practice, then, discrimination between normal, logistic, and
angle specifications of the dose-response relationship is unlikely
to be possible, and no doubt other transformations could be suggested
that are also indistinguishable.   This may seem at first a serious

difficulty, but in reality it removes the major problem of deciding which transformation is to be used for a particular set of data. If data cannot discriminate between alternative hypotheses, conclusions drawn from them are not likely to be seriously influenced by the choice of hypothesis. An argument like that of Chapter 15 may be invoked, and the choice made primarily on the score of convenience.

In illustration of this contention, three assays have been analysed by use of each of the three transformations now under discussion (the rectangular is omitted, because it would never be used in practice and it gives trouble when none or all of the subjects at a dose respond). The first assay chosen for this purpose is the insulin assay for which data are given in Table 18.1. This includes many doses of each preparation and, as shown by Fig. 18.1, the linearity on the probit scale is good ; hence it might be expected to be fairly sensitive to changes in the metameter. Table 17.1 summarizes the validity tests, potency estimate, and fiducial limits for each transformation, the iterations having been continued until close approximation to the solution of the maximum likelihood equations was attained. The numerical values are, of course, different, but the practical conclusions to be drawn are essentially the same : the assay gives no evidence of invalidity, the potency of the test preparation is estimated to be about 13·4 i.u. per mg. and almost certainly lies between 11·1 i.u. per mg. and 16·1 i.u. per mg.

TABLE 17.1—Comparison between analyses of the data in Table 18.1
by alternative metametric transformations

Transformation	Probit	Logit	Angle
$\chi^2_{[10]}$ for linearity ...	5·124	6·037	3·543
$\chi^2_{[1]}$ for parallelism ...	0·278	0·351	0·167
R (i.u. per mg.) ...	13·41	13·38	13·50
R_L (i.u. per mg.) ...	11·11	11·04	11·31
R_U (i.u. per mg.) ...	16·12	16·16	16·05

Tables 17.2 and 17.3 contain data for an 8-point and a 6-point assay respectively. They used fewer subjects, and the second of them is very unlikely to give any discrimination between alternative

transformations.   Tables 17·4 and 17·5 summarize analyses of these assays in a manner similar to that of Table 17.1.   Again the alternative metameters agree in their evidence on assay validity, both statistical and fundamental ; for the neoarsphenamine assay, there is a slight indication of non-linearity with each of the metameters, but this does not attain significance and may easily be due to the very small numbers of subjects.   For all practical purposes, the estimates of potency and their fiducial limits are the same by the three transformations.   Figs. 17.3 and 17.4 show the probit regression lines fitted to the data of Tables 17.2 and 17.3.

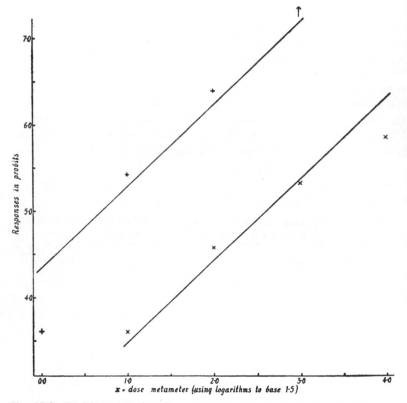

Fig. 17.3—Probit regression lines fitted to the data for the insulin assay in Table 17.2

× : Empirical probits for standard preparation

+ : Empirical probits for test preparation

The arrow indicates a 100 per cent. response rate.

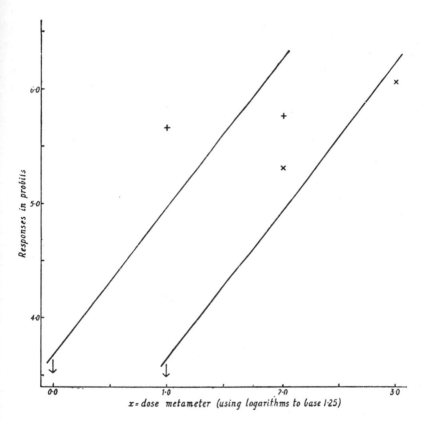

Fig. 17.4—Probit regression lines fitted to the data for the neoarsphenamine assay in Table 17.3

× : Empirical probits for standard preparation

+ : Empirical probits for test preparation

The arrows indicate 0 per cent. response rates.

TABLE 17.2—Data for an assay of insulin by the mouse convulsion method
(Hemmingsen, 1933)

Standard preparation			Test preparation		
Dose (i.u.)	No. of mice	No. convulsed	Dose (g.)	No. of mice	No. convulsed
0·004	12	1	0·000267	12	1
0·006	24	8	0·0004	24	16
0·009	24	15	0·0006	24	22
0·0135	10	8	0·0009	10	10

TABLE 17.3—Data for an assay of neoarsphenamine, by production of negative blood smears in female rats inoculated with

Trypanosoma equiperdum

(Morrell, Chapman, and Allmark, 1938)

Canadian standard			Preparation ' 610 '		
Dose	No. of rats	Negative smears	Dose	No. of rats	Negative smears
12·0	8	0	9·6	7	0
15·0	8	5	12·0	8	6
18·75	7	6	15·0	9	7

Morrell *et al.* record the highest dose of the standard preparation as 19·5 ; for illustrative examples here, this has been altered to 18·75 in order to make equal intervals of log dose and so to simplify the computing. To this extent, the example may be regarded as artificial, but the difference from the true data is practically negligible.

TABLE 17.4—Comparison between analyses of the data in Table 17.2
by alternative metametric transformations

Transformation	Probit	Logit	Angle
$\chi^2_{[4]}$ for linearity ...	1·324	1·148	2·298
$\chi^2_{[1]}$ for parallelism ...	2·876	3·096	1·952
R (i.u. per g.)	21·83	21·74	22·03
R_L (i.u. per g.)... ...	17·74	17·65	17·92
R_U (i.u. per g.)... ...	28·26	28·12	28·69

TABLE 17.5—Comparison between analyses of the data in Table 17.3
by alternative metametric transformations

Transformation	Probit	Logit	Angle
$\chi^2_{[2]}$ for linearity ...	5·607	5·614	5·679
$\chi^2_{[1]}$ for parallelism ...	0·291	0·304	0·226
R	1·255	1·261	1·248
R_L	1·068	1·062	1·089
R_U	1·493	1·522	1·440

17.15 Choice of a transformation

The three metametric transformations under discussion have been shown to be very similar over a wide range of responses, and no doubt others could be devised that would also behave like them. Not surprisingly, therefore, their use in three illustrative examples leads to practically indistinguishable results ; Miller (1950) found the same for a fourth set of data, and Berkson (1950) found similar good agreement between probits and logits in ten estimations of LD50's. Armitage and Allen (1950) have made probit, logit, and angle computations, using several cycles of iteration, for estimating the LD50 in twelve series of data (some of which may be the same as Berkson chose, but his paper does not state the sources of the data). They found probits and logits to agree very satisfactorily in their estimates. In no instance did the χ^2 test show poorer agreement with one hypothesis than with the other. The angle transformation was less satisfactory; in one instance of 11 doses with about 500 subjects per dose, the angle estimate differed from the probit by only 2 per cent. but had $\chi^2_{[9]} = 73 \cdot 8$, and in four others (with few subjects per dose and many extreme response rates) the estimates were very different from those obtained by probits. Biggers (1952) reported good agreement of calculations based on all three transformations (and also the rectangular) for 17 dose-response lines.

How is the choice between transformations to be made ? Ideally, of course, the ' correct ' transformation should be chosen, that is to say the one corresponding to the true tolerance distribution, or the true relationship between P and x. In fact, this is never possible, because knowledge of which is correct cannot be acquired. When the underlying structure of the dose-response relationship is that of a tolerance distribution, and in the absence of evidence to the contrary, the assumption of normality seems the most reasonable approximation to truth (§ 2.9). As mentioned in § 17.10, the dependence of response on dose does not always derive from variations in individual tolerance, and the assumption of a relationship such as the logistic may on occasion be preferred. Validity tests (especially that for linearity) will reject a violently wrong assumption, but can seldom discriminate between two as alike as the probit and logit. Narrowness of the fiducial range, of course, is irrelevant to this question : the fact that, in Table 17.1, the quantities called R_L and R_U are further apart for the logit than for the probit transformation is no argument against the logit (and would not be however great the difference), because correctness of the metameter is a necessary condition for the strict interpretation of R_L, R_U as fiducial limits (cf. § 15.6).

Ease of computation also is no criterion for the choice of a ' correct ' transformation, though it is often a consideration of practical importance. If different transformations are going to lead to conclusions as closely similar as Tables 17.1, 17.4, and 17.5 show, greater weight can be given to expediency than to theoretical appropriateness. Berkson's (1944, 1946) suggestion that the logit calculations could be handled more easily than the probit involved substituting the minimization of χ^2 for the maximization of the likelihood as a principle of estimation. This is discussed more fully in § 20.3, where the conclusion is reached that minimum

χ^2 is not known to have any general theoretical advantages over maximum likelihood, although in some respects it appears to be as good. Indeed, the two are closely related, as Berkson (1949) has shown for the quantal response problem, and, provided that the number of subjects per dose is not unduly small (as in the neoarsphenamine assay of Table 17.3), minimum χ^2 may be used if found more convenient. An ingenious approximation devised by Berkson (1944) makes some simplification of formulae possible in the application of minimum χ^2 to the logit metameter, though it must be used with due regard to its inappropriateness at extremes of response (see also Armitage and Allen, 1950). This must not be regarded as implying that, in any theoretical sense, minimum χ^2 is the best method for logits, maximum likelihood for probits.

For the angle transformation, no theoretical advantage has ever been claimed, but the constancy of w simplifies computations (§ 18.6). Knudsen and Curtis (1947) suggested this as an important consideration in routine assays. If doses are not so extreme as to emphasize the effect of the limited range of the tolerance distribution, conclusions from angles will usually be practically the same as if probits or logits were used. When use of very few subjects per dose causes frequent occurrence of extreme response rates and consequently affects estimation of the range of the tolerance distribution, or use of very many subjects per dose allows the theoretical weakness of the angle transformation to become clear (Armitage and Allen, 1950), probits or logits are preferable. Appendix Tables XIV and XV are intended to assist a compromise when irregular data obviously make several cycles necessary. Angles may be used in simple computations for the first one or two cycles, and then expected angles can be converted to probits or logits for further iteration.

17.16 Polytomous quantal responses

Occasionally responses may be recorded in more than two classes, as when moribund subjects are distinguished from ' dead ' and ' alive '. Analysis by collapsing the classification into a dichotomy is always permissible but may involve serious sacrifice of information. Gurland et al. (1960) have described a full minimum χ^2 procedure, and Ashford (1959) has discussed maximum likelihood more briefly (see also Aitchison and Silvey, 1957).

CHAPTER 18

ASSAYS BASED ON QUANTAL RESPONSES

18.1 The computational scheme

As explained in § 17.1, the data for an assay based on quantal responses will usually consist of records from two or more doses of each preparation, at each of which several subjects were tested and the number responding noted. The estimate of potency is then calculated by a procedure based upon § 17.5, and in many ways similar to that for quantitative responses (Chapter 4). The successive steps in the first cycle of iteration will be listed here for the probit transformation ; a numerical example follows in § 18.2, and the reader will be helped in the understanding of the present section by referring to Table 18.1. Except that different tables must be employed, the same method applies to other two-parameter transformations, such as those of §§ 17.9–17.13, but a simple detailed account for the most commonly used metameter is likely to be more helpful than a more general presentation. The systematic arrangement and the checking of the calculations have been described more fully elsewhere (Finney, 1952, Appendix I), and the inexperienced computer should study that description.

The first cycle proceeds as follows :—

   (i) For each dose tested, tabulate x ; x is defined as the log dose, or as some linear transformation of the log dose when this enables x to be expressed more simply in integers (*cf.* § 4.2).

  (ii) Tabulate n, the number of subjects tested at each dose (n need not be the same for all doses).

 (iii) Tabulate r, the number of subjects responding at each dose.

 (iv) Evaluate the empirical response rate,

$$p = \frac{r}{n} \qquad (18.1)$$

at each dose. Two places of decimals should suffice for
p, unless most values of n exceed 200.

(v) From Appendix Table V, obtain the empirical probit
of each p to two places of decimals. More detailed tables
of this transformation have been published (Finney,
1952, Table I ; Fisher and Yates, 1963, Table IX), but
their additional accuracy is rarely needed.

(vi) Plot the empirical probits against x, and draw, by eye
judgment, two parallel regression lines. Care at this
stage may save a cycle of iteration later ; experienced
users of the method will find that, in their judgment of
the positions of the lines, they are able to make approximate
allowance for the fact that the weight of each point is
proportional to n and that the weight is much greater for
probits between 4·0 and 6·0 than for more extreme values.
Doses at which $p = 0$ or $p = 1$ will have infinite empirical
probits ; the points cannot be plotted, but, in judging the
positions of the regression lines, allowance should be made
for points below or above the lines at these values of x.

(vii) From the regression line, read values of Y, the first
approximation to the expected probit at each dose. One
decimal place in Y is almost always enough. Some may
prefer to obtain the Y column by other methods, such
as by fitting unweighted linear regressions to the empirical
probits, or, when the doses are as few and as regularly
spaced as in the example of angle calculations in § 18.6,
even by simple inspection of the column of empirical
probits in relation to x. These alternatives are quite
legitimate, but, as for other types of assay, a diagram is
usually desirable and the method recommended here
therefore seems the best.

The values of Y are, of course, $(a_1 + b_1 x)$ of § 17.5,
but a_1, b_1 need not be evaluated explicitly.

(viii) For each Y, read the weighting coefficient, w, from
Appendix Table VI, multiply by n, and tabulate. One,
or at most two, decimal places in nw will suffice.

(ix) For each Y and p determine the working probit, y. This may be found from Appendix Table VI using any of the formulæ

$$y = Y_0 + pA, \tag{18.2}$$

$$y = Y_1 - qA, \tag{18.3}$$

$$y = qY_0 + pY_1, \tag{18.4}$$

according to convenience, each of which is equivalent to equation (17.24). Here Y_0, Y_1 are the *minimum working probit* and *maximum working probit* respectively,

$$Y_0 = Y - P/Z, \tag{18.5}$$

$$Y_1 = Y + Q/Z, \tag{18.6}$$

and A is the range,

$$A = 1/Z \tag{18.7}$$

(*cf.* § 3.13). Alternatively, working probits may be read directly from Appendix Table VII with an accuracy that suffices for most purposes. Unless the number of subjects per dose exceeds 200, two decimals in y are usually enough.

(x) Form columns of products, nwx and nwy.

(xi) Sum the nw, nwx, nwy columns for each preparation, and form

$$\bar{x} = \frac{Snwx}{Snw}, \tag{18.8}$$

$$\bar{y} = \frac{Snwy}{Snw}. \tag{18.9}$$

(xii) For each preparation multiply the nwx, nwy columns by x, y in turn, make adjustments for means in the usual manner, and obtain

$$S_{xx} = Snwx^2 - \frac{(Snwx)^2}{Snw}, \tag{18.10}$$

$$S_{xy} = Snwxy - \frac{(Snwx)\,(Snwy)}{Snw}, \tag{18.11}$$

$$S_{yy} = Snwy^2 - \frac{(Snwy)^2}{Snw}. \tag{18.12}$$

(xiii) Use these weighted means and weighted sums of squares and products, just as similar unweighted quantities were used in § 4.11, to give parallel linear regression equations for the two preparations.

(xiv) Evaluate Y_S, Y_T, for each x. If these differ much from the expected probits used in the first cycle, repeat the computations with Y_S, Y_T substituted for the original Y column. Continue to iterate until good agreement is obtained. When one place of decimals is used in Y, a reasonable standard to adopt is that no value of Y at the end of the last cycle should differ from the corresponding Y at the beginning by as much as 0·2, and that the signs of the differences should not show any obvious association with dose (as would occur if the slope of the regression lines on which the cycle was based were noticeably wrong).

(xv) When this agreement has been obtained, use

$$\chi^2_{[f]} = \Sigma S_{yy} - \Sigma \left\{ \frac{(S_{xy})^2}{S_{xx}} \right\} \tag{18.13}$$

as a test of linearity or statistical validity, with f, the number of degrees of freedom, 4 less than the total number of doses tested. This calculation is analogous to that for the linearity component in Table 4.2 ; the linearity component for quantal responses cannot be subdivided by orthogonal coefficients, even for a symmetrical assay design, on account of the differential weighting of the responses. If the χ^2 calculated by equation (18.13) is not significantly large, the hypothesis of the normality of the log tolerance distribution is not contradicted, and subsequent calculations will be based on it. In particular, the variance per unit weight will be taken as unity, this being a theoretical instead of an estimated variance : calculations of fiducial limits will use $t = 1·960$, which is the normal deviate for a probability of 0·05, in Fieller's theorem. If this χ^2 is significant, the deviations from linearity must be considered in the light of § 4.22. In circumstances which appear to justify retention of the hypothesis of linearity, the variance per unit weight must be taken as

$$s^2 = \frac{\chi^2}{f}, \tag{18.14}$$

a quantity known as the *heterogeneity factor* (Finney, 1952, § 11). All variances must be multiplied by s^2, and must then be regarded as having f degrees of freedom.

(xvi) Calculate

$$\chi^2_{[1]} = \Sigma \left\{ \frac{(S_{xy})^2}{S_{xx}} \right\} - \frac{(\Sigma S_{xy})^2}{\Sigma S_{xx}} \qquad (18.15)$$

as a test of parallelism, and thus of fundamental validity. This is equivalent to a test of equality of variance for the standard and test tolerance distributions (§ 2.9). If a heterogeneity factor has been found necessary, the test must be replaced by a variance ratio test, taking F to be the ratio of the quantity calculated in equation (18.15) to s^2 ; for this test, the degrees of freedom are 1 and f (Appendix Table II).

(xvii) For a valid assay, complete the estimation of potency in the usual manner, as for a parallel line assay ; the log potency is given by equation (4.11)

$$M = \bar{x}_S - \bar{x}_T - \frac{\bar{y}_S - \bar{y}_T}{b}, \qquad (18.16)$$

and fiducial limits to M are calculated by Fieller's theorem with

$$V(\bar{y}_S - \bar{y}_T) = \Sigma \left(\frac{1}{Snw} \right), \qquad (18.17)$$

$$V(b) = \frac{1}{\Sigma S_{xx}}. \qquad (18.18)$$

If a heterogeneity factor is required, both these variances must be multiplied by s^2 and assigned the appropriate number of degrees of freedom before Fieller's theorem is applied ; it is important to remember that g is affected by this as well as the main formula for M_L, M_U. Without any heterogeneity factor, the formulæ are

$$M_L, M_U = \bar{x}_S - \bar{x}_T + \left[(M - \bar{x}_S + \bar{x}_T) \right.$$
$$\left. \pm \frac{t}{b} \left\{ (1-g) \Sigma \left(\frac{1}{Snw} \right) + \frac{(M - \bar{x}_S + \bar{x}_T)^2}{\Sigma S_{xx}} \right\}^{\frac{1}{2}} \right] \div (1-g)$$
$$(18.19)$$

where

$$g = \frac{t^2}{b^2 \Sigma S_{xx}} ; \qquad (18.20)$$

the likeness to equations (4.12) and (4.13) is apparent. Here t is a normal deviate (1·960 for 95 per cent. limits), as explained in (xv) above. A heterogeneity factor, if required, must multiply g and also the term within { } in equation (18.19) ; t then reverts to its usual status as a t-deviate.

This scheme is, in its essentials, the same as that first proposed for biological assay by Gaddum (1933 ; see § 17.8 above).

If logits were to be used instead of probits, Appendix Tables VIII and IX would be employed exactly as were Tables V and VI in the above instructions. Table X is analogous to Table VII ; although it is rather less detailed, working logits may be read from it, with sufficient accuracy for most purposes, more rapidly than by calculation from Table IX. For these tables, the metameter has been re-defined to correspond to the Wilson-Worcester form, equation (17.50), rather than to Berkson's equation (17.47), and, as for probits, 5 has been added in order to give values that are almost invariably positive. This metameter perhaps ought not to be called the logit, but the name is convenient and to coin a new one would cause as much confusion as it would save. The advantage of this definition is that, for all but very extreme response rates, the probit and the logit are very similar in numerical value. The logit transformation as used here is therefore defined by

$$Y = 5 + \tfrac{1}{2} \log_e (P/Q). \qquad (18.21)$$

It has a weighting coefficient

$$w = 4PQ, \qquad (18.22)$$

minimum and maximum working logits,

$$Y_0 = Y - \frac{1}{2Q}, \qquad (18.23)$$

$$Y_1 = Y + \frac{1}{2P} \qquad (18.24)$$

and a range

$$A = \frac{1}{2PQ}. \qquad (18.25)$$

For the angle transformation, Appendix Tables XI, XII, and XIII replace Tables VIII, IX, and X. These have been expressed in degrees of arc, rather than in radian measure, so that equations (17.55) and (17.56) are modified slightly. The constant weighting coefficient is

$$w = \frac{4\pi^2}{(180)^2} = 0.0012185 \; ; \qquad (18.26)$$

the minimum and maximum working angles are

$$Y_0 = Y - 28.6479 \tan Y, \qquad (18.27)$$
$$Y_1 = Y + 28.6479 \cot Y, \qquad (18.28)$$

and the range is

$$A = 57.2958 \operatorname{cosec} 2Y, \qquad (18.29)$$

where Y is measured in degrees throughout.* Working logits and working angles are obtainable by using equations (18.1)–(18.3) with the appropriate definitions of Y_0, Y_1, and A.

18.2   An assay of insulin

The instructions for analysis given in § 18.1 will be made clearer by a numerical example. One of the earliest assays of which details have been published and for which a complete statistical analysis was attempted was an assay of insulin by the mouse convulsion method (Hemmingsen and Krogh, 1926). At each of nine doses of the standard preparation and five doses of the test preparation, batches of mice were injected with a dose of insulin, and the numbers of mice showing the symptoms of collapse or convulsions were recorded. Unfortunately for the present purpose, Hemmingsen and Krogh published their data in diagrammatic form only. As the assay illustrates a number of interesting points very satisfactorily, and as it is also of some historical interest, an attempt has been made to reconstruct the data from Hemmingsen and Krogh's diagram, with the aid of a statement in their paper that seems to imply that the number of subjects at each dose was between thirty and forty. Values of n and r have therefore been taken arbitrarily in such a way that each r/n agrees with the percentage in that diagram and that the average value of n is about thirty-five. The data analysed are thus in some degree artificial.

The first cycle of calculations is shown in Table 18.1. Doses of the standard preparation were measured in units of 0.001 i.u.,

---

* The factor 57.2958 arises as the number of degrees in 1 radian ; 28.6479 is the half of this.

and doses of the test preparation were measured in the same units
on the assumption that the potency was 20 i.u. per mg. The first
four columns of the table show the dose (z), the dose metameter
($x = \log_{10} z$), the number of mice tested (n), and the number
convulsed (r). The empirical response rate, p, is calculated from
equation (18.1) ; though often shown as a percentage, its expression
as a fraction of unity is more convenient for computation. The
empirical probit of p is found from Appendix Table V and plotted
against x in Fig. 18.1. In this figure, two parallel regression lines

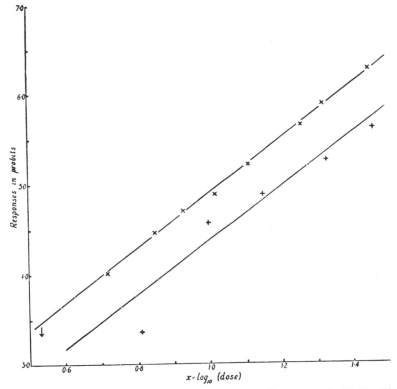

Fig. 18.1—Probit regression lines for the insulin assay in Table 18.1
  × : Empirical probits for standard preparation
  + : Empirical probits for test preparation
      The arrow indicates a 0 per cent response.
      The lines are those mentioned in § 18.2 as having been drawn
      by eye, but are very close to the lines represented by equations
      (18.32).

have been judged by eye, an easy task when the points lie as close to the lines as do these ; allowance was made for a point below the line for the standard at $x = 0.53$. The horizontal distance between these lines may be measured in order to give some preliminary indication of potency ; it is

$$M = -\,0.175, \tag{18.30}$$

which leads to

$$R = 20 \text{ antilog } \bar{1}.825$$
$$= 13.4. \tag{18.31}$$

The Y column in Table 18.1 is read from the lines in Fig. 18.1, and is used in Appendix Table VI to give the weighting coefficients. For example, for $Y = 3.5$, $w = 0.26907$, which is multiplied by 33 to give 8.9 as the first value of nw. The same table shows 2.98 for Y_0, the minimum working probit ; since $p = 0$, this is the value of y. For the second dose, $Y = 4.0$, and, by equation (18.2),

$$y = 3.3443 + 0.16 \times 4.1327$$
$$= 4.01.$$

Alternatively, one of equations (18.3), (18.4) might have been used, or y might have been read directly from Appendix Table VII. The columns nwx, nwy, and the sums of squares and products S_{xx}, S_{xy}, S_{yy}, may then be found as described in § 18.1.

The regression coefficient calculated from this cycle of calculations, by equation (4.8), is

$$b = \frac{42.298}{13.2664}$$
$$= 3.1884.$$

Insertion of mean values gives the regression lines, as based on this cycle :

$$\left.\begin{aligned}
Y_S &= 4.9331 + b(x - 1.0287) \\
&= 1.653 + 3.188x, \\
Y_T &= 4.8277 + b(x - 1.1709) \\
&= 1.094 + 3.188x.
\end{aligned}\right\} \tag{18.32}$$

If the values of these expressions for the doses tested are compared with the Y column of Table 18.1, they will be found to satisfy the criterion suggested in (xiv) of § 18.1, in that all the differences are less than 0.2. A new column of Y could be formed and a second

TABLE 18.1—First cycle of calculations for the assay of insulin

x	x	n	r	p	Empirical probit	Y	nw	y	nwx	nwy
Standard preparation										
3·4	0·53	33	0	0·00	—	3·5	8·9	2·98	4·717	26·522
5·2	0·72	32	5	0·16	4·01	4·0	14·0	4·01	10·080	56·140
7·0	0·85	38	11	0·29	4·45	4·4	21·2	4·45	18·020	94·340
8·5	0·93	37	14	0·38	4·69	4·7	22·8	4·70	21·204	107·160
10·5	1·02	40	18	0·45	4·87	4·9	25·4	4·87	25·908	123·698
13·0	1·11	37	21	0·57	5·18	5·2	23·2	5·18	25·752	120·176
18·0	1·26	31	23	0·74	5·64	5·7	16·5	5·64	20·790	93·060
21·0	1·32	37	30	0·81	5·88	5·9	17·4	5·88	22·968	102·312
28·0	1·45	30	27	0·90	6·28	6·3	10·1	6·28	14·645	63·428
							159·5		164·084	786·836
Test preparation										
6·5	0·81	40	2	0·05	3·36	3·8	14·8	3·46	11·988	51·208
10·0	1·00	30	10	0·33	4·56	4·4	16·7	4·57	16·700	76·319
14·0	1·15	40	18	0·45	4·87	4·8	25·1	4·88	28·865	122·488
21·5	1·33	35	21	0·60	5·25	5·4	21·0	5·25	27·930	110·250
29·0	1·46	37	27	0·73	5·61	5·8	18·6	5·60	27·156	104·160
							96·2		112·639	464·425

	S_{xx}	S_{xy}	S_{yy}
Standard preparation:	177·5536	838·171	3,977·32
	168·7997	809·450	3,881·57
	8·7539	28·721	95·75
Test preparation: ...	136·3997	557·365	2,285·81
	131·8872	543·788	2,242·11
	4·5125	13·577	43·70
Total:	13·2664	42·298	139·45

cycle calculated, but the consequent change in the conclusions would be small. This question is considered again in § 18.3, but for the present the first cycle will be supposed adequate.

Equation (18.13) gives

$$\chi^2_{[10]} = 139 \cdot 45 - 94 \cdot 23 - 40 \cdot 85$$
$$= 4 \cdot 37 \ ;$$

this is calculated exactly as is the sum of squares for deviations from linearity in an ordinary parallel line assay (§ 4.4). Since the χ^2 is well below the significance level (Appendix Table IV), the possibility that the iteration has not been continued far enough for the quantity to behave as a true χ^2, or that small expectations in some classes may have caused serious disturbance, can be ignored as unimportant (*cf.* § 17.6). Had the value been large, calculation of expected numbers in each class would have been needed. For example, the lowest dose of the standard preparation has $Y_S = 3 \cdot 34$, corresponding to a convulsion rate of $0 \cdot 05$; hence the expected number of responses in this group is only $1 \cdot 6$, and the usual practice with χ^2 tests would require that the data be pooled with those for the next dose before calculation of χ^2 by equation (17.33). As a test of parallelism, equation (18.15) gives

$$\chi^2_{[1]} = 94 \cdot 23 + 40 \cdot 85 - 134 \cdot 86$$
$$= 0 \cdot 22,$$

and no fundamental invalidity need be feared.

The log potency is obtained from the usual formula, repeated as equation (18.16), and is

$$M = 1 \cdot 0287 - 1 \cdot 1709 - \frac{4 \cdot 9331 - 4 \cdot 8277}{3 \cdot 1884}$$
$$= - 0 \cdot 1422 - 0 \cdot 0331$$
$$= - 0 \cdot 1753,$$

very close to the value in equation (18.30). Moreover, by equations (18.17) and (18.18),

$$V(\bar{y}_T - \bar{y}_S) = \frac{1}{159 \cdot 5} + \frac{1}{96 \cdot 2},$$

and

$$V(b) = \frac{1}{13 \cdot 2664}.$$

Hence, by equation (18.20),

$$g = \frac{(1 \cdot 960)^2}{(3 \cdot 1884)^2 \times 13 \cdot 2664}$$
$$= 0 \cdot 0285,$$

the deviate $t = 1 \cdot 960$ being used because no heterogeneity factor was required and all weights are therefore regarded as reciprocals of true variances. By Fieller's theorem, equation (18.19),

$$M_L, M_U = -0 \cdot 1422 - \left[0 \cdot 0331 \pm \frac{1 \cdot 960}{3 \cdot 1884} \left\{ 0 \cdot 9715 \left(\frac{1}{159 \cdot 5} + \frac{1}{96 \cdot 2} \right) + \frac{(0 \cdot 0331)^2}{13.2664} \right\}^{\frac{1}{2}} \right] \div 0 \cdot 9715$$

$$= -0 \cdot 1422 - [0 \cdot 0331 \pm 0 \cdot 0784] \div 0 \cdot 9715$$
$$= -0 \cdot 2570, -0 \cdot 0956.$$

Finally, as for equation (18.31),

$$R = 20 \text{ antilog } \bar{1} \cdot 8247 = 13 \cdot 36,$$
$$R_L = 20 \text{ antilog } \bar{1} \cdot 7430 = 11 \cdot 07,$$
$$R_U = 20 \text{ antilog } \bar{1} \cdot 9044 = 16 \cdot 05.$$

The potency of the test preparation is estimated to be $13 \cdot 36$ i.u. per mg., with fiducial limits at $11 \cdot 07$ i.u. per mg. and $16 \cdot 05$ i.u. per mg. Hemmingsen and Krogh stated their estimate to be ' $13 \cdot 34 \pm 0 \cdot 46$ ' i.u. per mg. The difference in R is trivial ; whether their figure of $0 \cdot 46$ is intended to represent a standard error or a probable error is not clear. Their method of analysis is not fully described, but appears to be related to the characteristic curve method (§ 20.1).

18.3 Speed of convergence

The calculations in § 18.2 have used only one cycle of iteration, yet the theory on which they are based states that the maximum likelihood estimate is obtained as the limit of the iterative process. It might be expected that several cycles would always be needed in order to approximate to this limit satisfactorily, but experience shows that, unless the irregularity of the data is so great as to make difficult the construction of the provisional regression lines and the first set of expected probits, two cycles almost always suffice ; with good data, one cycle is often enough. Table 18.2 shows results obtained in three successive cycles of the calculations for this assay ; in the construction of this table, one extra digit was carried in the p, Y, nw, and y columns of each cycle, in order to give small changes from one cycle to the next a better opportunity of showing. The regression equations obtained from cycle III would have given a Y column for a fourth cycle identical (to two places of decimals) with that for cycle III, and iteration was therefore stopped at this stage.

TABLE 18.2—Summarized results from three cycles of iteration on the insulin assay in Table 18.1

Cycle	I	II	III
b	3·195	3·218	3·219
$\chi^2_{[10]}$ (linearity) ...	4·203	5·039	5·124
$\chi^2_{[1]}$ (parallelism) ...	0·266	0·276	0·278
M	− 0·1739	− 0·1735	− 0·1735
g	0·0284	0·0294	0·0295
R (i.u. per mg.) ...	13·40	13·41	13·41
R_L (i.u. per mg.) ...	11·11	11·12	11·11
R_U (i.u. per mg.) ...	16·10	16·12	16·12

The potency estimates and their fiducial limits in Table 18.2 differ only to a trivial extent. Though they are a little higher than the corresponding values in § 18.2, presumably on account of the inclusion of extra digits in p and elsewhere, the change is of no importance : response rates cannot be satisfactorily estimated to three places of decimals from batches of forty subjects. An estimate of potency as 13·4 i.u. per mg., with fair confidence that the true potency lies between 11·1 i.u. per mg. and 16·1 i.u. per mg., is a conclusion in accord with all the analyses. Other quantities have also been included in Table 18.2, notably the two χ^2 values needed for validity tests. The probit method does not necessarily minimize χ^2 (*cf.* § 20.3). Moreover, unless the maximum likelihood limit has been attained, χ^2 calculated according to equations (18.13) and (18.15) is only an approximation to what would be obtained by comparison of observed and expected frequencies. Consequently, the quantities termed χ^2 in the system of calculation recommended may sometimes increase in successive cycles of iteration ; a slight increase is seen for both the criteria in Table 18.2, although the changes are too small to affect the conclusions.

Tables 18.3 and 18.4 have been computed for the insulin assay in Table 17.2 and the neoarsphenamine assay in Table 17.3 respectively, and are analogous to Table 18.2. Even for the neoarsphenamine data, based on very few subjects and consequently very irregular in its response rates, the first cycle gave results that for all practical purposes have the same interpretation as the last. Finney (1951*d*) used the data of this insulin assay in an experimental study of the success with which scientists without previous experience of probit methods would draw their provisional lines. As may be seen from Fig. 17.3 the instruction to draw two parallel regression lines by eye is not very easy to obey for these data, yet the experiment showed that, in every one of twenty-one independent trials, a single cycle of iteration sufficed to give R, R_L, R_U near

TABLE 18.3—Summarized results from three cycles of iteration on the insulin assay in Table 17.2

Cycle	I	II	III
b	0·943	0·951	0·951
$\chi^2_{[4]}$ (linearity) ...	1·504	1·343	1·324
$\chi^2_{[1]}$ (parallelism)	2·995	2·843	2·876
M	0·9151	0·9256	0·9252
g	0·1124	0·1061	0·1070
R (i.u. per g.) ...	21·74	21·83	21·83
R_L (i.u. per g.) ...	17·64	17·75	17·74
R_U (i.u. per g.) ...	28·32	28·27	28·26

enough to their maximum likelihood values for most practical purposes. Nevertheless, the inexperienced user of probits would be wise to calculate two cycles, unless his data agree very closely with the regression equations ; with practice, the provisional lines drawn on a diagram can almost always be made so satisfactory that one cycle is sufficient, unless the data are exceptionally erratic.

TABLE 18.4—Summarized results from four cycles of iteration on the neoarsphenamine assay in Table 17.3

Cycle	I	II	III	IV
b	1·162	1·289	1·306	1·307
$\chi^2_{[2]}$ (linearity) ...	4·670	5·016	5·549	5·607
$\chi^2_{[1]}$ (parallelism)	0·446	0·244	0·289	0·291
M	0·0235	0·0214	0·0175	0·0171
g	0·2244	0·1962	0·2152	0·2182
R	1·257	1·256	1·255	1·255
R_L	1·050	1·075	1·069	1·068
R_U	1·503	1·486	1·492	1·493

18.4 Calculations based on scores

The scheme of calculations described in § 18.1 and illustrated in § 18.2 is perhaps the most convenient for general purposes, because of its close analogy with that for parallel line assays using quantitative responses. Nevertheless, alternative schemes that give either identically or essentially the same results can be devised and have certain advantages.

For example, instead of using the working equivalent deviate for each dose, a *score* may be assigned to each subject, of magnitude

$$Y_0 = Y - \frac{P}{Z} \text{ if the subject did not respond,}$$

$$Y_1 = Y + \frac{Q}{Z} \text{ if the subject responded.}$$

(18.33)

Comparison with equation (18.4) shows that the total score at any dose is then ny. Black (1950) has published a table of weighting coefficients and of weighted probit scores wY_0, wY_1, at intervals of 0·01 in Y, and has suggested a computational routine based upon them. The values of S_{xx}, S_{xy}, can be formed rather more rapidly from weighted scores than from working equivalent deviates. Black's method is an example of the scoring schemes for the estimation of parameters that have been found useful in other branches of statistical science, notably in genetics (Finney, 1950a ; Rao, 1950). It can be applied for any metameter transformation as soon as tables of weighted scores have been prepared.

The disadvantages of Black's scheme are that its relationship to the diagrammatic representation of the assay is less obvious and that the calculation of S_{yy} is laborious. The latter would be a serious objection if the test of statistical validity was to be computed by equation (18.13). When n is small, however, this formula for χ^2 will usually have to be replaced by equation (17.33), after the pooling of some classes so as to eliminate small expectations ; S_{yy} is then not required. Black devised his scheme especially for use with small n.

Black's modification of the standard computational routine might prove valuable in the extreme type of experiment mentioned at the end of § 19.2, namely that having only one subject at each dose. The chief difficulty is then to obtain the column of expected equivalent deviates, Y, with which to initiate the iteration. Cornfield and Mantel (1950) have drawn attention to the merits of the Spearman-Kärber method (§ 20.6) for obtaining provisional estimates of the parameters in this type of assay ; they found estimates so obtained to be far superior to those derived by Finney (1947c) from a crude grouping of data in his discussion of a numerical example.

18.5   Calculations based on empirical weights

In the theoretical development of the maximum likelihood method presented in § 17.5, the expected values of the second differential coefficients of the log likelihood were employed. Garwood (1941) suggested that replacement of these by the empirical values would result in more rapid convergence to the maximum likelihood estimates, as measured by the number of cycles of iteration needed ; the estimates of the parameters are unaltered by this change, although the assessments of their variances will be slightly different. In Garwood's presentation of the calculations, the advantage for the empirical differential coefficients was offset by the more laborious calculations required in each cycle. More recently, however, Cornfield and Mantel (1950) have tabulated (for the normal tolerance distribution)

$$\left.\begin{array}{l} w_0 = \dfrac{Z^2}{Q^2} - \dfrac{YZ}{Q}, \\[2mm] w_1 = \dfrac{Z^2}{P^2} + \dfrac{YZ}{P}, \end{array}\right\} \tag{18.34}$$

at intervals of 0·01 in Y, from which the empirical weight for the subjects at a particular dose may be found as

$$nw' = (n - r)w_0 + rw_1. \tag{18.35}$$

If r were replaced by nP, its expectation, nw' would become nw, the weight used in the ordinary method of analysis, but the whole virtue of the Cornfield-Mantel method lies in its use of the empirical weight. In the formation of the second differential coefficients of the log likelihood, whence come the coefficients in equations (17.26) (cf. Finney, 1949b), w' must be used to give Snw', $Snw'x$, $Snw'x^2$. Cornfield and Mantel have described an iterative scheme for the computations ; they have assisted its use by preparing a table of weighted equivalent deviates, which are essentially the same as Black's weighted probits but expressed as deviations from the expected values.

When the Cornfield-Mantel tables are used, calculations with empirical weights are possibly no more laborious than the scheme of § 18.1. They are, however, a little more confusing, especially as the analogy with weighted linear regression is impaired. Validity tests must be made the long way, by insertion of observed and expected frequencies into equation (17.33), which would have to be done in any event if the numbers of subjects per dose were small but for large n is often avoidable. Calculation of the variances of the estimates is more troublesome than in the scheme of § 18.1.

Though no formal proof has been given, the arguments advanced by Garwood and by Cornfield and Mantel undoubtedly suggest that computations based on empirical weights would give satisfactory convergence in fewer cycles of iteration than would the standard scheme of § 18.1. With the intention of illustrating this, the data for the assays in Tables 17.2 and 17.3 were re-analysed by iteration of the Cornfield-Mantel scheme, the process being started from the same sets of provisional probits as for the first cycles in Tables 18.3 and 18.4. The χ^2 criteria for validity tests were not calculated, as the conclusion from these is obvious and the limiting values must be the same as those obtained in § 18.3. For the insulin assay, three cycles sufficed to determine the Y column to two places of decimals : a fourth cycle would begin with a difference of 0·01 for one entry, and further calculations would show only erratic changes attributable to the limitations of the numbers of decimal places retained. For the neoarsphenamine assay, four cycles sufficed. The results are summarized in Tables 18.5 and 18.6.

TABLE 18.5—Summarized results from three cycles of Cornfield-Mantel iteration on the insulin assay in Table 17.2

Cycle	I	II	III
b	0·944	0·948	0·949
M	0·9260	0·9250	0·9240
g	0·1104	0·1062	0·1063
R	21·84	21·83	21·82
R_L	17·62	17·60	17·59
R_U	27·54	27·37	27·36

TABLE 18.6—Summarized results from four cycles of Cornfield-Mantel iteration on the neoarsphenamine assay in Table 17.3

Cycle	I	II	III	IV
b	1·223	1·306	1·309	1·309
M	0·0311	0·0177	0·0157	0·0155
g	0·1981	0·2098	0·2241	0·2243
R	1·259	1·255	1·254	1·254
R_L	1·070	1·078	1·075	1·075
R_U	1·499	1·505	1·513	1·512

The differences between entries for b, M, and R in the final columns of Tables 18.3 and 18.5 or Tables 18.4 and 18.6 merely reflect the inaccuracy resulting from working with a limited number of decimal places, and would disappear if more digits were retained throughout ; these differences are clearly too small to be important. Differences between corresponding final values of g or of the fiducial limits are due to the different weighting systems ; they cannot themselves indicate the superiority of either method of calculation, since they would disappear if the data showed response rates identical with their expectations. The Cornfield-Mantel method gives slightly narrower limits for the first of the two assays, slightly wider limits for the second. The important comparison between the tables is in respect of the speed of convergence. For the insulin assay, one Cornfield-Mantel cycle brought the estimate of potency almost as close to its maximum likelihood value as did two cycles of the usual type. For the neoarsphenamine assay, on the other hand, the first Cornfield-Mantel cycle is less good than the first in Table 18.4, but two Cornfield-Mantel cycles are as good as three of the others. What is remarkable, however, is that even for two assays that used very few subjects, and consequently gave rather erratic response rates, a single cycle of either kind gives an approximation to the maximum likelihood estimate and its fiducial limits sufficiently close for all practical purposes. With data as extensive as those for the first insulin assay, Table 18.1, the efficacy of a single cycle would be still more evident, and for these a comparison of the two methods of iteration is pointless.

Further study of the Cornfield-Mantel scheme is desirable. When the data are so erratic as to make several cycles of iteration necessary, or when lack of experience of the behaviour of equivalent deviate calculations makes the user unreliable in his drawing of provisional regression lines, it seems likely to save one or two cycles. A comparison of results from one cycle of iteration by the standard and the Cornfield-Mantel method, beginning from each of many different sets of provisional lines in the assay of Table 17.2, was reported by Finney (1951d) ; the advantage for the Cornfield-Mantel method was usually small, but was most marked where it was most desirable, namely where the provisional lines were far from the maximum likelihood positions. If the principles of Chapter 19 be followed, however, one cycle of the scheme of § 18.1 will usually suffice, except for experiments of complex design (§§ 19.3, 19.4), and only very rarely will more than two cycles be needed. In view of the extra labour of the fiducial limit calculations when empirical weights are used, and the general familiarity with the expected weight process, the scheme in § 18.1 is recommended here. The reader who is troubled by time spent on slow convergence in the assays that he encounters should study Cornfield and Mantel's proposals.

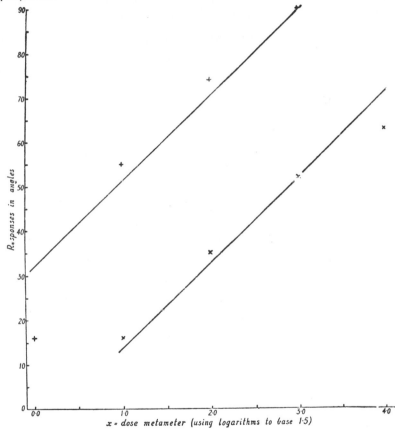

Fig. 18.2—Angle regression lines for the insulin assay in Table 17.2
   × : Empirical angles for standard preparation
   + : Empirical angles for test preparation
       The regression lines are those calculated in § 18.6, but are very similar to the lines drawn by eye and used to give the Y column of Table 18.7.

18.6   An example of the angle transformation

As an illustration of the simplification in the calculations that occurs when doses are equally spaced on the logarithmic scale and of the additional advantage of using the angle metametric transformation, an analysis of the insulin assay in Table 17.2 will now be shown. Table 18.7 contains the first stages of the calculations, and may be compared with Table 18.1. By use of logarithms to base 1·5, the dose metameter may be expressed in integers, since successive doses increase in this ratio.*   The column nw may be omitted,

TABLE 18.7—First cycle of calculations for the analysis of the insulin assay in Table 17.2 by the angle transformation

x	n	r	p	Empirical angle	Y	y	nx	ny
Standard preparation								
0	12	1	0·08	16	12	17·2	0	206·4
1	24	8	0·33	35	32	35·1	24	842·4
2	24	15	0·62	52	52	52·0	48	1,248·0
3	10	8	0·80	63	72	61·8	30	618·0
	70						102	2,914·8
Test preparation								
0	12	1	0·08	16	29	18·5	0	222·0
1	24	16	0·67	55	49	54·8	24	1,315·2
2	24	22	0·92	74	69	73·2	48	1,756·8
3	10	10	1·00	90	89	89·5	30	895·0
	70						102	4,189·0

		$Sn(x - \bar{x})^2$	$Sn(x - \bar{x})(y - \bar{y})$	$Sn(y - \bar{y})^2$
Standard preparation :		210·0000	5,192·40	136,207
		148·6286	4,247·28	121,372
		61·3714	945·12	14,835
Test preparation :		210·0000	7,513·80	284,880
		148·6286	6,103·97	250,682
		61·3714	1,409·83	34,198
Total :		122·7428	2,354·95	49,033

* As in Chapter 5, the dose metameter could be made to take the values $- 3$, $- 1$, 1, 3, by using $(1·5)^{\frac{1}{2}}$ as the base of logarithms. For quantal responses, this has little advantage, as it will not make $\bar{x} = 0$ unless angles are being used and n is constant.

and n itself used as the weight, provided that, in the calculation of validity tests and fiducial limits, all total weights and sums of squares are multiplied by w from equation (18.26) ; in a perfectly symmetrical assay, n also would be constant, and no weighting would be necessary until later in the calculations. The empirical angles, read from Appendix Table XI, have been plotted in Fig. 18.2, and two provisional parallel regression lines, drawn by eye, have been used to give Y (to the nearest degree). Working angles are next obtained, either from equations (18.2)–(18.4) with the aid of Table XII or by interpolation in Table XIII, and Table 18.7 is completed in the obvious manner.

The regression coefficient given by this first cycle is

$$b = \frac{2,354 \cdot 95}{122 \cdot 7428}$$

$$= 19 \cdot 186.$$

The regression lines are then calculated as

$$Y_S = 13 \cdot 68 + 19 \cdot 19x,$$

$$Y_T = 31 \cdot 89 + 19 \cdot 19x.$$

These are sufficiently different from the Y values in Table 18.1 to suggest the desirability of a second cycle of iteration, one change being as much as $3°$ (a maximum of $2°$ might be suggested for routine work). Further cycles were computed in the construction of Table 17.4, but, for this illustration of method, completion of the calculations on the basis of the first cycle will suffice.

For the linearity test,

$$\chi^2_{[4]} = (49,033 - 14,555 - 32,387) \times 0 \cdot 0012185$$

$$= 2 \cdot 55,$$

and, for parallelism,

$$\chi^2_{[1]} = (14,555 + 32,387 - 45,182) \times 0 \cdot 0012185$$

$$= 2 \cdot 14.$$

The assay shows no evidence of invalidity, and estimation proceeds in the usual manner. The symmetry has made $\bar{x}_S = \bar{x}_T$, and therefore

$$M = \frac{\bar{y}_T - \bar{y}_S}{b}$$

$$= \frac{59\cdot843 - 41\cdot640}{19\cdot186}$$

$$= 0\cdot9488.$$

Also,

$$g = \frac{(1\cdot960)^2}{(19\cdot186)^2 \times 122\cdot7428 \times 0\cdot0012185}$$

$$= 0\cdot0698.$$

The fiducial limits to M are therefore

$$M_L,\ M_U = \left[0\cdot9488 \pm \frac{1\cdot960}{19\cdot186} \left\{ \left(0\cdot9302 \left(\frac{1}{70} + \frac{1}{70} \right) \right. \right. \right.$$
$$\left. \left. \left. + \frac{(0\cdot9488)^2}{122\cdot7428} \right) \div 0\cdot0012185 \right\}^{\frac{1}{2}} \right] \div 0\cdot9302$$

$$= [0\cdot9488 \pm 0\cdot5389] \div 0\cdot9302$$

$$= 0\cdot4407,\ 1\cdot5993.$$

Hence, after multiplication by $\log_{10}1\cdot5$,

$$R = 15\ \text{antilog}\ 0\cdot1671 = 22\cdot04,$$
$$R_L = 15\ \text{antilog}\ 0\cdot0776 = 17\cdot93,$$
$$R_U = 15\ \text{antilog}\ 0\cdot2816 = 28\cdot69.$$

The test preparation is estimated to contain 22·0 i.u. of insulin per mg., with fiducial limits at 17·9 i.u. per mg. and 28·7 i.u. per mg. In spite of being based on only one cycle, this result is almost identical with that shown in the last column of Table 17·4, which was obtained after several cycles of more exact computations. More important still from the point of view of the practical application of the angle transformation, the result is very little different from that obtainable by one or more cycles of the more laborious probit or logit calculations.

CHAPTER 19

THE DESIGN OF ASSAYS BASED ON QUANTAL RESPONSES

19.1 General principles of good design

The principles of good design for biological assays based upon quantal responses are very similar to those for parallel line assays based upon quantitative responses, and at this stage §§ 6.1–6.7 can be re-read with profit. The complexities of the maximum likelihood estimation prevent as simple an analysis of the situation as was given in §§ 6.8–6.10, primarily because of the dependence of the weighting coefficient upon the expected value of the response metameter (for all transformations except the angle). Nevertheless, a discussion analogous to that in § 6.8 can be given, the conclusions being only in part dependent upon the choice of metameter and the behaviour of w.

Once again, the basic problem is that of the most economic use of a fixed total number of subjects, N. In the simple scheme of assay involving tests on batches of subjects (selected at random from the available stock) at a series of doses of each preparation, the requirements for high precision may be seen by study of the expression for the quarter-square of the fiducial interval for M; this is analogous to equation (6.1), and may be taken from equation (18.19) as

$$I = \frac{t^2 s^2}{b^2 (1 - g)^2} \left[(1 - g) \Sigma \left(\frac{1}{Snw} \right) + \frac{(M - \bar{x}_S + \bar{x}_T)^2}{\Sigma S_{xx}} \right]. \quad (19.1)$$

If no heterogeneity factor (§ 18.1) is needed, s^2 will be taken as unity and t read from the normal distribution; for heterogeneous data, s^2 is the heterogeneity factor and t is read from the t distribution with the appropriate number of degrees of freedom. The investigator will desire to assign subjects to doses in such a way as to make I small, with the constraint that $\Sigma (Sn) = N$; he will therefore attempt to choose a design for which

(i) the data are homogeneous,

(ii) b is large,

(iii) g is small,

(iv) $\Sigma \left(\dfrac{1}{Snw} \right)$ is small,

(v) $(M - \bar{x}_S + \bar{x}_T)$ is small,

(vi) ΣS_{xx} is large.

The notes that follow indicate how these ends may be attained (cf. Miller, Bliss, and Braun, 1939).

(i) The only sure way of securing homogeneity is by proper randomization. The subjects for each dose should be selected either completely at random from the whole set of N available or randomly within the framework of suitable block restrictions (§ 19.3). Failure to comply with this condition is likely to result in a large χ^2 for deviations from linearity. At worst, this may cause doubts of the validity of the assay ; at best, it necessitates the use of a heterogeneity factor and of a t distribution with a small number of degrees of freedom, and so reduces the reliability (cf. § 4.22).

(ii) Selection of the subjects for homogeneity in respect of tolerance, possibly by a selective breeding programme, should reduce the variance of the tolerance distribution. For a normal log tolerance distribution, the regression coefficient is equal to the reciprocal of this standard deviation, and for other distributions (such as the logistic and angle types) it is proportional to this reciprocal. Thus the regression coefficient is a property of the source of subjects and is unaffected by the experimental design. Trevan (1927, 1929) recognized its importance to assay precision before methods of equivalent deviate analysis had been developed. Gaddum's claim (1933) that closely inbred Wistar rats showed higher regression coefficients than a mixed group has been challenged by Biggers and Claringbold (1954). Morrell and Allmark (1941) reported only a small, non-significant increase in b as a result of inbreeding their stock used in assaying the trypanocidal activity of neoarsphenamine. As suggested in § 6.8, possibly the best hope of breeding for assay precision lies in using F_1 hybrids of carefully chosen inbred lines.

(iii) As usual, a small value of g is desirable in order that imprecision in b shall be without serious effect on the reliability of R. Ideally, g will be so small that approximate fiducial limits obtained by use of a formula for $V(M)$ will be practically the same as those calculated with the aid of Fieller's theorem. Reduction of g below 0·05 is of negligible importance, but a value in excess of 0·2 is very undesirable. The measures taken under headings (i), (ii), (iv), and (vi) will also benefit g.

(iv) Equal division of N between the standard and test preparations will generally be advantageous for the reduction

of $\Sigma\left(\dfrac{1}{Snw}\right)$. Unlike the parallel line assays discussed in

Chapter 6, the choice of doses also affects this quantity (except for the angle transformation). For most metameters likely to be used, including the probit and the logit, w has a maximum when the response rate is 0·50 ; hence,

if minimizing $\Sigma\left(\dfrac{1}{Snw}\right)$ were the only consideration, N

would be equally divided between two doses guessed to be about the ED50s of the two preparations. In practice, this would be useless because of the need for estimating the regression coefficient also. For probits, if the response rate is kept between 0·05 and 0·95, w will never fall below one-third of its maximum, but if P is allowed to become as extreme as 0·01 or 0·99, w can fall to one-tenth of its maximum. For logits, w decreases more rapidly as the value of P is moved away from 0·50, being one-fifth of its maximum at $P = 0·05$ or 0·95 and only one-twenty-fifth at $P = 0·01$ or 0·99. Doses should therefore be chosen, in the light of any pre-existing information on potency, so as to be reasonably sure to give responses between 0·05 and 0·95. Unless there are special circumstances dictating otherwise, N should be equally divided between all doses that are used.

(v) Exactly as for parallel line assays (§ 6.8), when the doses
for the standard preparation have been chosen, with each
should be associated a dose of the test preparation determined by equation (6.2) :

$$x_T = x_S - \log R_0,$$

where R_v is a guessed value of ρ. If R_0 is near to the truth,
$(M - \bar{x}_S + \bar{x}_T)$ should thus be made small in absolute
value.

(vi) The largest contributions to ΣS_{xx} will arise from doses
for which $w(x - \bar{x})^2$ is a maximum. If doses for the assay
have been successfully chosen to be symmetrical with
respect to the ED50 of each preparation and equal numbers
of subjects are used at every dose, $\bar{x}$ will be the ED50 and
the maximum contribution to S_{xx} will arise when
$w(Y - Y_{50})^2$ is a maximum (where Y_{50} is the value of the
response metameter at the ED50). For a normal tolerance
distribution, the maximum is at probit values of 3·42 and
6·58, or approximately response rates of 0·06 and 0·94.
For the logistic distribution, the maximizing logits are
3·80 and 6·20, corresponding to responses of 0·08 and
0·92. For angles, since w is constant, the maximum would
be at responses of 0·00 and 1·00, but the angle distribution
is to be regarded only as an approximation and is almost
certainly incorrect at extremes of dose.

The optimal requirements under headings (iv) and (vi) conflict,
but a compromise is possible without too great a loss on either
Snw or S_{xx}. For the probit transformation, the contributions to
Snw and S_{xx} from subjects tested at doses for which $P = 0·15$
or $P = 0·85$ are both about 70 per cent. of the maximum possible.
For logits, this standard is achieved by doses for which $P = 0·20$ or
$P = 0·80$.

19.2 The choice of doses

To compare the efficiencies of alternative assay schemes in as
much detail as was done in Chapter 6 would entail tremendous
labour, on account of the differential weighting. Tables 19.1 and
19.2 give some information of a simpler character. For an assay
using N subjects in a symmetrical $2k$-point design, Table 19.1

shows values of Ng and $Nb^2V(M)$, on the assumption that the probit metameter is applicable and that the responses are exactly those at which the experimenter aimed when he chose the doses. The quantity described as the variance of M, $V(M)$, has been obtained by equation (2.10), and is therefore what has been called elsewhere a 'naive' variance assuming g negligible (cf. equation (4.14)). Hence, unless N is large, $V(M)$ gives a somewhat optimistic representation of precision. Moreover, any failure to obtain exactly the response rates planned will make $(M - \bar{x}_S + \bar{x}_T)$ no longer zero, will increase $V(M)$, and may increase g. Nevertheless, comparison of the entries for $Nb^2V(M)$ gives some idea of the relative efficiencies of the alternative arrangements of doses. The formulæ for the quantities tabulated may easily be seen to be

$$Ng = \frac{(1 \cdot 960)^2 \times k}{Sw\,(Y - Y_{50})^2},\qquad(19.2)$$

and

$$Nb^2V(M) = \frac{4k}{Sw},\qquad(19.3)$$

where k is the number of doses of each preparation (2, 3, or 4 in the table) and S denotes summation over those doses of one preparation only. For example, corresponding to values of $-1\cdot80$, $-0\cdot60$, $0\cdot60$, $1\cdot80$ for $(Y - Y_{50})$ in probits are weighting coefficients $0\cdot17994$, $0\cdot55788$, $0\cdot55788$, $0\cdot17994$ respectively. These probits represent response rates of $0\cdot04$, $0\cdot27$, $0\cdot73$, $0\cdot96$ respectively ; hence, for the first of the 8-point assays in Table 19.1,

$$Ng = \frac{(1 \cdot 960)^2 \times 4}{2 \times 3 \cdot 2400 \times 0 \cdot 17994 + 2 \times 0 \cdot 3600 \times 0 \cdot 55788}$$
$$= 9 \cdot 8$$

and

$$Nb^2V(M) = \frac{16}{2 \times (0 \cdot 17994 + 0 \cdot 55788)}$$
$$= 10 \cdot 84.$$

All the entries in Table 19.1 have been calculated for equally spaced values of $(Y - Y_{50})$, and therefore for equally spaced doses, to which the response rates shown correspond approximately. When $(M - \bar{x}_S + \bar{x}_T)$ is zero, the effect of g in widening the fiducial limits of M is equivalent to a division of $V(M)$ by $(1 - g)$: if $V_E(M)$, the *effective variance* of M, be defined by

$$V_E(M) = \frac{V(M)}{1 - g}, \qquad (19.4)$$

use of the square root of $V_E(M)$ as though it were a standard error will give the right fiducial limits. Further columns of Table 19.1 show this effective variance for $N = 48$ and for $N = 240$. Table 19.2 has been similarly calculated for logits.

TABLE 19.1—Values of g, the variance of M, and the effective variance of M for two sizes of assay, in various schemes using a total of N subjects and the probit transformation

Subjects divided equally between doses giving percentage responses shown below				Ng (5% probability)	$Nb^2V(M)$	$b^2V_E(M)$ $N = 48$	$b^2V_E(M)$ $N = 240$
4,	96			6·6	22·23	0·537	0·0952
7,	93			6·3	14·87	0·357	0·0636
12,	88			7·2	10·80	0·265	0·0464
18,	82			10·1	8·48	*0·224*	0·0369
27,	73			19·1	7·17	0·248	*0·0325*
33,	67			32·1	6·77	0·425	0·0326
38,	62			69·3	6·49	—	0·0380
44,	56			270·	6·33	—	—
46,	54			606·	6·31	—	—
4,	50,	96		9·9	12·04	0·316	0·0523
7,	50,	93		9·5	10·21	0·265	0·0443
12,	50,	88		10·8	8·71	0·234	0·0380
18,	50,	82		15·1	7·60	*0·231*	0·0338
27,	50,	73		28·7	6·85	0·355	*0·0324*
33,	50,	67		48·1	6·60	—	0·0344
38,	50,	62		104·	6·42	—	0·0472
44,	50,	56		406·	6·32	—	—
46,	50,	54		909·	6·30	—	—
4,	27,	73,	96	9·8	10·84	0·284	0·0471
7,	31,	69,	93	10·2	9·41	0·249	0·0410
12,	34,	66,	88	12·2	8·24	*0·230*	0·0362
18,	38,	62,	82	17·6	7·36	0·242	0·0331
27,	42,	58,	73	34·0	6·75	0·482	*0·0328*
33,	44,	56,	67	57·4	6·54	—	0·0358
38,	46,	54,	62	124·	6·40	—	0·0553

Italics indicate the tabulated value nearest to the minimum ; a dash indicates that the fiducial range would be infinite because b would not differ significantly from zero.

TABLE 19.2—Values of g, the variance of M, and the effective variance of M for two sizes of assay, in various schemes using a total of N subjects and the logit transformation

Subjects divided equally between doses giving percentage responses shown below	Ng (5% probability)	$Nb^2V(M)$	$b^2V_E(M)$	
			$N = 48$	$N = 240$
3, 97	11·4	38·62	1·057	0·1690
5, 95	9·4	22·13	0·574	0·0960
8, 92	8·7	13·11	0·334	0·0567
14, 86	9·7	8·21	0·215	0·0357
23, 77	15·0	5·62	*0·170*	0·0250
29, 71	23·1	4·87	0·195	*0·0225*
35, 65	46·6	4·37	3·223	0·0226
43, 57	175·	4·09	—	0·0626
45, 55	388·	4·04	—	—
3, 50, 97	17·2	9·94	0·322	0·0446
5, 50, 95	14·2	8·81	0·261	0·0390
8, 50, 92	13·1	7·45	0·214	0·0328
14, 50, 86	14·6	6·08	*0·182*	0·0270
23, 50, 77	22·5	4·95	0·194	0·0228
29, 50, 71	34·6	4·54	0·339	*0·0221*
35, 50, 65	70·0	4·24	—	0·0249
43, 50, 57	262·	4·06	—	—
45, 50, 55	582·	4·03	—	—
3, 23, 77, 97	13·0	9·81	0·280	0·0432
5, 27, 73, 95	12·7	8·27	0·235	0·0364
8, 31, 69, 92	13·3	6·89	0·199	0·0304
14, 35, 65, 86	16·1	5·71	*0·179*	0·0255
23, 40, 60, 77	26·1	4·78	0·218	0·0224
29, 43, 57, 71	40·8	4·44	0·615	*0·0223*
35, 45, 55, 65	83·3	4·20	—	0·0268

Italics indicate the tabulated value nearest to the minimum ; a dash indicates that the fiducial range would be infinite because b would not differ significantly from zero.

Tables 19.1 and 19.2 illustrate how important the precision of estimation of b is to the reliability of an assay. If in the planning of the assay attention were limited to $V(M)$, the naive variance formula, doses near to the ED50 would be chosen (so far as the experimenter could guess these), irrespective of the number of subjects to be used. For probits, the column of values of $Nb^2V(M)$ might suggest that any doses giving responses between $P = 0.30$ and $P = 0.70$ would be satisfactory. In fact, even if as many as

240 subjects are available, the optimal design will have its extremes of dose just outside this range, in the neighbourhood of one of the arrangements for which the entry in the last column of Table 19.1 is italicized. If the number of subjects is smaller, the doses should be spaced more widely. For example, to a rough approximation with which both tables agree, an 8-point assay with 240 subjects should be designed with the aim of giving response rates of about 0·25, 0·40, 0·60, and 0·75 for both preparations. The same set of doses with only 48 subjects, however, would give an effective variance of the log potency nearly twice the optimal, this optimal being obtained with doses that produce response rates of about 0·15, 0·35, 0·65, and 0·85.

The value of this information in the designing of a particular assay is limited, because the experimenter does not know the doses to choose in order to get the desired responses—if he did know, he would have no need of an assay! Nevertheless, an experimenter will often have some idea of the ED50 of his standard preparation, and perhaps of the test preparation ; from previous experience of the assay technique, he may also be able to guess b, the reciprocal of the standard deviation of log tolerances. With the aid of these, he can attempt to select doses that will lead to a reliable potency estimate. The objections to a 4-point design have been sufficiently stated in earlier chapters, and need only a brief mention here. Unless the experimenter has very strong evidence from past experience, or clear *a priori* knowledge both that the test preparation is a dilution of the standard and that the tolerance distribution is of a particular form, on the basis of which he can assert both fundamental and statistical validity, he must choose a design that allows him to make validity tests. Tables 19.1 and 19.2 indicate that 6-point and 8-point designs need not be appreciably less reliable than 4-point ; provided that doses near to the optimal are used, values of $V_E(M)$ are nearly the same for all three. The optimal for any specified number of subjects may easily be found by constructing a column of values of $b^2 V_E(M)$ for the appropriate N, by means of Table 19.1 or Table 19.2 and equation (19.4). When the number of subjects is small, a 6-point design with doses that give 0·15, 0·50, 0·85 as the response rates, or an 8-point design with doses that give 0·15, 0·35, 0·65, 0·85, seems to be about ideal ; when the number of subjects is much larger, the doses can with advantage be put closer

together.* In choosing the doses on the basis of rather inadequate
information, however, it is wise to err in the direction of wide spacing.
This is well illustrated by consideration of 4-point assays with 48
subjects. An experimenter might try to choose doses that would
give him 0·25, 0·75 as the response rates, so as to be near the
optimal whether he used probits or logits ; if his spacing were
too narrow, and his response rates were about 0·35, 0·65, the assay
would be practically worthless, whereas if his spacing were too wide,
even to the extent of giving 0·05, 0·95 as the response rates, the
increase in $V_E(M)$ would be much less serious. This discussion
assumes perfect symmetry, so that $(M - \bar{x}_S + \bar{x}_T)$ is zero ; failure
to achieve this will increase all variances, to an extent that depends
also upon ΣS_{xx} and is therefore minimized by fairly widely spaced
doses (§ 19.1, (vi)). Moreover, the effective variance, $V_E(M)$, as
defined by equation (19.4), depends upon the probability level
to be used in the fiducial limits. The numerical values in Tables
19.1 and 19.2, and the discussion in this section, relate only to 95
per cent. limits ; adoption of 99 per cent. limits would make wider
spacing of doses desirable. The contrast with the recommendations
in §§ 6.8, 6.9 that, for quantitative responses, the widest possible
range of doses should always be used, must be carefully noted.
If very little is known about the potency of the test preparation,
however, additional doses might be tested at either end of the scale,
data obviously off the linear section of the regression being discarded
later.

Healy (1950) has considered the problem of the choice of doses
for an assay with quantal responses that is to be analysed by probits.
His approach is closely related to that used here, but he has concerned
himself with determining the least number of subjects needed for a
specified reliability of estimate, rather than with maximizing the
reliability obtainable from a specified total number of subjects.
His assumptions about the information available to the experimenter
for use in planning also differ slightly from those adopted here.
His recommendations, which he presents in convenient graphical
form, are qualitatively similar to those obtained above.

---

* The most convenient procedure is first to decide what response rates are
to be aimed at, then to use existing information for the prediction of the appropriate
doses, and finally to modify these doses slightly if that be necessary to make them
equally spaced.

In some circumstances, exact measurement of dose may be impossible until after a subject has been tested. For example, a subject may be allowed to eat food containing approximately the desired dose, but the exact amount ingested depends upon the amount of food the subject chooses to consume. Although the experimenter can exercise some control upon the doses given, he will in general find that no two subjects have had quite the same dose. The probit method (or any of the analogous methods) can still be applied to the estimation of potency, but validity tests are rather unsatisfactory unless the number of subjects is very large. The calculations follow the standard form, every working probit being a maximum or a minimum value, although they are usually laborious because of slow convergence. An example, though not in connexion with an assay, has been given by Finney (1947c), from which the procedure should be apparent (cf. Bliss, 1938 ; Finney, 1952, § 43).

19.3 Block restrictions

For assays based upon quantitative responses, incorporation into the design of constraints serving to balance inherent differences in the experimental material, or unavoidable differences in the conditions of experimentation, has been found to improve the precision of potency estimation. Examples of such designs have been given frequently in earlier chapters, notably in Chapters 9 and 10. Similar constraints of design may be expected also to benefit assays based upon quantal responses. For example, mice from the same litter are likely to vary less in their individual insulin tolerances than are mice from different litters : randomized complete or incomplete block designs, using litters as blocks, might be used in order to balance doses within litters and so to improve the precision of an assay by the mouse convulsion method.

To suggest such a design is easier than to analyse the results. In accordance with what would certainly be assumed in a direct assay, at least until evidence showed the hypothesis to be untenable, the litters may be supposed to differ only in the means of their tolerance distributions, the variance being constant. Probit * regression lines could be fitted to the data for each litter separately (a pair of

---

* The same procedure would be used whatever the preferred metameter, but for convenience the description is here given in terms of probits.

lines for the two preparations), with the constraint that all the lines should be parallel. Unless the litters were large, each would have only one mouse at each dose, but, when a set of first approximations to the expected probits had been constructed, the routine of computation would proceed in the ordinary manner.

Each cycle would use one line for each preparation in each litter, and the regression coefficient,

$$b = \frac{\Sigma S_{xy}}{\Sigma S_{xx}}, \tag{19.5}$$

would be calculated by summations over all litters. Each litter would then give its own value of M, and the final estimate of potency would be found from a mean of these. For simplicity, the unweighted arithmetic mean might be taken ; an illustration of the calculations has been given elsewhere (Finney, 1946b ; 1952, § 51). This would allow litters of very high or very low mean tolerance to exert undue influence on the final estimate, and a better procedure would be to weight the values of M inversely in proportion to $\Sigma \left(\dfrac{1}{Snw} \right)$ for each litter, or to apply the methods of Chapter 14.

The same system of calculation could be applied to incomplete block designs, provided that both preparations were tested at one or more doses in every litter. When the complete block scheme is

TABLE 19.3—Design for a 6-point assay using six subjects per day balanced over six litters

Litter no.	Dose on day no.					
	1	2	3	4	5	6
I	S_1	T_1	T_3	T_2	S_3	S_2
II	S_2	S_1	T_1	T_3	T_2	S_3
III	T_1	T_2	S_2	S_3	S_1	T_3
IV	S_3	S_2	T_2	T_1	T_3	S_1
V	T_2	T_3	S_3	S_1	S_2	T_1
VI	T_3	S_3	S_1	S_2	T_1	T_2

abandoned, however, the need for using a weighted mean of M increases because of the differing precisions of the separate values (*cf.* Moore and Bliss, 1942). Fitzhugh *et al.* (1944) have described a comparative assay of selenium preparations in respect of their toxicity to rats ; this was arranged as a balanced incomplete block design for ten treatments (three doses of each of three preparations plus a control) with litters of six, but the litter classification was ignored in the statistical analysis.

When the design uses two or more classes of block restriction simultaneously, as in a Latin square, the difficulties are greater. The method of analysis now to be described is indeed the correct one even for randomized complete block designs, but that suggested above is likely to be a good enough approximation. Consider the direct assay in § 2.12 (omitting the covariance discussion and confining attention to the tolerances of the 144 cats). The application of the analysis of variance to this Latin square design implicitly assumed that the log tolerance of any cat could be expressed as the sum of four components : a general mean, a deviation attributable to the day of experiment, a deviation attributable to the combination of operator and time of day, and a random element for the particular cat. A statement that the log tolerance distribution is normal means that the random elements have a normal distribution. If a Latin square is used for an assay with quantal responses, it is reasonable to make the same assumption that would be made if each quantal response were replaced by a direct measurement of the corresponding tolerance. For example, a 6-point assay using six litters of six animals might be arranged as the 6×6 Latin square in Table 19.3, in order that only six animals would have to be tested each day. Six litters would scarcely give adequate precision, and the assay might be improved by adding further sets of six with other Latin square arrangements, but the scheme shown will serve for illustration here. If the tolerance of each of the thirty-six subjects can be expressed as the sum of four components (as in § 2.12), and the random elements are normally distributed with constant variance, the general theory of equivalent deviate transformations (§ 17.4) shows that the expected probit for each subject must be expressible as the sum of a general mean, a component for the litter, a component for the day of experimentation, a component for the preparation, and a linear function of the log dose.

Thus

$$Y = \bar{y} + r_i + c_j + p_k + bx, \tag{19.6}$$

where r_i is the component for a row or litter in Table 19.3 ($i =$ I, II, ... VI), c_j is the component for a column or day ($j =$ 1, 2, ... 6), p_k takes one of the two values p_S and p_T, and b is a regression coefficient. A set of expected probits conforming to this pattern must first be guessed. This is not easy, but perhaps a sufficiently good set will be obtained by taking $\bar{y}$ as the empirical probit of the total proportion of responses (from the thirty-six subjects), r_i and c_j as the deviations of empirical probits for the appropriate rows from $\bar{y}$, and p_S, p_T, and b from a diagram ; if the dose metameters are written $-$ 1, 0, 1, for each preparation, p_S and $- p_T$ are each half the vertical distance between two parallel regression lines in that diagram, and b is the slope of the lines. Sets of thirty-six weights and thirty-six working probits (all minimum or maximum values) are then formed in the usual way. Weighted totals of working probits for each row, column, and preparation are equated to the similarly weighted totals of parametric representations of which (19.6) is typical, and ΣS_{xy} is equated to ΣS_{xY}. Thus a set of linear equations for the r_i, c_j, p_k and b is obtained, the solutions of which are inserted in equation (19.6) to give a revised set of expected probits for the second cycle of iteration. The process is basically the same as for the fitting of constants in an experiment of non-orthogonal design (Yates, 1933), the non-orthogonality arising here because of differential weighting. From the final cycle of iteration,

$$M = \frac{1}{b} (p_T - p_S) \tag{19.7}$$

is the estimate of log ρ. Inversion of the matrix for the last set of linear equations would provide assessments of variances and covariances for all the parameters, and R_L, R_U would be found by Fieller's theorem as usual.

In theory, the problem of the analysis of data from an assay of complex design is solved, for the above method may be adapted to any design. In practice, the calculations are clearly very laborious, and a complete analysis leading to assessment of the precision of R would be prohibitively so. Provided that the data did not extend over an extreme range of doses, the angle transformation might replace the probit ; this would reduce the labour very considerably, since the constancy of w would preserve the orthogonality of the Latin square, and the linear equations for the parameters would be solved by simple evaluation of arithmetic means. Even when angles are not satisfactory, one or two cycles of iteration using angles might start the analysis, expected angles being replaced by the corresponding expected probits or logits (Appendix Tables XIV or XV) for later cycles (*cf.* § 17.15).

The gain in precision should show itself by a larger value of b (a smaller standard deviation of log tolerances) than if no restrictions of design were used ; in fact, the standard deviation of tolerances within litters and within days is wanted. Whether the gain in precision can ever justify the labour of the calculations and whether satisfactory approximate methods of analysis can be devised are questions that cannot now be answered. To analyse data from the 6×6 Latin square as though they related to a simple 6-point assay with six subjects at each dose, without any other restrictions, would in theory be regrettable ; the analysis might give about the right estimate of potency, but would seriously underestimate the precision if inter-litter or inter-day variation were large. Nevertheless, this is the procedure likely to be adopted as long as the method just described is the only alternative. No example of the full calculations will be given here.

19.4   Cross-over designs

If the quantal response of a subject is some minor reaction of a kind that can be repeated indefinitely, without affecting the sensitivity of the subject, the possibility of using a cross-over design needs to be considered. One of the simplest is the twin cross-over (§ 10.2). Each subject might be tested once or several times with the first dose before passing to the second, so giving either a single quantal record or the proportion of responses in a short series. A more elaborate design would be the 6×6 Latin square in Table 19.3, with rows now representing six subjects and columns six occasions of testing (one or several tests on each occasion). As with quantitative responses (Chapter 10), the experimenter might hope to improve the precision of estimation by testing doses of each preparation on every subject and so eliminating inter-subject variation. Unfortunately, the difficulties of analysis encountered in § 19.3

arise again. All designs suggested in Chapters 9, 10 and 11 can also be used for quantal responses; the general method of estimation outlined in § 19.3 is always applicable, but the more complex the design the more laborious will the analysis be and the less safely can any simple approximation be adopted.

Among the few published examples of quantal cross-over assays are Somers and Edge (1947) on anaesthetics using guinea pigs, Miller *et al.* (1948) on spasmolytic drugs using isolated pieces of tissue, and Blackith (1950) on the paralytic action of insecticides. These authors did not attempt to take account of the cross-over constraints in the analysis, and simply used total response rates at each dose as though each subject had been used only once, although Blackith used an approximate angle analysis to indicate some substantial gain over a design that used each insect only once. Claringbold (1956) has suggested analysing exactly as for quantitative responses, using $y = 1$ for a response and $y = 0$ for a non-response; he claims that if the expected responses lie between $P = 0.05$ and $P = 0.95$ this will approximate well to the correct result. The evidence at present is small, but the idea is at least reasonable and undoubtedly attractive.

19.5 Multiple assays

The problem of assaying several test preparations simultaneously against one standard does not of itself present new features for quantal responses. If c test preparations are to be included, the analysis will involve constraining $(c + 1)$ regression lines to be parallel, and the χ^2 for the test of fundamental validity (parallelism) will have c degrees of freedom. The method of calculation for an assay with no block restrictions should be obvious from Chapters 11 and 18, and an example has been given elsewhere (Finney, 1952, § 20). The rule of allocating more subjects to the standard preparation than to each of the test preparations, in the ratio of $c^{\frac{1}{2}} : 1$ (§ 11.6), remains applicable, and the choice of dose levels follows the principles of § 19.2. As already pointed out (§ 19.3) complications will occur if, like those in §§ 11.2, 11.3, and 11.5, the assay design involves block restrictions.

19.6 Sequential procedures

In the study of quantal responses, two interesting techniques of sequential sampling have recently been suggested. Bartlett (1946 ; Finney, 1952, § 54) discussed the estimation of very high or very low percentiles of the tolerance distribution, and pointed out the need for basing such estimation on data from doses giving responses in the neighbourhood of the required percentage. If the dose giving $P = 0.95$ were to be estimated from data relating to tests at doses between $P = 0.10$ and $P = 0.90$, the estimate might be completely untrustworthy because the true tolerance distribution was not exactly of the form assumed (even though the apparent precision based upon the usual formulæ were good). Bartlett's scheme of *inverse sampling* is planned to make a reasonable allocation of subjects to doses on either side of that giving the required response rate, and so to avoid extrapolatory estimation. There is no reason to suppose that precision will be increased, and indeed the apparent precision of the estimate may be decreased by this procedure, but relevance of the estimate is assured. The estimation of extreme percentiles, however, is not of interest for biological assay (at least in the sense of this book), since a well-planned assay will concentrate on the more informative doses. The inverse sampling method will therefore not be described here.

Dixon and Mood (1948) proposed a system of *staircase sampling* for the estimation of an ED50. Since M, the log potency, is equal to the difference between two ED50 values, and a good assay will generally concentrate its tests about the ED50 of each preparation, this may be useful for assays. The staircase method can be applied only when subjects are tested one at a time, when the result of any test is known before the next is begun, and when the experimenter can so readily change the dose he is using that he is willing to make every test at a dose different from its predecessor. A series of doses, in ascending order, is chosen and designated as ... x_{-3}, x_{-2}, x_{-1}, x_0, x_1, x_2, x_3, ... , where x_0 is guessed to be about the ED50 ; the doses are for preference equally spaced on the logarithmic scale, although this is not essential. The particular dose used for any subject is determined by the result of the previous test with the same preparation, according to the *staircase rule*. This rule states that the first subject shall be tested at x_0 ; if it responds, the next subject is tested at a dose one step lower, and if it fails to respond, the next is tested at a dose one step higher. Subsequent doses are determined in the same way. The rule ensures that the further from the ED50 any dose happens to be the greater is the probability that the next dose is one step nearer ; it therefore tends to concentrate tests in the neighbourhood of the ED50.

If the doses are equally spaced, a method akin to the Spearman-Kärber method (§ 20.6) may be used for estimating the ED50. Dixon and Mood have made a careful study of this method, and have found a formula for the standard error of their estimate. Unfortunately, however, the formula involves the true standard deviation of the tolerance distribution, and the authors have not discussed the consequences of replacing this by a standard deviation estimated from the data ; hence the assessment of the precision of the estimated ED50 from the internal evidence of the experiment is unsatisfactory. Finney (1952, § 55) has pointed out that the probit method (or any similar technique making use of an appropriate equivalent deviate transformation) may legitimately be applied to the records of response and non-response, and is preferable to the scheme for maximum likelihood estimation developed by Dixon and Mood.

Like that of Bartlett's inverse sampling, the merit of staircase sampling is not that it is inherently more precise than the more usual experimentation with pre-selected numbers of subjects per dose, but that its rule of experimentation concentrates attention on the doses of chief interest for a particular purpose. Suppose pre-existing information to suggest that an ED50 almost certainly lies between $x - 1.7$ and $x = 2.3$. If a total of N subjects were divided equally between several doses ranging from $x = 1.4$ to $x = 2.6$, the ED50 ought to be satisfactorily included, but the experiment might show many of these subjects to have been practically wasted because their doses were far above or far below the ED50. A staricase experiment based on doses 1·4, 1·6, 1·8, 2·0, 2·2, 2·4, 2·6 would ensure that at worst the first one or two subjects were wasted, and the others would all be tested near the ED50. If the standard deviation of the tolerance distribution were shown by the tests on the first few subjects to be much smaller than 0·2, the steps between doses might later be shortened to 0·1 or 0·05. The probit method still applies, and no doubt Dixon and Mood's approximate method could be modified to suit this experiment. The staircase rule may sometimes be the ideal way of making a pilot investigation for the location of the ED50, especially when the experimenter begins in almost complete ignorance.

For assay purposes, staircase tests would be made on each preparation. If the investigator were content to use the Dixon and Mood method of calculation, the estimate of potency would be formed from the two estimates of ED50 ; assessment of the precision would then be rather unsatisfactory, because it would require an assumption that a standard deviation estimated from the data could be taken as the true value. Alternatively, probit calculations could be applied exactly as described in § 18.1.

The scheme of staircase sampling of doses described here is only the simplest of many that might be devised. The theory needs much further study ; even in its present stage of development, however, the staircase principle might be useful in some types of bioassay.

19.7 Quality control

The use of control charts was commended in § 5.10, as a means of ensuring that assays of a routine character were behaving in accordance with statistical theory. These methods of quality control may readily be adapted for assays based on quantal responses. If a particular experimental technique and assay design is in regular use, the regression coefficient, b, should remain in control, as also should the values of χ^2 for linearity and parallelism ; hence each might be made the subject of a control chart. As mentioned in § 5.10, the possibility of pooling information on b from several consecutive assays may be considered as an aid to precision, though this procedure is not to be encouraged unless there is great confidence that variations in b are due only to the chances of sampling.

In all the assays of this book, the emphasis has been on the estimation of the potency of a test preparation. When the need is only to inspect the quality of the test preparation, in order to ensure that preparations accepted as satisfactory conform to certain minimal requirements, the statistical problems that arise are different. For example, the permissible level of toxicity of a drug might be defined, either in absolute terms or relative to simultaneous trials with a standard preparation, by the mortality produced in a certain stock of test subjects. Perry (1950) has given an interesting discussion of the relative merits of different experimental designs, with particular reference to the efficiency with which they discriminate between acceptable and unacceptable preparations. He illustrated his argument by considering a requirement that the toxicity of a test preparation shall not exceed the value $\rho = 1 \cdot 2$ relative to that of the standard ; for various designs, he obtained curves to show the probability of a test preparation failing to comply with the appropriate criterion as a function of the true relative toxicity.

Perry's approach is closely related to the use of operating characteristics in industrial quality control. Since this book is concerned with assays for the estimation of potency, rather than with routine checks on the quality of drug production, his methods will not be described here.

19.8   The comparison of assay techniques

The foregoing discussion of assay design has been concerned only with statistical aspects of the problem. It has assumed that all comparisons related to alternative designs to be used with the same population of subjects and the same quantal response. The regression coefficient of equivalent deviate on log dose, however, is dependent upon the variability of individual log tolerances in that population ; in fact, for a normal tolerance distribution, $1/b$ is an estimate of the standard deviation of log tolerances, while for the logistic distribution $\pi/2b\sqrt{3}$ and for the angle distribution $(\pi^2 - 8)^{\frac{1}{2}}/4b$ are estimates of the standard deviation ($0 \cdot 9069/b$ and $19 \cdot 59/b$ respectively, if b for angles is measured in degrees ; see Armitage and Allen, 1950). Any change in the population or modification in technique that tends to increase b will improve the precision of assays.

In a direct assay, whatever the form of the log tolerance distribution, the standard error of a log potency ratio is, by equation (2.32),

$$\text{S.E. } (M) = s \left(\frac{1}{N_S} + \frac{1}{N_T} \right)^{\frac{1}{2}}, \tag{19.8}$$

where s is an estimate of the standard deviation per response. For a quantal response assay, if g is small and $(M - \bar{x}_S + \bar{x}_T)$ nearly zero,

$$\text{S.E.}(M) \doteqdot \frac{1}{b} \left\{ \Sigma \left(\frac{1}{Snw} \right) \right\}^{\frac{1}{2}}. \tag{19.9}$$

Equation (19.9) shows that, for probits, w can be regarded as the value of the information from a single subject in a good assay relative to its unit value in a direct assay. For logits, w must be multiplied by $0 \cdot 8225$, and for angles by $383 \cdot 6$, in order to give this comparison.

More exactly, this is true of an assay for which b is known in advance ; when b is unknown the comparison cannot be made without taking account of g. A symmetrical direct assay using N subjects will assign $N/2$ to each preparation and give a log potency for which

$$V(M) = \frac{4s^2}{N}. \qquad (19.10)$$

Consequently the value of $b^2 V_E(M)$ in Table 19.1 may be compared with $4/N$ in order to show the loss consequent upon restriction to quantal responses. Even for optimal designs, the variance is trebled for $N = 48$ and doubled for $N = 240$; for these numbers of subjects, quantal responses can give effectively only 37 per cent. and 51 per cent. of the information that direct tolerance measurements would contain. As N becomes large, this percentage information approaches its limiting value, 63·7 per cent., corresponding to the maximum value of w, 0·637. For logits, the values of $V_E(M)$ in Table 19·2 must first be divided by 0·8225, in order to convert $1/b^2$ into a measure of the variance of log tolerances ; the efficiencies of optimal designs are 40 per cent. for $N = 48$, 62 per cent. for $N = 240$, and 82·2 per cent. in the limit.

Alternative assay techniques for estimating the potency of a particular stimulus by quantal response records may be compared in terms of the magnitudes of $1/b$ (or the appropriate multiple of this for equivalent deviates other than the probit). Bliss and Cattell (1943) reported values ranging from 0·01 to 0·76 in a miscellaneous series of thirty-five assays analysed by probits ; four methods for digitalis assay gave values between 0·05 and 0·14. Gaddum (1933) earlier reported another series of twenty-five assays for which $1/b$ ranged from 0·04 to 0·91. The value of $1/b$ is comparable with the inherent standard error per response, s/b, for an assay using quantitative responses (§ 6.11). For example, Bliss and Cattell reported five assays of vitamin B_1, based on weight gains of depleted rats, for which s/b ranged from 0·06 to 0·24 ; in three assays using time to recurrence of polyneuritis in rats as a response, s/b ranged from 0·03 to 0·14. They also recorded a value of 0·28 for $1/b$ for an assay of this vitamin in which cure of polyneuritis in rats was used as a quantal response, and a value of 0·60 when a similar technique was adopted with pigeons. These findings point strongly to the superiority of assays based on quantitative responses in respect of their efficiency for estimating vitamin B_1.   Miller (1944) has given a good elementary account of the comparison of alternative techniques for digitalis assay in terms of their efficiency.

The conclusion to be drawn is that an indirect assay based upon quantal responses will always give less information on potency per subject tested than would the corresponding direct assay, and will often (but not inevitably) give less information than an indirect assay based upon quantitative responses.   On the other hand, quantal response techniques can be used in circumstances where neither of the others is possible ;   even when all three types are possible, quantal responses may involve simpler and less costly experimental techniques.   If values of $1/b$ for quantal responses, s for a direct assay, and s/b for quantitative responses are known, as well as the relative costs of the techniques, a complete comparison between their economic efficiencies is possible.

CHAPTER 20

ALTERNATIVE METHODS OF ANALYSIS FOR QUANTAL RESPONSES

20.1 The characteristic curve

Methods of assay based upon a standard regression curve are no more satisfactory with quantal responses than they are with quantitative. An assumption that the curve representing the regression of response rate on dose, as determined once for the standard preparation, can thereafter be used for an indefinite period is rarely justified. The example of the standardization of X-rays by their effect on the survival of eggs of *Drosophila melanogaster* has been quoted in § 3.14, but this is exceptional. As for quantitative responses, such methods should never be used without strong theoretical or experimental reasons for belief in the constancy of the regression for the standard preparation.

A method that has frequently been used is that of the *characteristic curve* (Trevan, 1927). Extensive data for the standard preparation are used to estimate the percentage change in dose required to produce various responses, as compared with the ED50, the relationship between relative dose and response rate being known as the characteristic curve. Subsequent single-dose trials of the standard and a test preparation can then be used to give comparable estimates of the ED50 for each, on the assumption that the doses for different response rates remain in the same relation to one another as for the original determination of the characteristic curve. In fact, each of the two doses tested is divided by the value from the characteristic curve corresponding to the observed response, and the results are regarded as estimates of the ED50 ; the ratio of these is then the estimate of relative potency.

An example will make this clear. In Fig. 20.1, the response rates for the standard preparation of insulin in Table 18.1 have been plotted against dose. The points lie so close to a sigmoidal curve that freehand drawing could give a very satisfactory representation, and the original users of the characteristic curve method would

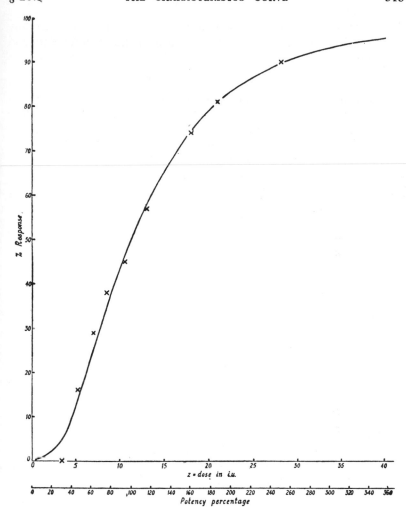

Fig. 20.1—Construction of characteristic curve from the data of Table 18.1 on the standard preparation of insulin

× : Empirical response rates

The curve has the equation

$$P = \int_{-\infty}^{Y} \frac{1}{\sqrt{2\pi}} \exp\left(-\tfrac{1}{2}\theta^2\right) . d\theta$$

In this, $Y = 1\cdot653 + 3\cdot188 \log z$, obtained from equation (18.32), where z is the dose in i.u.

The lower dose scale expresses each z as a percentage of the ED50.

almost certainly have been content with this. The curve actually shown in Fig. 20.1 has been constructed from the probit regression equation *

$$Y = 1{\cdot}653 + 3{\cdot}188x$$

obtained in equation (18.32), by evaluating Y for a series of doses and plotting the corresponding values of P against z. From the curve may be read the doses corresponding to different response rates. For the characteristic curve, the response rate must be plotted against the dose expressed as a percentage of the ED50 : Fig. 20.1 may be regarded as the characteristic curve if the scale of z is replaced by the lower scale of percentage potency. Table 20.1 shows the characteristic curve in tabular form.

TABLE 20.1—Characteristic curve for insulin
Based on the data of Table 18.1

Response rate	% potency	Response rate	% potency
0·05	30	0·50	100
0·10	40	0·55	109
0·15	47	0·60	120
0·20	54	0·65	132
0·25	61	0·70	146
0·30	68	0·75	163
0·35	76	0·80	184
0·40	83	0·85	211
0·45	91	0·90	252
0·50	100	0·95	328

An assay based upon this characteristic curve assumes that it remains unchanged for an indefinite period, and therefore that, although the absolute magnitudes of doses corresponding to two different rates of response may vary, their ratio is constant provided that the conditions of the experiment are standardized. This is equivalent to an assumption that, although its location may change, the mathematical form and scale parameter of the tolerance dis-

---

* This equation was obtained under the constraint of parallelism to the line for the test preparation in Table 18.1, whereas for the present purpose an equation for the standard preparation alone is wanted. The small value for the χ^2 used as a test of parallelism in § 18.2 shows that the difference between the two equations would be negligible. Since all that is needed for the characteristic curve is a reasonably well-fitting, objectively constructed, curve, to confuse the reader by introducing yet another equation seemed undesirable.

tribution may safely be regarded as fixed. The curve may then be used quite simply, in practically the same way as was the standard slope method of § 3.15. Single doses of the standard and test preparations are chosen, and each is given to a batch of subjects. For example, in a new assay, mice receiving 0·01 i.u. of the standard insulin might show a proportion 0·29 convulsed, while a simultaneous trial of other mice with 0·0015 mg. of the test preparation might show a proportion of 0·72 convulsed. The equivalent potencies of these response rates are read from Fig. 20.1, or found by interpolation in Table 20.1, as 67 per cent. and 153 per cent. respectively. Hence

$$R = \frac{0 \cdot 01}{0 \cdot 0015} \times \frac{153}{67} ,$$

and the potency is estimated to be 15·2 i.u. per mg.

The method is fairly trustworthy if the two experimental doses show nearly equal response rates, for the form of the characteristic curve is then of little importance ; they should therefore be chosen with this intention, on the basis of any existing information. On the other hand, if the two response rates are very different, the potency estimate may be seriously in error because the characteristic curve has altered slightly or was never exactly correct. Though Table 19.1 records a potency percentage of 328 for a 0·95 response, no critical experimenter would use this in forming a potency estimate; obviously the data on which the characteristic curve was based provided no information on what happens at so extreme a dose, and the figure of 328 per cent. is a wild extrapolation. Moreover, the method gives no validity tests. It should therefore be regarded only as a rough guide, resting on very unsure foundations. Even within one laboratory, the variance of the tolerance distribution is not likely to remain constant for a very long period. Still less justifiable would be attempts to apply a curve determined in one laboratory to assays performed in another ; different stocks of subjects, bred under different conditions and tested by techniques that inevitably differ slightly in spite of efforts at standardization, are almost certain to have different tolerance variances. Published accounts of determinations of *the* characteristic curve for a certain type of assay often suggest that the experimenter had such universal use in mind.

If experience showed the characteristic curve method to be valid for some type of assay, the initial determination of the curve ought to be made with considerable care, using many doses and a large number of subjects. In theory, use of the method need not then be restricted to any approximately linear portion of the curve, although the consequences of slight changes in the tolerance distribution would be the most serious in assays involving very high or very low responses. A scheme of computation for the assessment of fiducial limits to the potency could be set up on the analogy of that for quantitative responses in § 3.15, though this cannot be regarded as very satisfactory. Unless the investigator is certain of the applicability of a characteristic curve, he should follow the practice recommended for quantitative responses and prefer self-contained assay designs (§ 3.16; Chapter 19).

20.2   Graphical and semi-graphical methods

For quantal responses, as for quantitative, the drawing of a dose-response diagram is almost always a desirable first step in the statistical analysis of an assay. Usually this will be drawn in terms of log dose and equivalent deviate, so that the regressions for the two preparations are linear and parallel. The horizontal distance between two lines drawn by eye, subject to the constraint of parallellism, will be a first approximation to M ; an experienced worker will often draw lines that are very close to those obtained as the limit of the iterative calculations, and even the inexperienced, with moderately good data, will find the distance between the lines to differ little from the maximum likelihood estimate. These lines, or some equivalent process for obtaining a provisional set of expected probits, are required as a preliminary to the maximum likelihood calculations described in § 18.1, but they may also be regarded as in themselves estimating the relative potency. The estimate of M obtained by this graphical construction is always interesting as a first indication, and is sometimes sufficiently good in itself without recourse to further calculation (as when the data chance to show exceptionally good linearity and parallelism), but is never free from the taint of subjectivity of judgment.

A further objection to the purely graphical method is that it does not give any assessment of precision, yet some idea of precision is generally required before decisions relating to the test preparation can be taken. Numerous attempts have been made to devise semi-graphical methods that should supplement the graphical and lead to satisfactory assessments of variances and fiducial limits. One of the earliest was due to Litchfield and Fertig (1941) ; this accepted a considerable crudity of approximation as the price of extreme simplicity. Working with the probit transformation, Litchfield and Fertig proposed to draw the regression lines by eye (as described in the previous paragraph), then to assume $w = 0.5$ for each subject at a dose within $1/b$ of the ED50, $w = 0$ elsewhere, to estimate $V(b)$ by a simple rule based upon the range of x values, and thus to construct an approximation to $V(M)$. This method has been quite widely adopted, and may on occasion be a useful guide, but clearly it is too crude to be uncritically recommended for general use. One of the dangers of all approximate methods of analysis, of which Litchfield and Fertig's method is an extreme example, is that their appeal is primarily to the investigator who has little knowledge of or inclination for statistical science, and who is therefore least qualified to judge of their adequacy in any particular circumstances. In the hands of an experienced statistician, a method such as that just described may be valuable : he will recognize the situations in which its use could be seriously misleading, and will reserve it for data showing no abnormal features, from which a conclusion is wanted speedily rather than efficiently.

Several methods less crude than, but necessarily more laborious than, that of Litchfield and Fertig have been proposed. Another very simple one is that of Miller and Tainter (1944). Approaching more closely to the maximum likelihood procedure, de Beer (1945) described a scheme of nomographs for the probit calculations ; these use weights appropriate to the provisional regression lines, in order to provide variances for the parameters, but no iteration is involved. Curtis, Umberger, and Knudsen (1947), and Knudsen and Curtis (1947) have given nomographs to aid the assessment of fiducial limits for 4-point assays, and no doubt their method could be extended to other designs ; they used the angle transformation (§ 17.11), in which constancy of w eases the computations. Litchfield and Wilcoxon (1949) have published ' A simplified method of evaluating dose-effect experiments ' which, at first sight, looks far more complicated than the standard probit method in § 18.1 ! So hasty a criticism is unfair, however, for the authors have in fact devised an exceedingly ingenious system of nomographs ; with a minimum of arithmetic, these give a test of heterogeneity for the deviations from linearity of a single preparation, after which the ED50 and its fiducial limits are obtained, with allowance for a heterogeneity factor if that is needed. For two preparations a test of parallelism can also be included, and the relative potency and its limits are then formed if the assay seems fundamentally valid. The authors set themselves the aim of producing a method that should give all the tests and estimates that the iterative calculations provide, that ' should not unduly sacrifice accuracy in favour of simplicity and speed,' yet ' should make it possible to carry out the necessary calculations within 10-15 minutes without a calculating machine, and without resort to logarithms.' Once the rules of operation for the method have been read carefully, they can be applied easily, even by the worker with no statistical experience, and the incorporation of validity tests is some safeguard against the misuse to which these approximate methods are prone. Exclusion of calculating machines and logarithms, however, with the implication that these are unnecessarily complex refinements rather than aids to simplicity, seems an extraordinary limitation to adopt : an organization that has need of analysing enough assays to make especially rapid computing techniques economically important might reasonably be expected to afford, not only a table of logarithms and a calculating machine, but also a member of staff able to use both.

The papers by Goyan and Dufrenoy (1947) and de Beer (1941) mentioned in § 5.8 suggest mechanical aids that assist the estimation of potency from a dose-response diagram. Haley (1947) has made similar suggestions with particular reference to quantal responses.

These graphical methods of assay analysis do not introduce any new principles ; their aim is to simulate the maximum likelihood process, and their sole merit (sometimes a very important advantage) lies in speed and simplicity. The reader, whether statistician or not, who has mastered the general principles of bio-assay and the analysis of quantal responses will have no difficulty in adapting any of them to his use. Research workers who lack that mastery will be wise to resist the temptations that the methods present. When graphical method and iterative calculation give conclusions that for all practical purposes are identical, of course either may be used ; when the discrepancy in respect of either validity tests or potency estimation is large, the fault is most likely to lie in the graphical method. Without considerable experience of exact statistical methods, the chemist or biologist is not likely to be able to distinguish which of his assays are safe for graphical analysis merely by inspection of the raw data.

Cornfield and Mantel (1950) have mentioned an important flaw in graphical methods which has frequently been overlooked. They point out that ' a variance should be appropriate to the estimator being used rather than to the ideal estimator being approximated.' Methods such as that of Litchfield and Wilcoxon attempt to obtain the maximum likelihood estimate ; the value they do obtain is an approximation, but to it they ascribe a variance appropriate to the true maximum likelihood estimate (or rather a numerical approximation to this variance). No allowance is made for ' the additional errors inherent in the process of graphical estimation ' ; even supposing that the person who draws the line is unbiased (and this is hard to ensure !), he would not obtain exactly the same line each time he was presented with the same set of data, and appreciable extra error may enter from this source.

In accordance with the general policy of this book, no details of graphical methods will be given here. Two final points may be noted. Though most of the suggestions for graphical analysis have been based on the probit transformation, they could easily be modified for use with logits, angles, or any similar metameter transformations. Preparation of the graphs is made easier by specially ruled paper, which enables the proportionate response, p, to be plotted directly without recourse to tables such as Appendix Tables V, VIII, and XI. *Probability paper*, having a ruled grid based upon the normal distribution and either an absolute or a logarithmic dose metameter, may be obtained from several suppliers of graph papers,* and similar papers for logits and angles at least from the first firm mentioned in the footnote. Some workers find these papers helpful also for the drawing of provisional regression lines, with which to initiate iterative calculations.

---

* Those known to the author are the Codex Book Company, Inc., 74 Broadway, Norwood, Mass., U.S.A. ; the Special Chemicals Division of Winthrop-Stearns Inc., New York ; Messrs. Wightman, Mountain and Co., Artillery House, Artillery Row, Westminster, London, S.W.1 ; and Messrs. W. Heffer and Sons Ltd., 19 Sidney Street, Cambridge.

20.3 Estimation by minimum χ^2

Quantal response data involve dichotomous frequency classifications, and validity tests are usually made in terms of the statistic χ^2. A method of estimation of the parameters that aimed at minimizing the heterogeneity χ^2 might seem to be more appropriate than maximum likelihood. Indeed, Berkson's proposals for a method of minimum χ^2 in association with the logit transformation have already been mentioned (§ 17.14). By χ^2 is meant here the quantity resulting from the comparison of all observed frequencies with a set of expected frequencies calculated according to some theory, in the manner usual for a significance test of the deviations from the theory.* Thus, for a single preparation, if $S(\ )$ denotes summation over all doses,

$$\chi^2 = S \left\{ \frac{(np - nP)^2}{nP} + \frac{(nq - nQ)^2}{nQ} \right\},$$

which simplifies to

$$\chi^2 = S \left\{ \frac{n(p - P)^2}{PQ} \right\}. \tag{20.1}$$

The method of minimum χ^2 requires that the parameters of P, in a specification such as that of equation (17.7), be chosen so as to minimize the expression in (20.1) for the particular data obtained. General statistical theory shows that estimates of parameters based upon the minimization of χ^2 tend to equality with maximum likelihood estimates as the number of observations is increased, and that they also have the properties of consistency, asymptotic normality of distribution and asymptotic efficiency (§ 3.12; Cramér, 1946, § 30.3; Kendall & Stuart, 1961). Why then should one method be preferred to the other? Minimum χ^2 estimates will not usually have the properties listed as (iv) and (v) in § 3.12, but the existence of efficient (in finite samples) or sufficient estimates for the quantal response problem has not been conjectured, still less proved, so that maximum likelihood has no advantages on this count. Perhaps the most serious objection to the minimum χ^2 approach

---

* The mathematical statistician might prefer to define χ^2 as the sum of squares of a number of independent normal deviates, and to allow its use for an expression such as that in equation (20.1) only when observations are sufficiently numerous to make the probability distribution of this expression approximate to that of χ^2. In applied statistics, such an expression is commonly denoted by χ^2, whatever its distribution may be, and this usage is convenient here. The minimization of this χ^2 is always a legitimate procedure for estimation ; whether or not it is a good procedure is now to be discussed.

is that, when the number of subjects per dose is small, either or
both of the expected frequencies (responses and non-responses)
will be small and the value of χ^2 unstable; this is related to the
fact that the loss of information inherent in estimation by minimum
χ^2 increases without limit as the number of classes increases, even
though the total number of observations is large (Kendall & Stuart,
1961). The difficulty of using minimum χ^2 when class numbers
are small may constitute a serious practical difficulty in data of the
extent usual in assays.

An important point in connexion with both maximum likelihood
and minimum χ^2, and one that has in the past been too often forgotten, is that their virtues are primarily optimal properties in large
samples. Little is known about their biases or their efficiencies
when applied to data from experiments of small or moderate size.
Even the words ' large ' and ' small ' cannot at present be given
exact meaning in this context ; on the basis of existing information,
it would be unwise to assume that an experiment with one hundred
subjects at each of eight doses of a preparation was large enough
for the maximum likelihood (or the minimum χ^2) estimate of the
ED50 to be for all practical purposes unbiased and of maximum
efficiency, and equally unwise to assume that an experiment with
five subjects at each of three doses was too small for this. There
is no *a priori* reason why minimum χ^2, or some third method
(Tukey, 1949) should not be superior to maximum likelihood in
small samples. Neyman (1949) has shown both these methods to
fall within a wider class of estimation principles, so indicating a
possible line for further development.

Maximum likelihood is more generally applicable than minimum
χ^2 both because it does not run into difficulties when class numbers
are small, and because it can be used for quantitative data as well as
for frequencies. Though future developments of theory may lead
to the supersession of maximum likelihood by some other method for
quantal responses, instructions and tables to assist the use of minimum χ^2 seem unnecessary in the absence of evidence of its
superiority. The results obtained by Berkson (1949) show that
replacement of the usual weighting coefficient by

$$w = \frac{Z^2(qP + pQ)}{2P^2Q^2} \tag{20.2}$$

for probits,
$$w = 2(qP + pQ) \qquad (20.3)$$
for logits, and
$$w = \frac{0\cdot0006092(qP + pQ)}{P\underset{\sim}{Q}} \qquad (20.4)$$

for angles, in the iterative process of § 18.1, will convert that process into one for estimation by minimum χ^2. These are simply the maximum likelihood values of w multiplied by $\frac{1}{2}\left(\dfrac{p}{P} + \dfrac{q}{Q}\right)$, and tables to facilitate their use could easily be constructed. In large samples, p will tend to equality with P, and the two weighting coefficients for any metameter will become identical.

20.4 Estimation by least squares

One of the oldest and most widely used principles for the estimation of unknown parameters is the *method of least squares*. For it, the estimates are taken as those values which minimize the sum of squares of the difference between the observations and their corresponding theoretical values or expectations. In § 3.13, the method of maximum likelihood as applied to the estimation of the regression of a quantitative response on dose (under conditions there explained) was shown to be equivalent to the method of least squares. The statement is sometimes made that the probit calculations, as described in § 18.1 or any of the recognized modifications of this process, have as their object the determination of the least squares estimates of the parameters, and presumably the same would be said of the generalization in § 17.5. This is not true. For quantal responses, minimization of the quantity
$$S\{n(p - P)^2\}$$
has no merits as a method of estimation : it takes no account of the fact that $V(p)$ depends on P, so that large deviations from P can occur much more easily in the neighbourhood of $P = 0\cdot50$ than at the extremes. If the method is modified and based upon a weighted sum of squares, with the reciprocals of the variances as weights, the quantity to be minimized becomes
$$S\left\{\frac{n(p - P)^2}{PQ}\right\} ;$$
the least squares method is then identical with that of minimum χ^2.

20.5 Estimation of equivalent doses

Many methods of analysis that have been proposed involve separate estimation of equivalent doses for the two preparations, after which the relative potency is estimated as the ratio of the two. The level of comparison usually chosen is that of 50 per cent. response, the ED50, because, when the data are well distributed over a wide range of doses, this dose is likely to be more precisely determinable than any other. Use of a different percentage point, such as the ED90, however, would be quite legitimate, as the condition of similarity ensures that the same relative potency is being estimated ; for some data, this might give more precise results. The ED50, of course, is the median of the tolerance distribution, and estimation of the mean of that distribution is yet another procedure that could be adopted. Whatever the choice, if m_S, m_T are estimates of equivalent log doses for the standard and test preparations,

$$M = m_S - m_T \tag{20.5}$$

is an estimate of the logarithm of the relative potency. Moreover, the variances of m_S, m_T will usually be obtained quite independently, and the variance of M will be estimated by

$$V(M) = V(m_S) + V(m_T). \tag{20.6}$$

In the discussion of these methods, therefore, attention may be restricted to one preparation.

One criticism of all such methods should be immediately apparent. In an assay for which the condition of similarity is satisfied, the true relative potency does not depend upon any particular level of response, and both its estimate and the fiducial limits ought to be independent of any such choice, whereas if the condition of similarity is not satisfied the relative potency no longer exists as a unique value. A method of estimation that uses entirely separate calculations for each preparation will lead to a numerical value of M that is to some extent dependent upon whether equation (20 5) is based on the ED50, the ED70, or the ED95 ; therefore, it cannot be making the best possible use of the data. Moreover, the test of fundamental validity will usually be imperfect or even completely absent. The same objections might be raised to many graphical methods, at least in their common form of presentation, but these may always be improved by introducing the constraint that the regression lines be drawn parallel. As for graphical methods, the chief reason for the popularity of methods based upon separate estimation of equivelant doses is their arithmetical simplicity, though arguments relating to intrinsic merits have been advanced for some (see also Finney, 1952, § 13; Miller, 1950).

The discussion of particular methods in §§ 20.6–20.10 will relate almost entirely to symmetrical tolerance distributions, for which the distinction between the median and the mean disappears. Theoretical results relating to precision must be restricted to the normal tolerance distribution, because at the time of writing the corresponding results for the logistic or any other distribution are not known.

20.6   The Spearman-Kärber method

One of the best known and most easily understood of methods for estimating equivalent doses is usually attributed to Kärber (1931), but essentially the same idea was put forward much earlier by Spearman (1908).* Suppose that doses of one preparation, having logarithms $x_1, x_2, \ldots x_k$, are tested, and that r_i of the n_i subjects at dose x_i respond. Then

$$p_i = r_i/n_i \tag{20.7}$$

is an estimate of the response rate at x_i. Suppose further that $p_1 = 0$ and $p_k = 1$. Now $(p_{i+1} - p_i)$ is an estimate of the proportion of subjects whose tolerances lie between x_i and x_{i+1}. If successive doses are fairly close together, the mean of the log tolerance distribution may be estimated by

$$m = S \left\{ (p_{i+1} - p_i) \frac{(x_i + x_{i+1})}{2} \right\}, \tag{20.8}$$

on the analogy of the calculation commonly made for a grouped frequency distribution. The method is not exactly that of a grouped frequency distribution, however, since p_i and p_{i+1} are obtained from different groups of subjects. The chances of sampling may happen to make some values of $(p_{i+1} - p_i)$ negative, but equation (20.8)

---

* An ingenious proposal for the comparison of quantal response data was put forward by Christensen and Kerrich (1948), apparently without knowledge of the Spearman-Kärber method to which it is clearly related. It has little practical interest, because it does not lead to any estimate of potency and has no compensating advantages.

will still apply. There is an implicit assumption that doses below x_1, if tested, would have given no responses, and that doses above x_k would have given a response for every subject, so that doses outside the range actually tested would make no contribution to equation (20.8). This contradicts the hypothesis of a normal or other unlimited distribution of log tolerances, for which the probability of response is never quite zero or unity at any finite dose, but, if the interval between x_1 and x_k is wide relative to the standard deviation of log tolerances, the contradiction will be unimportant. Of course x_1 and x_k need not be the only doses for which $p = 0$ and $p = 1$; when the number of subjects per dose is small, several intermediate doses may have $p_i = 0$ or $p_i = 1$.

If the doses are equally spaced, so that

$$x_{i+1} - x_i = d \tag{20.9}$$

for all i, equation (20.8) may be written

$$m = x_k + \tfrac{1}{2}d - dSp_i. \tag{20.10}$$

If the number of subjects per dose is also constant and equal to n, equation (20.10) becomes

$$m = x_k + \tfrac{1}{2}d - \frac{dSr_i}{n}, \tag{20.11}$$

the form most suitable for computing. For such a regular set of doses, a rule is sometimes stated that if $p_1 \neq 0$ or $p_k \neq 1$ the next dose in the series, though untested, should be assumed to have given the desired result $p_0 = 0$ or $p_{k+1} = 1$; the estimation is then completed as for the longer series. This fabrication of 'data' is obviously without any theoretical basis ; though often it may do little harm, it could be seriously misleading if applied uncritically (but see § 20.11), and a better way of surmounting the difficulty is by the method of § 20.10. Only the case of equally spaced doses will be considered here, but the possibility of extending the ideas and formulæ to the more general case will be obvious to the reader.

The variance of the estimate given by equation (20.10) is (Irwin and Cheeseman, 1939)

$$V(m) = d^2 S\left(\frac{P_i Q_i}{n_i}\right), \tag{20.12}$$

where P is the expected response rate at x_i. A freehand curve representing the regression of p_i on x_i is sometimes used to give values for the P_i that are sufficiently accurate for equation (20.12). Alternatively, the variance may be estimated by

$$V(m) = d^2 S \left(\frac{p_i q_i}{n_i - 1} \right) ; \qquad (20.13)$$

the divisor $(n_i - 1)$ makes the estimate unbiased, a modification that may be important when the n_i are small. If n_i is constant, this variance may be more rapidly computed as

$$V(m) = \frac{d^2}{n^2(n - 1)} S \{ r_i(n - r_i) \} . \qquad (20.14)$$

For assay purposes, equation (20.6) gives the variance of M in equation (20.5), and fiducial limits are found by assuming a normal distribution for M, an assumption that is not likely to be far wrong unless the total number of subjects is very small.

The account of the usual computations for the Spearman-Kärber method given in previous paragraphs needs a more critical examination before it is accepted. In particular, the variance of m requires closer study. For a specified set of doses, m may be neither an unbiased nor a consistent estimate (§ 3.12) of μ, the true mean : repeated experimentation need not give values of m whose mean tends to μ, nor need increase in the n_i ensure that m tends to μ. Irwin (1937) and Finney (1950b) have discussed this in relation to the normal tolerance distribution. They found that, when a set of equally-spaced doses is specified, the expectation of m differs from μ by an amount independent of the n_i but dependent upon the location of μ relative to the nearest x_i. If the deviation of μ from the nearest x_i is selected at random between $\frac{1}{2}d$ and $-\frac{1}{2}d$, as is effectively done when the experimenter begins without knowledge of μ, the bias will be removed ; with this condition,

$$E(m) = \mu,$$

but the variance of m about μ will be increased by a component due to the location of μ relative to the nearest x_i. Development of this theory shows that the formula for $V(m)$ ought to be revised to read

$$V(m) = d^2 S \left(\frac{P_i Q_i}{n_i} \right) + V_B , \qquad (20.15)$$

where V_B is the additional component. Finney (1950b) has examined $V(m)$ for the perfectly symmetrical arrangement having all the n_i

equal ; he showed that $\bar{V}(m)$, the value of $V(m)$ averaged over all positions of the doses relative to μ, is then

$$\bar{V}(m) = \sigma d \left(\frac{0 \cdot 5642}{n} + B \right), \tag{20.16}$$

where

$$B = V_B / \sigma d \tag{20.17}$$

and B is a function only of the ratio d/σ^*. Since the second term in equation (20.16) is independent of n, the extent to which the precision of m as an estimator of μ can be improved by increase in n is limited. Even for d/σ as large as $4 \cdot 0$ (a much higher value than would usually be encountered), however, B is only $0 \cdot 0172$; for $d/\sigma = 3 \cdot 0$, B is $0 \cdot 0019$, and for smaller values of d/σ it is negligible. Thus, even for a wide spacing of doses, the contribution of V_B to $V(m)$ is scarcely important unless n is 100 or more. The obvious way of avoiding troubles from this source is to use a few subjects at each of many closely spaced doses, rather than an equal total number divided into larger groups at more widely spaced doses. The formula

$$\bar{V}(m) \doteqdot \frac{0 \cdot 564 \sigma d}{n}, \tag{20.18}$$

originally given by Gaddum (1933), will then be sufficiently close to the truth for use in the comparison of methods. The variance for any particular set of doses, equation (20.12) with $n_i = n$, will differ from its average for all locations of μ, equation (20.18), but unless d/σ is large the difference is unimportant ; when $d/\sigma = 4 \cdot 0$, the highest and lowest possible values of $S \left(\frac{P_i Q_i}{n} \right)$ differ by a factor of $5 \cdot 6$, when $d/\sigma = 3 \cdot 0$ this factor is reduced to $2 \cdot 0$, and when $d/\sigma \leqslant 2 \cdot 0$ this factor is less than $1 \cdot 1$. Thus, provided that d is not greater than 2σ, equation (20.18) can be regarded as a close approximation to $V(m)$ for any set of doses and any reasonable value of n (not unless n exceeded 10,000 would V_B be important).

---

* More exactly, the factor $0 \cdot 5642$ is $1/\sqrt{\pi}$, as was proved by van der Waerden (1940a, b) ; from its closeness to the corresponding quantity in $\bar{V}(m)$ for the probit method (§ 20.11), he concluded that the Spearman-Kärber method was of high efficiency, but did not take into account the considerations of design advanced in § 20.11.

The corresponding properties of the Spearman-Kärber method for tolerance distributions other than normal have not yet been investigated. Cornfield and Mantel (1950), however, have shown that for a logistic distribution the method is essentially the same as maximum likelihood estimation. They also pointed out that, even when the estimate is not to be accepted as the final summary of the data, it may be valuable as a first stage in the maximum likelihood calculations. To this end, they would use Epstein and Churchman's (1944) formula for σ^2, the variance of the tolerance distribution, and estimate it by

$$s^2 = d^2 \left[S\{(2k + 1 - 2i)p_i\} - (Sp_i)^2 - \frac{1}{12} \right]. \qquad (20.19)$$

The maximum likelihood process might then be initiated with a provisional set of expected probits calculated from

$$Y = 5 + \frac{x - m}{s}, \qquad (20.20)$$

where m and s are determined by equations (20.11) and (20.19). For irregular data, this may be superior to the usual practice of drawing a provisional line on a diagram (§ 18.1).

Epstein and Churchman (1944) have proposed the use of the Spearman-Kärber method as a standard procedure, in preference to the probit method, because ' it does not necessitate the assumption of some type of distribution prior to analysis, and hence resembles the standard treatment of independent observations made on the same object.' Their reasoning seems confused, since most methods of statistical analysis in common use for quantitative measurements assume an underlying normal distribution (cf. §§ 2.9, 15.4, 20.11). They then investigated the mean and the variance of the tolerance distribution (as well as higher moments), and discussed the optimal allocation of subjects to doses. Their approach seems unprofitable, however, because they did not consider problems of estimation ; their formulæ are applicable only when the true response rates at different doses are known. They neglect entirely the component of variance termed B in equation (20.16).

Enough has been said here of the theory of the Spearman-Kärber method ; its merits relative to other methods will be discussed in § 20.11. The present section concludes with a numerical example. Reed and Muench (1938) gave the data in Table 20.2 as obtained in

TABLE 20.2—Dosage-mortality data

Log dose, x	No. of subjects, n	No. dead, r	Mortality rate, p
1	6	0	0·00
2	6	0	0·00
3	6	1	0·17
4	6	0	0·00
5	6	2	0·33
6	6	4	0·67
7	6	4	0·67
8	6	6	1·00
9	6	5	0·83

mortality tests of groups of six subjects at each of nine doses of a stimulus. They did not describe the nature of the experiment, but the data are conveniently simple for the illustration of various methods of analysis. The highest dose tested failed to give a complete kill of all the subjects, but, especially as $p = 1·00$ for the next lower dose, an assumption that the kill would have been complete for $x = 10$ and all higher doses is not unreasonable : on strictly logical grounds, this is indefensible, but for data that are no more irregular than these it is likely to be good enough. Hence, by equation (20.11), the Spearman-Kärber estimate of the ED50 is

$$m = 10 + \tfrac{1}{2} - 1 \times (1 + 2 + 4 + 4 + 6 + 5 + 6) \div 6$$
$$= 5·83$$

(fictitious data of $r = n = 6$ being inserted for $x = 10$). Moreover, equation (20.14) gives

$$V(m) = (1 \times 5 + 2 \times 4 + 4 \times 2 + 4 \times 2 + 5 \times 1) \div (36 \times 5)$$
$$= 0·189.$$

Alternatively, the sequence of values of p_i might be crudely smoothed, arithmetically or by a freehand curve, to give a set of approximations to P_i. If these are taken as 0·00, 0·00, 0·10, 0·20, 0·35, 0·55, 0·75, 0.85, 0·95, 1·00 for x between 1 and 10*, equation (20.12) gives

$$V(m) = (0·10 \times 0·90 + \ . \ . \ . \ + 0·95 \times 0·05) \div 6$$
$$= 0·181,$$

which agrees closely with the value calculated from the p_i. Yet again, if a normal tolerance distribution were assumed, equation (20.18) might be used. If 2σ is estimated by the difference between x-values for $P = 0·16$ and $P = 0·84$, the sequence of smoothed values just used suggests

$$2\sigma \doteqdot 7·9 - 3·6$$
$$= 4·3,$$

and therefore

$$V(m) \doteqdot \frac{0·564 \times 2·15}{6}$$
$$= 0·202,$$

also in reasonably good agreement. The standard error of m is thus about 0·43. No exact theory of fiducial limits for this estimate of μ is available, but the obvious approximation based upon a normal distribution is likely to be adequate for many purposes; this would simply allow a range of $1·96 \times 0·43$, or 0·84, on either side of m, and so gives 4·99 and 6·67 as the 95 per cent. limits.

20.7 The method of extreme effective doses

Gaddum (1933) mentioned the method of extreme effective doses as being that usually adopted when only one subject is tested at each dose: the estimate of the ED50 is the mean of the lowest effective and the highest ineffective doses. The method should not be applied unless the doses are equally spaced (logarithmically), so giving data of the same kind as for the fully symmetrical Spearman-Kärber scheme. If $n = 1$, the estimate, n, is immediately written down; if $n > 1$, the data may be divided into n series, by allocating the subjects at each dose randomly between the series, and m is the mean of the n separate estimates that can be formed. The only

---

* This smoothing is obviously far from the best that could be done, but to demand that an elaborate smoothing process be used would defeat the primary purpose of the method, speed of computing. The values used for P_i were chosen, from inspection of Table 20·2, as a regular series not too widely discrepant from the observations, and were rounded to the nearest 0·05.

process at present known for obtaining the variance of m from the data themselves is to form a sum of squares of deviations between the estimates from the n series, and this is clearly unsatisfactory if n is small.

Finney (1950b) has investigated the properties of this method for a normal tolerance distribution. As for the Spearman-Karber method, the variance of m has a component, independent of n, that is due to the location of μ (the mean log tolerance, now identical with the log ED50) relative to the doses. Indeed, the average variance can be expressed by a formula of the same type as equation (20.16):

$$\bar{V}(m) = \sigma d \left(\frac{A}{n} + B \right), \qquad (20.21)$$

but both A and B are functions of d/σ. When d/σ is large, this method and the Spearman-Kärber tend to give exactly the same results, and when d/σ exceeds 4·0 both A and B are indistinguishable from the corresponding values in § 20.6. If d/σ is reduced, B decreases, rather more slowly than for the Spearman-Kärber method, but sufficiently to be negligible when d/σ is less than 2·0 ; A also decreases at first, though to a trivial extent (its minimum occurs near $d/\sigma = 1·5$ and is about 99·98 per cent. of the constant value for Kärber's method), after which it increases, so that when $d/\sigma < 0·5$ it is substantially greater than the value 0·564 in equation (20.16). The effect of the location of μ on the magnitude of $V(m)$ for a particular set of doses is practically the same as in Kärber's method for any value of d/σ.

Table 20.3 shows steps in the calculation of m for the data of Table 20.2. At each dose for which both deaths and survivals were recorded, the number of deaths was divided randomly between the six series ; thus, for $x = 5$, two series were chosen at random out of the six and the two deaths recorded in Table 20.2 were assigned to these. The series have no real existence in this example, and are used merely as an aid to the application of the method of calculation. If the order of testing were fully randomized, the natural procedure would be to assign the first subject at every dose to series I, the second to series II, and so on. For each series, the value of m is written down by averaging the values of x for the first ' — ' and the last ' + ' in the column. An assumption analogous to that in § 20.6,

**TABLE 20.3—Application of the method of
extreme effective doses to the
data of Table 20.2**

x	I	II	III	IV	V	VI
			Series			
1	+	+	+	+	+	+
2	+	+	+	+	+	+
3	+	+	+	+	+	⊖
4	+	⊕	+	+	+	+
5	⊕	⊖	⊖	+	+	+
6	⊖	–	–	⊕	⊖	⊕
7	–	–	+	⊖	⊕	–
8	–	–	–	–	–	–
9	–	–	⊕	–	–	–
m	5·5	4·5	7·0	6·5	6·5	4·5

+ indicates survival
− indicates death
m is the mean of the extreme effective doses
in each column, these corresponding to the
responses ringed.

and equally open to objection, has been made, namely that no subjects
could have died at doses lower than those tested and none could have
survived doses higher than those tested. The final estimate is

$$m = (5·5 + 4·5 + 7·0 + 6·5 + 6·5 + 4·5) \div 6$$
$$= 34·5/6$$
$$= 5·75.$$

An estimate of the variance of m, with 5 degrees of freedom, is
obtained from the mean square between the six series :

$$V(m) = \left\{ (5·5)^2 + (4·5)^2 + \dots + (4·5)^2 - \frac{(34·5)^2}{6} \right\} \div (5 \times 6)$$
$$= 0·196.$$

Nothing is known about the theoretical distribution of m, though it is likely to tend to normality for large n.   On the assumption that $n = 6$ is large enough for this to be a reasonable approximation here, 'fiducial limits' may be calculated from the standard error, 0·44 : for 5 degrees of freedom, $t = 2$·57, and the limits are 4·62, 6·88.   The results agree well with those obtained in § 20.6 ; although d/σ is only about 0·5, so that Kärber's method in theory ought to be appreciably more precise than that of extreme effective doses, in so small a sample the difference may easily fail to show.

20.8   The Reed-Muench method

Reed and Muench (1938) made an ingenious suggestion for rapid estimation of an ED50.   From data obtained in tests of n subjects at equally spaced doses, they would form for each dose :

$$
\left.
\begin{aligned}
S_-(r, x) &= \text{sum of all values of } r \text{ for this and} \\
&\quad \text{lower doses,} \\
S_+(\overline{n - r}, x) &= \text{sum of all values of } (n - r) \text{ for this} \\
&\quad \text{and higher doses.}
\end{aligned}
\right\} \quad (20.22)
$$

As x increases, S_- increases and S_+ decreases.   If one of the doses used in the experiment has

$$
S_-(r_i, x_i) = S_+(\overline{n - r_i}, x_i) , \qquad (20.23)
$$

then x_i is taken as m, the estimate of μ ; if not, the estimate is formed by linear interpolation between successive values of S_- and S_+ in order to find m for which equation (20.23) might be true.   Although the linear interpolation is obviously crude, more elaborate interpolatory schemes would so increase the labour as to make the method of questionable value in speedy calculation, and appear unlikely to have much theoretical advantage unless d/σ is small.   A superficial consideration might suggest that the method was valid whatever the form of the tolerance distribution, but in fact it requires that distribution to be symmetrical.   The reader may satisfy himself of this by calculations with hypothetical data, conforming perfectly to a smooth asymmetrical distribution ; he will find that m is displaced from the true ED50.   Reed and Muench did not suggest how the precision of m might be assessed from the data of a single experiment, nor is any way of doing this yet known.

If the interpolation is to be made between doses x_i and x_{i+1}, then

$$S_-(r_i, x_i) < S_+(\overline{n - r_i}, x_i),$$

and

$$S_-(r_{i+1}, x_i) > S_+(\overline{n - r_{i+1}}, x_{i+1}).$$

The estimate is given by the equation

$$S_- + r_{i+1}(m - x_i)/d = S_+ - (n - r_i)(m - x_i)/d,$$

where S_-, S_+ are the values of the functions at x_i ; therefore

$$m = x_i + \frac{d(S_+ - S_-)}{n - r_i + r_{i+1}}. \tag{20.24}$$

If the number of subjects per dose is not constant, a similar formula could be based on summations of the p_i and q_i, but might be very misleading if the variations in n_i were large. The formulæ can obviously still be applied to data for which the dose interval is not constant, but this is undesirable and may give a very distorted picture. Theoretical investigation of the precision of the estimate in equation (20.24) is difficult, and the only results at present known (Finney, 1950b) are based on the assumption that n is large. The mean variance of m can then again be expressed in the form of equation (20.21). For the normal tolerance distribution, $\bar{V}(m)$ is always a little larger than in the Spearman-Kärber method. Thus A has a maximum of about 0·63 in the neighbourhood of $d/\sigma = 1$, and for larger or smaller values of d/σ decreases slightly, being 0·60 at $d/\sigma = 4·0$ and 0·58 at $d/\sigma = 0·1$; B is also larger than in Kärber's method, though it is unlikely to be important in practice unless n is large. The value of $V(m)$ for a particular set of doses is more unstable than in Kärber's method, the ratio of extremes being 17·0 when $d/\sigma = 4·0$ and not falling to negligible proportions unless d/σ is less than 1·0.

The application of the Reed-Muench method to the data of Table 20.2 is readily illustrated. Columns 2 and 3 of Table 20.4 show the values of S_- and S_+, from which it appears that interpolation between $x = 5$ and $x = 6$ is needed. Equation (20.24) gives

$$m = 5·00 + \frac{9 - 3}{6 - 2 + 4}$$

$$= 5·75,$$

a result which happens to be identical with the estimate in § 20.7.

TABLE 20.4—Application of the Reed-Muench and Dragstedt-Behrens methods to the data of Table 20.2

x	S_-	S_+	$p^* = \dfrac{S_-}{S_- + S_+}$
1	0	32	0·00
2	0	26	0·00
3	1	20	0·05
4	1	15	0·06
5	3	9	0·25
6	7	5	0·58
7	11	3	0·79
8	17	1	0·94
9	22	1	0·96

20.9 The Dragstedt-Behrens method

In 1928, Dragstedt and Lang proposed a method very closely allied to that of Reed and Muench, though the latter seem to have been unaware of it. Behrens (1929) independently proposed the same method. Concerned to interpret very scanty data on cocaine poisoning, Dragstedt and Lang remarked ‘ It seems to us obvious that a rabbit that died from 100 mgm. would have died from any higher dose and one that survived from 150 mgm. per kilogram would have survived from any lesser dose,’ and they therefore estimated their ED50 by a double summation process. In fact, in the notation of equations (20.22), they used

$$p^* = \frac{S_-}{S_- + S_+},\qquad (20.25)$$

calculated for each x_i, as a smoothed value for the response rate at x_i, basing this upon the argument that S_- was the total of all subjects demonstrated by the experiment to be certain to respond at x_i and S_+ was the total demonstrated to be non-responders at that dose. If any p^* so calculated is exactly 0·50, the corresponding x_i is taken as m, the estimated ED50 ; if not, m is obtained by linear interpolation between two successive values of p^* on either side of 0·50.

Whether the authors ever intended their method to be regarded as more than a conveniently quick scheme for finding a rough assessment of the ED50 may be doubted. Nevertheless, it has come to be regarded as a general technique, on a par with the Spearman-Kärber and Reed-Muench methods. The form of equation (20.25) has encouraged the misconception that each p^* is an estimate of p_i with the precision appropriate to $(S_- + S_+)$ subjects. Thus Wright (1941) stated

'The usefulness of the " Dragstedt method " of calculating percentage mortalities lies in the fact that the statistical procedure of simultaneous integration of survivors and deaths gives an accuracy to the percentage mortality equivalent to that which would be obtained without integration only by the use of several times the number of animals employed with integration.'

Even more explicitly, Barr and Nelson (1949) wrote that

'The low margin of error produced in the mouse method of assay is brought about by several factors : (a) the double integration method of statistical interpretation, making it possible to interpret results in terms of approximately three times as many animals as actually used in the assay . . .

Unfortunately, the statistical legerdemain that will enable experimenters to draw conclusions from animals that have not been used in their experiments has yet to be discovered !

The estimation of m is a valid procedure for the ED50, provided that the tolerance distribution is symmetrical, but it must not be applied to unsymmetrical distributions or to any other ED value (such as the ED90). The relationship between p^* and x does not estimate the original dose-response relationship, but instead gives a steeper curve, as may easily be seen by performing the summations on data conforming perfectly to a smooth curve. The underestimation of the standard error that will result from assuming p^* to be based on $(S_- + S_+)$ subjects cannot be too strongly emphasized (Winder, 1947) ; in reality, both this and the Reed-Muench method are merely devices for interpolation in the series of values of p_i, and no deeper meaning should be attributed to them.

An approximate method of assessing the precision of m from experimental results was suggested by Pizzi (1950). When n is large, the mean variance will be expressible by equation (20.21), but, even for the normal tolerance distribution, nothing is known about the magnitude of A; Finney (1950b) found B to be considerably larger than for the Reed-Muench method. Experimental sampling by Behrens himself and by Gaddum (1933) indicates that for $d/\sigma = 0.4$, A is about 0.66, also larger than for the Reed-Muench method, though of course this need not be true of all values of d/σ. Interpolation in terms of the Dragstedt-Behrens ratio seems *a priori* less likely to be satisfactory than interpolation in terms of the Reed-Muench sums, and the evidence available supports this view.

The last column of Table 20.4 shows the Dragstedt-Behrens ratios for the data of Table 20.2. The estimate of the ED50 is obtained by interpolation between $x = 5$ and $x = 6$, and is clearly

$$m = 5 + \frac{0.25}{0.33}$$
$$= 5.76,$$

in this instance almost the same as for the Reed-Muench method. The importance of having a dose range sufficiently wide to give near certainty that the lowest will show no responses and the highest will show n responses must be emphasized for both the Reed-Muench and the Dragstedt-Behrens methods. For example, if the data in Table 20.2 for $x = 7, 8, 9$ were absent, both methods would lead to $m = 5.38$, a serious underestimate of what the values of p indicate.

20.10 The moving average method

Thompson (1947) suggested a moving average method for estimating the median of a tolerance distribution. A moving average of span K is obtained for any integer K by calculating

$$p^* = (p_i + p_{i+1} + p_{i+2} + \cdots + p_{i+K-1})/K \qquad (20.26)$$

for every set of K consecutive doses, and associating this with a dose

$$x = (x_i + x_{i+1} + x_{i+2} + \cdots + x_{i+K-1})/K. \qquad (20.27)$$

Thompson's technique is then to interpolate linearly between successive values of p^* on either side of 0.50 in order to estimate m, the value of x for which p^* would be 0.50. As for the Dragstedt-Behrens ratio, p^* is not in reality an estimate of P for the x-value associated with it, and the method must not be used for estimating any other percentage point. Indeed, the moving average method is like the

Reed-Muench and Dragstedt-Behrens methods in being valid for the estimation of the ED50 only when the tolerance distribution is symmetrical. The estimate depends upon K, the span of the moving average; Thompson suggested $K = 3$ as reasonable, but did not discuss the relative merits of alternatives. Thompson and Weil (1952) and Weil (1952) have published tables to expedite moving average calculations.

For the fully symmetrical experiment having n subjects at each of a series of equally spaced doses, if values of p^* involving x_i, x_{i+1} as the lowest doses in equation (20.27) fall on either side of 0·50, the estimate of the ED50 is

$$m = x_i + \tfrac{1}{2}d(K + 1) - df, \qquad (20.28)$$

where

$$f = \frac{(p_{i+1} + p_{i+2} + \ldots + p_{i+K} - \tfrac{1}{2}K)}{(p_{i+K} - p_i)}. \qquad (20.29)$$

Equation (20.28) is obviously related to equation (20.10), the estimate for the Spearman-Kärber method ; indeed, equation (20.10) is the limit of equation (20.28) as K becomes large. The advantage for the moving average method is that its validity does not require an unlimited series of doses : provided that tests have been made at all doses from x_i to x_{i+K}, the estimate may be used.

Since m is the ratio of two linear functions of the empirical response rates, full discussion of its sampling distribution is difficult. If n is large, the dispersion may be adequately represented by a naive variance formula, akin to equation (2.10) :

$$V(m) = d^2\{f^2 P_i Q_i + P_{i+1}Q_{i+1} + P_{i+2}Q_{i+2} + \ldots$$
$$+ P_{i+K-1}Q_{i+K-1} + (1 - f)^2 P_{i+K}Q_{i+K}\}$$
$$\div n\,(P_{i+K} - P_i)^2. \qquad (20.30)$$

If n is small, but still large enough for the distribution of p_i to be approximately normal, Fieller's theorem may be used; an alternative, employing an angle transformation, has been suggested by Harris (1959). If $V(m)$ is to be estimated from within one experiment, either the P_i must be approximated from a smooth freehand curve for p plotted against x or equation (20.30) must be replaced by

$$V(m) = d^2\{f^2 p_i q_i + p_{i+1}q_{i+1} + p_{i+2}q_{i+2} + \ldots$$
$$+ p_{i+K-1}q_{i+K-1} + (1 - f)^2 p_{i+K}q_{i+K}\}$$
$$\div (n - 1)\,(p_{i+K} - p_i)^2. \qquad (20.31)$$

For theoretical investigations, however, equation (20.30) may be used ; with its aid, Finney (1950b) has studied the precision of m in the same manner as was done for the methods in §§ 20.6–20.9. The mean value of $V(m)$ is again expressible in the form of equation (20.21), though A and B now depend upon K as well as upon d/σ. For large K, $\bar{V}(m)$ must tend to the same value as in the Spearman-Kärber method, but the approach is slow when d/σ is small. If Kd/σ exceeds 6·0, the variance is not much greater than the Spearman-Kärber value. Under other conditions, $\bar{V}(m)$ is much greater, the A component becoming especially large when d/σ is small. The instability of the variance is also more marked. This makes clear that, for any set of data to which the method can be applied, the span selected should be as large as possible. In planning an experiment, however, the doses should not necessarily be chosen with a view to using a large K, because allocation of more subjects to each of a smaller number of doses may be the better policy (Table 20.7) ; the decision should depend upon existing information about μ and σ.

The ED50 for the data in Table 20.2 might be estimated by the method of moving averages using any one of several different spans. For example, with $K = 4$, equation (20.28) gives

$$m = 4 \cdot 00 + 2 \cdot 50 - \frac{0 \cdot 33 + 0 \cdot 67 + 0 \cdot 67 + 1 \cdot 00 - 2 \cdot 00}{1 \cdot 00 - 0 \cdot 00}$$

$$= 5 \cdot 83.$$

The number of subjects per dose, six, can scarcely be regarded as large, and the irregularities in the last column of Table 20.2 indicate that equation (20.31) is not likely to be very satisfactory ; if this objection were ignored, the variance would be calculated as

$$V(m) = \left(\frac{4}{9} \times 0 + \frac{2}{6} \times \frac{4}{6} + \frac{4}{6} \times \frac{4}{6} + \frac{4}{6} \times \frac{2}{6} + \frac{1}{9} \times 0 \right)$$
$$\div \{ 5 \times (1 \cdot 00)^2 \}$$

$$= 0 \cdot 133.$$

Alternatively, using equation (20.30) with the smoothed values of P adopted for the Spearman-Kärber method in § 20.6,

$$V(m) = \left(\frac{4}{9} \times 0 \cdot 1600 + 0 \cdot 2275 + 0 \cdot 2475 + 0 \cdot 1875 + \frac{1}{9} \times 0 \cdot 1275 \right)$$
$$\div \{ 6 \times (0 \cdot 65)^2 \}$$

$$= 0 \cdot 295.$$

Table 20.5 summarizes similar calculations for different values of K. The variances calculated from equation (20.31) are very erratic, as may be expected when n is small. Those from equation (20.30) show a regular decrease as K increases, but are unsatisfactory for other reasons, notably for their dependence upon a smoothing process. Nor is it known how far these calculations, based upon the use of 6 as a ' large ' number, can give trustworthy indications of the sampling errors in m.

TABLE 20.5—Estimates of the log ED50 for the data of Table 20.2, by the method of moving averages

Span, K	Estimate, m	Variance of estimate, $V(m)$	
		Equation (20.31)	Equation (20.30)
1	5·50	0·200	0·495
2	5·50	0·800	0·495
3	5·75	0·256	0·325
4	5·83	0·133	0·295
5	5·80	0·194	0·269
6	5·75	0·339	0·232
7	5·80	0·258	0·198
8*	5·83	0·189	0·181

* for $K = 8$, the assumption was made that, if 6 subjects had been tested at $x = 10$, all would have died.

20.11 Comparison of methods

Of the methods described in §§ 20.6–20.10, the Spearman-Kärber estimates the mean log tolerance ; the method of extreme effective doses estimates the ED50 or median log tolerance ; the Reed-Muench, Dragstedt-Behrens, and moving average methods should be applied only to symmetrical tolerance distributions, and then estimate both the mean log tolerance and the ED50 since the two coincide. The chief argument advanced in support of any of these methods is that of arithmetical speed and simplicity. Thompson (1947), indeed, advocated the moving average method because it is ' free from assumption as to the precise type of fundamental curve involved ' (though symmetry is essential), and the same merit can be claimed for the others. There seems to be no clear reason, however, why freedom from assumptions about the nature of a distribution should be especially desirable for quantal response experiments. If normality of distribution, for example, would be an acceptable assumption for tolerances that were directly measurable, the mere fact that experimental circumstances permit only quantal records does not destroy this acceptability. On the other hand, if, in a particular type of quantal response experiment, freedom from assumption were important, this would also be true in an experiment that permitted the same tolerances to be directly measured. The value of non-parametric methods in statistical science is undeniable, but the need for them is quite unconnected with whether or not data are quantal or quantitative. When nothing at all is known about a distribution, their use is mandatory ; when a distribution is known to be, say, approximately normal in form, neglect of this knowledge almost certainly reduces the precision of estimation.

In the discussion that follows, attention will be restricted to experiments of symmetrical design, having n subjects at each of a series of equally spaced doses, the most important arrangement for actual use. At this stage, the number of doses need not be specified, but, as will become clear in the argument that follows, the question of whether the range over which the doses are spaced shall be limited or long enough to be regarded as unlimited is unavoidable in any consideration of efficiency and economy of experimentation. Although the conclusions need not apply to unsymmetrical designs, in general qualitative terms they are likely to do so. Numerical values relate to a normal tolerance distribution.

When the tolerance distribution is symmetrical, the five methods estimate the same quantity, the mean or median of the distribution. For the normal distribution, the variance of the estimate from the Spearman-Kärber method has been shown to be smaller than that given by any of the others (with a trivial exception for extreme effective doses). Admittedly, this statement is not fully proved for the Dragstedt-Behrens method, and for the Reed-Muench and moving average methods has been demonstrated only for the asymptotic variance when n is large, but the evidence (Finney, 1950*b*) leaves little hope that these will be relatively more precise when n is small.

Since the extreme effective dose, the Reed-Muench, and the Dragstedt-Behrens methods all require an unlimited range of doses, and none has any obvious advantages in respect of speed of computing (except for extreme effective doses with $n = 1$), they may be considered as no longer eligible for practical use ; the decision is reinforced by the lack of any satisfactory method of assessing their precision from the internal evidence of a single experiment. The situation may be different for other tolerance distributions, but is scarcely likely to be so for any as closely resembling the normal as does the logistic.

The moving average method is in a rather different category, because of its freedom from the condition that the range of doses be unlimited.   When d/σ is small, it is hopelessly imprecise, but, for spans of 3 or more, when d/σ exceeds $1\cdot0$ the precision of m is comparable with that for the Spearman-Kärber estimate with the same number of subjects per dose.   If the dose range really were unlimited, the Spearman-Kärber method would be preferable.   What is meant in practice by an unlimited range of doses ?   The experimenter will always take into account any existing knowledge of the tolerance distribution.   If he wishes to obtain data to which the Spearman-Kärber method may legitimately be applied, he should so choose his doses that he believes himself almost certain to obtain no responses with the lowest, 100 per cent. responses with the highest.   Even if the mean tolerance were known, an interval of 3σ on either side of it (a total of 6σ) would be needed in order to ensure this, and in practice a total range of at least 10σ would usually be desirable. For the moving average method, on the other hand, all that is necessary is a range wide enough to be sure to include the ED50 and to allow sufficient doses on either side for calculation of a moving average with the desired span ; how much the range may be restricted will depend upon what knowledge the investigator possesses in respect of a particular assay technique, but a range of 6σ should often suffice and sometimes this might be reduced to 4σ.   Of course, the experimenter would judge the range by its absolute extent, since he would not know σ : the ratios $10:6$ and $6:4$ seem reasonable representations of what might arise in practice, and expression as multiples of σ is convenient for the argument that follows.

If the interval between extremes of log dose is to be at least X, the number of doses to be tested for each preparation is

$$k = \frac{X}{d} + 1, \qquad (20.32)$$

or the integer next above this. Hence, if N subjects are available for a $2k$-point design assaying one test preparation against a standard, the number of subjects per dose is given by

$$2n \left(\frac{X}{d} + 1 \right) = N. \qquad (20.33)$$

In practice, n will usually be small enough for B in equation (20.21) to be neglected, whatever the method of estimation, and therefore, by equations (20.6) and (20.33), the mean variance of M may be written

$$\bar{V}(M) = 4A\sigma(X + d)/N. \qquad (20.34)$$

TABLE 20.6—Mean variance of log potency, by the Spearman-Kärber method applied to a symmetrical assay using N subjects (normal tolerance distribution)

d/σ	Values of $N\bar{V}(M)/\sigma^2$	
	$X = 10\sigma$	$X = 6\sigma$
3·0	(29·3)	20·3
2·0	27·1	18·1
1·5	(26·0)	16·9
1·0	24·8	15·8
0·5	23·7	14·7
0·3	(23·2)	14·2
0·2	23·0	14·0
0·1	22·8	13·8

( ) indicates that k, given by equation (20.32), is not an integer ; use of the next larger integer for k, without alteration in d, would make $N\bar{V}(M)/\sigma^2$ greater than the value tabulated.

For the Spearman-Kärber method, since $A = 0.5642$, equation (20.34) leads to

$$N\bar{V}(M)/\sigma^2 = 2.257(X + d)/\sigma. \qquad (20.35)$$

Table 20.6 shows this quantity for $X = 10\sigma$ and $X = 6\sigma$, with various values of d/σ. Table 20.7 shows $N\bar{V}(M)/\sigma^2$ by the moving average method for $H = 6\sigma$ and $H = 4\sigma$, with spans of 1, 2, 3, or 4 and various values of d/σ ; the numerical values of A have been taken from Finney's paper (1950b), on the assumption that equation (20.30) is applicable. For both tables, the experimenter is assumed to have been successful in selecting a range of doses that has the ED50 near its centre.

TABLE 20.7—Mean variance of log potency, by the moving average method applied to a symmetrical assay using N subjects (normal tolerance distribution)

	Values of $N\bar{V}(M)/\sigma^2$							
d/σ	$X = 6\sigma$				$X = 4\sigma$			
	$K = 1$	$K = 2$	$K = 3$	$K = 4$	$K = 1$	$K = 2$	$K = 3$	$K = 4$
3·0	25·7	20·5	—	—	(20·0)	—	—	—
2·0	24·6	19·3	18·2	—	18·5	14·5	—	—
1·5	26·4	19·7	17·6	17·0	(19·3)	(14·4)	—	—
1·0	32·8	22·7	18·5	16·8	23·4	16·2	13·2	12·0
0·5	56·2	36·1	26·8	21·9	38·9	25·0	18·6	15·2
0·3	88·8	56·1	40·6	32·1	(60·6)	(38·3)	(27·7)	(21·9)
0·2	130·6	82·0	58·7	45·8	88·4	55·5	39·8	31·1
0·1	257·1	160·4	114·2	88·5	172·8	107·8	76·7	59·5

( ) indicates that k, given by equation (20.32), is not an integer ; use of the next larger integer for k, without alteration in d, would make $N\bar{V}(M)/\sigma^2$ greater than the value tabulated.

— indicates that k is too small to give a moving average of the span required.

Exact numerical comparisons between the two methods are impossible, because so much depends upon the success with which the mean and σ are guessed at the time when the doses are chosen. Tables 20.6 and 20.7 present both in a rather favourable light. They show that the precision of the Spearman-Kärber estimate is improved by narrowing the interval between successive doses, though the gain by reduction below an interval of 0.5σ is slight : the experimenter who intends to employ the Spearman-Kärber method will be wise to use a few subjects at each of many doses, rather than the same total number of subjects distributed between fewer doses over the same total range, even though he may appear to be estimating individual values of p_i with low precision. For equal total dose ranges, and when d/σ is large, the moving average method behaves like the Spearman-Kärber, although its variance is always slightly greater ; when d/σ is small, however, the moving average method with any moderately short span becomes markedly inferior.

The advantages claimed for the moving average method derive from the possibility of using a smaller range of doses. If, on the basis of the argument put forward earlier, $X = 10\sigma$ for Spearman-Kärber and $X = 6\sigma$ for moving averages are regarded as comparable, the moving average method with span 3 or 4 has a maximum precision about 30 per cent. or 35 per cent. better than the other; this maximum occurs when the dose interval, d, lies between σ and 2σ, the gain being assessed relative to the optimal conditions for the Spearman-Kärber method (a very small dose interval). The danger in the moving average method is that, if d/σ differs markedly from what the experimenter believes it to be, the estimate may be very much less precise than was expected. For instance, an experimenter might choose his doses in the belief that his value of d was about equal to σ ; if in reality $d = \sigma/3$, his precision may be less than half what he had hoped. Moreover, in the construction of Table 20.7, the ED50 was assumed to be near the centre of the series of doses used, and failure to achieve this, on account of inadequate previous information, would make the precision even lower. Either type of misjudgment might make the data definitely unsuitable for application of the Spearman-Kärber method, because the doses would not extend from one giving a very low response rate to one giving a very high rate. The rapid increase in $\bar{V}(M)$ as d/σ decreases, characteristic of the moving average method, may be a high price to pay for the possible gain in precision, especially when the near-independence of $\bar{V}(M)$ and d/σ in the Spearman-Kärber method is remembered.

If circumstances seem to warrant the discounting of these dangers, and the moving average method is to be adopted, planning of the experiment on the basis of a span of 3 or 4 is probably the most reasonable course, as for longer spans the number of doses needed becomes large. Nevertheless, when the experiment has been completed, the moving average adopted for calculation should have the largest span that the data permit without recourse to speculations about doses outside the range tested ; as Tables 20.5 and 20.7 illustrate, this will most effectively utilize the available information, and so lead to maximum precision.

The merits of these methods relative to estimation by probits, according to the recommendations of Chapters 17 and 18, must next be considered. Finney (1950b) has discussed the application of probit analysis to the data from an experiment on n subjects at each of an unlimited series of equally spaced doses. When n is large enough for a naive variance formula to replace Fieller's theorem in the assessment of fiducial limits, the mean variance of m can again be expressed by equation (20.21). In this equation, the component represented by B may be ignored, however, since it is no longer a constant but instead must tend to zero more rapidly than n^{-1}. The value of A is almost exactly 0·5536 for any value of d/σ less than 2·0, but increases rather rapidly for larger values of d, being as much as 1·171 for $d/\sigma = 4·0$. Thus, at best, $\bar{V}(m)$ from the probit analysis of such an experiment will be 2 per cent. smaller than $\bar{V}(m)$ from a Spearman-Kärber analysis, a state of affairs that has led a number of writers to conclude that the general use of the more laborious maximum likelihood processes has little to recommend it in problems of quantal responses. Indeed, if d/σ exceeds 2·5, $\bar{V}(m)$ for probits will be greater than the Spearman-Kärber value unless n is large. This possibility does not controvert the theoretical maximal efficiency of the maximum likelihood (probit) method (§ 3.12), because of the B component in equation (20.16) : as n is increased, this component remains constant, so that $\bar{V}(m)$ does not tend to zero, whereas the consistency of maximum likelihood estimation ensures that, for it, $\bar{V}(m)$ may be made as small as desired by use of a sufficiently large n. In practice, the interval between successive doses is unlikely to exceed 3σ. Unless n is so small as to reduce the effective precision of the probit estimate on account of a large value of g, the difference between the precisions achieved when the two methods of analysis are applied to data for which either is suitable will then be negligible. This negative virtue of the probit method, however, is not the complete story. Both the Spearman-Kärber and the moving average methods require a rather specialized experimental design before they can be safely applied. Although the general formulæ for m are capable of use however irregular the design, the underlying theory is much more open to objection if the doses are unequally spaced or if the number of subjects per dose is not constant. Moreover, the number of doses needed is usually large, and, even though a wide range of doses be adopted, the methods may sometimes break down because an ED50 is much greater or much smaller than was believed when the doses were chosen. The probit method, on the other hand, can be applied whatever the doses or the numbers of subjects per dose may be. This is not intended as advocacy of experiments of irregular design : circumstances sometimes compel irregularity, and, even in a symmetrically designed experiment, accidental losses may destroy the symmetry. Most important of all, the methods in §§ 20.6–20.10 do not provide any validity tests, yet they require a number of doses in excess of the recommendations in § 19.2. Tables 20.6 and 20.7, indeed, may be compared with Table 19.1 ; the values of $N\bar{V}(M)/\sigma^2$ measure essentially the same thing as $Nb^2V_E(M)$ in Table 19.1. With $X = 10\sigma$ for the Spearman-Kärber method, $N\bar{V}(M)/\sigma^2$ is at least 22·6, and with $X = 6\sigma$ for moving averages of span 4, it is at least 16·8 : a well-designed experiment analysed by probits, having 48 subjects and three or four doses of each preparation, may give $Nb^2V_E(M)$ as small as 11·0. If X could be reduced to 6σ for the Spearman-Kärber method or to 4σ for moving averages, the difference would almost disappear, but so small a dose range is scarcely to be recommended with these methods. The comparison has been made for an assay using practically the smallest number of subjects that could ever be regarded as worth while for quantal responses (that in Table 17.3 had $N = 47$), and is therefore most unfavourable to probits. When N is larger, the difference is more marked ; the $N = 240$ column of Table 19.1 shows values of $Nb^2V_E(M)$ less than 8·0. In the limit for a large number of subjects, the relevant comparison is that of $Nb^2V(M)$ in Table 19.1 with the entries in Tables 20.6,

20.7 :   the efficiency of the Spearman-Kärber and moving average methods is then at best about 50 per cent., and quite probably below 30 per cent. The values in Table 19.1 may present the probit method in too favourable a light, because they assume that the experimenter has succeeded in obtaining responses very close to those at which he aimed when he chose his doses. The apparent loss of 50 per cent. of the potential information from N subjects, through bad assay design and poor statistical analysis, cannot be entirely explained away by this argument, however, since Tables 20.6 and 20.7 are, for similar reasons, unduly favourable to their methods. The loss of 50 per cent. is possibly about the true figure.

In all that has been said above, the necessity for an unlimited range of doses as a basis for the Spearman-Kärber and various other methods has been emphasized. Nevertheless, m can be calculated from formulæ such as equation (20.10) and (20.24) whatever the range of doses may be, and undoubtedly quantities so calculated have often been used by experimenters as estimates of the ED50. From one point of view, this involves the assumption that, had doses outside the range been tested, all lower doses would have given $p_i = 0$ and all higher doses would have given $p_i = 1$. From another point of view, the procedure may be regarded as an arbitrary rule for the calculation of a quantity whose merits as an estimator of m have yet to be investigated, adopted with the full understanding that addition to the data of results from more extreme doses would alter the estimate ; for example, in equation (20.10) if $p_i \neq 1$ for $i = k$ and all higher doses, inclusion of results from the next higher dose would increase m by an amount dq_{k+1}. For a specified set of doses, the bias in m regarded as an estimator of μ will presumably be greater than that discussed in § 20.6. Examination of the effect of working with a randomly located set of doses is more troublesome, because of the necessity of placing some limitation on the range within which the agreed number of doses may be located, but the bias would again be replaced by a component of variance independent of n, so as to give a mean variance with the form of equation (20.21). It is to be expected that the B component would be appreciably larger than that found in previous sections (and tabulated elsewhere, by Finney, 1950b), especially if the total range of doses happened only just to include or even to exclude μ.

Bross (1950) has made extensive calculations relating to the ideas of the previous paragraph, but the amount of labour involved restricted him to consideration of one or two particular cases and much remains to be done before the whole problem can be seen in proper perspective. Bross compared the Spearman-Kärber, Reed-Muench, and maximum likelihood methods in small samples, by complete enumeration of cases. He chose the logistic distribution as the basis of his calculations, but probably would have obtained qualitatively similar results with the normal distribution. He used four doses, these being such as to have expected response rates of either 0·10, 0·32, 0·68, 0·90, or 0·59, 0·86, 0·96, 0·99 ; the first set is symmetric with respect to the ED50, the second is so violently skewed that it does not bracket the ED50. The doses corresponding to these response rates for the logistic distribution are equally spaced, and correspond roughly with a spacing defined by $d/\sigma = 0·8$ for probits. He enumerated all possible sets of experimental results with either two subjects at each dose or five at each dose, and apparently adopted equations (20.10) and (20.24) for the Spearman-Kärber and Reed-Muench estimations. His assessment of the success of different estimation procedures was based upon the relative frequencies with which the absolute value of the difference $(m - \mu)$ lay in various intervals, and so is not directly comparable with the variance criteria used in this chapter.

Bross's conclusions agree with those of this chapter in their rejection of the Reed-Muench method, but, for his special cases, he found the Spearman-Kärber method to give closer approximation to the true ED50 than did the maximum likelihood. The difference was not great, but was sufficient to suggest that the Spearman-Kärber method may be genuinely superior when the number of subjects per dose is very small. The apparent disagreement with the earlier finding that, when d/σ is small, the variances for probit and Spearman-Kärber estimation are almost equal may reflect the inadequacy of the variance as a measure of deviation from the truth when n is very small. Certainly, to assume that the numerator and denominator of the probit estimator are normally distributed when calculated from an experiment with $n = 2$ at each of four doses is likely to be somewhat misleading, even though the theory of maximum likelihood ensures that it may be used safely for large n. The whole question needs much further study, in order to discover the circumstances under which the asymptotic efficiency of maximum likelihood estimation begins to assert itself, but such study is likely to be exceedingly laborious because it must be based upon separate analyses for the many different possible outcomes of an experiment. Bross's results are surprising, especially in their indications that the Spearman-Kärber method gives estimates from his skew set of doses of a quality comparable with those from the symmetrical set; their present importance, however, is perhaps as a demonstration that a more intensive examination of the problem may be profitable, rather than as justifying his unduly confident conclusion on the general superiority of Spearman-Kärber estimation. Cornfield and Mantel (1951) showed that assumptions about responses for the unobserved next lower and next higher doses may have influenced Bross's findings.

The numerical example in Table 20.2 can easily be analysed by the probit method. The calculations need not be shown, but the equation to the regression line,

$$Y = 1 \cdot 994 + 0 \cdot 511x$$

is of some interest. The regression coefficient is an estimate of $1/\sigma$, and therefore σ is estimated as $1 \cdot 96$, in good agreement with the value $\sigma = 2 \cdot 15$ used in § 20.6. Substitution of the values of x gives as the nine expected response rates, P_i, the quantities $0 \cdot 01$, $0 \cdot 02$, $0 \cdot 07$, $0 \cdot 17$, $0 \cdot 33$, $0 \cdot 52$, $0 \cdot 72$, $0 \cdot 86$, $0 \cdot 94$; these differ a little from the set used in § 20.6 and again in § 20.10 as a smoothed series, primarily because of the crude smoothing. Insertion of $Y = 5 \cdot 0$ gives the logarithm of the ED50 as

$$m = 5 \cdot 882,$$

and limits obtained by application of Fieller's theorem are

$$m_L, m_U = 4 \cdot 960, 6 \cdot 892.$$

Table 20.8 summarizes various estimates of ED50 and fiducial limits for these data. For moving averages, variances obtained from equation (20.30) and shown as smoothed values in Table 20.5 have been used, with an assumption that the normal deviate, $1 \cdot 960$, will give approximate 95 per cent. limits. As the preceding discussion might suggest, differences between methods are not tremendous for an experiment using only 54 subjects. In a paper describing alternative methods of analysis for an immunological assay (Finney, 1959), another set of comparisons is summarized.

TABLE 20.8—Summary of estimates of the median lethal dose for the data of Table 20.2

Method of analysis	ED50 ($\times 10^5$)	Limits ($\times 10^5$)	
		Lower	Upper
Spearman-Kärber . .	6·8	0·98	47·
Extreme effective doses .	5·6	0·42	76·
Reed-Muench . . .	5·6	—	—
Dragstedt-Behrens . .	5·8	—	—
Moving average, span 1 .	3·2	0·13	76·
,, ,, ,, 2 .	3·2	0·13	76·
,, ,, ,, 3 .	5·6	0·43	74·
,, ,, ,, 4 .	6·8	0·59	78·
,, ,, ,, 5 .	6·3	0·60	66·
,, ,, ,, 6 .	5·6	0·65	49·
,, ,, ,, 7 .	6·3	0·85	47·
,, ,, ,, 8 .	6·8	1·00	46·
Probits	7·6	0·91	78·

Armitage and Allen (1950) have made extensive comparisons between different methods of estimation of an ED50 for twelve series of dose-mortality data. Their conclusions on the relative merits of maximum likelihood, minimum χ^2, Spearman-Kärber, Reed-Muench, and moving average estimation are in general agreement with this chapter. In particular, they have emphasized the computational simplicity of the Spearman-Kärber and moving average methods, and have illustrated the close agreement with the results of iterative calculations, but have drawn attention to the advantages of maximum likelihood or minimum χ^2 for discussions of precision, validity, and the properties of the tolerance distribution. They have also discussed the most convenient manner of modifying the Spearman-Kärber, Reed-Muench, and moving average methods in the analysis of data with unequal intervals between successive pairs of doses and unequal numbers of subjects per dose.

20.12   Recommendations on the choice of method

The discussion in §§ 20.6–20.11 may be summarized as follows:—
(i) The extreme effective dose, Reed-Muench, and Dragstedt-Behrens methods ought never to be used. They do not

permit the assessment of precision from the data of a single assay, they give no validity tests, and they are less efficient than alternatives that are equally simple computationally.

(ii) If the experimenter knows nothing about the ED50's for his two preparations before the experiment is performed, he must choose a very wide dose range in order to be sure of bracketing them. He should space his doses fairly closely, but not excessively so (if he can give any meaning to that instruction when he is so ignorant about his materials !). He may use the Spearman-Kärber method. The moving average method, with the largest possible span, is preferable because of its avoidance of flaws at the ends of the dose range, but is likely to give almost the same result after more laborious calculation. The probit (or other equivalent deviate) method may be used ; it will give little or no increase in precision, and will certainly be more laborious, but it will provide the validity tests that the others lack.

(iii) If existing information makes the experimenter fairly sure that each ED50 lies between known limits which are not very far apart (of the order of 4σ, say), his doses should extend over a range rather wider than these limits but not as wide as in (ii). The doses should not be very closely spaced. If enough doses are used, moving average estimation with a span of 3 or greater will be preferable to the Spearman-Kärber method. Whatever the intention at the time of planning the experiment, in the analysis of the results the longest span permitted by the data should be adopted. Probits may be used instead if an unfortunate choice of doses causes the data to be unsuitable for moving average estimation, and again must be used if validity tests are wanted.

(iv) If existing information is more trustworthy, so that both the ED50's and the standard deviation of the tolerance distributions can be guessed before the assay is begun, the design should be planned carefully in accordance with the principles of §§ 19.1, 19.2. The most economic utilization of subjects will almost certainly demand a design to which neither Spearman-Kärber nor moving average estimation can safely be applied, and probits must be used if all available information is to be extracted from the records.

(v) The recommendations in (ii)–(iv) above have assumed that statistical advice is sought by the experimenter at the right time, namely during the planning of an assay. The statistician who is not consulted then, but is later asked to assist in the analysis of data, should of course use the method that appears likely to be most economical and efficient for the assay as actually performed. For example, in the insulin assay for which the data are given in Table 18.1, probably little harm would be done by adoption of a modified moving average or Spearman-Kärber estimation. The neoarsphenamine data in Table 17.3, on the other hand, are obviously quite unsuitable for methods of this type and maximum likelihood estimation (or something like it) must be used.

Considerations of simplicity and computing speed, such as have been in the minds of advocates of the various methods described in §§ 20.6–20.10, are by no means of negligible importance. The methods rejected in (i) are no easier than those accepted in (ii) and are theoretically less satisfactory. Under the conditions of (ii) and (iii), the probit method is very little more efficient than the Spearman-Kärber or the moving average. Under the conditions of (iv), however, to plan the experiment so that either of the others could be used would be too high a price to pay for avoiding probits : a good design and maximum likelihood (or similar) estimation are essential in any economic programme of experimentation (*cf.* § 6.6).

Finney (1953) has made a study of the logistic response curve similar to his earlier one of the normal (1950*b*), and has found very similar results. It is reasonable to conclude that the recommendations above, though based upon a normal curve, will apply with little modification to the logistic and many other similar curves.

The reader is reminded that the methods in §§ 20.6–20.10 have been presented in the form of methods of estimating an ED50. For the estimation of a relative potency and the assessment of the precision of the estimate, they must be used in association with equations (20.5) and (20.6).

CHAPTER 21

SPECIAL PROBLEMS WITH QUANTAL RESPONSES

21.1 Concomitant variation

For an assay based upon quantal responses, the analysis of covariance can be used in order to estimate the allowance that should be made for the effect of a concomitant variate, such as the initial weights of subjects, on tolerances. All sums of squares and products must be weighted with the weights appropriate to the equivalent deviate transformation adopted. The calculations are likely to be lengthy, but should present no special difficulties to those who have mastered the techniques described in Chapters 12 and 18. In most assays, a batch of subjects will be tested at each dose, and the analysis may then be based upon the mean value of the concomitant for each batch rather than upon values for individual subjects.

21.2 The combination of estimates

When several assays of one test preparation have been performed, a single estimate of potency may be wanted. The methods for calculating this are similar to those described in Chapter 14. If g is small for each assay, the simple weighted mean (§ 14.1) may be used (Perry, 1950). If some or all of the values of g are not small, the method of § 14.3 must be adapted ; the chief modification required is that the weight to be attached to each H_i is now

$$\omega_i = \frac{1}{\Sigma\left(\dfrac{1}{Snw}\right)} \, , \qquad (21.1)$$

the Σ relating to summation over the standard and test preparations for the assay.

The calculations will be understood from a study of the example that follows. Gaddum (1933) reported two assays of a test preparation of strophanthus by means of mortality trials with the frog *Rana temporaria*. The assays were both 4-point designs, using

two concentrations of each preparation and having all doses injected
subcutaneously at a rate of 0·02 c.c. per g. body weight of frog
(*cf.* § 2.11).   The data are shown in Table 21.1.   In the first assay,
the dose range was too small, and the doses of the standard preparation too high, so that the results were little use except as suggesting
better doses for the second.

**TABLE 21.1—Data for two assays of a preparation of strophanthus based on
the mortality of *Rana temporaria***

(*a*) Assay 1 (15 subjects per dose)

Standard preparation		Test preparation	
Concentration (c.c. per litre saline)	No. killed	Concentration (c.c. per litre saline)	No. killed
6	11	6	3
7	12	7	6

(*b*) Assay 2 (20 subjects per dose)

Standard preparation		Test preparation	
Concentration (c.c. per litre saline)	No. killed	Concentration (c.c. per litre saline)	No. killed
4	2	6	7
6	16	9	19

A rapid indication that the first assay is useless by itself is given
by forming a contingency table for numbers killed and survived
at low and high doses, the two preparations being grouped together.
This is :—

	Killed	Survived	Total
Low dose . . .	14	16	30
High dose . . .	18	12	30
Total . . .	32	28	60

To test the significance of the deviation from proportionality in this table by the ordinary χ^2 test is not legitimate, because of the heterogeneous origin of the data (two preparations, with very different response rates). Nevertheless, in this instance the data are so close to perfect proportionality as to make clear that the deviation is not significant : the data give little evidence that the mortality rate is increased by increasing the dose, and therefore are of no use for potency estimation. The same conclusion may be reached more laboriously by fitting parallel regression lines to the data of assay 1. The slope is

$$b = 6{\cdot}17 \pm 5{\cdot}22,$$

which obviously does not differ significantly from zero.

Assay 2 can be analysed alone, by the method of § 18.1, in order to give a potency estimate. The details need not be set out here (see Burn *et al.*, 1950, pp. 135-43). Logarithms to base 10 rather than to base 1·5 were used, in order to simplify the subsequent combination with assay 1 which had a different dose interval. A 4-point assay gives no degrees of freedom for a test of linearity or heterogeneity, and therefore

$$S_{yy} - \frac{S_{xy}^2}{S_{xx}} = 0$$

is an arithmetical check for each preparation. For the test of parallelism, equation (18.15) gives

$$\chi^2_{[1]} = 0{\cdot}02,$$

which clearly does not suggest any serious non-parallelism. It must be remembered, however, that 20 subjects at each of four doses is far too small a total for any non-validity but the grossest to be detected, and the present assays should not be regarded as adequate unless the experimenter has considerable prior evidence of validity. The estimate of log potency is

$$M = -\,0{\cdot}1031,$$

with

$$M_L,\ M_U = -\,0{\cdot}1634,\ -\,0{\cdot}0392.$$

Hence

$$R = \text{antilog } \bar{1}{\cdot}8969 = 0{\cdot}789,$$
$$R_L = \text{antilog } \bar{1}{\cdot}8366 = 0{\cdot}686,$$
$$R_U = \text{antilog } \bar{1}{\cdot}9608 = 0{\cdot}914\ ;$$

1 c.c. of the test preparation is estimated to be equivalent to 0·789 c.c. of the standard, with fiducial limits at 0·686 c.c. and 0·914 c.c.

TABLE 21.2—Summary of computations for the strophanthus assays in Table 21.1, with separate regression coefficients

	Assay 1	Assay 2
$G = \bar{x}_T - \bar{x}_S$	0·0060	0·1157
$H = \bar{y}_T - \bar{y}$	— 1·2316	0·1483
b	6·166	11·799
$H - bG$	— 1·269	— 1·217
$\omega = \dfrac{1}{\Sigma\left(\dfrac{1}{Snw}\right)}$	8·232	8·230
ΣS_{xx}	0·03672	0·22029
$V(b)$	27·233	4·539
g	2·75	0·1253

For the combination of the results of the two assays by the method of § 14.3, certain quantities require to be abstracted from the separate calculations ; these, as obtained after two cycles of iteration on each assay, are summarized in Table 21.2. The low value of ΣS_{xt} for the first assay, arising because the doses were closely spaced, means that b for this assay has a large variance and g is greater than unity (as already noted). The two values of ω, the weights to be used in combining the assays, in this instance chance to be almost equal, and no harm would result from taking them as equal ; the exact values will be used, however, in order to illustrate the general procedure. Since

$$\Sigma\omega(H - bG) = - 20·462$$

and

$$\Sigma\omega b = 147·864,$$

equation (14.13) gives

$$\bar{M} = - \frac{20·462}{147·864}$$
$$= - 0·1384,$$

Also, by equations (14.21)–(14.23), with s^2 taken as unity,

$$V\{\Sigma\omega(H - bG)\} = 8\cdot232 + 8\cdot230 + 0\cdot066 + 4\cdot116$$
$$= 20\cdot644,$$
$$V(\Sigma\omega b) = 1{,}845\cdot5 + 307\cdot4$$
$$= 2{,}152\cdot9,$$

and

$$C\{\Sigma\omega(H - bG),\ \Sigma\omega b\} = -11\cdot07 - 35\cdot57$$
$$= -46\cdot64.$$

Hence

$$g = \frac{(1\cdot960)^2 \times 2{,}152\cdot9}{(147\cdot864)^2}$$
$$= 0\cdot3783,$$

a value which may be compared with that of $0\cdot1253$ for Assay 2 alone. The cause of this apparent anomaly is that the weights for forming the most precise mean regression coefficient are the values of ΣS_{xx} for the two assays, and the ratio of these is very different from that of the ω_i ; in consequence, b, defined by

$$b = \frac{\Sigma\omega b}{\Sigma\omega},$$

has a greater variance than has b in Assay 2, and g is increased. In such circumstances, $\bar{M}$ is likely to be a less reliable estimate of $\log \rho$ than is M_2, because the approximations by which equation (21.1) is obtained (cf. § 14.3) as a condition for the minimization of $V(\bar{M})$ are too far from the truth. This is found to be so : application of Fieller's theorem gives

$$\bar{M}_L,\ \bar{M}_U = \left[-0\cdot1384 + \frac{0\cdot6217 \times 46\cdot44}{2{,}152\cdot9} \right.$$
$$\pm \frac{1\cdot960}{147\cdot864}(20\cdot644 - 12\cdot910 + 41\cdot238$$
$$\left. - 0\cdot3783 \times 19\cdot634)^{\frac{1}{2}} \right] \div 0\cdot6217$$
$$= [-0\cdot1384 + 0\cdot0135 \pm 0\cdot0854] \div 0\cdot6217$$
$$= -0\cdot3383,\ -0\cdot0635.$$

The antilogarithms of the several M values give the potency estimate for the test preparation as $0\cdot727$ c.c. of the standard per c.c., with fiducial limits at $0\cdot459$ c.c. and $0\cdot864$ c.c. These are substantially wider than the limits for the second assay alone ; inclusion of the first assay has lowered the reliability !

This paradoxical conclusion is primarily due to the failure to achieve the true minimization of $V(\bar{M})$. For quantitative responses, the variances of H_i will usually be in nearly the same ratio as the variances of b_i, so that the weighting that is optimal for combining one set will be near to optimal for the other. For quantal responses, as the present example illustrates, this need not be true even in assays of exceedingly simple design. The difficulty may be easily overcome if the values of b_i are not too widely discrepant. Thus here the high standard error of b_1 makes clear that, although it is not significantly different from zero, it is also not significantly different from b_2. If the experimenter is prepared to accept the assumption that the frogs for the two assays had equal tolerance variances, he may recompute his analysis with the condition that one value of b shall serve both. The condition of similarity then requires that $(H - bG)$, the vertical distance between the regression lines, shall also be the same for both assays. The iterative estimation of regression lines must therefore be carried out for the two assays

TABLE 21.3—Summary of computations for the strophanthus assays in Table 21.1, constrained to have equal regression coefficients

	Assay 1	Assay 2
$G = \bar{x}_T - \bar{x}_S$	0·0118	0·1329
$H = \bar{y}_T - \bar{y}_S$	− 1·1749	0·3383
b	11·029	
$H - bG$	− 1·305	− 1·127
$\omega = \dfrac{1}{\Sigma\left(\dfrac{1}{Snw}\right)}$	7·960	8·879
ΣS_{xx}	0·28858	
$V(b)$	3·4652	
g	0·1094	

simultaneously, with the additional constraint that in each cycle the four lines are parallel and the vertical distances between pairs, $(Y_T - Y_S)$, are equal. Calculations of this type need not be described in detail ; their results are summarized in Table 21.3 (the apparent difference in the values of $(H - bG)$ would disappear if further cycles were computed).

When b is the same for all the assays to be combined, equation (14.13) may be written

$$\bar{M} = - \frac{\Sigma \omega G}{\Sigma \omega} + \frac{\Sigma \omega H}{b \Sigma \omega}$$

or

$$\bar{M} = - \bar{G} + \frac{\bar{H}}{b} \tag{21.2}$$

$$= - 0 \cdot 0757 - \frac{0 \cdot 3770}{b}$$

$$= - 0 \cdot 0757 - 0 \cdot 0342$$

$$= - 0 \cdot 1099,$$

where

$$\left.\begin{array}{l} \bar{G} = \dfrac{\Sigma \omega G}{\Sigma \omega} \ , \\[3mm] \bar{H} = \dfrac{\Sigma \omega H}{\Sigma \omega} \ . \end{array}\right\} \tag{21.3}$$

The advantage of writing $\bar{M}$ as in equation (21.2) is that b does not enter into the first term, and fiducial limits can be calculated by application of Fieller's theorem to the ratio of $\bar{H}$ and b. Now

$$V(\bar{H}) = 1/\Sigma \omega$$
$$= 0 \cdot 059386,$$
$$V(b) = 1/\Sigma S_{xx}$$
$$= 3 \cdot 4652,$$

and, since each H_i is uncorrelated with b,

$$C\{\bar{H}, b\} = 0.$$

Hence

$$g = \frac{(1 \cdot 960)^2 \times 3 \cdot 4652}{(11 \cdot 029)^2}$$
$$= 0 \cdot 1094,$$

a value smaller than that for Assay 2 alone. The fiducial limits are

$$\bar{M}_L, \bar{M}_U = -0.0757 - \left[0.0342 \pm \frac{1.960}{11.029} \left\{ 0.8906 \times 0.059386 \right. \right.$$
$$\left. \left. + \frac{(0.0342)^2}{0.28858} \right\}^{\frac{1}{2}} \right] \div 0.8906$$
$$= -0.0757 - [0.0342 \pm 0.0424] \div 0.8906$$
$$= -0.1617, -0.0665,$$

an appreciably narrower range than for the second assay alone. The assumption of a common tolerance variance has undoubtedly increased the reliability of the estimated potency ; that assumption, of course, is not in any way justified by the narrower fiducial range, and must rest on other grounds. The several analyses of the data in Table 21.1 are summarized in Table 21.4.

TABLE 21.4—Potency estimates for the strophanthus assays in Table 21.1

	Assay 1	Assay 2	Combined (separate b_1, b_2)	Combined (common b)
R (c.c. per c.c.)	0·623	0·789	0·727	0·776
R_L (c.c. per c.c.)	—	0·686	0·459	0·689
R_U (c.c. per c.c.)	—	0·914	0·864	0·858
R_L as % of R	—	87	63	89
R_U as % of R	—	116	119	111

21.3 Natural response rates

The theory developed in § 17.5 has not been required in its most general form for the types of assay so far discussed ; in all the problems encountered, J and K have been known, so that equations for their estimation were unnecessary. The general formulæ are needed because, in some types of experiment, direct estimation of P for any dose as the ratio of the number of subjects responding and the number tested is impossible.

As already noted, one important instance is that of certain subjects being liable to show the response even at zero dose of the stimulus, others perhaps being incapable of responding however high a dose they receive. For example, if death is the response, some subjects may die during the course of the experiment from causes quite unconnected with the stimulus : in assays of insecticides, insects kept as untreated controls (or perhaps treated only with the non-toxic carrier used for the insecticide) may die between the time of treatment and the time of examination. Again, in assays of fungicides by tests of spore germination, some spores may fail to germinate even when untreated or treated with very low doses, and evidence from very high doses may indicate that others are effectively immune to the fungicide since they germinate however high the dose. Subjects of either of these types can themselves give no information on potency : their reactions are independent of dose. Unfortunately, they cannot be discarded before the assay is begun, because they are indistinguishable from the others. Neither can they be rejected from the results ; the experimenter cannot discover whether a subject that responds does so because of the dose received or would have done so in any case, or whether a subject that fails to respond did not receive a high enough dose or was naturally immune. For some investigations, *post mortem* examinations of the subjects may throw light on these matters, and to reject all subjects shown by such examination to have died from natural causes or to be immune to the stimulus would be quite legitimate, provided that *all* subjects were examined, irrespective of their dose or response. For many subjects, and for most routine assays, this course is impossible, and allowance for the two classes must be made in the statistical analysis.

Suppose that a proportion C_1 of the population of subjects will respond whatever dose is given, a proportion C_2 is immune to the stimulus, and the remaining proportion $(1 - C_1 - C_2)$ behaves according to the tolerance distribution. Then, if $P(= 1 - Q)$ is defined by equation (17.7) as the proportion of subjects in this third section of the population that responds to the dose x of the stimulus, the expected response rate for responses from all sources is

$$P^* = (1 - C_2) - Q(1 - C_1 - C_2). \qquad (21.4)$$

Equation (21.4) involves an assumption that natural response and immunity are entirely independent of the action of the stimulus. In some circumstances this may be absolutely true, in others only an approximation. Experience has shown it to be adequate for many sets of data, and Finney (1949a) has defended its use in the absence of evidence favouring some alternative model of the behaviour of the population. If n subjects receive a dose x, the probability that exactly r respond is

$$P(r) = \binom{n}{r} P^{*^r} Q^{*^{(n-r)}} \tag{21.5}$$

which has the form of equation (17.13) with

$$\left.\begin{array}{l} J = 1 - C_2 \\ K = - (1 - C_1 - C_2) \end{array}\right\} . \tag{21.6}$$

An iterative process for the estimation of the parameters α, β, J, K from data on several doses of one preparation may be set up exactly as described in § 17.5. The weight, equation (17.23), may easily be seen to have the form

$$W = nw = \frac{nZ^2}{\left(P + \dfrac{C_1}{1 - C_1 - C_2} \right) \left(Q + \dfrac{C_2}{1 - C_1 - C_2} \right)} . \tag{21.7}$$

The weighting coefficient, w, could be tabulated as a function of Y, C_1, C_2, though the table would perforce be rather large. As would be expected, any increase in C_1 or C_2 decreases w, since fewer of the subjects tested are really able to give information on the tolerance distribution. The auxiliary variates would most easily be used in the form

$$\lambda_1 = 1/Z, \tag{21.8}$$

$$\lambda_2 = Q/Z, \tag{21.9}$$

the factor $- 1/(1 - C_1 - C_2)$ being introduced at the end ; λ_1 is already familiar as the ' range ' used in forming working equivalent deviates, and λ_2 also is easily tabulated as a function of Y. The working equivalent deviate is unaltered and is still defined by equation (17.24) or equations (18.2)–(18.4). The methods of §§ 17.3–17.5 may be applied to the estimation of the four parameters for a single preparation exactly as there described. In an assay, C_1 and C_2 are the same for both preparations (by virtue of their definitions), and the computational scheme may easily be extended in a manner analogous to that of Chapter 18.

The process will be made clearer by discussion of the most frequently encountered problem of this character, that in which

C_2 is zero and only C_1 has to be considered. If the natural mortality rate be written C, equation (21.4) is equivalent to

$$P = \frac{P^* - C}{1 - C} ; \qquad (21.10)$$

this formula for calculating the response rate attributable to the stimulus from the total response rate is familiar to workers with insecticides under the name of *Abbott's Formula* (Abbott, 1925 ; Finney, 1952, § 26), but its basis is so simple that no special name is necessary. Equations (21.6) reduce to

$$\left.\begin{array}{l} J = 1, \\ K = -(1 - C). \end{array}\right\} \qquad (21.11)$$

Thus J is specified by the conditions of the problem, and only three equations of estimation are needed. The weighting coefficient, by equation (21.7), is now

$$w = \frac{Z^2}{Q\left\{\dfrac{1}{1 - C} - Q\right\}} . \qquad (21.12$$

For the normal tolerance distribution, Finney (1952, Appendix Table II) has tabulated w as a function of Y and C, with $Y = 1\cdot1(0\cdot1)9\cdot0$, $C = 0\cdot00(0\cdot01)0\cdot90$; Fisher and Yates (1963, Table XI$_1$) give a similar but less detailed table. Unless C is very small, w may be considerably less than its value for $C = 0$ (especially when P is small), and the values of w are no longer symmetrical about $Y = 5\cdot0$. Tables for other tolerance distributions have not been prepared.

Direct estimation of C, rather than of $(1 - C)$ is convenient, and is secured by defining the auxiliary variate as

$$\lambda = Q/Z ; \qquad (21.13)$$

this also has been tabulated for the normal tolerance distribution (Finney, 1952, Appendix Table II ; Fisher and Yates, 1963, Table XI$_1$). With the aid of a first approximation from which Y, λ, w, and y are determined, the iteration proceeds by calculation of the regression of y on x and λ :

$$\left.\begin{array}{l} bS_{xx} + \dfrac{\delta C}{1 - C} S_{x\lambda} = S_{xy}, \\[2mm] bS_{x\lambda} + \dfrac{\delta C}{1 - C} S_{\lambda\lambda} = S_{\lambda y}, \end{array}\right\} \qquad (21.14)$$

and

$$a = \bar{y} - b\bar{x}\,\frac{\delta C}{1-C}\,\bar{\lambda}, \qquad (21.15)$$

are the appropriate versions of equations (17.26) and (17.25), giving new values of a, b, C with which to continue the iteration. Though not essential to the validity of the method or to the statistical calculations, a control batch of subjects giving a direct estimate of C will often be used, and may give most of the information on C. If n_c subjects are untreated controls (for which $x \longrightarrow -\infty$), and r_c of them respond,

$$c = r_c/n_c \qquad (21.16)$$

is an estimate of C from them alone ; this will be a good guide to the first approximation with which to initiate the iteration. Even without this, however, the evidence from low doses may be used to give a provisional value for C. In accordance with the general instructions of § 17.5, if C is the natural mortality rate on which any cycle of iteration is based,

$$\frac{n_o(1-C)}{C} \qquad (21.17)$$

must be added to $S_{\lambda\lambda}$. Moreover, the empirical response rates, as defined by equation (17.20), are given by

$$q = \frac{q^*}{1-C}, \qquad (21.18)$$

where

$$p^* = 1 - q^* = 1 - \frac{r}{n} \qquad (21.19)$$

is the observed total response rate at a dose. Substitution of c for p^* in equation (21.18) gives $(1-c)/(1-C)$ as the ' empirical response rate ' for the controls, and therefore

$$\frac{n_c(c-C)}{C} \qquad (21.20)$$

must be added to $S_{\lambda y}$. In the formation of χ^2 for a test of homogeneity, S_{yy} must be increased by the contribution

$$\frac{n_c(c-C)^2}{C(1-C)}$$

from the controls.

In any cycle of the iteration, C may happen to be greater than c or than some of the p^* ; the corresponding empirical response rate, p, is then negative. This is purely an accident of sampling, and in itself no cause for alarm. The corresponding expected rates, P, are by definition positive, and application of the formulæ for working probits without modification will enable the results for these doses to exert their proper influence in the calculations.

Examples of these calculations for a single preparation, and of the simple extension required when two parallel lines have to be fitted to the data for two preparations, in order that one may be assayed against the other, have been given elsewhere (Finney, 1944a ; 1949a, b ; 1952, § 28). The method does not seem to be often needed for assay purposes, and no numerical example is included here. Both for a fuller explanation of the computations and for the tables of w and λ in a normal tolerance distribution, the reader is referred to *Probit Analysis* (Finney, 1952).

21.4 Assays with unknown numbers of subjects tested

Assays are sometimes encountered in which a quantal response is used but determination of the number of subjects tested at each dose is either impossible or impracticable. For example, in assaying a bactericide, counts of bacteria surviving treatment may be made by plating or some similar technique, but no count of the total number exposed to treatment can be made. Again, in the assay of materials for the control of immature stages of fruit flies, the numbers of flies developing and emerging from treated samples of fruit can easily be counted ; the total number of individuals treated, however, could be discovered only by dissection of the fruit and laborious counting of those that had been killed. For this second type of experiment, a natural procedure is to take parallel samples of untreated fruit, and to ascertain the numbers of flies emerging from them. If these samples are of the standard size, an estimate is thereby given of the numbers that would have emerged from the treated samples but for the insecticide. In some respects, the estimate so obtained is more useful than a direct count, since it automatically excludes natural mortality, leaving a value truly comparable with the numbers emerging from treated samples. Response rates calculated from these parallel samples must not be analysed by the methods of Chapter 18, however, for the denominator of equation (18.1) is now only an estimate of the number of subjects treated. Wadley (1949a) first discussed the statistical analysis of this kind of experiment and the maximum likelihood estimation of the parameters ; Finney (1949b) modified Wadley's method, and showed that it came within the general theory developed in § 17.5. The method proposed by Wadley and Finney requires that the subjects are initially distributed entirely at random within the bulk from which samples are to be drawn. The number of subjects in a randomly selected sample of specified size (such as a fixed volume of a bacterial suspension) will then follow a Poisson distribution : if the mean number of subjects per sample is v, the probability that exactly n occur in a particular sample is

$$\frac{e^{-v} v^n}{n!} \tag{21.21}$$

Suppose now that a particular sample receives a dose sufficient to cause response in a proportion of P of all subjects. The experiment under discussion is of a type that permits only one of the two classes, response and non-response, to be observed. Whether this class is named ' response ' or ' non-response ' is entirely a matter of convention*, but in applications the observable class is usually the one that is most naturally described as ' non-response ' (e.g. survival). The argument that follows is therefore given in terms of non-responding subjects.

The probability that exactly s non-responses occur in the sample is the probability that the sample contained exactly n subjects, multiplied by the probability that s out of n survive, and summed for all possible values of n. This probability may be written

$$P(s) = \sum_{n=s}^{\infty} e^{-v} \left\{ \frac{v^n}{n!} \binom{n}{s} P^{n-s} Q^s \right\}$$

$$= \frac{e^{-vQ} (vQ)^s}{s!} . \tag{21.22}$$

Thus s has a Poisson distribution with mean vQ. Now the theory that follows from equation (17.13) could equally well have been developed from the probability of s non-responses. Hence equation

---

* The assay in § 18.2 would have given exactly the same conclusions if non-occurrence of convulsions had been regarded as the response.

(21.22) shows the general theory of § 17.5 to be applicable to the present problem with

$$J = 0, \\ K = \nu.$$ \hfill (21.23)

The computations required for estimating the parameters a, β, ν from data on several doses of a single preparation are in some respects similar to those described in § 21.3. If the same size of sample is used at each dose, the weight to be attached to the equivalent deviate for that dose is

$$W = \nu w,$$ \hfill (21.24)

where the weighting coefficient is

$$w = Z^2/Q.$$ \hfill (21.25)

If the sample sizes vary, W must be increased in proportion to the size of the particular sample. An auxiliary variate

$$\lambda = - Q/Z$$ \hfill (21.26)

is defined. From a provisional set of estimates of the parameters, numerical values of the weight, auxiliary variate, and working equivalent deviate are formed, the last by any of equations (17.24), (18.2)–(18.4) ; equation (17.20) shows the empirical response rate to be

$$p = 1 - q = \frac{\nu - s}{\nu},$$ \hfill (21.27)

and so to accord with the suggestions of common sense. The weighted regression of y on x, λ is then calculated, equations (17.26) and (17.25) taking the form

$$bS_{xx} + \frac{\delta\nu}{\nu} S_{x\lambda} = S_{xy}, \\ bS_{x\lambda} + \frac{\delta\nu}{\nu} S_{\lambda\lambda} = S_{\lambda y},$$ \hfill (21.28)

and

$$a = \bar{y} - b\bar{x} - \frac{\delta\nu}{\nu}\bar{\lambda}.$$ \hfill (21.29)

Iteration continues in the usual manner, and the extension to assay calculations with two parallel lines is easily made.

The existence of control batches of untreated subjects is not essential to the calculations, though usually the greatest part of the information on ν will come from them. Without these, a value of ν may be guessed by inspection of results for low doses, but the estimates of the parameters may be of low precision because of inadequate information on ν. If a sample of the standard size is untreated and shows s_c non-responses, this is a direct estimate of ν ; in the formation of equations (21.28), for each cycle of iteration, $S_{\lambda\lambda}$ must be increased by the provisional value of ν and $S_{\lambda y}$ by $(s_c - \nu)$. In the formation of a χ^2 for heterogeneity, S_{yy} must be increased by $(s_c - \nu)^2/\nu$. If several samples are untreated, each gives its contribution to $S_{\lambda\lambda}$, $S_{\lambda y}$, and S_{yy}.

Sampling variation in the true numbers of individuals tested at different doses may cause values of s for some low doses to exceed ν ; the empirical response rate, according to equation (21.27), is then negative. The data for these doses will play their proper part in increasing the estimate of ν if the calculations are performed exactly as described here, using a negative p in the formation of the working equivalent deviate. Although the method of calculation has a close resemblance to multiple regression methods, it is in reality a method of solving the complicated non-linear maximum likelihood equations : the anomaly of p being negative is an indication that the analogy is imperfect, not a condemnation of the method.

No restriction has yet been placed upon the form of the tolerance distribution. Wadley's original discussion related to the normal tolerance distribution, for which probits are used as the equivalent deviates ; Finney (1949b) generalized this along the lines of Chapter 17. For the normal tolerance distribution, a table of w having $Y = 1 \cdot 1(0 \cdot 1)9 \cdot 0$ has been published (Finney, 1952, Table VIII), and λ is the same as in equation (21.13) except for the reversal of sign. Tables for other distributions have not been prepared. Finney (1949b) has given a numerical example for a single preparation ; no example need be shown here, as the problem is not one that often arises. The method is so similar to that of § 21.3 that familiarity with one is a great aid to use of the other.

The condition that the distribution of n between samples should be that of (21.21) ought to apply to a well-stirred suspension of micro-organisms, but may be far from correct as a representation of an insect population in fruit. Anscombe (1949) has suggested that a negative binomial distribution might be nearer to the truth for the latter type of investigation. This also has the property that the numbers of survivors at any one dose will follow the same type of distribution with modified parameters ; unfortunately, however, two parameters replace v, and the weighting coefficient is a function of both. Anscombe has indicated a change in experimental design that might help to overcome this difficulty, but no complete scheme of statistical analysis has yet been put forward.

21.5 Dilution series

One more type of estimation based on quantal responses will be discussed. This is generally regarded as a method for population estimation by sampling, rather than as an assay, but, since the estimation depends upon a growth reaction manifested by living matter, it can justifiably be classed as a biological assay. Moreover, its consideration here is instructive because of its relationship to the general equivalent deviate method of Chapter 17. A further point of interest is that no standard preparation is used, and the potency is assessed in absolute units from the behaviour of the test preparation alone.

If the density of a bacterial suspension, in terms of the number of bacteria per unit volume, is to be estimated, the obvious procedure to adopt is to incubate samples of the suspension (or of a dilution by a known factor) and to count the number of colonies that form. On the assumption that each colony has developed from one bacterium, the mean number of colonies per sample can be used to provide the estimate required. Colony counting, however, is laborious and may be impracticable if the number of colonies in a sample is large. An alternative that has often been adopted, because of the simplicity with which each observation can be made, is to record only the presence or absence of bacterial growth, and to use this record as equivalent to a statement of whether a sample is fertile or sterile. No attempt is made to count the number of colonies in a fertile sample : the data are therefore quantal. Although the information on bacterial density obtained from a particular set of samples will be less than if accurate colony counts were made, it will be preferable to the uncertain indications of inaccurate counts ; moreover, the loss may be compensated by the possibility of using a far greater number of samples.

Whereas colony counts are readily interpretable as estimators of bacterial density, the quantal classification of samples must be followed by application of some statistical theory before it yields an estimate of density. Two conditions must be fulfilled if the procedure is to be valid :—

(i) The organisms must be distributed entirely at random in the bulk suspension from which small samples are to be removed, so that the distribution of numbers of organisms in replicate samples will be Poissonian, formula (21.21).

(ii) The nature of the culture medium and incubation must be such as to ensure that visible growth will occur in every sample containing one or more organisms.

The first condition is required in both procedures, and implies that the suspension be thoroughly mixed so as to ensure that organisms neither cluster nor repel one another. The second is less stringent than is required for colony counts, for there every organism must be certain to develop into a visible and separately identifiable colony.

For convenience of notation, the unit of volume may be taken as the volume of suspension used in each sample. With this convention, suppose that the original, undiluted, suspension has μ organisms per unit volume. Any dilution may be represented by a ' dose ' variate z, such that the density in the dilution is μz per unit volume ; usually z will be less than unity, but values greater than unity (corresponding to concentrations of the original suspension) can be treated by the same theory. The number of organisms per sample in samples of unit volume from the dilution z will therefore follow a Poisson distribution with mean μz. If colonies are counted on n samples from this dilution, and have a mean value $\bar{y}$, the estimate of μ will be taken as

$$m = \frac{\bar{y}}{z}. \tag{21.30}$$

From the properties of a Poisson distribution,

$$V(\bar{y}) = \frac{\mu z}{n}, \tag{21.31}$$

and therefore

$$V(m) = \frac{\mu}{nz}, \tag{21.32}$$

a quantity which would be estimated from the data by

$$V(m) = \frac{\bar{y}}{nz^2}.$$ (21.33)

Now the probability that a sample is sterile is the probability that it contains no organisms ; this is the first term of the Poisson distribution

$$P = e^{-\mu z}.$$ (21.34)

If an estimate were to be formed from a fertile-sterile classification alone, and if r of the n samples were sterile, the estimate would naturally be taken as m, the solution of the equation

$$e^{-mz} = p,$$ (21.35)

where

$$p = \frac{r}{n}$$ (21.36)

is an estimate of P from the data. Hence for this form of estimation

$$m = -\frac{\log p}{z}.$$ (21.37)

Since

$$V(p) = \frac{PQ}{n},$$

it is easily proved that, to a first order approximation,

$$V(m) = \frac{Q}{nPz^2}.$$ (21.38)

The utility of this formula is limited ; when P or n is small, the sampling distribution of r is far from normal, and the formula will not indicate limits of error for m satisfactorily. Still more open to criticism is the variance calculated from the data,

$$V(m) = \frac{n-r}{nrz^2}.$$ (21.39)

Nevertheless, comparison of equations (21.32) and (21.38) is interesting as indicating the efficiency of the quantal method by comparison with that of colony counting. This efficiency is the inverse ratio of the two variances :

$$\text{Eff.} = \frac{\mu z P}{Q}$$

$$= \frac{\mu z}{e^{\mu z} - 1}.$$ (21.40)

When the density is high, the loss of information consequent upon making only quantal records is large, and the efficiency of the quantal method is low ; when the density is low, the number of organisms per sample will be nearly always 0 or 1, and the quantal method will be of relatively high efficiency because it distinguishes between these two types almost as satisfactorily as would colony counts.

The expression for $V(m)$ in equation (21.38) is a minimum when $P \doteqdot 0.203$, and therefore when $\mu z \doteqdot 1.59$. Thus the ideal dilution to take in order that the quantal method. shall give as much information as possible on μ is one that has about 1.59 organisms per unit volume. Provided that the number of organisms can be kept between 1 and 2.5 per unit volume, the loss through

TABLE 21.5—Efficiency of fertile-sterile classification of samples for the estimation of the density of a bacterial suspension

Density of organisms per sample μz	Probability of sterile sample, P	Efficiency relative to optimal μz	Efficiency relative to colony counts at this density
16	0·000 000 113	0·000	0·000
8	0·000 335	0·033	0·003
4	0·018 3	0·461	0·075
2	0·135	0·967	0·313
1·5936	0·203	1·000	0·406
1	0·368	0·899	0·582
1/2	0·607	0·595	0·771
1/4	0·779	0·340	0·880
1/8	0·882	0·181	0·939
1/16	0·939	0·094	0·969
1/32	0·969	0·047	0·984
1/64	0·984	0·024	0·992
1/128	0·992	0·012	0·996
1/256	0·996	0·006	0·998

failing to attain optimal conditions is at worst about 10 per cent. : the experimenter ought to use any knowledge he may have about the value of μ in order to select a dilution that will give

$$1\cdot0 < \mu z < 2\cdot5. \tag{21.41}$$

The variance of the estimate of μ in direct colony counting, equation (21.32), decreases steadily as z increases. Table 21.5 shows the efficiency of the quantal method for various densities in the sample, reckoned relative to the optimal conditions with $\mu z = 1\cdot5936$ and also relative to colony counts on the same samples ; the first is obtained from equation (21.38), the second from equation (21.40).

The discussion so far has related to counts or tests made at one dilution only. If the experimenter has initially no idea what the density of organisms is, he will try samples at several dilutions. The impossibility of making satisfactory counts when the density in a sample is high will force him to do this even if he adopts the colony count method ; the same policy is desirable for the quantal method in order to ensure that some dilutions have between 4 and 1/4 organisms per sample and so can give a reasonable amount of information on μ. The problem of combining information from different dilutions then arises.

Suppose that n_i samples (of unit volume) are taken at a dilution z_i, and that $\bar{y}_i$ is the mean colony count in these samples. Then

$$m = \frac{Sn_i\bar{y}_i}{Sn_iz_i}, \tag{21.42}$$

where S, as usual, represents summation over the various doses, will be taken as the estimate of μ ; this is a generalization of equation (21.30), and is appropriate because $Sn_i\bar{y}_i$ is a Poisson variate with mean μSn_iz_i. Moreover

$$V(m) = \frac{\mu}{Sn_iz_i}. \tag{21.43}$$

Equation (21.42) is easily verified to be the maximum likelihood estimation of μ.

What is to be done if only quantal records of fertility and sterility are available ? The probability of finding r sterile plates at dilution z is

$$P(r) = \binom{n}{r} P^r Q^{n-r}, \tag{21.44}$$

where P is as defined by equation (21.34). If now Y is defined by

$$P = e^{-Y}, \qquad (21.45)$$

or

$$Y = -\log_e P, \qquad (21.46)$$

it is clear that

$$Y = \mu z. \qquad (21.47)$$

The likeness of equations (21.44), (21.45), and (21.47) to equations (17.11), (17.8), and (17.9) respectively suggests that the maximum likelihood estimate of μ may be obtained by an iterative process using an 'equivalent deviate transformation' defined by equation (21.46). Indeed, the formulæ are the same as would be given by application of the methods of Chapter 17 to the tolerance distribution

$$\mu e^{-\mu z}\, dz \qquad (z \geqslant 0,\ \mu > 0); \qquad (21.48)$$

here the tolerance distribution has no real meaning, but the general maximum likelihood theory will still apply. Only one parameter, μ, has to be estimated, and this is the slope of a regression (of equivalent deviate on z) constrained to pass through $z = 0$, $Y = 0$.

A response is now formally the occurrence of a sterile plate. At each dose, p_i is defined by equation (21.36), equation (21.46) gives the empirical equivalent deviate, and the working equivalent deviate is obtained from equation (17.24) as

$$y = Y + 1 - pe^Y. \qquad (21.49)$$

Equation (17.31) gives the weighting coefficient

$$w = \frac{1}{e^Y - 1}. \qquad (21.50)$$

The weighted regression coefficient of y on z, with the constraint that the regression line passes through the origin, is then m, the estimate of μ. This is

$$m = \frac{Snwzy}{Snwz^2}. \qquad (21.51)$$

For iterative calculation, a provisional value of m is guessed, and used in equation (21.47) to give the expected equivalent deviate for each dilution ; a revised approximation then follows from equations (21.49)–(21.51). If only one dilution is used, equation (21.51) is easily seen to reduce to equation (21.37), since the provisional

Y will naturally be taken to be $- \log_e P$, thus showing that equation (21.37) gives the maximum likelihood estimate.

The problem of estimating μ from this type of quantal experiment has long interested bacteriologists and statisticians. Halvorson and Ziegler (1933 a, b) first gave the maximum likelihood equation in a form suitable for calculation, though Fisher (1922) had indicated the method earlier ; McCrady (1915) had proposed essentially the same estimation process under the title of estimation of the *most probable number*, and other bacteriologists had followed him in this. Cochran (1950) has published a useful account of the relationship between the two approaches. Eisenhart and Wilson (1943) have surveyed the history of the problem very fully. Various authors, including Halvorson and Ziegler (1933a, b) and Swaroop (1938 ; 1940 ; 1941a, b), have given tables from which the maximum likelihood estimate can be read directly for certain assay designs (i.e. particular sets of dilutions and numbers of samples), and have discussed the precision of the estimate. Barkworth and Irwin (1938) showed how an iterative scheme for solving the maximum likelihood equation could be set up whatever the arrangement of dilutions and numbers of samples. Ziegler and Halvorson (1935) made an interesting experimental comparison between the precisions obtained in estimation by colony counting and by dilution series for the same suspensions ; their findings were in general agreement with theory.

Finney (1947a) developed the equivalent deviate method of solving the maximum likelihood equation, in the manner shown above, and suggested a further simplification. If a fairly long series of dilutions has been used, both y and w, as defined by equations (21.49) and (21.50) will range from very small to very large values, one being small when the other is large. This makes the computations awkward, especially in respect of the retention of a proper number of digits at each stage. Finney's suggestion was that the response metameter be re-defined as

$$Y = -\frac{1}{z} \log_e P. \tag{21.52}$$

The estimate of μ is then obtained as a weighted mean, instead of as a regression coefficient. A closely related plan of computation has been proposed by Peto (1953). However, the sampling distribution of the estimate is likely to be far from normal. This and other difficulties can be overcome by estimating log μ instead of μ, to which end a transformation proposed by Mather (1949) for a slightly different purpose may be adapted (Finney, 1951c).

Define a new response metameter, the *loglog*, by

$$Y = \log_e (- \log_e P), \qquad (21.53)$$

and a dose metameter

$$x = \log_e z. \qquad (21.54)$$

Then equation (21.34) may be written

$$Y = \log_e \mu + x. \qquad (21.55)$$

The estimation of $\log_e \mu$ may be put into the form of calculating a weighted regression of a working loglog on x, subject to the condition that the regression coefficient is unity. Because of this constancy of the regression coefficient, the arithmetic is made easier by arranging that each iterative cycle gives an adjustment to equation (21.55) instead of a new version of the equation. The general method of § 17.5 leads to a working loglog

$$y = Y + \frac{p - P}{P \log_e P},$$

but the recommended alternative is to use a working deviate

$$\eta = \frac{P - p}{P \log_e P}. \qquad (21.56)$$

If minimum and maximum working deviates corresponding to any expected loglog are defined by

$$\eta_0 = - e^{-Y}, \qquad (21.57)$$

$$\eta_1 = e^{(e^Y - Y)} - e^{-Y}, \qquad (21.58)$$

and the range is

$$A = e^{(e^Y - Y)}, \qquad (21.59)$$

then the working deviate may be found from any one of equations (18.2)–(18.4) with η, η_0, η_1 replacing y, Y_0, Y_1; thus

$$\eta = \eta_0 + p\, A, \qquad (21.60)$$

$$\eta = \eta_1 - q\, A, \qquad (21.61)$$

$$\boldsymbol{\eta} = q\eta_0 + p\, \eta_1. \qquad (21.62)$$

The weighting coefficient is now

$$w = \frac{e^{2Y}}{e^{e^Y} - 1}.$$

(21.63)

The iterative procedure follows a very simple pattern. A value of μ is guessed, and equation (21.55) is used to determine expected loglogs at each dilution. Equations (21.60)–(21.63) give the working deviate and the weight, nw, for each dilution, and a weighted mean of the working deviates is calculated

$$\bar{\eta} = \frac{Snw\eta}{Snw}.$$

(21.64)

This $\bar{\eta}$ is *subtracted from* the provisional estimate of $\log_e\mu$, to give a revised estimate with which the iteration may be repeated. When satisfactory approximation to the maximum likelihood solution has been attained,

$$\chi^2 = Snw\eta^2 - \frac{(Snw\eta)^2}{Snw}$$

(21.65)

is a homogeneity test for the data, equivalent to a χ^2 test on observed and expected numbers of fertile and sterile plates for each dilution ; of course, the usual troubles arise with small frequencies, and in cases of doubt appeal must be made to calculations based on equation (17.33). For data that are satisfactorily homogeneous, if $\log_e m$ is the final estimate,

$$V(\log_e m) = 1/Snw$$

(21.66)

and fiducial limits to m may be obtained by first assigning fiducial limits to $\log_e m$.

This process may sound complicated, but, with the aid of tables (Mather, 1949 ; Finney, 1951c), it is completed much more rapidly than are probit computations. Appendix Table XVI gives the loglog transformation, and is used for finding the empirical loglogs. Appendix Table XVII gives the minimum and maximum working deviates, range, and weighting coefficient as functions of the expected loglog. A table of natural logarithms, such as Fisher and Yates's Table XXVI, is also helpful, but logarithms to base 10 can always be used instead, by the rule

$$\log_e \theta = 2{\cdot}3026 \; \log_{10}\theta.$$

(21.67)

An example will make this clearer. Fisher and Yates (1963) report tests of a potato flour for the estimation of the density of spores of 'rope' (*Bacillus mesentericus*). Five samples, each of 1 c.c., were withdrawn from each of ten dilutions of a suspension of the flour, each sample was plated, and the number of sterile plates was recorded. The results are shown in Table 21.6. The empirical loglogs of each p are entered in the table ; their indication that the expected loglog is zero at or about a dilution of 1/8 g. per 100 c.c. may be used as the basis of a first cycle. Successive dilutions differ by a factor of 2, and, using $\log_e 2 = 0.69$, the Y column in Table 21.6 is easily constructed from equation (21.55).

TABLE 21.6—Estimation of the density of rope spores in a potato flour. from a dilution series

Dilution (z) in g. per 100 c.c.	n	r	p	Empirical loglog	Y	w	η
4	5	0	0·0	—	3·5	0·000	− 0·03
2	5	0	0·0	—	2·8	0·000	− 0·06
1	5	0	0·0	—	2·1	0·019	− 0·12
1/2	5	0	0·0	—	1·4	0·290	− 0·25
1/4	5	1	0·2	0·48	0·7	0·625	0·25
1/8	5	2	0·4	− 0·09	0·0	0·582	0·09
1/16	5	3	0·6	− 0·67	− 0·7	0·383	− 0·03
1/32	5	3	0·6	− 0·67	− 1·4	0·217	− 0·94
1/64	5	5	1·0	—	− 2·1	0·115	1·06
1/128	5	5	1·0	--	− 2·8	0·059	1·03

The values of w for each Y are read directly from Table XVII ; for the computations they need not be multiplied by n, since in this assay n is the same for all dilutions. The working deviates are found from Table XVII by any one of equations (21.60)–(21.62). Summations give

$$Sw = 2.290,$$
$$Sw\eta = 0.1010,$$

and therefore
$$\bar{\eta} = 0.1010/2.290$$
$$= 0.0441.$$
The expected loglogs were constructed from the guess that the density was such as to give $Y = 0$ at $z = 1/8$; $\bar{\eta}$ must now be subtracted from this value of Y and a new column of expected loglogs based upon this. No new cycle of computation is needed, as the values of Y are scarcely altered (see Finney, 1951c, for the results of a second cycle). Equation (21.65) gives
$$\chi^2 = 5 \times \left\{ 0.446 - \frac{(0.1010)^2}{2.290} \right\}$$
$$= 2.21,$$
which might be regarded as having 7 degrees of freedom, since only eight dilutions had non-zero weights and one parameter has been estimated. Here the test is practically worthless, however, because the numbers of samples are so small ; if inferences are to be drawn from data of this kind, in which the test of validity will be insensitive to all but the grossest discrepancies, the *a priori* evidence for validity of the mathematical model must be strong. If the expected frequencies are small only in some classes, expected values of r may be calculated as
$$E(r) = ne^{-e^Y} \tag{21.68}$$
and equation (17.33) applied after the pooling of classes.

If the present analysis be accepted as valid,
$$V(\bar{\eta}) = \frac{1}{5 \times 2.290}$$
$$= 0.08734,$$
and therefore a standard error of 0.296 may be attached to $\bar{\eta}$. Multiplication by 1.960 gives the fiducial interval on either side of $\bar{\eta}$, so that the limits are $- 0.536, 0.624$. These and $\bar{\eta}$ itself are in natural logarithms (base e), and equation (21.67) may be used to express them in common logarithms. Subtraction from 0.0 (the trial value for the computed cycle) gives the estimated log density and its fiducial limits at $z = 1/8$. Hence, in terms of the number of organisms per gram,
$$m = 800 \text{ antilog } \bar{1}.981 = 766,$$
$$m_L = 800 \text{ antilog } \bar{1}.729 = 429,$$
$$m_U = 800 \text{ antilog } 0.233 = 1,370 ;$$

the density is estimated to be 766 spores per gram, and is almost certain to be between 429 and 1,370 spores per gram.

When very little is known in advance about the value of μ, a common practice is to test n plates at each of a long series of dilutions ; n is kept constant, the dilutions are arranged in geometrical progression (successive dilution factors of 2, 4, or 10 are the favourites), and the series is made long enough to be almost certain to have P very small at one end, very large at the other. For such an experiment, Fisher (1922) suggested an ingenious method of estimation that bears some resemblance to the Spearman-Kärber method (§ 20.6). The estimate is based on the total number of sterile plates, T, where
$$T = S(r). \tag{21.69}$$
The expected value of T, by equation (21.34), is
$$E(T) = n(e^{-\mu z_0} + e^{-\mu z_0/a} + e^{-\mu z_0/a^2 +} \dots), \tag{21.70}$$
where z_0 is the first dilution tested and a is the dilution factor. Fisher's method involves taking as the estimate of μ that value which satisfies
$$E(T) = T. \tag{21.71}$$
He proved his method to be 87·7 per cent. efficient, in the sense that when n is large the method of maximum likelihood would give an estimate whose variance was 87·7 per cent. of that for the estimate obtained by solving equation (21.71). Fisher and Yates (1963, Table VIII$_2$) have given a table that enables equation (21.71) to be solved very easily and allows limits of error to be assigned to the estimate. The existing table applies only when $a = 2$, 4, or 10, but could be extended to include other dilution factors*. For the data in Table 21.6, Fisher and Yates obtained an estimate of 760 spores per gram, with limits at 407 and 1,440 spores per gram. This range is 10 per cent. wider than for the maximum likelihood estimate.

The Fisher method of estimation is undoubtedly easier and quicker for data to which it is applicable. It involves a sacrifice of 12 per cent. of the information provided by a set of data, but, for

---

* As for the Spearman-Kärber method, and various other methods of estimation discussed in Chapter 20, the variance of Fisher's estimate contains a component, independent of n, representing the effect of the location of the set of doses used. Unless n is very large, or a at least 10, this component is negligible (Cochran, 1950a).

an experiment so simple in execution, compensation by testing a larger number of samples may be a more economic procedure than use of maximum likelihood estimation. The Fisher method applied to data from an experiment with eight samples at each dilution would have the same precision as maximum likelihood with seven samples at each dilution, and the experimenter may legitimately choose whichever of the two courses seems to him the simpler.

Like the Spearman-Kärber method for an ED50, however, the Fisher method of estimating μ lacks flexibility, and in circumstances where the experimenter has moderately good advance information on μ it compels an uneconomic experimental design. It is valid only when the range of dilutions extends from one extreme of P to the other.

Fisher proposed his method only for the type of experiment in which a long series of dilutions has been tested ; the theoretical requirement of an infinite series extending from $P = 0$ to $P = 1$ may be interpreted practically as a series giving 10 or more organisms per sample at one end, 0·01 or less per sample at the other*. The existence of tables that enable equation (21.71) to be solved rapidly, however, may tempt experimenters either to design their experiments so as to have an economically undesirable range of dilutions or even to use the tables when $S(r)$ is only a summation over a short series of dilutions (in which event, the tables will not yield the true solution of the equation). Such misuse of the method is obviously as strongly opposed to the intentions of its originator, who was himself responsible for developing the general maximum likelihood theory from which the loglog method is derived, as it is to the recommendations of this section. To refer to the method of estimation expressed by equation (21.71) as the 'Fisher method' is convenient, but is in no sense intended to imply that Fisher regarded it as suitable or desirable for every use of dilution series. At extreme dilutions, the weighting coefficient for the loglog method is very small by comparison with its maximum at 1·59 organisms per sample. Thus, in an experiment to which the Fisher method can be applied, many samples will be contributing little direct information for the estimate, but are included to ensure the validity of the method by adequate coverage of the range. Moreover, that method requires the dilutions to be spaced

---

* On this basis, the dilutions in the experiment of Table 21.4 scarcely go low enough, and two more steps ought to have been included.

regularly in a geometrical progression and the number of samples per dilution to be constant, or rather the method becomes much more troublesome to operate if these restrictions are relaxed. These may often be desirable features of an assay for estimating the density of organisms, but special circumstances or accidents may sometimes intervene ; the loglog method, or any other variant of maximum likelihood estimation, has the advantage that it then presents no new difficulties.

When the experimenter has moderately good advance information on μ, he should certainly not adopt a wide range of dilutions merely in order that he may be able to estimate his density by a table of the solutions of equation (21.71). If N, the total number of samples to be used, is fixed, the ideal allocation of these would be to use all at the dilution giving 1·59 organisms per sample. Obviously there can be no certainty of achieving this, but any prior knowledge of μ should be used in order to approximate to it. Several dilutions will have to be tested as an insurance against a bad guess, but not necessarily as many as would be needed if estimation by equation (21.71) were intended ; values of the number of organisms per sample greater than 4·0 or less than 0·25 should be avoided, if possible, in order to avoid very small weighting coefficients. For example, in the experiment recorded in Table 21.6, if the experimenter had guessed in advance that the density was about 1,000 spores per gram, he might have restricted attention to dilutions of 1/2, 1/4, 1/8, 1/16, 1/32 g. per 100 c.c. Had he then assigned 10 plates to each of these, so keeping his total at 50, the value of Snw would have been increased from 11·45 to 20·97 ; had he been still more confident in his guess and assigned his plates as 5, 10, 20, 10, 5 to the five dilutions, Snw would have been 24·26. These represent great improvements over the design actually used, and relative to them the design of Table 21·6 with estimation according to equation (21.71) is only 48 per cent. or 41 per cent. efficient. The convenience of the estimation based on T alone, and its high efficiency for data to which it is applicable, must not blind the experimenter to the fact that more useful experimental designs may be available.

If μ can be approximately located in advance, economy is likely to be achieved by concentration of effort in the neighbourhood of 1·6 organisms per sample and use of the loglog estimation process ; the additional time required for computation may then be compensated by a reduction in the number of samples needed. This is yet one more example of the truth that the choice of a satisfactory experimental design depends upon the pre-existing knowledge of the question under investigation. If this knowledge is unreliable, and the experimenter fails to admit its unreliability, the experiment may be bad. In the rope spore assay, for example, if the spore density had been guessed as 100 per gram when in fact it was 766 per gram, the experiment might have been designed to have 10 plates at each of the dilutions 4, 2, 1, 1/2, 1/4, g. per 100 c.c. ; Snw would have been 9·34, and the estimate by maximum likelihood would have been less precise than by the use of Fisher's method on the original design. A guess of 10 spores per gram might have had disastrous consequences, unless the experimenter had realized that it was untrustworthy, and had therefore adopted a wide range of dilutions.

In planning an assay of a density of organisms, the experimenter ought first to decide limits between which he is practically certain that his true density lies. If these limits are μ_L and μ_U per unit volume $(\mu_L < \mu_U)$, he should choose his dilutions so as to cover a range of ' doses ' from $2/\mu_L$ to $1/2\mu_U$, thus ensuring that his first dilution has at least 2 organisms per sample and his last has at most 1/2 per sample. The dilution factor should be as small as is practicable ; 2 and 4 are definitely preferable to 10, but the convenience of using a few widely spaced dilutions may be allowed to have some influence on the choice. Thus, if the experimenter is sure that his density lies between 100 and 600 organisms per gram, he must have dilutions ranging at least as widely as 1/50 and 1/1,200. A suitable set would be 1/40, 1/80, 1/160, 1/320, 1/640, 1/1,280 (dilution factor 2), or 1/25, 1/100, 1/400, 1/1,600 (dilution factor 4), these being preferable to a design with the same total number of plates distributed between dilutions of 1/30, 1/300, 1/3,000 (dilution factor 10).

If inclusion of extra dilutions is little extra trouble by comparison with the labour of loglog calculations, the experimenter may choose to extend his series so as to be confident that he is for all practical purposes covering the range from $P = 0$ to $P = 1$, and, assigning equal numbers of plates to each level, he will plan to base his estimate on T alone. If he can locate μ reasonably closely in advance, he will probably do better to concentrate his efforts in the centre of the range and plan to use the loglog method. Whatever design he adopts, if the outcome of the experiment shows clearly the legitimacy of the method based on T, he may use it with little loss of efficiency, but he must be prepared to use the loglog method if circumstances show the other to be unsuitable. At the stage of design, considerations of potential precision in relation to the amount of work put into an experiment should dominate the attention; when the data have been obtained, the primary consideration is likely to be whether or not the Fisher and Yates tables for solving equation (21.71) can legitimately be applied.

The reader is warned against attempting to use any analogue of the Dragstedt-Behrens, Reed-Muench, or moving average methods for dilution assays. The exponential formula for the probability of a sterile plate, equation (21.34), is not symmetrical about any central point, and these methods are therefore even less appropriate than with normal or logistic sigmoid response curves.

The test of significance given by equation (21.65) is appropriate for detecting unspecified types of deviation from equation (21.34). In some circumstances, it may be possible to specify more exactly the pattern of deviation most likely to occur and to choose a test more susceptible to this. For example, the essential statistical features of the dilution series appear to be fulfilled in certain techniques of virus assay involving injection of different dilutions of a virus preparation into eggs and subsequent classification of the eggs as sterile or fertile. However, if the eggs themselves differ in their liability to infection, a source of variation additional to the Poisson is introduced; the general effect will be to draw out the series of results so as to lengthen the dilution interval between complete sterility and complete fertility.

Various tests of significance have been proposed. Moran (1954) and Armitage and Spicer (1956) gave interesting theoretical developments of their tests, and concluded that Moran's was likely to be the better; this is based on summing $r(n - r)$ over all dilutions, and examining its excess over a theoretical value. Stevens (1958) has discussed a very simple test, unfortunately without comparing it with Moran's. He used as test criterion the *range of transition*, the number of dilutions from the first at which $r \neq 0$ to the last at which $r \neq n$, counted inclusively. In Table 21.6, these intermediate dilutions are 1/4, 1/8, 1/16, and 1/32, so that the range is 4. In general, dilutions with $r = 0$ or $r = n$ may occur within the range, since this is defined solely by the extreme occurrences of $r \neq 0$ and $r \neq n$; if the results in Table 21.6 were changed by having $r = 5$ instead of $r = 3$ at $z = 1/16$, the range would still be 4. Appendix Table XVIII is an abridged version of Stevens's tabulation of probability levels for the range of transition. For example, with a dilution factor $a = 2$, the probability of the range being 4 or greater is 0·18 for an assay with 1 plate per dilution, 0·42 for $n = 2$, and certainly greater for $n = 5$ although this has not been tabulated. For Table 21.6, the test agrees with the χ^2 test in showing no sign of departure from the exponential model.

The Stevens test is strictly correct only for series that extend to infinity in both directions. Its use in an experiment of finite size assumes that the probability of a sterile plate at any higher value of z than those in the assay and the probability of a fertile plate at any lower value of z are both negligible. The test should therefore be used with caution for any assay in which values of r different from 0, n occur near the ends of the dilution series, as it may be appreciably biased by a tendency to underestimate the range. The test is primarily suitable for dilution series in which n is constant over all dilutions, although in some instances approximate allowances for inequalities of n will permit a near certainty about the outcome of a correct test.

21.6   Information from different types of assay

The reader who has appreciated the problems underlying §§ 14.1–14.3 and 21.2 will realize that no satisfactory general method is available for combining a series of assays of the same preparation when some are parallel line, some slope ratio, and some quantal. If the assays are individually good, with small values of g, the method of weighted means of M (§ 14.1) should be adequate, and nothing better can be proposed at present, even when some g are large. This method has been used in a number of instances of international collaboration for the establishment of a new standard: perhaps the earliest example is the report by Miles and Perry (1950) on a new international digitalis standard, using results from collaborators who had been permitted great freedom in the choice of assay technique.

Table 21.7 summarizes results from 47 usable assays. There was some indication of heterogeneity of estimates, since $\chi^2_{[46]} = 72 \cdot 84$, and possibly the guinea-pig assays by " other " methods should have

been omitted, but this is subsidiary to the present discussion. Miles
and Perry suggested using the average weight contributed by an
animal as a measure of the information provided by one animal in a
particular type of assay. Thus, they found the frog to be much less

TABLE 21.7—**Combination of results for assays of third international
digitalis standard against second**

Animal	Assay	No. of assays	Mean potency	95 per cent. limits	No. of animals	Σω	Information per animal
Frog ...	Quantal	12	1·020	0·977–1·064	874	11,090	13
Cat ...	Par. line	16	1·087	1·057–1·117	226	25,820	114
Guinea-pig*	Par. line	6	1·036	0·997–1·077	152	13,930	92
Guinea-pig†	Par. line	6	1·033	0·995–1·072	142	14,650	103
Pigeon ...	Par. line	7	1·074	1·037–1·113	94	16,540	176

* Recommended method.   † Other methods .
Weighted mean potency: 1·057; 95 per cent. limits: 1·040–1·074.

informative than the other animals (to a far greater extent than the
use of a quantal technique can explain), and the pigeon to be much
better than either cat or guinea-pig. These quantities can be
compared with costs per animal in any consideration of economic
choice of assay technique.

CHAPTER 22

TIME AS A RESPONSE

22.1 Time responses

For some assay techniques, the most obvious response to measure is a time, usually the time that elapses between application of the stimulus to the subject and the occurrence of some reaction ; death of the subject or recovery from some morbid condition, as indicated by the disappearance of certain symptoms, are reactions frequently used for this purpose. Such a time measurement is, of course, a quantitative response, and in many instances the assay may be analysed by the methods of earlier chapters. If the range of doses is wide, the data are likely to show a considerable increase in variance as the response increases ; in the choice of a response metameter, special attention must be paid to the essentially positive nature of the response and to the homoscedasticity of the dose-response regression (Perry, 1950).

22.2 Incomplete records

One difficulty that frequently arises is peculiar to time responses. For some subjects, the assay may end before any reaction occurs, so that no measure of response is available for them. This may happen because bad planning causes the experimenter to end his observations prematurely ; even in a good assay, however, the mean time to response at one extreme of dose may be so great as to make continuation of the experiment until all subjects have responded impracticable. If a subject is removed from the assay because it suffers damage or death by an accident completely independent of the stimulus, it may be expunged from the records without introducing any bias : the statistical analysis may be made more complicated because of non-orthogonality of the remaining data, but the validity of that analysis is not disturbed. On the other hand, to discard a subject from the analysis merely because experiment showed it to have a long reaction time would obviously bias the estimation of the mean reaction time for the corresponding dose.

Three methods of dealing with data of this kind may be considered :—

(i) The data might be converted to quantal form by classifying the subjects as ' reacted ' or ' not reacted ' at some arbitrary time. Analysis then proceeds as in Chapters 17–20.

(ii) An arbitrary value might be assigned as the response for all subjects that have not reacted when the experiment ends, this value being, of course, independent of dose.

(iii) A mathematical model of the process of the reaction might be set up, on which could be based a method of estimation (maximum likelihood or other) that would take full account of the uncompleted records.

The third of these would be almost essential to a research programme whose chief object was the study of the reaction, but the statistical analysis is likely to be too complicated for general use in assays ; it will be furthei discussed in § 22.4. If the number of subjects that have not reacted at the end of the experiment is a high proportion of the total, analysis as in (i) is unlikely to entail much sacrifice of information. If only a few subjects have incomplete records, neglect of the information conveyed by the detailed time measurements may seriously reduce the precision, and method (ii) will be preferable. The introduction of an entirely arbitrary value may seem an undesirable feature, but in fact the choice that is made will usually have little influence on the conclusions because few subjects are concerned. The argument will be made clearer by consideration of a numerical example.

22.3   An assay of a virus

Gard (1943) reported the data in Table 22.1 as the results of tests of a standard preparation (No. 21) of the virus of poliomyelitis and of four test preparations. The tests were made by inoculation of five male and five female mice at each of five doses of the standard and two doses of the test preparations. The table shows the number of days elapsing before each mouse became sick. Observations were continued for sixteen days, at the end of which time five subjects were still apparently well. The doses were dilutions of the preparations, at ten-fold intervals for the standard preparation, hundred-fold for each of the others. The design

TABLE 22.1—Responses of mice to inoculation with poliomyelitis virus

Preparation number	Dilution (as $\log_{10}$)	Sex	Day on which subject fell sick														
			3	4	5	6	7	8	9	10	11	12	13	14	15	16	>16
21 (Standard)	2	♂	4	1	1	1											
		♀	4	1	1	1											
	3	♂	1	2	3	1											
		♀		2		3											
	4	♂		1		2											
		♀		1		3		1									
	5	♂					1	1	1		1						
		♀					1	1	1					1			1
	6	♂							2	1							1
		♀					1	1								1	1
8	2	♂	1		2	1	1		1								
		♀	4		1	1	1	1									
	4	♂		1	1	1					1						
		♀			2												1
10	2	♂	4			3	1										
		♀	5	1		4											
	4	♂			1												
		♀															
11	2	♂	1	1		2	1	1									
		♀		5	3	2	1										
	4	♂								2							
		♀															1
12	2	♂	5	1	1	2											
		♀	4	2	3												
	4	♂		2													
		♀															

thus conforms fairly well to the recommendations in Chapter 11 for multiple assays, by having more subjects for the standard preparation than for any of the others ; the arrangement of the doses permits a wider range to be covered for the standard preparation than for the others, an advantage if little is known about the potency of the test preparations as thereby an insurance against bad guesses is effected. On the other hand, if the existing knowledge of the relative potencies were reasonably good, use of equal dose ranges for each preparation would have been preferable. The incomplete records naturally occur on the less potent doses.

The three methods of analysis mentioned in § 22.2 here take the forms :—

(i) Choose some convenient day, perhaps that at which about 50 per cent. of all mice have fallen sick, and use the methods of quantal response analysis on the proportions sick. At day 4, for example, the percentage responses would be 100 for both sexes at the first dose of the standard preparation, 60 and 40 at the next, and so on. Clearly this will not be very satisfactory, as many doses will show 100 per cent. or 0 per cent. response, even though quite useful information on the day of sickness is available.

(ii) An arbitrary value, say 18, might be assigned to the five mice unaffected at day 16 ; within reasonable limits, the exact choice for this value will have little effect on the results. Inspection of Table 22.1 discloses that the variances of the response time increases as the level of response increases. A reciprocal transformation is often useful as an aid to the equalization of variance of time responses (Box and Cullumbine, 1947 ; Brownlee and Hamre, 1951) ; if the animals falling sick on any one day are regarded as grouped at the midpoint of the preceding time interval, the response metameter may be taken as

$$y = \frac{1,000}{\text{No. of days} - 0.5}. \tag{22.1}$$

This metameter is likely to be more nearly normally distributed than the time itself, since the transformation will remove the positive skewness usually found in distributions of survival times and like measurements. Hence the metameter is to be recommended from considerations of normality as well as of scedasticity, though more data than are available here would be needed for any adequate confirmation of this. Even an ' infinite ' time can be transformed by equation (22.1) since its metametric value is zero. To assume that the five unaffected mice would remain unaffected indefinitely, however, would be just as arbitrary as to assign them to 18 days, and the latter seems more in keeping with the remainder of the data.* Moreover, no alternative value greater than 18 would make any appreciable difference to the estimates of potency.

(iii) Method (i) is obviously wasteful of information ; method (ii) has an appearance of being not quite honest. Any method that is logically more satisfying, however, will almost certainly be much more laborious. The distribution of times would have to be formulated mathematically, perhaps with allowance for the possibility that mice unaffected by day 16 might be either merely slow to react or immune to the virus, and this could not be done satisfactorily on the evidence of only one experiment. No full discussion can be given here, though § 22.4 is a brief introduction to the method.

In fact, method (ii) is not as objectionable as it may at first appear. The value assigned to the mice that fail to react may be regarded as part of the definition of the response metameter, and, in the light of the discussion in Chapter 15, the only fault in the metameter then is that it has been chosen to suit a single assay. If a series of assays which stopped at day 16 were all found to be satisfactorily analysable in terms of this metameter, the choice would be as sound as that for other types of quantitative assay. For illustrative purposes, the analysis will be completed in terms of the assumed value of 18 for the incomplete records, though in practice evidence from a number of assays on the most suitable metametric transformation is desirable.

The only evidence on the deviations from linearity of the regression of y on x comes from the standard preparation ; a preliminary analysis of variance shows these deviations to be significant, primarily because of a flattening of the regression at $x = 6$. That the regression

---

* Note that these are not missing values in the ordinary sense of the term (*cf.* § 4.14), since the times are known to exceed 16 days.

is not perfectly linear is not surprising, and the best procedure seems to be to omit the data for $x = 6$; the loss of information from this omission must be small, because the values of y fall well outside the range that is of interest for the test preparations. The analysis of variance for the remaining 120 responses should cause no great difficulty, although care is needed because of the lack of symmetry arising from the extra doses of the test preparation. Table 22.2 shows this analysis ; there is still some suspicion of non-linearity (not enough to cause any serious alarm), but no other indication of invalidity. Some heterogeneity of variance might be expected. If the mean square with 4 degrees of freedom is calculated for each of the twenty-four groups of five mice, it is found to range from 0 to 7,300 ; this is largely attributable to the coarseness of grouping, since, for example, the five female mice at $x = 2$ for preparation 10 are all assigned to $y = 400$, but might in reality

TABLE 22.2—Analysis of variance of the data in Table 22.1, transformed by equation (22.1)

Adjustment for mean		7,923,824	
Nature of variation	d.f.	Sum of squares	Mean square
Preparations	4	144,902	36,226
Sex	1	875	875
Preparations × Sex	4	17,608	4,402
Regression	1	778,180	778,180
Linearity	2	15,647	7,824
Preparations × Regression ...	4	10,616	2,654
Sex × Regression	1	823	823
Sex × Linearity	2	6,886	3,443
Preparations × Sex × Regression	4	14,539	3,635
Doses	23	990,076	
Error	96	278,754	2,904
Total	119	1,268,830	

have had any values between 500 and 333. There is no indication of any association between the mean and the variance of y, as may be seen by dividing the doses into two sets according to whether the mean value of y is less than or greater than 250 and evaluating the mean square for each set ; the two mean squares are 2,523 (52 degrees of freedom) and 3,353 (44 degrees of freedom) respectively. Consequently, no ill effects of heteroscedasticity need be feared.

Table 22.2 also shows no sign of any differential effects for the two sexes. Had there been a significant interaction of sex and regression, separate analyses for males and females would have been needed, and the final potency estimates would have been obtained by methods such as those of Chapter 14. Here, relative potencies may be calculated from all the data at once, with the aid

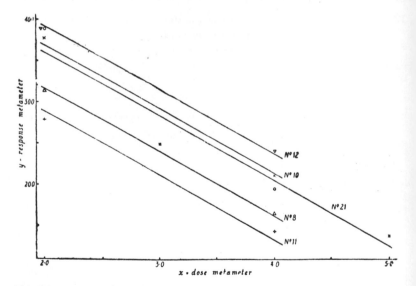

Fig. 22.1—Linear dose-response regressions for the assay of poliomyelitis virus in Table 22.1

     × : Mean response metameters for standard preparation No. 21

     △ : Mean response metameters for preparation No. 8

     ○ : Mean response metameters for preparation No. 10

     + : Mean response metameters for preparation No. 11

     ▽ : Mean response metameters for preparation No. 12

of the regression coefficient obtained by pooling contributions from the five preparations :

$$b = -\frac{3{,}784 + 1{,}488 + 1{,}950 + 1{,}346 + 1{,}490}{50 + 20 + 20 + 20 + 20}$$

$$= -\frac{10{,}058}{130}$$

$$= -77{\cdot}37. \tag{22.2}$$

From totals already used in the calculations for the analysis of variance are obtained the means :

Preparation no.	$\bar{x}$	$\bar{y}$
21	3·5	243·35
8	3·0	239·00
10	3·0	291·10
11	3·0	210·90
12	3·0	314·10

A little care is needed in the calculation of M, because x is measured as a log dilution instead of the more usual log concentration, and b is negative ; consideration of a diagram (Fig. 22.1) shows that equation (4.11) needs to be altered to

$$M = \bar{x}_T - \bar{x}_S - \frac{\bar{y}_T - \bar{y}_S}{b}$$

$$= -0{\cdot}5 + \frac{\bar{y}_T - 243{\cdot}35}{77{\cdot}37}. \tag{22.3}$$

Hence
$$M_8 = \bar{1}{\cdot}4438,$$
$$M_{10} = 0{\cdot}1172,$$
$$M_{11} = \bar{1}{\cdot}0806,$$
$$M_{12} = 0{\cdot}4144.$$

The ratio of the regression to the error mean square is so large that g is only 0·0147, a value that might almost be neglected. The usual method, however, may easily be applied to the calculation of fiducial limits. The conclusions are summarized in Table 22.3.

TABLE 22.3—Summary of relative potencies estimated from
the data of Table 22.1

Preparation no.	Potency relative to no. 21	Fiducial limits	
		Lower	Upper
8	0·278	0·115	0·668
10	1·31	0·546	3·27
11	0·210	0·0489	0·288
12	2·60	1·07	6·70

Comparison of these potency estimates with results obtained by
analysing the data by quantal response methods, as suggested in
(i) above, is of some interest. If falling sick on or before day 4
is regarded as a quantal response, and the data are analysed by
probits, several cycles of calculation are necessary before close
approximation to maximum likelihood estimates is attained. The
fifth cycle of the standard technique described in § 18.1 gave

$$b = -1 \cdot 6333,$$

and

$$g = 0 \cdot 1355.$$

From the regression coefficient, the standard deviation of the tolerance distribution is estimated as 0·6123, a value which may be compared with the inherent standard error per response,

$$\frac{s}{b} = \frac{53 \cdot 89}{77 \cdot 37}$$

$$= 0 \cdot 6965,$$

in the analysis based on equation (22.1). The agreement is good
(*cf.* Perry, 1950). On the other hand, the weight per subject in
the quantal analysis is small, the total of all the *Snw* values being
only 34·6 by comparison with an effective total weight of 120 in
the other analysis. This explains the marked increase in *g* and the
widening of the fiducial intervals. Table 22.4 contains the summarized results of the quantal analysis ; the estimates (except for preparation no. 8) agree well with those in Table 22.3, but the fiducial
limits are so widely spaced as to leave no doubt of the advantage

that lies in the use of quantitative responses. Had the quantal response been defined in terms of any day other than day 4, the results would have been still less satisfactory.

TABLE 22.4—Summary of relative potencies estimated from the data of Table 22.1 by analysis of quantal responses.

Preparation no.	Potency relative to no. 21	Fiducial limits	
		Lower	Upper
8	0·0833	0·0196	0·380
10	1·15	0·202	5·45
11	0·121	0·0285	0·590
12	4·19	0·915	17·8

22.4 The complete analysis

The major criticism of the method used in § 22.3 is that it does not take account of the exact form of the regression relationship. All the assay methods described in earlier chapters are open to this criticism, but reasons have been given for regarding the dose response relationships used as adequate for the representation of the exact regressions over a limited range of doses. Use of a response metameter such as that of equation (22.1), with the assumption of a linear regression, is perhaps more obviously imperfect : the reason for this may be not so much that it is intrinsically worse than the procedure in other types of assay, but that improvements could more easily be suggested.

Rigorous analysis of the relationship between time to response and dose, however, introduces many complications, and comparatively little work on the general theory has been done. Even if the time, or some simple function of it, is assumed to be normally distributed, estimation of the parameters of the distribution when some records are incomplete involves laborious calculations. Yet this model of the behaviour of the subjects is obviously not sufficiently complex. Of the subjects that do not respond within the period of the experiment, some may be naturally of low responsiveness to (or high tolerance for) the stimulus, so that they would not respond until a longer time had elapsed ; some may be absolutely immune to the stimulus, and therefore would never respond ; and others may have had a subliminal reaction, after which they have recovered and so have never been observed as responding. All these will be classified together as incomplete records, though their mathematical representations would be different. Natural responses may occur in addition to those experimentally stimulated ; for example, if the reaction to be used were death of the subject and at some doses the survival times were long, natural deaths might be indistinguishable from those due to treatment. Models of these phenomena in terms of mathematical probabilities can be constructed, but will require considerably more than the number of parameters usually estimated as part of the statistical analysis of a biological assay.

Bliss (1937) and Stevens (1937) made a start on the problem of the analysis of time-mortality data for a single treatment. They discussed the artificial truncation of the distribution of times brought about by early conclusion of the experiment, and, less completely, the recovery of subjects from the effects of treatment. They did not consider the simultaneous occurrence of both phenomena in one experiment, the possibility of immunity, or the occurrence of natural responses. Boag (1949) has investigated some of these problems, with particular reference to cures effected by cancer therapy. The statistical analysis of samples of observations from truncated distributions has been discussed in a number of other papers ; except for a paper by Ipsen (1949), the special application to bio-assay has been somewhat neglected. For assay purposes, as usual, two or more doses of two preparations must be considered simultaneously, and all the relevant parameters must be estimated. This may not introduce further theoretical difficulties, but it will certainly increase the already heavy arithmetic.

Since publication of the first edition of this book, many papers on the estimation of parameters of distributions from truncated records have appeared. The nearest in thought to the presentation I have adopted are those of Sampford (1952, a, b, 1954), a series on maximum likelihood techniques for time–mortality studies. Even these say little about applications to biological assay. In § 4 of the third paper, however, Sampford briefly described the calculations appropriate to assays; they will not be summarized here because of the infrequency of their use. Dr. Sampford informs me that he and Dr. J. Taylor expect soon to publish a method that will enable assays based on survival times to be analysed with calculations no more unwieldy than those of iterated probit regressions. However, extensive use of time as the response in routine biological assays is unlikely, at any rate under conditions that give rise to many of the complications mentioned above.

Even if reasonable computing schemes were available, data such as those of Gard for the assay of poliomyelitis virus (Table 22.1) are clearly quite inadequate for the estimation of all the parameters that would be needed in anything approaching a full mathematical model. Despite its theoretical shortcomings, an analysis such as that in § 22.3 is not only easy to compute, but is in practice often as good an approximation to the ideal as the data and the knowledge of the experimenter can justify.

REFERENCES

ABBOTT, W. S. (1925). A method of computing the effectiveness of an insecticide. *Journal of Economic Entomology*, **18**, 265–267.

AITCHISON, J., & SILVEY, S. D. (1957). The generalization of probit analysis to the case of multiple responses. *Biometrika*, **44**, 131–140.

ANDERSON, R. L. (1946). Missing-plot techniques. *Biometrics*, **2**, 41–47.

ANON. (1946). Tests and methods of assay for antibiotic drugs—penicillin. *Federal Register*, **11**, 12,128–12,136.

ANON. (1963). *Fifteenth Report of the Expert Committee on Biological Standardization*. World Health Organization Technical Report Series.

ANSCOMBE, F. J. (1949). Note on a problem in probit analysis. *Annals of Applied Biology*, **36**, 203–205.

ARMITAGE, P., & ALLEN, I. (1950). Methods of estimating the LD50 in quantal response data. *Journal of Hygiene*, **48**, 298–322.

ARMITAGE, P., & SPICER, C. C. (1956). The detection of variation in host susceptibility in dilution counting experiments. *Journal of Hygiene*, **54**, 401–414.

ASHFORD, J. R. (1959). An approach to the analysis of data for semi-quantal responses in biological assay. *Biometrics*, **15**, 573–581.

BACHARACH, A. L. (1945). Biological assay and chemical analysis. *Analyst*, **70**, 394–403.

BACHARACH, A. L., COATES, M. E., & MIDDLETON, T. R. (1942). A biological test for vitamin P activity. *Biochemical Journal*, **36**, 407–412.

BARKWORTH, H., & IRWIN, J. O. (1938). Distribution of coliform organisms in milk and the accuracy of the presumptive coliform test. *Journal of Hygiene*, **38**, 446–457,

BARR, M., & NELSON, J. W. (1949). An accurate and economical method for the biological assay of aconite tincture. *Journal of the American Pharmaceutical Association*, **38**, 518–521.

BARRACLOUGH, C. G. (1955). Statistical analysis of multiple slope ratio assays. *Biometrics*, **11**, 186–200.

BARTLETT, M. S. (1937). Properties of sufficiency and statistical tests. *Proceedings of the Royal Society of London*, **A 160**, 268–282.

BARTLETT, M. S. (1946). A modified probit technique for small probabilities. *Journal of the Royal Statistical Society, Supplement*, **8**, 113–117.

BARTLETT, M. S. (1947). The use of transformations. *Biometrics*, **3**, 39–52.

BEHRENS, B. (1929). Zur Auswertung der Digitalisblätter im Froschversuch. *Archiv für Experimentelle Pathologie und Pharmakologie*, **140**, 237–256.

BERKSON, J. (1944). Application of the logistic function to bio-assay. *Journal of the American Statistical Association*, **39**, 357–365.

BERKSON, J. (1946). Approximation of chi-square by " probits " and by " logits ". *Journal of the American Statistical Association*, **41**, 70–74.

BERKSON, J. (1949). Minimum χ^2 and maximum likelihood solution in terms of a linear transformation, with particular reference to bio-assay. *Journal of the American Statistical Association*, **44**, 273–278.

BERKSON, J. (1950). Some observations with respect to the error of bio-assay. *Biometrics*, **6**, 432–434.

BIGGERS, J. D. (1952). The calculation of the dose-response line in quantal assays with special reference to oestrogen assays by the Allen–Doisy technique. *Journal of Endocrinology*, **8**, 169–178.

BIGGERS, J. D., & CLARINGBOLD, P. J. (1954). Why use inbred lines? *Nature*, **174**, 596–597.

BIRCH, T. W., & HARRIS, L. J. (1934). Bradycardia in the vitamin B_1 deficient rat and its use in vitamin B_1 determinations. *Biochemical Journal*, **28**, 602–621.

BLACK, A. N. (1950). Weighted probits and their use. *Biometrika*, **37**, 158–167.

BLACKITH, R. E. (1950). Bio-assay systems for the pyrethrins. III. Application of the twin cross-over design to crawling insect *assays*. *Annals of Applied Biology*, **37**, 508–515.

BLISS, C. I. (1934a). The method of probits. *Science*, **79**, 38–39.

BLISS, C. I. (1934b). The method of probits—a correction. *Science*, **79**, 409–410.

BLISS, C. I. (1935a). The calculation of the dosage-mortality curve. *Annals of Applied Biology*, **22**, 134–167.

BLISS, C. I. (1935b). The comparison of dosage-mortality data. *Annals of Applied Biology*, **22**, 307–333.

BLISS, C. I. (1937). The calculation of the time-mortality curve. *Annals of Applied Biology*, **24**, 815–852.

BLISS, C. I. (1938). The determination of dosage-mortality curves from small numbers. *Quarterly Journal of Pharmacy and Pharmacology*, **11**, 192–216.

BLISS, C. I. (1939). Fly spray testing. *Soap and Sanitary Chemicals*, **15**, no. 4, 103–111.

BLISS, C. I. (1940a). Factorial design and covariance in the biological assay of vitamin D. *Journal of the American Statistical Association*, **35**, 498–506.

BLISS, C. I. (1940b). Quantitative aspects of biological assay. *Journal of the American Pharmaceutical Association*, **29**, 465–475.

BLISS, C. I. (1944a). The U.S.P. collaborative cat assay for digitalis. *Journal of the American Pharmaceutical Association*, **33**, 225–245.

BLISS, C. I. (1944b). A simplified calculation of the potency of penicillin and other drugs assayed biologically with a graded response. *Journal of the American Statistical Association*, **39**, 479–487.

BLISS, C. I. (1944c). Relative potency as applied to the assay of penicillin. *Science*, **100**, 577–578.

BLISS, C. I. (1945). Confidence limits for biological assays. *Biometrics*, **1**, 57–65.

BLISS, C. I. (1946a). A revised cylinder-plate assay for penicillin. *Journal of the American Pharmaceutical Association*, **35**, 6–12.

BLISS, C. I. (1946b). An experimental design for slope-ratio assays. *Annals of Mathematical Statistics*, **17**, 232–237.

BLISS, C. I. (1946c). Collaborative comparison of three rations for the chick assay of vitamin D. *Journal of the Association of Official Agricultural Chemists*, **29**, 396–408.

BLISS, C. I. (1947a). 2 × 2 factorial experiments in incomplete groups for use in biological assays. *Biometrics*, **3**, 69–88.

BLISS, C. I. (1947b). The biological measurement of the depth dose of roentgen rays with lettuce seedlings. *American Journal of Roentgenology and Radium Therapy*, **58**, 222–233.

BLISS, C. I. (1950). The design of biological assays. *Annals of the New York Academy of Sciences*, **52**, 877–888.

BLISS, C. I. (1952a). *The Statistics of Bioassay*, New York: Academic Press Inc.

BLISS, C. I. (1952b). Estimation of the error in a clinical assay. *Biometrics*, **8**, 237–245.

BLISS, C. I. (1956). Analysis of biological assays in *U.S.P. XV*. *Drug Standards*, **24**, 33–68.

BLISS, C. I., & ALLMARK, M. G. (1944). The digitalis cat assay in relation to rate of injection. *Journal of Pharmacology and Experimental Therapeutics*, **81**, 378–389.

BLISS, C. I., & BARTELS, B. L. (1946). The determination of the most efficient response for measuring drug potency. *Proceedings, Part II, Federation of American Societies for Experimental Biology*, **5**, 167–168.

BLISS, C. I., & CATTELL, McK. (1943). Biological assay. *Annual Review of Physiology*, **5**, 479–539.

BLISS, C. I., & HANSON, J. C. (1939). Quantitative estimation of the potency of digitalis by the cat method in relation to secular variation. *Journal of the American Pharmaceutical Association*, **28**, 521–530.

BLISS, C. I., & MARKS, H. P. (1939a). The biological assay of insulin. I. Some general considerations directed to increasing the precision of the curve relating dosage and graded response. *Quarterly Journal of Pharmacy and Pharmacology*, **12**, 82–110.

BLISS, C. I., & MARKS, H. P. (1939*b*). The biological assay of insulin. II. The estimation of drug potency from a graded response. *Quarterly Journal of Pharmacy and Pharmacology*, **12**, 182–205.

BLISS, C. I., & PABST, M. L. (1955). Assays for standardizing adrenal cortex extract in production. *Bulletin of the International Statistical Institute*, **34** (4), 317–338.

BLISS, C. I., & PACKARD, C. (1941). Stability of the standard dosage-effect curve for radiation. *American Journal of Roentgenology and Radium Therapy*, **46**, 400–404.

BLISS, C. I., & ROSE, C. L. (1940). The assay of parathyroid extract from the serum calcium of dogs. *American Journal of Hygiene*, **31**, A 79–98.

BOAG, J. W. (1949). Maximum likelihood estimates of the proportion of patients cured by cancer therapy. *Journal of the Royal Statistical Society*, **B 11**, 15–53.

BOX, G. E. P. (1953). Non-normality and tests on variances. *Biometrika*, **40**, 318–335.

BOX, G. E. P., & CULLUMBINE, H. (1947). The relationship between survival time and dosage with certain toxic agents. *British Journal of Pharmacology and Chemotherapy*, **2**, 27–37.

BOX, G. E. P., & HAY, W. A. (1953). A statistical design for the efficient removal of trends occurring in a comparative experiment with an application in biological assay. *Biometrics*, **9**, 304–319.

BRAUN, H. A., & SIEGFRIED, A. (1947). The assay of digitalis. V. The guinea-pig method. *Journal of the American Pharmaceutical Association*, **36**, 363–368.

BRITISH PHARMACOPOEIA (1958). London: Pharmaceutical Press.

BRITISH STANDARDS INSTITUTION (1940). *British Standard Method for the Biological Assay of Vitamin D_3 by the Chick Method.* British Standard no. 911.

BROSS, I. (1950). Estimates of the LD_{50}: A critique. *Biometrics*, **6**, 413–423.

BROWNLEE, K. A., DELVES, C. S., DORMAN, M., GREEN, C. A., GRENFELL, E., JOHNSON, J. D. A., & SMITH, N. (1948). The biological assay of streptomycin by a modified cylinder plate method. *Journal of General Microbiology*, **2**, 40–53.

BROWNLEE, K. A., & HAMRE, D. (1951). Studies on chemotherapy of vaccinia virus. I. An experimental design for testing antiviral agents. *Journal of Bacteriology*, **61**, 127–134.

BROWNLEE, K. A., LORAINE, P. K., & STEPHENS, J. (1949). The biological assay of penicillin by a modified plate method. *Journal of General Microbiology*, **3**, 347–352.

BÜLBRING, E., & BURN, J. H. (1935). The estimation of oestrin and of male hormone in oily solution. *Journal of Physiology*, **85**, 320–333.

BURN, J. H. (1930). The errors of biological assay. *Physiological Reviews*, **10**, 146–169.

BURN, J. H., FINNEY, D. J., & GOODWIN, L. G. (1950). *Biological Standardization* (2nd edition) London: Oxford University Press.

CHEN, K. K., BLISS, C. I., & ROBBINS, E. B. (1942). The digitalis-like principles of *Calotropis* compared with other cardiac substances. *Journal of Pharmacology and Experimental Therapeutics*, **74**, 223–234.

CHRISTENSEN, P. A., & KERRICH, J. E. (1948). A note on enzyme-purified antitoxin and anaphylaxis in guinea-pigs. *Journal of Immunology*, **59**, 21–29.

CLARINGBOLD, P. J. (1956). The within-animal bioassay with quantal responses. *Journal of the Royal Statistical Society*, **B 18**, 133–137.

CLARINGBOLD, P. J. (1959). Orthogonal contrasts in slope ratio investigations. *Biometrics*, **15**, 307–322.

CLARKE, P. M. (1952). Statistical analysis of symmetrical slope-ratio assays of any number of test preparations. *Biometrics*, **8**, 370–379.

COCHRAN, W. G. (1950a). Estimation of bacterial densities by means of the " most probable number ". *Biometrics*, **6**, 105–116.

COCHRAN, W. G. (1950b). The comparison of percentages in matched samples. *Biometrika*, **37**, 256–266.

COCHRAN, W. G., & BLISS, C. I. (1948). Discriminant functions with covariance. *Annals of Mathematical Statistics*, **19**, 151–176.

COCHRAN, W. G., & COX, G. M. (1957). *Experimental Designs* (2nd edition). New York: John Wiley and Sons, Inc.

COHEN, H., VAN RAMSHORST, J. D., & TASMAN, A. (1959). Consistency in potency assay of tetanus toxoid in mice. *Bulletin of the World Health Organization*, **20**, 1133–1150.

CORNFIELD, J., & MANTEL, N. (1950). Some new aspects of the application of maximum likelihood to the calculation of the dosage response curve. *Journal of the American Statistical Association*, **45**, 181–210.

CORNFIELD, J., & MANTEL, N. (1951). Some comments on "Estimates of the LD_{50}: A Critique". *Biometrics*, **7**, 295–298.

COWARD, K. H. (1947). *The Biological Standardisation of the Vitamins* (2nd edition). London: Baillière, Tindall & Cox.

COX, D. R. (1958). *Planning of Experiments*. New York: John Wiley & Sons, Inc.

CRAMÉR, H. (1946). *Mathematical Methods of Statistics*. Princeton: University Press.

CURTIS, J. M., UMBERGER, E. J., & KNUDSEN, L. F. (1947). The interpretation of estrogenic assays. *Endocrinology*, **40**, 231–240.

DALE, H. (1939). Biological standardisation. *Analyst*, **64**, 554–567.

DEBEER, E. J. (1941). A scale for graphically determining the slopes of dose-response curves. *Science*, **94**, 521–522.

DEBEER, E. J. (1945). The calculation of biological assay results by graphic methods. The all-or-none type of response. *Journal of Pharmacology and Experimental Therapeutics*, **85**, 1–13.

DEBEER, E. J., & SHERWOOD, M. B. (1945). The paper-disc agar-plate method for the assay of antibiotic substances. *Journal of Bacteriology*, **50**, 459–467.

DIXON, W. J., & MOOD, A. M. (1948). A method for obtaining and analyzing sensitivity data. *Journal of the American Statistical Association*, **43**, 109–126.

DRAGSTEDT, C. A., & LANG, V. F. (1928). Respiratory stimulants in acute cocaine poisoning in rabbits. *Journal of Pharmacology and Experimental Therapeutics*, **32**, 215–222.

DUFRENOY, J., & GOYAN, F. M. (1947). A graphical calculator for statistical analysis. *Journal of the American Pharmaceutical Association*, **36**, 309–314.

EISENHART, C., & WILSON, P. W. (1943). Statistical method and control in bacteriology. *Bacteriological Reviews*, **7**, 57–137.

EMMENS, C. W. (1940). The dose/response relation for certain principles of the pituitary gland, and of the serum and urine of pregnancy. *Journal of Endocrinology*, **2**, 194–225.

EMMENS, C. W. (1948). *Principles of Biological Assay*. London: Chapman & Hall.

EPSTEIN, B., & CHURCHMAN, C. W. (1944). On the statistics of sensitivity data. *Annals of Mathematical Statistics*, **15**, 90–96.

FECHNER, G. T. (1860). *Elemente der Psychophysik* (2 Vols.). Leipzig: Breitkopf und Härtel.

FIELLER, E. C. (1940). The biological standardization of insulin. *Journal of the Royal Statistical Society, Supplement*, **7**, 1–64.

FIELLER, E. C. (1944). A fundamental formula in the statistics of biological assay, and some applications. *Quarterly Journal of Pharmacy and Pharmacology*, **17**, 117–123.

FIELLER, E. C. (1947). Some remarks on the statistical background in bio-assay. *Analyst*, **72**, 37–43.

FIELLER, E. C. (1954). Some problems in interval estimation. *Journal of the Royal Statistical Society*, **B 16**, 175–185.

FIELLER, E. C., IRWIN, J. O., MARKS, H. P., & SHRIMPTON, E. A. G. (1939a). The dosage-response relation in the cross-over rabbit test for insulin. Part I. *Quarterly Journal of Pharmacy and Pharmacology*, **12**, 206–211.

FIELLER, E. C., IRWIN, J. O., MARKS, H. P., & SHRIMPTON, E. A. G. (1939b). The dosage-response relation in the cross-over rabbit test for insulin. Part II. *Quarterly Journal of Pharmacy and Pharmacology*, **12**, 724–742.

FINNEY, D. J. (1941). The joint distribution of variance ratios based on a common error mean square. *Annals of Eugenics*, **11**, 136–140.

FINNEY, D. J. (1944a). The application of the probit method to toxicity test data adjusted for mortality in the controls. *Annals of Applied Biology*, **31**, 68–74.

FINNEY, D. J. (1944*b*). Mathematics of biological assay. *Nature*, **153**, 284.

FINNEY, D. J. (1945*a*). The microbiological assay of vitamins: The estimate and its precision. *Quarterly Journal of Pharmacy and Pharmacology*, **18**, 77–82.

FINNEY, D. J. (1945*b*). Some orthogonal properties of the 4 × 4 and 6 × 6 Latin squares. *Annals of Eugenics*, **12**, 213–219.

FINNEY, D. J. (1946*a*). Standard errors of yields adjusted for regression on an independent measurement. *Biometrics*, **2**, 53–55.

FINNEY, D. J. (1946*b*). The analysis of a factorial series of insecticide tests. *Annals of Applied Biology*, **33**, 160–165.

FINNEY, D. J. (1946*c*). Orthogonal partitions of the 6 × 6 Latin squares. *Annals of Eugenics*, **13**, 184–196.

FINNEY, D. J. (1947*a*). The principles of biological assay. *Journal of the Royal Statistical Society, Supplement*, **9**, 46–91.

FINNEY, D. J. (1947*b*). The construction of confounding arrangements. *Empire Journal of Experimental Agriculture*, **15**, 107–112.

FINNEY, D. J. (1947*c*). The estimation from individual records of the relationship between dose and quantal response. *Biometrika*, **34**, 320–334.

FINNEY, D. J. (1947*d*). Statistical aspects of microbiological assay. *Biochemical Journal*, **41**, v–vii.

FINNEY, D. J. (1947*e*). The adjustment of biological assay results for variation in concomitant observations. *Journal of Hygiene*, **45**, 397–406.

FINNEY, D. J. (1949*a*). The adjustment for a natural response rate in probit analysis. *Annals of Applied Biology*, **36**, 187–195.

FINNEY, D. J. (1949*b*). The estimation of the parameters of tolerance distributions. *Biometrika*, **36**, 239–256.

FINNEY, D. J. (1949*c*). The choice of a response metameter in bio-assay. *Biometrics*, **5**, 261–272.

FINNEY, D. J. (1950*a*). Scores for the estimation of parameters. *Biometrics*, **6**, 221–225.

FINNEY, D. J. (1950*b*). The estimation of the mean of a normal tolerance distribution. *Sankhyā*, **10**, 341–360.

FINNEY, D. J. (1951*a*). The statistical analysis of slope-ratio assays. *Journal of General Microbiology*, **5**, 223–230.

FINNEY, D. J. (1951*b*). Two new uses of the Behrens–Fisher distribution. *Journal of the Royal Statistical Society*, **B 12**, 296–300.

FINNEY, D. J. (1951*c*). The estimation of bacterial densities from dilution series. *Journal of Hygiene*, **49**, 26–35.

FINNEY, D. J. (1951*d*). Subjective judgment in statistical analysis— An experimental study. *Journal of the Royal Statistical Society*, **B 13**, 284–297.

FINNEY, D. J. (1952). *Probit Analysis: A Statistical Treatment of the Sigmoid Response Curve* (2nd edition). London: Cambridge University Press.

FINNEY, D. J. (1953). The estimation of the ED50 for a logistic response curve. *Sankhyā*, **12**, 121–136.

FINNEY, D. J. (1955). *Experimental Design and its Statistical Basis*. Chicago: Chicago University Press.

FINNEY, D. J. (1956). Cross-over designs in bioassay. *Proceedings of the Royal Society*, **B 145**, 42–61.

FINNEY, D. J. (1959). *An Introduction to the Theory of Experimental Design*. Chicago: Chicago University Press.

FINNEY, D. J. (1961). The design and analysis of an immunological assay. *Acta Microbiologica*, **6**, 341–368.

FINNEY, D. J., & OUTHWAITE, A. D. (1956). Serially balanced sequences in bioassay. *Proceedings of the Royal Society*, **B 145**, 493–507.

FINNEY, D. J., & STEVENS, W. L. (1948). A table for the calculation of working probits and weights in probit analysis. *Biometrika*, **35**, 191–201.

FINNEY, D. J., & WOOD, E. C. (1951). Intra-litter replication in biological assays. *Nature*, **167**, 903–904.

FISHER, R. A. (1912). On an absolute criterion for fitting frequency curves. *Messenger of Mathematics*, **41**, 155–160.

FISHER, R. A. (1922). On the mathematical foundations of theoretical statistics. *Philosophical Transactions of the Royal Society*, **A 222**, 309–368.

FISHER, R. A. (1925). Theory of statistical estimation. *Proceedings of the Cambridge Philosophical Society*, **22**, 700–725.

FISHER, R. A. (1935). Appendix to Bliss (1935*a*): The case of zero survivors. *Annals of Applied Biology*, **22**, 164–165.

FISHER, R. A. (1949*a*). A biological assay of tuberculins. *Biometrics*, **5**, 300–316.

FISHER, R. A. (1958). *Statistical Methods for Research Workers* (13th edition). Edinburgh: Oliver & Boyd.

FISHER, R. A. (1960). *The Design of Experiments* (7th edition). Edinburgh: Oliver & Boyd.

FISHER, R. A. (1961*a*). Sampling the reference set. *Sankhyā*, **A 23**, 3–8.

FISHER, R. A. (1961*b*). The weighted mean of two normal samples with unknown variance ratio. *Sankhyā*, **A 23**, 103–114.

FISHER, R. A., & YATES, F. (1963). *Statistical Tables for Biological, Agricultural and Medical Research* (6th edition). Edinburgh: Oliver & Boyd.

FITZHUGH, O. G., NELSON, A. N., & BLISS, C. I. (1944). The chronic oral toxicity of selenium. *Journal of Pharmacology and Experimental Therapeutics*, **80**, 289–299.

GADDUM, J. H. (1933). Reports on biological standards. III. Methods of biological assay depending on a quantal response. *Medical Research Council, Special Report Series*, no. 183.

GADDUM, J. H. (1948). *Pharmacology* (3rd edition). London: Oxford University Press.

GADDUM, J. H. (1950). Hormone assay: Introduction. *Analyst*, **75**, 530–533.

GARD, S. (1943). *Purification of Poliomyelitis Viruses*. Uppsala: Almqvist & Wiksell.

GARWOOD, F. (1941). The application of maximum likelihood to dosage-mortality curves. *Biometrika*, **32**, 46–58.

GAUTIER, R. (1945). The Health Organization and biological standardisation. *Bulletin of the Health Organization of the League of Nations*, **12**, 1–75.

GEARY, R. C. (1947). Testing for normality. *Biometrika*, **34**, 209–242.

GOYAN, F. M., & DUFRENOY, J. (1947). A graphical calculator for bio-assays. *Journal of the American Pharmaceutical Association*, **36**, 305–308.

GRIDGEMAN, N. T. (1943). The technique of the biological vitamin A assay. *Biochemical Journal*, **37**, 127–132.

GRIDGEMAN, N. T. (1944a). Mathematics of biological assay. *Nature*, **153**, 461–462.

GRIDGEMAN, N. T. (1944b). *The Estimation of Vitamin A*. London: Lever Brothers & Unilever Ltd.

GRIDGEMAN, N. T. (1946). The transformation of biological responses with special reference to vitamin-D assays. *Analyst*, **71**, 376–379.

GRIDGEMAN, N. T. (1950). Design and evaluation of biological assays. *Nature*, **165**, 843–844.

GRIDGEMAN, N. T. (1951). On the errors of biological assays with graded responses, and their graphical derivation. *Biometrics*, **7**, 201–221.

GULD, J., BENTZON, M. W., BLEIKER, M. A., GRIEP, W. A., MAGNUSSON, M., & WAALER, H. (1958). Standardization of a new batch of purified tuberculin (PPD) intended for international use. *Bulletin of the World Health Organization*, **19**, 845–951.

GURLAND, J., LEE, I., & DAHM, P. A. (1960). Polychotomous quantal response in biological assay. *Biometrics*, **16**, 382–398.

GYÖRGY, P. (1951). *Vitamin Methods*. (Vol. 2). New York: Academic Press Inc.

HALEY, T. J. (1947). An instrument for plotting ED_{50} curves. *Science*, **106**, 151.

HALVORSON, H. O., & ZIEGLER, N. R. (1933a). Application of statistics to problems in bacteriology. I. A means of determining bacterial population by the dilution method. *Journal of Bacteriology*, **25**, 101–121.

HALVORSON, H. O., & ZIEGLER, N. R. (1933b). Application of statistics to problems in bacteriology. III. A consideration of the accuracy of dilution data obtained by using several dilutions. *Journal of Bacteriology*, **26**, 559–567.

HARRIS, E. K. (1959). Confidence limits for the LD_{50} using the moving average-angle method. *Biometrics*, **15**, 424–432.

HARTE, R. A. (1948). A simple graphical solution for potency calculations of multidose assays. *Science*, **107**, 401–402.

HARTLEY, P. (1935). International biological standards. *Pharmaceutical Journal*, **81**, 625–627.

HARTLEY, P. (1945a). Notes on the international standards for antitoxins and antisera. *Bulletin of the Health Organisation of the League of Nations*, **12**, 76–97.

HARTLEY, P. (1945b). International biological standards: Prospect and retrospect. *Proceedings of the Royal Society of Medicine*, **39**, 45–58.

HATCHER, R. A., & BRODY, J. G. (1910). The biological standization of drugs. *American Journal of Pharmacy*, **82**, 360–372.

HEALY, M. J. R. (1949). Routine computation of biological assays involving a quantitative response. *Biometrics*, **5**, 330–334.

HEALY, M. J. R. (1950). The planning of probit assays. *Biometrics*, **6**, 424–431.

HEMMINGSEN, A. M. (1933). The accuracy of insulin assay on white mice. *Quarterly Journal of Pharmacy and Pharmacology*, **6**, 39–80 & 187–218.

HEMMINGSEN, A. M., & KROGH, A. (1926). The assay of insulin by the convulsive-dose method on white mice. *Publications of the League of Nations*, III. Health, 1926. III. **7**, 40–46.

HUMPHREY, J. H., LIGHTBOWN, J. W., MUSSETT, M. V., & PERRY, W. L. M. (1953). The international standard for aureomycin. *Bulletin of the World Health Organization*, **9**, 851–860.

IPSEN, J. (1941). *Contribution to the Theory of Biological Standardization*. Copenhagen: Nyt Nordisk Forlag (Arnold Busck).

IPSEN, J. (1949). Biometric analysis of graded response with incomplete measurements in assays of analgetic drugs. *Acta Pharmacologica et Toxicologica*, **5**, 321–346.

IRWIN, J. O. (1937). Statistical method applied to biological assays. *Journal of the Royal Statistical Society, Supplement*, **4**, 1–60.

IRWIN, J. O. (1943). On the calculation of the error of biological assays. *Journal of Hygiene*, **43**, 121–128.

IRWIN, J. O. (1950). Biological assays with special reference to biological standards. *Journal of Hygiene*, **48**, 215–238.

IRWIN, J. O., & CHEESEMAN, E. A. (1939). On an approximate method of determining the median effective dose and its error in the case of a quantal response. *Journal of Hygiene*, **39**, 574–580.

JERNE, N. K., & PERRY, W. L. M. (1956). The stability of biological standards. *Bulletin of the World Health Organization*, **14**, 167–182.

JERNE, N. K., & WOOD, E. C. (1949). The validity and meaning of the results of biological assays. *Biometrics*, **5**, 273–299.

JONES, J. I. M. (1945). The biological estimation of vitamin D. *Quarterly Journal of Pharmacy and Pharmacology*, **18**, 92–108.

KAPTEYN, J. C. (1903). *Skew Frequency Curves in Biology and Statistics*. Groningen: P. Noordhoff.

KAPTEYN, J. C., & VAN UVEN, M. J. (1916). *Skew Frequency Curves in Biology and Statistics*. Groningen: Hoitsema Brothers.

KÄRBER, G. (1931). Beitrag zur kollektiven Behandlung pharmakologischer Reihenversuche. *Archiv für Experimentelle Pathologie und Pharmakologie*, **162**, 480–487.

KENDALL, M. G., & STUART, A. *The Advanced Theory of Statistics*, Vol. 1 (1958, 1963), Vol. 2 (1961). London: Charles Griffin & Co., Ltd.

KENT-JONES, D. W., & MEIKLEJOHN, M. (1944). Some experiences of microbiological assays of riboflavin, nicotinic acid and other nutrient factors. *Analyst*, **69**, 330–336.

KNUDSEN, L. F. (1945a). Penicillin assay. *Science*, **101**, 46–48.

KNUDSEN, L. F. (1945b). The use of statistics in biological experimentation and assay. *Journal of the Association of Official Agricultural Chemists*, **28**, 806–813.

KNUDSEN, L. F. (1950). Statistics in microbiological assay. *Annals of the New York Academy of Sciences*, **52**, 889–902.

KNUDSEN, L. F., & CURTIS, J. M. (1947). The use of the angular transformation in biological assays. *Journal of the American Statistical Association*, **42**, 282–296.

KNUDSEN, L. F., & RANDALL, W. A. (1945). Penicillin assay and its control chart analysis. *Journal of Bacteriology*, **50**, 187–200.

614 REFERENCES

KNUDSEN, L. F., SMITH, R. B., VOS, B. J., & McCLOSKY, W. T. (1946). The biological assay of epinephrine. *Journal of Pharmacology and Experimental Therapeutics*, **86**, 339–343.

KOCH, W. (1947). A rapid method for the evaluation of microbiologic tests. *American Journal of Clinical Pathology*, **17**, 897–903.

KOLB, R. W., CUTCHINS, E. C., JONES, W. P. & AYLOR, H. T. (1961). A comparison of the rabbit scarification technique with titrations in cell cultures for the potency assay of smallpox vaccine. *Bulletin of the World Health Organization*, **25**, 25–32.

LEES, K. A. (1949). A semi-automatic calculating machine for the computation of microbiological plate assay results. *Chemistry and Industry*, 378.

LIDDLE, G. W., CORNFIELD, J., CASPER, A. G. T., & BARTTER, F. C. (1955). The physiological basis for a method of assaying aldosterone in extracts of human urine. *Journal of Clinical Investigation*, **34**, 1410–1416.

LITCHFIELD, J. T., & FERTIG, J. W. (1941). On a graphic solution of the dosage-effect curve. *Bulletin of the Johns Hopkins Hospital*, **69**, 276–286.

LITCHFIELD, J. T., & WILCOXON, F. (1949). A simplified method of evaluating dose-effect experiments. *Journal of Pharmacology and Experimental Therapeutics*, **96**, 99–113.

LORD, E. (1947). The use of range in place of standard deviation in the t-test. *Biometrika*, **34**, 41–67.

McCRADY, M. H. (1915). The numerical interpretation of fermentation-tube results. *Journal of Infectious Diseases*, **17**, 183–212.

McLAREN, A., & MICHIE, D. (1954). Are inbred strains suitable for bioassay? *Nature*, **173**, 686–687.

MARTIN, J. T. (1940). The problem of the evaluation of rotenone-containing plants. V. The relative toxicities of different species of derris. *Annals of Applied Biology*, **27**, 274–294.

MARTIN, J. T. (1942). The problem of the evaluation of rotenone-containing plants. VI. The toxicity of l-elliptone and of poisons applied jointly, with further observations on the rotenone equivalent method of assessing the toxicity of derris root. *Annals of Applied Biology*, **29**, 69–81.

MATHER, K. (1946). *Statistical Analysis in Biology* (2nd edition). London: Methuen & Co., Ltd.

MATHER, K. (1949). The analysis of extinction time data in bioassay. *Biometrics*, **5**, 127–143.

MERRINGTON, M. (1942). Table of percentage points of the t-distribution. *Biometrika*, **32**, 300.

MERRINGTON, M., & THOMPSON, C. M. (1943). Tables of percentage points of the inverted beta (F) distribution. *Biometrika*, **33**, 73–88.

MILES, A. A. (1948). Some observations on biological standards. *Analyst*, **73**, 530–538.

MILES, A. A. (1950). The biological unit of activity. *Bulletin of the World Health Organization*, **2**, 205–213.

MILES, A. A. (1952). The concept of biological potency as applied to closely related antibiotics. *Bulletin of the World Health Organization*, **6**, 131–147.

MILES, A. A., & PERRY, W. L. M. (1950). Third international digitalis standard. *Bulletin of the World Health Organization*, **2**, 655–672.

MILLER, L. C. (1944). The U.S.P. collaborative digitalis study using frogs (1939–1941). *Journal of the American Pharmaceutical Association*, **33**, 245–266.

MILLER, L. C. (1950). Biological assays involving quantal responses. *Annals of the New York Academy of Sciences*, **52**, 903–919.

MILLER, L. C., BECKER, T. J., & TAINTER, M. L. (1948). The quantitative evaluation of spasmolytic drugs in vitro. *Journal of Pharmacology and Experimental Therapeutics*, **92**, 260–268.

MILLER, L. C., BLISS, C. I., & BRAUN, H. A. (1939). The assay of digitalis. I. Criteria for evaluating various methods using frogs. *Journal of the American Pharmaceutical Association*, **28**, 644–657.

MILLER, L. C., & TAINTER, M. L. (1944). Estimation of the ED_{50} and its error by means of logarithmic-probit graph paper. *Proceedings of the Society for Experimental Biology and Medicine*, **57**, 261–264.

MONGAR, J. L. (1959). Use of randomized blocks in local anaesthetic assays. In *Quantitative Methods in Human Pharmacology and Therapeutics*, edited by D. R. Laurence, London: Pergamon Press.

MOORE, W., & BLISS, C. I. (1942). A method for determining insecticidal effectiveness using *Aphis rumicis* and certain organic compounds. *Journal of Economic Entomology*, **35**, 544–553.

MORAN, P. A. P. (1954). The dilution assay of viruses. *Journal of Hygiene*, **52**, 189–193.

MORRELL, C. A., & ALLMARK, M. G. (1941). The toxicity and trypanocidal activity of commercial neoarsphenamine. *Journal of the American Pharmaceutical Association*, **30**, 33–38.

MORRELL, C. A., CHAPMAN, C. W., & ALLMARK, M. G. (1938). On the therapeutic assay of neoarsphenamine with *Trypanosoma equiperdum*. *Journal of Pharmacology and Experimental Therapeutics*, **64**, 14–42.

MUNSON, P. L., & SHEPS, M. C. (1958). An improved procedure for the biological assay of androgens by direct application to the combs of baby chicks. *Endrocrinology*, **62**, 173–188.

MURRAY, C. A. (1937). A statistical analysis of fly mortality data. *Soap and Sanitary Chemicals*, **13**, no. 8, 89–105.

MYERSCOUGH, P. R., & SCHILD, H. O. (1958). Quantitative assays of oxytocic drugs on the human postpartum uterus. *British Journal of Pharmacology*, **13**, 207–212.

NEYMAN, J. (1949). Contribution to the theory of the χ^2 test. *Proceedings of the Berkeley Symposium on Mathematical Statistics and Probability*, University of California Press, 239–273.

NOEL, R. H. (1945). The biological assay of epinephrine. *Journal of Pharmacology and Experimental Therapeutics*, **84**, 278–283.

OSGOOD, E. E. (1947). Assay of penicillin, streptomycin, trivalent organic arsenicals, and other bactericidal and bacteriostatic agents. *Journal of Laboratory and Clinical Medicine*, **32**, 444–460.

OSGOOD, E. E., & GRAHAM, S. M. (1947). A simple rapid method for assay of bactericidal and bacteriostatic agents. *American Journal of Clinical Pathology*, **17**, 93–107.

PATTERSON, H. D. (1950). The analysis of change-over trials. *Journal of Agricultural Science*, **40**, 375–380.

PATTERSON, H. D. (1951). Change-over trials. *Journal of the Royal Statistical Society*, **B 13**, 256–271.

PERRY, W. L. M. (1950). Reports on biological standards. VI. The design of toxicity tests. *Medical Research Council, Special Report Series*, no. 270.

PETO, S. (1953). A dose-response equation for the invasion of micro-organisms. *Biometrics*, **9**, 320–335.

PHARMACOPOEA INTERNATIONALIS (1951, 1955, 1959). Geneva: World Health Organization.

PIZZI, M. (1950). Sampling variation of the fifty per cent end-point determined by the Reed–Muench (Behrens) methods. *Human Biology*, **22**, 151–190.

PRATT, R., & DUFRENOY, J. (1947). Practical three-hour and two-hour cylinder-plate assays for penicillin. *Nature*, **159**, 576–577.

PRICE, W. C. (1945). Accuracy of the local-lesion method for measuring virus activity. IV. Southern bean mosaic virus. *American Journal of Botany*, **32**, 613–619.

PRICE, W. C. (1946). Measurement of virus activity in plants. *Biometrics*, **2**, 81–86.

PRICE, W. C., & SPENCER, E. L. (1943). Accuracy of the local-lesion method for measuring virus activity. III. The standard deviation of the log-ratio of potencies as a measure of the accuracy of measurement. *American Journal of Botany*, **30**, 720–735.

PUGSLEY, L. I. (1946). The application of the principles of statistical analysis to the biological assay of hormones. *Endocrinology*, **39**, 161–176.

QUENOUILLE, M. H. (1950). *Introductory Statistics*. London: Butterworth-Springer.

RAO, C. R. (1950). Methods of scoring linkage data giving the simultaneous segregation of three factors. *Heredity*, **4**, 37–59.

RAO, C. R. (1954). Estimation of relative potency from multiple response data. *Biometrics*, **10**, 208–220.

REED, L. J., & MUENCH, H. (1938). A simple method of estimating fifty per cent. endpoints. *American Journal of Hygiene*, **27**, 493–497.

SAMPFORD, M. R. (1952a). The estimation of response-time distributions. I. Fundamental concepts and general methods. *Biometrics*, **8**, 13–32.

SAMPFORD, M. R. (1952b). The estimation of response-time distributions. II. Multi-stimulus distributions. *Biometrics*, **8**, 307–369.

SAMPFORD, M. R. (1954). The estimation of response-time distributions. III. Truncation and survival. *Biometrics*, **10**, 531–561.

SAMPFORD, M. R. (1957). Methods of construction and analysis of serially balanced sequences. *Journal of the Royal Statistical Society*, **B 19**, 286–304.

SCHILD, H. O. (1942). A method of conducting a biological assay on a preparation giving repeated graded responses illustrated by the estimation of histamine. *Journal of Physiology*, **101**, 115–130.

SCHILD, H. O. (1950). General approach to biological assays. *Analyst*, **75**, 533–536.

SCHILD, H. O. (1959). The use of incomplete randomized blocks in an oxytocic assay. In *Quantitative Methods in Human Pharmacology and Therapeutics*, edited by D. R. Laurence, London: Pergamon Press.

SHEPS, M. C. & MUNSON, P. I. (1957). The error of replicated potency estimates in a biological assay method of the parallel line type. *Biometrics*, **13**, 131–148.

SHERWOOD, M. B. (1947). Simple formulas for calculating percentage potency in three- and four-dose assay procedures. *Science*, **106**, 152–153.

SHERWOOD, M. B. (1951). A universal line graph for estimating percentage potency in multidose assays. *Science*, **113**, 185–187.

SHERWOOD, M. B., FALCO, E. A., & DeBEER, E. J. (1944). A rapid, quantitative method for the determination of penicillin. *Science*, **99**, 247–248.

SHEWHART, W. A. (1931). *Economic Control of Quality of a Manufactured Product*. New York: Van Nostrand.

SMITH, B., & VOS, B. J. (1943). The biological assay of posterior pituitary solution. *Journal of Pharmacology and Experimental Therapeutics*, **78**, 72–78.

SMITH, K. W., MARKS, H. P., FIELLER, E. C., & BROOM, W. A. (1944). An extended cross-over design and its use in insulin assay. *Quarterly Journal of Pharmacy and Pharmacology*, **17**, 108–117.

SNEDECOR, G. W. (1956). *Statistical Methods* (5th edition). Ames, Iowa: State College Press.

SOLOMON, L. (1948*a*). Statistical estimation. *Journal of the Institute of Actuaries Students' Society*, **7**, 144–173.

SOLOMON, L. (1948*b*). Statistical estimation (continued). *Journal of the Institute of Actuaries Students' Society*, **7**, 213–234.

SOMERS, G. F. (1950). The measurement of thyroidal activity. *Analyst*, **75**, 537–541.

SOMERS, G. F., & EDGE, N. D. (1947). Comparative activities of amethocaine, cinchocaine and procaine as local anaesthetics. *Quarterly Journal of Pharmacy and Pharmacology*, **20**, 380–387.

SPEARMAN, C. (1908). The method of ' right and wrong cases ' ('constant stimuli') without Gauss's formulae. *British Journal of Psychology*, **2**, 227–242.

STEVENS, W. L. (1937). Appendix to Bliss (1937). The truncated normal distribution. *Annals of Applied Biology*, **24**, 847–850.

STEVENS, W. L. (1958). Dilution series: a statistical test of technique. *Journal of the Royal Statistical Society*, **B 20**, 205–214.

SWAROOP, S. (1938). Numerical estimation of *B. coli* by dilution method. *Indian Journal of Medical Research*, **26**, 353–378.

SWAROOP, S. (1940). Error in the estimation of the most probable number of organisms by the dilution method. *Indian Journal of Medical Research*, **27**, 1129–1147.

SWAROOP, S. (1941*a*). A modification of the routine dilution tests and table showing the most probable number of organisms and the standard error of this number. *Indian Journal of Medical Research*, **29**, 499–510.

SWAROOP, S. (1941*b*). A consideration of the accuracy of estimation of the most probable number of organisms by dilution test. *Indian Journal of Medical Research*, **29**, 511–521.

THOMPSON, C. M. (1941). Table of percentage points of the χ^2 distribution. *Biometrika*, **32**, 187–191.

THOMPSON, R. E. (1944). Biological assay of posterior pituitary. *Journal of Pharmacology and Experimental Therapeutics*, **80**, 373–382.

THOMPSON, R. E. (1945). Biological assay of epinephrine. *Journal of the American Pharmaceutical Association*, **34**, 265–269.

THOMPSON, W. R. (1947). Use of moving averages and interpolation to estimate median-effective dose. I. Fundamental formulas, estimation of error, and relation to other methods. *Bacteriological Reviews*, **11**, 115–145.

THOMPSON, W. R. (1948). On the use of parallel or non-parallel systems of transformed curves in bio-assay: Illustrations in the quantitative complement-fixation test. *Biometrics*, **4**, 197–210.

THOMPSON, W. R., & WEIL, C. S. (1952). On the construction of tables for moving-average interpolation. *Biometrics*, **8**, 51–54.

TREVAN, J. W. (1927). The error of determination of toxicity. *Proceedings of the Royal Society*, **B 101**, 483–514.

TREVAN, J. W. (1929). A statistical note on the testing of anti-dysentery sera. *Journal of Pathology and Bacteriology*, **32**, 127–134.

TUKEY, J. W. (1948). Approximate weights. *Annals of Mathematical Statistics*, **19**, 91–92.

TUKEY, J. W. (1949). Answer to Question 21. *The American Statistician*, **3**, no. 4, 12.

UNITED STATES PHARMACOPEIA (1960). Washington, D.C.: United States Pharmacopeial Convention, Inc.

URBAN, F. M. (1909). Die psychophysischen Massmethoden als Grundlagen empirischer Messungen. *Archiv für die gesamte Psychologie*, **15**, 261–355.

URBAN, F. M. (1910). Die psychophysischen Massmethoden als Grundlagen empirischer Messungen (continued). *Archiv für die gesamte Psychologie*, **16**, 168–227.

VAN DER WAERDEN, B. L. (1940a). Biologische Konzentrazionsauswertung. *Berichte über die Verhandlungen der Sächsischen Akademie der Wissenchaften zu Leipzig*, **92**, 41–44.

VAN DER WAERDEN, B. L. (1940*b*). Wirksamkeits- und Konzentrationsbestimmung durch Tierversuche. *Archiv für Experimentelle Pathologie und Pharmakologie*, 195, 389–412.

VOS, B. J. (1943). Use of the latent period in the assay of ergonovine on the isolated rabbit uterus. *Journal of the American Pharmaceutical Association*, 32, 138–141.

VOS, B. J. (1950). Statistics in biological assay: An example of the graded response. *Annals of the New York Academy of Sciences*, 52, 920–921.

WADLEY, F. M. (1948). Experimental design in comparison of allergens on cattle. *Biometrics*, 4, 100–108.

WADLEY, F. M. (1949*a*). Dosage-mortality correlation with number treated estimated from a parallel sample. *Annals of Applied Biology*, 36, 196–202.

WADLEY, F. M. (1949*b*). The use of biometric methods in comparison of acid-fast allergens. *American Review of Tuberculosis*, 60, 131–139.

WEIL, C. S. (1952). Tables for convenient calculation of median-effective dose (LD_{50} or ED_{50}) and instructions in their use. *Biometrics*, 8, 249–263.

WILLIAMS, E. J. (1949). Experimental designs balanced for the estimation of residual effects of treatments. *Australian Journal of Scientific Research*, A 2, 149–168.

WILLIAMS, E. J. (1950). Experimental designs balanced for pairs of residual effects. *Australian Journal of Scientific Research*, A 3, 351–363.

WILLIAMS, E. J. (1959). *Regression Analysis*. New York: John Wiley & Sons, Inc.

WILSON, E. B., & WORCESTER, J. (1943*a*). The determination of L.D.50 and its sampling error in bio-assay. *Proceedings of the National Academy of Sciences*, 29, 79–85.

WILSON, E. B., & WORCESTER, J. (1943*b*). The determination of L.D.50 and its sampling error in bio-assay. II. *Proceedings of the National Academy of Sciences*, 29, 114–120.

WILSON, E. B., & WORCESTER, J. (1943*c*). Bio-assay on a general curve. *Proceedings of the National Academy of Sciences*, 29, 150–154.

WILSON, E. B., & WORCESTER, J. (1943*d*). The determination of L.D.50 and its sampling error in bio-assay. III. *Proceedings of the National Academy of Sciences*, **29**, 257–262.

WINDER, C. V. (1947). Misuse of ' deduced ratios ' in the estimation of median effective doses. *Nature*, **159**, 883.

WOOD, E. C. (1944*a*). Mathematics of biological assay. *Nature*, **153**, 84–85.

WOOD, E. C. (1944*b*). Mathematics of biological assay. *Nature*, **153**, 681–682.

WOOD, E. C. (1945). Calculation of the results of microbiological assays. *Nature*, **155**, 632–633.

WOOD, E. C. (1946*a*). The theory of certain analytical procedures, with particular reference to micro-biological assays. *Analyst*, **71**, 1–14.

WOOD, E. C. (1946*b*). Computation of biological assays. *Nature*, **158**, 835.

WOOD, E. C. (1947*a*). The computation of microbiological assays of amino-acids and other growth factors. *Analyst*, **72**, 84–90.

WOOD, E. C. (1947*b*). Short cuts to the estimation of standard errors, particularly in microbiological assays. *Chemistry and Industry*, 334–336.

WOOD, E. C., & FINNEY, D. J. (1946). The design and statistical analysis of microbiological assays. *Quarterly Journal of Pharmacy and Pharmacology*, **19**, 112–127.

WORCESTER, J., & WILSON, E. B. (1943). A table determining L.D.50 or the fifty per cent. end point. *Proceedings of the National Academy of Sciences*, **29**, 207–212.

WRIGHT, H. N. (1941). A simple statistical method for the calculation of mortality percentage in digitalis assay. *Journal of the American Pharmaceutical Association*, **30**, 177–180.

YATES, F. (1933*a*). The analysis of replicated experiments when the field results are incomplete. *Empire Journal of Experimental Agriculture*, **1**, 129–142.

YATES, F. (1933*b*). The principles of orthogonality and confounding in replicated experiments. *Journal of Agricultural Science*, **23**, 108–145.

YATES, F. (1937a). The design and analysis of factorial experiments. *Imperial Bureau of Soil Science, Harpenden, Technical Communication*, no. 35.

YATES, F. (1937b). Incomplete randomized blocks. *Annals of Eugenics*, 7, 121–140.

YATES, F. (1939). An apparent inconsistency arising from tests of significance based on fiducial distributions of unknown parameters. *Proceedings of the Cambridge Philosophical Society*, 35, 579–591.

YATES, F. (1940). The recovery of inter-block information in balanced incomplete block designs. *Annals of Eugenics*, 10, 317–325.

YOUDEN, W. J. (1937). Use of incomplete block replications in estimating tobacco-mosaic virus. *Contributions from the Boyce Thompson Institute*, 9, 41–48.

YOUDEN, W. J. (1940). Experimental designs to increase accuracy of greenhouse studies. *Contributions from the Boyce Thompson Institute*, 11, 219 228.

YOUNG, D. M., & ROMANS, R. G. (1948). Assays of insulin with one blood sample per rabbit per test day. *Biometrics*, 4, 122–131.

ZIEGLER, N. R., & HALVORSON, H. O. (1935). Application of statistics to problems in bacteriology. IV. Experimental comparison of the dilution method, the plate count, and the direct count for the determination of bacterial populations. *Journal of Bacteriology*, 29, 609–634.

APPENDIX TABLES

A set of tables of standard statistical functions is as essential to the regular user of bioassay techniques as are tables of elementary mathematical functions. In their *Statistical Tables for Biological, Agricultural and Medical Research*, R. A. Fisher and F. Yates have given tables of both kinds to an accuracy sufficient for most practical purposes. Since this or a similar collection of tables ought to be available to all who apply statistical methods, full reproduction of the relevant tables here is unnecessary. Nevertheless as an aid to the reader who is studying, rather than practising, the techniques described in this book, abridged versions of tables of the distributions of t, χ^2, the variance ratio, and the Behrens ratio are included in the following pages. For many applications, indeed, the accuracy and detail of these abridgements is sufficient, but for the numerical examples of this book the full tables have generally been used.

The analysis of assays based on quantal responses requires tables that are not always so readily available. These appear as Tables V-XVII, which are of the full accuracy generally needed.

I am indebted to Professor Fisher and Dr. Yates, and to their publishers, Messrs. Oliver & Boyd Ltd., for permission to include from their collection abridgements of Tables III, V, V_1, and IV and Table XII in full as Tables I, II, III, IV and XI of this Appendix, and also to the Cambridge University Press for permission to include Tables III and IV from my *Probit Analysis* as Tables VI and VII of this Appendix.

TABLE I—The distribution of t

[Abridged from Fisher & Yates (1963, Table III). Merrington (1942) has given a table for some additional percentage points]

Degrees of freedom (f)	Probability			
	10%	5%	1%	0·1%
1	6·31	12·7	63·7	637·0
2	2·92	4·30	9·92	31·6
3	2·35	3·18	5·84	12·9
4	2·13	2·78	4·60	8·61
5	2·02	2·57	4·03	6·86
6	1·94	2·45	3·71	5·96
7	1·90	2·36	3·50	5·40
8	1·86	2·31	3·36	5·04
9	1·83	2·26	3·25	4·78
10	1·81	2·23	3·17	4·59
12	1·78	2·18	3·06	4·32
14	1·76	2·14	2·98	4·14
16	1·75	2·12	2·92	4·02
18	1·73	2·10	2·88	3·92
20	1·72	2·09	2·84	3·85
22	1·72	2·07	2·82	3·79
24	1·71	2·06	2·80	3·74
26	1·71	2·06	2·78	3·71
28	1·70	2·05	2·76	3·67
30	1·70	2·04	2·75	3·65
40	1·68	2·02	2·70	3·55
60	1·67	2·00	2·66	3·46
120	1·66	1·98	2·62	3·37
∞ (normal distribution)	1·645	1·960	2·576	3·291

TABLE II—The distribution of the variance ratio

[Abridged from Fisher & Yates (1963, Table V). Merrington & Thompson (1943) have given a table for some additional percentage points and additional values of f_1]

(a) 5% probability

Values of f_2	Values of f_1						
	1	2	3	4	6	12	∞
1	161·	200·	216·	225·	234·	244·	254·
2	18·5	19·0	19·2	19·2	19·3	19·4	19·5
3	10·1	9·6	9·3	9·1	8·9	8·7	8·5
4	7·7	6·9	6·6	6·4	6·2	5·9	5·6
5	6·6	5·8	5·4	5·2	5·0	4·7	4·4
6	6·0	5·1	4·8	4·5	4·3	4·0	3·7
7	5·6	4·7	4·3	4·1	3·9	3·6	3·2
8	5·3	4·5	4·1	3·8	3·6	3·3	2·9
9	5·1	4·3	3·9	3·6	3·4	3·1	2·7
10	5·0	4·1	3·7	3·5	3·2	2·9	2·5
15	4·5	3·7	3·3	3·1	2·8	2·5	2·1
20	4·4	3·5	3·1	2·9	2·6	2·3	1·8
30	4·2	3·3	2·9	2·7	2·4	2·1	1·6
60	4·0	3·2	2·8	2·5	2·3	1·9	1·4
∞	3·8	3·0	2·6	2·4	2·1	1·8	1·0

(b) 1% probability

Values of f_2	Values of f_1						
	1	2	3	4	6	12	∞
1	4,052·	4,999·	5,403·	5,625·	5,859·	6,106·	6,366·
2	98·5	99·0	99·2	99·2	99·3	99·4	99·5
3	34·1	30·8	29·5	28·7	27·9	27·1	26·1
4	21·2	18·0	16·7	16·0	15·2	14·4	13·5
5	16·3	13·3	12·1	11·4	10·7	9·9	9·0
6	13·7	10·9	9·8	9·1	8·5	7·7	6·9
7	12·2	9·5	8·5	7·8	7·2	6·5	5·6
8	11·3	8·6	7·6	7·0	6·4	5·7	4·9
9	10·6	8·0	7·0	6·4	5·8	5·1	4·3
10	10·0	7·6	6·6	6·0	5·4	4·7	3·9
15	8·7	6·4	5·4	4·9	4·3	3·7	2·9
20	8·1	5·8	4·9	4·4	3·9	3·2	2·4
30	7·6	5·4	4·5	4·0	3·5	2·8	2·0
60	7·1	5·0	4·1	3·6	3·1	2·5	1·6
∞	6·6	4·6	3·8	3·3	2·8	2·2	1·0

TABLE III—The Behrens distribution
[Abridged from Fisher & Yates (1963, Table V_1)]

(a) 5% probability

Values of		Values of f_1				
f_2	θ	6	8	12	24	∞
	0°	2·45	2·45	2·45	2·45	2·45
	15°	2·44	2·43	2·42	2·42	2·41
6	30°	2·44	2·40	2·37	2·34	2·32
	45°	2·44	2·36	2·30	2·25	2·20
	0°	2·31	2·31	2·31	2·31	2·31
	15°	2·31	2·30	2·29	2·29	2·28
8	30°	2·33	2·29	2·26	2·24	2·22
	45°	2·36	2·29	2·23	2·18	2·13
	0°	2·18	2·18	2·18	2·18	2·18
	15°	2·19	2·18	2·18	2·17	2·16
12	30°	2·24	2·20	2·17	2·14	2·12
	45°	2·30	2·23	2·17	2·11	2·06
	0°	2·06	2·06	2·06	2·06	2·06
	15°	2·09	2·08	2·07	2·06	2·06
24	30°	2·16	2·12	2·08	2·06	2·04
	45°	2·25	2·18	2·11	2·06	2·01
	0°	1·96	1·96	1·96	1·96	1·96
	15°	1·99	1·98	1·97	1·97	1·96
∞	30°	2·08	2·04	2·01	1·98	1·96
	45°	2·20	2·13	2·06	2·01	1·96

TABLE III (*cont.*)—**The Behrens distribution**

(*b*) 1% probability

Values of		Values of f_1				
f_2	θ	6	8	12	24	∞
	0°	3·71	3·71	3·71	3·71	3·71
	15°	3·65	3·64	3·64	3·63	3·63
6	30°	3·56	3·50	3·45	3·42	3·40
	45°	3·51	3·36	3·25	3·16	3·09
	0°	3·36	3·36	3·36	3·36	3·36
	15°	3·33	3·32	3·31	3·30	3·30
8	30°	3·31	3·24	3·19	3·16	3·13
	45°	3·36	3·21	3·08	2·99	2·92
	0°	3·06	3·06	3·06	3·06	3·06
	15°	3·05	3·04	3·03	3·02	3·01
12	30°	3·10	3·03	2·98	2·94	2·91
	45°	3·25	3·08	2·95	2·85	2·78
	0°	2·80	2·80	2·80	2·80	2·80
	15°	2·82	2·80	2·79	2·78	2·78
24	30°	2·94	2·86	2·80	2·76	2·73
	45°	3·16	2·99	2·85	2·75	2·66
	0°	2·58	2·58	2·58	2·58	2·58
	15°	2·63	2·61	2·60	2·58	2·58
∞	30°	2·80	2·72	2·66	2·61	2·58
	45°	3·09	2·92	2·78	2·66	2·58

For $\theta > 45°$, note that the d-deviate for (f_1, f_2, θ) is identical with that for $(f_2, f_1, 90°-\theta)$.

TABLE IV—The distribution of χ^2

[Abridged from Fisher & Yates (1963, Table IV) ; Thompson (1941) has given a table for many additional percentage points and values of f]

Degrees of freedom (f)	Probability			
	10%	5%	1%	0·1%
1	2·7	3·8	6·6	10·8
2	4·6	6·0	9·2	13·8
3	6·3	7·8	11·3	16·3
4	7·8	9·5	13·3	18·5
5	9·2	11·1	15·1	20·5
6	10·6	12·6	16·8	22·5
7	12·0	14·1	18·5	24·3
8	13·4	15·5	20·1	26·1
9	14·7	16·9	21·7	27·9
10	16·0	18·3	23·2	29·6
12	18·5	21·0	26·2	32·9
14	21·1	23·7	29·1	36·1
16	23·5	26·3	32·0	39·3
18	26·0	28·9	34·8	42·3
20	28·4	31·4	37·6	45·3
22	30·8	33·9	40·3	48·3
24	33·2	36·4	43·0	51·2
26	35·6	38·9	45·6	54·1
28	37·9	41·3	48·3	56·9
30	40·3	43·8	50·9	59·7

When χ^2 is based on more than 30 degrees of freedom the tabular value may be taken as approximately $\{\sqrt{(f-\frac{1}{2})} + B\}^2$ where
$$B = 0\cdot91,\ 1\cdot16,\ 1\cdot64,\ \text{and}\ 2\cdot19$$
for the 10%, 5%, 1%, and 0·1% probabilities respectively.

TABLE V—The probit transformation

[Fisher & Yates (1963) & Finney (1952) have tabulated the probit at intervals of 0·001 in the response rate]

Res-ponse rate	0·00	0·01	0·02	0·03	0·04	0·05	0·06	0·07	0·08	0·09
0·00	—	2·67	2·95	3·12	3·25	3·36	3·45	3·52	3·59	3·66
0·10	3·72	3·77	3·82	3·87	3·92	3·96	4·01	4·05	4·08	4·12
0·20	4·16	4·19	4·23	4·26	4·29	4·33	4·36	4·39	4·42	4·45
0·30	4·48	4·50	4·53	4·56	4·59	4·61	4·64	4·67	4·69	4·72
0·40	4·75	4·77	4·80	4·82	4·85	4·87	4·90	4·92	4·95	4·97
0·50	5·00	5·03	5·05	5·08	5·10	5·13	5·15	5·18	5·20	5·23
0·60	5·25	5·28	5·31	5·33	5·36	5·39	5·41	5·44	5·47	5·50
0·70	5·52	5·55	5·58	5·61	5·64	5·67	5·71	5·74	5·77	5·81
0·80	5·84	5·88	5·92	5·95	5·99	6·04	6·08	6·13	6·18	6·23
0·90	6·28	6·34	6·41	6·48	6·55	6·64	6·75	6·88	7·05	7·33

Res-ponse rate	0·000	0·001	0·002	0·003	0·004	0·005	0·006	0·007	0·008	0·009
0·97	6·88	6·90	6·91	6·93	6·94	6·96	6·98	7·00	7·01	7·03
0·98	7·05	7·07	7·10	7·12	7·14	7·17	7·20	7·23	7·26	7·29
0·99	7·33	7·37	7·41	7·46	7·51	7·58	7·65	7·75	7·88	8·09

TABLE VI—Minimum and maximum working probits, range, and weighting coefficient

Minimum working probit		Range	Maximum working probit		Weighting coefficient
Expected probit Y	Y_0	A	Y_1	Expected probit Y	w
1·1	0·8579	5,034·	9·1421	8·9	·00082
1·2	0·9522	3,425·	9·0478	8·8	·00118
1·3	1·0462	2,354·	8·9538	8·7	·00167
1·4	1·1400	1,634·	8·8600	8·6	·00235
1·5	1·2334	1,146·	8·7666	8·5	·00327
1·6	1·3266	811·5	8·6734	8·4	·00451
1·7	1·4194	580·5	8·5806	8·3	·00614
1·8	1·5118	419·4	8·4882	8·2	·00828
1·9	1·6038	306·1	8·3962	8·1	·01104
2·0	1·6954	225·6	8·3046	8·0	·01457
2·1	1·7866	168·00	8·2134	7·9	·01903
2·2	1·8772	126·34	8·1228	7·8	·02458
2·3	1·9673	95·96	8·0327	7·7	·03143
2·4	2·0568	73·62	7·9432	7·6	·03977
2·5	2·1457	57·05	7·8543	7·5	·04979
2·6	2·2339	44·654	7·7661	7·4	·06168
2·7	2·3214	35·302	7·6786	7·3	·07564
2·8	2·4081	28·189	7·5919	7·2	·09179
2·9	2·4938	22·736	7·5062	7·1	·11026
3·0	2·5786	18·522	7·4214	7·0	·13112
3·1	2·6624	15·2402	7·3376	6·9	·15430
3·2	2·7449	12·6662	7·2551	6·8	·17994
3·3	2·8261	10·6327	7·1739	6·7	·20774
3·4	2·9060	9·0154	7·0940	6·6	·23753
3·5	2·9842	7·7210	7·0158	6·5	·26907
3·6	3·0606	6·6788	6·9394	6·4	·30199
3·7	3·1351	5·8354	6·8649	6·3	·33589
3·8	3·2074	5·1497	6·7926	6·2	·37031
3·9	3·2773	4·5903	6·7227	6·1	·40474
4·0	3·3443	4·1327	6·6557	6·0	·43863
4·1	3·4083	3·7582	6·5917	5·9	·47144
4·2	3·4687	3·4519	6·5313	5·8	·50260
4·3	3·5251	3·2025	6·4749	5·7	·53159
4·4	3·5770	3·0010	6·4230	5·6	·55788
4·5	3·6236	2·8404	6·3764	5·5	·58099
4·6	3·6643	2·7154	6·3357	5·4	·60052
4·7	3·6982	2·6220	6·3018	5·3	·61609
4·8	3·7241	2·5573	6·2759	5·2	·62742
4·9	3·7407	2·5192	6·2593	5·1	·63431
5·0	3·7467	2·5066	6·2533	5·0	·63662
5·1	3·7401	2·5192	6·2599	4·9	·63431
5·2	3·7187	2·5573	6·2813	4·8	·62742
5·3	3·6798	2·6220	6·3202	4·7	·61609
5·4	3·6203	2·7154	6·3797	4·6	·60052
5·5	3·5360	2·8404	6·4640	4·5	·58099
5·6	3·4220	3·0010	6·5780	4·4	·55788
5·7	3·2724	3·2025	6·7276	4·3	·53159
5·8	3·0794	3·4519	6·9206	4·2	·50260
5·9	2·8335	3·7582	7·1665	4·1	·47144
6·0	2·5229	4·1327	7·4771	4·0	·43863
6·1	2·1325	4·5903	7·8675	3·9	·40474
6·2	1·6429	5·1497	8·3571	3·8	·37031
6·3	1·0295	5·8354	8·9705	3·7	·33589
6·4	0·2606	6·6788	9·7394	3·6	·30199
6·5	− 0·7051	7·7210	10·7051	3·5	·26907

TABLE VII—Working probits

$$(Y = 2 \cdot 0 - 2 \cdot 9 ; \quad p = 0 \cdot 00 - 0 \cdot 33)$$

Response rate, p	Expected probit, Y									
	2·0	2·1	2·2	2·3	2·4	2·5	2·6	2·7	2·8	2·9
·00	1·695	1·787	1·877	1·967	2·057	2·146	2·234	2·321	2·408	2·494
·01	3·951	3·467	3·141	2·927	2·793	2·716	2·681	2·674	2·690	2·721
·02	6·207	5·147	4·404	3·886	3·529	3·287	3·127	3·027	·972	·949
·03	8·463	6·827	5·667	4·846	4·265	·857	·574	·380	3·254	3·176
·04		8·507	6·931	5·806	5·002	4·428	4·020	·733	·536	·403
·05			8·194	6·765	·738	·998	·467	4·086	·818	·631
·06			9·458	7·725	6·474	5·569	4·913	4·440	4·099	3·858
·07				8·684	7·210	6·139	5·360	·793	·381	4·085
·08				9·644	·946	·710	·806	5·146	·663	·313
·09					8·683	7·280	6·253	·499	·945	·540
·10					9·419	·851	·699	·852	5·227	·767
·11						8·421	7·146	6·205	5·509	4·995
·12						·992	·592	·558	·791	5·222
·13						9·562	8·039	·911	6·073	·449
·14							·486	7·264	·355	·677
·15							·932	·617	·636	·904
·16							9·379	7·970	6·918	6·132
·17							·825	8·323	7·200	·359
·18								·676	·482	·586
·19								9·029	·764	·814
·20								·382	8·046	7·041
·21								9·735	8·328	7·268
·22									·610	·496
·23									·892	·723
·24									9·173	·950
·25									·455	8·178
·26									9·737	8·405
·27										·633
·28										·860
·29										9·087
·30										·315
·31										9·542
·32										·769
·33										·997

TABLE VII (cont.)—Working probits

$$(Y = 3 \cdot 0 - 3 \cdot 9 \; ; \; p = 0 \cdot 00 - 0 \cdot 50)$$

Response rate, p	Expected probit, Y									
	3·0	3·1	3·2	3·3	3·4	3·5	3·6	3·7	3·8	3·9
·00	2·579	2·662	2·745	2·826	2·906	2·984	3·061	3·135	3·207	3·277
·01	2·764	2·815	2·872	2·932	2·996	3·061	3·127	3·193	3·259	3·323
·02	·949	·967	·998	3·039	3·086	·139	·194	·252	·310	·369
·03	3·134	3·120	3·125	·145	·176	·216	·261	·310	·362	·415
·04	·319	·272	·252	·251	·267	·293	·328	·369	·413	·461
·05	·505	·424	·378	·358	·357	·370	·395	·427	·465	·507
·06	3·690	3·577	3·505	3·464	3·447	3·447	3·461	3·485	3·516	3·553
·07	·875	·729	·632	·570	·537	·525	·528	·544	·568	·599
·08	4·060	·882	·758	·677	·627	·602	·595	·602	·619	·645
·09	·246	4·034	·885	·783	·717	·679	·662	·660	·671	·690
·10	·431	·186	4·012	·889	·808	·756	·728	·719	·722	·736
·11	4·616	4·339	4·138	3·996	3·898	3·834	3·795	3·777	3·774	3·782
·12	·801	·491	·265	4·102	·988	·911	·862	·835	·825	·828
·13	·986	·644	·391	·208	4·078	·988	·929	·894	·877	·874
·14	5·172	·796	·518	·315	·168	4·065	·996	·952	·928	·920
·15	·357	·948	·645	·421	·258	·142	4·062	4·010	·980	·966
·16	5·542	5·101	4·771	4·527	4·348	4·220	4·129	4·069	4·031	4·012
·17	·727	·253	·898	·634	·439	·297	·196	·127	·083	·058
·18	·913	·406	5·025	·740	·529	·374	·263	·185	·134	·104
·19	6·098	·558	·151	·846	·619	·451	·330	·244	·186	·149
·20	·283	·710	·278	·953	·709	·528	·396	·302	·237	·195
·21	6·468	5·863	5·405	5·059	4·799	4·606	4·463	4·361	4·289	4·241
·22	·653	6·015	·531	·165	·889	·683	·530	·419	·340	·287
·23	·839	·168	·658	·272	·979	·760	·597	·477	·392	·333
·24	7·024	·320	·785	·378	5·070	·837	·664	·536	·443	·379
·25	·209	·472	·911	·484	·160	·914	·730	·594	·495	·425
·26	7·394	6·625	6·038	5·591	5·250	4·992	4·797	4·652	4·546	4·471
·27	·580	·777	·165	·697	·340	5·069	·864	·711	·598	·517
·28	·765	·930	·291	·803	·430	·146	·931	·769	·649	·563
·29	·950	7·082	·418	·910	·520	·223	·997	·827	·701	·608
·30	8·135	·234	·545	6·016	·610	·300	5·064	·886	·752	·654
·31	8·320	7·387	6·671	6·122	5·701	5·378	5·131	4·944	4·804	4·700
·32	·506	539	·798	·229	·791	·455	·198	5·002	·855	·740
·33	·691	·692	·925	·335	·881	·532	·265	·061	·907	·792
·34	·876	·844	7·051	·441	·971	·609	·331	·119	·958	·838
·35	9·061	·996	·178	·548	6·061	·687	·398	·177	5·010	·884
·36	9·247	8·149	7·305	6·654	6·151	5·764	5·465	5·236	5·061	4·930
·37	·432	·301	·431	·760	·242	·841	·532	·294	·113	·976
·38	·617	·454	·558	·867	·332	·918	·599	·353	·164	5·022
·39	·802	·606	·685	·973	·422	·995	·665	·411	·216	·068
·40	·987	·758	·811	7·079	·512	6·073	·732	·469	·267	·113
·41		8·911	7·938	7·186	6·602	6·150	5·799	5·528	5·319	5·159
·42		9·063	8·065	·292	·692	·227	·866	·586	·370	·205
·43		·216	·191	·398	·782	·304	·932	·644	·422	·251
·44		·368	·318	·505	·873	·381	·999	·703	·473	·297
·45		·520	·445	·611	·963	·459	6·066	·761	·525	·343
·46		9·673	8·571	7·717	7·053	6·536	6·133	5·819	5·576	5·389
·47		·825	·698	·824	·143	·613	·200	·878	·628	·435
·48		·978	·825	·930	·233	·690	·266	·936	·670	·481
·49			·951	8·036	·323	·767	·333	·994	·731	·527
·50			9·078	·143	·414	·845	·400	6·053	·782	·572

TABLE VII (*cont.*)—Working probits

$$(Y = 3 \cdot 0 - 3 \cdot 9 \; ; \; p = 0 \cdot 51 - 1 \cdot 00)$$

Response rate, p	Expected probit, Y									
	3·0	3·1	3·2	3·3	3·4	3·5	3·6	3·7	3·8	3·9
·51			9·205	8·249	7·504	6·922	6·467	6·111	5·834	5·618
·52			·331	·355	·594	·999	·534	·170	·885	·664
·53			·458	·462	·684	7·076	·600	·228	·937	·710
·54			·585	·568	·774	·154	·667	·286	·988	·756
·55			·711	·674	·864	·231	·734	·345	6·040	·802
·56			9·838	8·781	7·954	7·308	6·801	6·403	6·091	5·848
·57			·965	·887	8·045	·385	·868	·461	·143	·894
·58				·993	·135	·462	·934	·520	·194	·940
·59				9·100	·225	·540	7·001	·578	·246	·986
·60				·206	·315	·617	·068	·636	·297	6·031
·61				9·312	8·405	7·694	7·135	6·695	6·349	6·077
·62				·419	·495	·771	·201	·753	·400	·123
·63				·525	·585	·848	·268	·811	·452	·169
·64				·631	·676	·926	·335	·870	·503	·215
·65				·738	·766	8·003	·402	·928	·555	·261
·66				9·844	8·856	8·080	7·469	6·986	6·606	6·307
·67				·950	·946	·157	·535	7·045	·658	·353
·68					9·036	·234	·602	·103	·709	·399
·69					·126	·312	·669	·162	·761	·445
·70					·216	·389	·736	·220	·812	·491
·71					9·307	8·466	7·803	7·278	6·864	6·536
·72					·397	·543	·869	·337	·915	·582
·73					·487	·621	·936	·395	·967	·628
·74					·577	·698	8·003	·453	7·018	·674
·75					·667	·775	·070	·512	·070	·720
·76					9·757	8·852	8·136	7·570	7·121	6·766
·77					·848	·929	·203	·628	·173	·812
·78					·938	9·007	·270	·687	·224	·858
·79						·084	·337	·745	·276	·904
·80						·161	·404	·803	·327	·950
·81						9·238	8·470	7·862	7·379	6·995
·82						·315	·537	·920	·430	7·041
·83						·393	·604	·978	·482	·087
·84						·470	·671	8·037	·533	·133
·85						·547	·738	·095	·585	·179
·86						9·624	8·804	8·154	7·636	7·225
·87						·701	·871	·212	·688	·271
·88						·779	·938	·270	·739	·317
·89						·856	9·005	·329	·791	·363
·90						·933	·072	·387	·842	·409
·91							9·138	8·445	7·894	7·454
·92							·205	·504	·945	·500
·93							·272	·562	·997	·546
·94							·339	·620	8·048	·592
·95							·405	·679	·100	·638
·96							9·472	8·737	8·151	7·684
·97							·539	·795	·203	·730
·98							·606	·854	·254	·776
·99							·673	·912	·306	·822
1·00							·739	·970	·357	·868

TABLE VII (*cont.*)—Working probits

$$(Y = 4.0 - 4.9 ; \quad p = 0.00 - 0.50)$$

Res-ponse rate, *p*	Expected probit, *Y*									
	4·0	4·1	4·2	4·3	4·4	4·5	4·6	4·7	4·8	4·9
·00	3·344	3·408	3·469	3·525	3·577	3·624	3·664	3·698	3·724	3·741
·01	3·386	3·446	3·503	3·557	3·607	3·652	3·691	3·724	3·750	3·766
·02	·427	·487	·538	·589	·637	·680	·719	·751	·775	·791
·03	·468	·521	·572	·621	·667	·709	·746	·777	·801	·816
·04	·510	·559	·607	·653	·697	·737	·773	·803	·826	·841
·05	·551	·596	·641	·685	·727	·766	·800	·829	·852	·867
·06	3·592	3·634	3·676	3·717	3·757	3·794	3·827	3·856	3·878	3·892
·07	·634	·671	·710	·749	·787	·822	·854	·882	·903	·917
·08	·675	·709	·745	·781	·817	·851	·882	·908	·929	·942
·09	·716	·747	·779	·813	·847	·879	·909	·934	·954	·967
·10	·758	·784	·814	·845	·877	·908	·936	·960	·980	·993
·11	3·799	3·822	3·848	3·877	3·907	3·936	3·963	3·987	4·005	4·018
·12	·840	·859	·883	·909	·937	·964	·990	4·013	·031	·043
·13	·882	·897	·917	·941	·967	·993	4·017	·039	·057	·068
·14	·923	·934	·952	·973	·997	4·021	·044	·065	·082	·093
·15	·964	·972	·986	4·005	4·027	·050	·072	·092	·108	·119
·16	4·006	4·010	4·021	4·038	4·057	4·078	4·099	4·118	4·133	4·144
·17	·047	·047	·056	·070	·087	·106	·126	·144	·159	·169
·18	·088	·085	·090	·102	·117	·135	·153	·170	·184	·194
·19	·130	·122	·125	·134	·147	·163	·180	·196	·210	·219
·20	·171	·160	·159	·166	·177	·192	·207	·223	·236	·245
·21	4·212	4·198	4·194	4·198	4·207	4·220	4·235	4·249	4·261	4·270
·22	·253	·235	·228	·230	·237	·248	·262	·275	·287	·295
·23	·295	·273	·263	·262	·267	·277	·289	·301	·312	·320
·24	·336	·310	·297	·294	·297	·305	·316	·327	·338	·345
·25	·377	·348	·332	·326	·327	·334	·343	·354	·363	·370
·26	4·419	4·385	4·366	4·358	4·357	4·362	4·370	4·380	4·389	4·396
·27	·460	·423	·401	·390	·387	·391	·397	·406	·415	·421
·28	·501	·461	·435	·422	·417	·419	·425	·432	·440	·446
·29	·543	·498	·470	·454	·447	·447	·452	·459	·466	·471
·30	·584	·536	·504	·486	·477	·476	·470	·485	·491	·496
·31	4·625	4·573	4·539	4·518	4·507	4·504	4·506	4·511	4·517	4·522
·32	·667	·611	·573	·550	·537	·533	·533	·537	·542	·547
·33	·708	·649	·608	·582	·567	·561	·560	·563	·568	·572
·34	·749	·686	·642	·014	·597	·589	·588	·590	·594	·597
·35	·791	·724	·677	·646	·627	·618	·615	·616	·619	·622
·36	4·832	4·761	4·711	4·678	4·657	4·646	4·642	4·642	4·645	4·648
·37	·873	·799	·746	·710	·687	·675	·669	·668	·670	·673
·38	·915	·836	·780	·742	·717	·703	·696	·695	·696	·698
·39	·956	·874	·815	·774	·747	·731	·723	·721	·721	·723
·40	·997	·912	·849	·806	·777	·760	·750	·747	·747	·748
·41	5·039	4·949	4·884	4·838	4·807	4·788	4·778	4·773	4·773	4·774
·42	·080	·987	·918	·870	·837	·817	·805	·799	·798	·799
·43	·121	5·024	·953	·902	·867	·845	·832	·826	·824	·824
·44	·163	·062	·988	·934	·897	·873	·859	·852	·849	·849
·45	·204	·099	5·022	·966	·927	·902	·886	·878	·875	·874
·46	5·245	5·137	5·057	4·998	4·957	4·930	4·913	4·904	4·900	4·900
·47	·287	·175	·091	5·030	·987	·959	·941	·931	·926	·925
·48	·328	·212	·126	·062	5·017	·987	·968	·957	·952	·950
·49	·369	·250	·160	·094	·047	5·015	·995	·983	·977	·975
·50	·411	·287	·195	·126	·078	·044	5·022	5·009	5·003	5·000

TABLE VII (cont.)—Working probits

$$(Y = 4 \cdot 0 - 4 \cdot 9 \; ; \; p = 0 \cdot 51 - 1 \cdot 00)$$

Response rate, p	Expected probit, Y									
	4·0	4·1	4·2	4·3	4·4	4·5	4·6	4·7	4·8	4·9
·51	5·452	5·325	5·229	5·158	5·108	5·072	5·049	5·035	5·028	5·025
·52	·493	·363	·264	·190	·138	·101	·076	·062	·054	·051
·53	·535	·400	·298	·222	·168	·129	·103	·088	·079	·076
·54	·576	·438	·333	·254	·198	·157	·131	·114	·105	·101
·55	·617	·475	·367	·286	·228	·186	·158	·140	·131	·126
·56	5·659	5·513	5·402	5·318	5·258	5·214	5·185	5·167	5·156	5·151
·57	·700	·550	·436	·351	·288	·243	·212	·193	·182	·177
·58	·741	·588	·471	·383	·318	·271	·239	·219	·207	·202
·59	·783	·626	·505	·415	·348	·299	·266	·245	·233	·227
·60	·824	·663	·540	·447	·378	·328	·294	·271	·258	·252
·61	5·865	5·701	5·574	5·479	5·408	5·356	5·321	5·298	5·284	5·277
·62	·907	·738	·609	·511	·438	·385	·348	·324	·310	·303
·63	·948	·776	·643	·543	·468	·413	·375	·350	·335	·328
·64	·989	·814	·678	·575	·498	·441	·402	·376	·361	·353
·65	6·031	·851	·712	·607	·528	·470	·429	·402	·386	·378
·66	6·072	5·889	5·747	5·639	5·558	5·498	5·456	5·429	5·412	5·403
·67	·113	·926	·781	·671	·588	·527	·484	·455	·437	·429
·68	·155	·964	·816	·703	·618	·555	·511	·481	·463	·454
·69	·196	6·001	·851	·735	·648	·583	·538	·507	·489	·479
·70	·237	·039	·885	·767	·678	·612	·565	·534	·514	·504
·71	6·279	6·077	5·920	5·799	5·708	5·640	5·592	5·560	5·540	5·529
·72	·320	·114	·954	·831	·738	·669	·619	·586	·565	·555
·73	·361	·152	·989	·863	·768	·697	·647	·612	·591	·580
·74	·402	·189	6·023	·895	·798	·725	·674	·638	·617	·605
·75	·444	·227	·058	·927	·828	·754	·701	·665	·642	·630
·76	6·485	6·265	6·092	5·959	5·858	5·782	5·728	5·691	5·668	5·655
·77	·526	·302	·127	·991	·888	·811	·755	·717	·693	·680
·78	·568	·340	·161	6·023	·918	·839	·782	·743	·719	·706
·79	·609	·377	·196	·055	·948	·868	·809	·770	·744	·731
·80	·650	·415	·230	·087	·978	·896	·837	·796	·770	·756
·81	6·692	6·452	6·265	6·119	6·008	5·924	5·864	5·822	5·796	5·781
·82	·733	·490	·299	·151	·038	·953	·891	·848	·821	·806
·83	·774	·528	·334	·183	·068	·981	·918	·874	·847	·832
·84	·816	·565	·368	·215	·098	6·010	·945	·901	·872	·857
·85	·857	·603	·403	·247	·128	·038	·972	·927	·898	·882
·86	6·898	6·640	6·437	6·279	6·158	6·066	6·000	5·953	5·923	5·907
·87	·940	·678	·472	·311	·188	·095	·027	·979	·949	·932
·88	·981	·716	·506	·343	·218	·123	·054	6·006	·975	·958
·89	7·022	·753	·541	·375	·248	·152	·081	·032	6·000	·983
·90	·064	·791	·575	·407	·278	·180	·108	·058	·026	6·008
·91	7·105	6·828	6·610	6·439	6·308	6·208	6·135	6·084	6·051	6·033
·92	·146	·866	·644	·471	·338	·237	·162	·110	·077	·058
·93	·188	·903	·679	·503	·368	·265	·190	·137	·102	·084
·94	·229	·941	·713	·535	·398	·294	·217	·163	·128	·109
·95	·270	·979	·748	·567	·428	·322	·244	·189	·154	·134
·96	7·312	7·016	6·783	6·600	6·458	6·350	6·271	6·215	6·179	6·159
·97	·353	·054	·817	·632	·488	·379	·298	·242	·205	·184
·98	·394	·091	·852	·664	·518	·407	·325	·268	·230	·210
·99	·436	·129	·886	·696	·548	·436	·353	·294	·256	·235
1·00	·477	·166	·921	·728	·578	·464	·380	·320	·281	·260

TABLE VII (cont.)—Working probits

$$(Y = 5{\cdot}0 - 5{\cdot}9 \; ; \; p = 0{\cdot}00 - 0{\cdot}50)$$

Response rate, p	Expected probit, Y									
	5·0	5·1	5·2	5·3	5·4	5·5	5·6	5·7	5·8	5·9
·00	3·747	3·740	3·719	3·680	3·620	3·536	3·422	3·272	3·079	2·834
·01	3·772	3·765	3·744	3·706	3·647	3·564	3·452	3·304	3·114	2·871
·02	·797	·790	·770	·732	·675	·593	·482	·336	·148	·909
·03	·822	·816	·795	·758	·702	·621	·512	·368	·183	·946
·04	·847	·841	·821	·785	·729	·650	·542	·400	·217	·984
·05	·872	·866	·846	·811	·756	·678	·572	·433	·252	3·021
·06	3·897	3·891	3·872	3·837	3·783	3·706	3·602	3·465	3·287	3·059
·07	·922	·916	·898	·863	·810	·735	·632	·497	·321	·097
·08	·947	·942	·923	·890	·838	·763	·662	·529	·356	·134
·09	·972	·967	·949	·916	·865	·792	·692	·561	·390	·172
·10	·997	·992	·974	·942	·892	·820	·722	·593	·425	·209
·11	4·022	4·017	4·000	3·968	3·919	3·848	3·752	3·625	3·459	3·247
·12	·047	·042	·025	·994	·946	·877	·782	·657	·494	·284
·13	·073	·068	·051	4·021	·973	·905	·812	·689	·528	·322
·14	·098	·093	·077	·047	4·000	·934	·842	·721	·563	·360
·15	·123	·118	·102	·073	·028	·962	·872	·753	·597	·397
·16	4·148	4·143	4·128	4·099	4·055	3·990	3·902	3·785	3·632	3·435
·17	·173	·168	·153	·126	·082	4·019	·932	·817	·666	·472
·18	·198	·194	·179	·152	·109	·047	·962	·849	·701	·510
·19	·223	·219	·204	·178	·136	·076	·992	·881	·735	·548
·20	·248	·244	·230	·204	·163	·104	4·022	·913	·770	·585
·21	4·273	4·269	4·256	4·230	4·191	4·132	4·052	3·945	3·804	3·623
·22	·298	·294	·281	·257	·218	·161	·082	·977	·839	·660
·23	·323	·320	·307	·283	·245	·189	·112	4·009	·873	·698
·24	·348	·345	·332	·309	·272	·218	·142	·041	·908	·735
·25	·373	·370	·358	·335	·299	·246	·172	·073	·942	·773
·26	4·398	4·395	4·383	4·362	4·326	4·275	4·202	4·105	3·977	3·811
·27	·423	·420	·409	·388	·353	·303	·232	·137	4·011	·848
·28	·449	·445	·435	·414	·381	·331	·262	·169	·046	·886
·29	·474	·471	·460	·440	·408	·360	·292	·201	·080	·923
·30	·499	·496	·486	·466	·435	·388	·322	·233	·115	·961
·31	4·524	4·521	4·511	4·493	4·462	4·417	4·352	4·265	4·149	3·999
·32	·549	·546	·537	·519	·489	·445	·382	·297	·184	4·036
·33	·574	·571	·563	·545	·516	·473	·412	·329	·219	·074
·34	·599	·597	·588	·571	·544	·502	·442	·361	·253	·111
·35	·624	·622	·614	·598	·571	·530	·472	·393	·288	·149
·36	4·649	4·647	4·639	4·624	4·598	4·559	4·502	4·425	4·322	4·186
·37	·674	·672	·665	·650	·625	·587	·532	·457	·357	·224
·38	·699	·697	·690	·676	·652	·615	·562	·489	·391	·262
·39	·724	·723	·716	·702	·679	·644	·592	·521	·426	·299
·40	·749	·748	·742	·729	·706	·672	·622	·553	·460	·337
·41	4·774	4·773	4·767	4·755	4·734	4·701	4·652	4·585	4·495	4·374
·42	·799	·798	·793	·781	·761	·729	·682	·617	·529	·412
·43	·825	·823	·818	·807	·788	·757	·712	·649	·564	·450
·44	·850	·849	·844	·833	·815	·786	·742	·682	·598	·487
·45	·875	·874	·869	·860	·842	·814	·772	·714	·633	·525
·46	4·900	4·899	4·895	4·886	4·869	4·843	4·802	4·746	4·667	4·562
·47	·925	·924	·921	·912	·897	·871	·832	·778	·702	·600
·48	·950	·949	·946	·938	·924	·899	·862	·810	·736	·637
·49	·975	·975	·972	·965	·951	·928	·892	·842	·771	·675
·50	5·000	5·000	·997	·991	·978	·956	·922	·874	·805	·713

TABLE VII (cont.)—Working probits

$$(Y = 5\cdot0 - 5\cdot9 \; ; \; p = 0\cdot51 - 1\cdot00)$$

Response rate, p	Expected probit, Y									
	5·0	5·1	5·2	5·3	5·4	5·5	5·6	5·7	5·8	5·9
·51	5·025	5·025	5·023	5·017	5·005	4·985	4·953	4·906	4·840	4·750
·52	·050	·050	·048	·043	·032	5·013	·983	·938	·874	·788
·53	·075	·075	·074	·069	·059	·041	5·013	·970	·909	·825
·54	·100	·100	·100	·096	·087	·070	·043	5·002	·943	·863
·55	·125	·126	·125	·122	·114	·098	·073	·034	·978	·901
·56	5·150	5·151	5·151	5·148	5·141	5·127	5·103	5·066	5·012	4·938
·57	·175	·176	·176	·174	·168	·155	·133	·098	·047	·976
·58	·201	·201	·202	·201	·195	·183	·163	·130	·082	5·013
·59	·226	·226	·227	·227	·222	·212	·193	·162	·116	·051
·60	·251	·252	·253	·253	·250	·240	·223	·194	·151	·088
·61	5·276	5·277	5·279	5·279	5·277	5·269	5·253	5·226	5·185	5·126
·62	·301	·302	·304	·305	·304	·297	·283	·258	·220	·164
·63	·326	·327	·330	·332	·331	·325	·313	·290	·254	·201
·64	·351	·352	·355	·358	·358	·354	·343	·322	·289	·239
·65	·376	·378	·381	·384	·385	·382	·373	·354	·323	·276
·66	5·401	5·403	5·406	5·410	5·412	5·411	5·403	5·386	5·358	5·314
·67	·426	·428	·432	·437	·440	·439	·433	·418	·392	·351
·68	·451	·453	·458	·463	·467	·467	·463	·450	·427	·389
·69	·476	·478	·483	·489	·494	·496	·493	·482	·461	·427
·70	·501	·504	·509	·515	·521	·524	·523	·514	·496	·464
·71	5·526	5·529	5·534	5·541	5·548	5·553	5·553	5·546	5·530	5·502
·72	·551	·554	·560	·568	·575	·581	·583	·578	·565	·539
·73	·577	·579	·585	·594	·603	·609	·613	·610	·599	·577
·74	·602	·604	·611	·620	·630	·638	·643	·642	·634	·615
·75	·627	·630	·637	·646	·657	·666	·673	·674	·668	·652
·76	5·652	5·655	5·662	5·673	5·684	5·695	5·703	5·706	5·703	5·690
·77	·677	·680	·688	·699	·711	·723	·733	·738	·737	·727
·78	·702	·705	·713	·725	·738	·752	·763	·770	·772	·765
·79	·727	·730	·739	·751	·765	·780	·793	·802	·806	·802
·80	·752	·755	·764	·777	·793	·808	·823	·834	·841	·840
·81	5·777	5·781	5·790	5·804	5·820	5·837	5·853	5·866	5·875	5·878
·82	·802	·806	·816	·830	·847	·865	·883	·898	·910	·915
·83	·827	·831	·841	·856	·874	·894	·913	·930	·944	·953
·84	·852	·856	·867	·882	·901	·922	·943	·962	·979	·990
·85	·877	·881	·892	·908	·928	·950	·973	·995	6·014	6·028
·86	902	5·907	5·918	5·935	5·956	5·979	6·003	6·027	6·048	6·066
·87	·927	·932	·943	·961	·983	6·007	·033	·059	·083	·103
·88	·953	·957	·969	·987	6·010	·036	·063	·091	·117	·141
·89	·978	·982	·995	6·013	·037	·064	·093	·123	·152	·178
·90	6·003	6·007	6·020	·040	·064	·092	·123	·155	·186	·216
·91	6·028	6·033	6·046	6·066	6·091	6·121	6·153	6·187	6·221	6·253
·92	·053	·058	·071	·092	·118	·149	·183	·219	·255	·291
·93	·078	·083	·097	·118	·146	·178	·213	·251	·290	·329
·94	·103	·108	·122	·144	·173	·206	·243	·283	·324	·366
·95	·128	·133	·148	·171	·200	·234	·273	·315	·359	·404
·96	6·153	6·159	6·174	6·197	6·227	6·263	6·303	6·347	6·393	6·441
·97	·178	·184	·199	·223	·254	·291	·333	·379	·428	·479
·98	·203	·209	·225	·249	·281	·320	·363	·411	·462	·517
·99	·228	·234	·250	·276	·309	·348	·393	·443	·497	·554
1·00	·253	·259	·276	·302	·336	·376	·423	·475	·531	·592

TABLE VII (*cont.*)—Working probits

$$(Y = 6\cdot0 - 6\cdot9 \; ; \; p = 0\cdot00 - 0\cdot50)$$

Response rate, p	6·0	6·1	6·2	6·3	6·4	6·5	6·6	6·7	6·8	6·9
·00	2·523	2·132	1·643	1·030	0·261					
·01	2·564	2·178	1·694	1·088	0·327					
·02	·606	·224	·746	·146	·394					
·03	·647	·270	·797	·205	·461					
·04	·688	·316	·849	·263	·528					
·05	·730	·362	·900	·321	·595					
·06	2·771	2·408	1·952	1·380	0·661					
·07	·812	·454	2·003	·438	·728					
·08	·854	·500	·055	·496	·795					
·09	·895	·546	·106	·555	·862					
·10	·936	·591	·158	·613	·928	0·067				
·11	2·978	2·637	2·209	1·671	0·995	0·144				
·12	3·019	·683	·261	·730	1·062	·221				
·13	·060	·729	·312	·788	·129	·299				
·14	·102	·775	·364	·846	·196	·376				
·15	·143	·821	·415	·905	·262	·453				
·16	3·184	2·867	2·467	1·963	1·329	0·530				
·17	·226	·913	·518	2·022	·396	·607				
·18	·267	·959	·570	·080	·463	·685				
·19	·308	3·005	·621	·138	·530	·762				
·20	·350	·050	·673	·197	·596	·839				
·21	3·391	3·096	2·724	2·255	1·663	0·916				
·22	·432	·142	·776	·313	·730	·993	0·062			
·23	·474	·188	·827	·372	·797	1·071	·152			
·24	·515	·234	·879	·430	·864	·148	·243			
·25	·556	·280	·930	·488	·930	·225	·333			
·26	3·598	3·326	2·982	2·547	1·997	1·302	0·423			
·27	·639	·372	3·033	·605	2·064	·379	·513			
·28	·680	·418	·085	·663	·131	·457	·603			
·29	·721	·464	·136	·722	·197	·534	·693			
·30	·763	·509	·188	·780	·264	·611	·784			
·31	3·804	3·555	3·239	2·838	2·331	1·688	0·874			
·32	·845	·601	·291	·897	·398	·766	·964			
·33	·887	·647	·342	·955	·465	·843	1·054	0·050		
·34	·928	·693	·394	3·014	·531	·920	·144	·156		
·35	·969	·739	·445	·072	·598	·997	·234	·262		
·36	4·011	3·785	3·497	3·130	2·665	2·074	1·324	0·369		
·37	·052	·831	·548	·189	·732	·152	·415	·475		
·38	·093	·877	·600	·247	·799	·229	·505	·581		
·39	·135	·923	·651	·305	·865	·306	·595	·688		
·40	·176	·969	·703	·364	·932	·383	·685	·794		
·41	4·217	4·014	3·754	3·422	2·999	2·460	1·775	0·900		
·42	·259	·060	·806	·480	3·066	·538	·865	1·007		
·43	·300	·106	·857	·539	·132	·615	·955	·113	0·035	
·44	·341	·152	·909	·597	·199	·692	2·046	·219	·162	
·45	·383	·198	·960	·655	·266	·769	·136	·326	·289	
·46	4·424	4·244	4·012	3·714	3·333	2·846	2·226	1·432	0·415	
·47	·465	·290	·063	·772	·400	·924	·316	·538	·542	
·48	·507	·336	·115	·830	·466	3·001	·406	·645	·669	
·49	·548	·382	·166	·889	·533	·078	·496	·751	·795	
·50	·589	·428	·218	·947	·600	·155	·586	·857	·922	

TABLE VII (cont.)—Working probits

$$(Y = 6 \cdot 0 - 6 \cdot 9 \; ; \; p = 0 \cdot 51 - 1 \cdot 00)$$

Res-ponse rate, p	Expected probit, Y									
	6·0	6·1	6·2	6·3	6·4	6·5	6·6	6·7	6·8	6·9
·51	4·631	4·473	4·269	4·006	3·667	3·233	2·677	1·964	1·049	
·52	·672	·519	·321	·064	·734	·310	·767	2·070	·175	0·022
·53	·713	·565	·372	·122	·800	·387	·857	·176	·302	·175
·54	·755	·611	·424	·181	·867	·464	·947	·283	·429	·327
·55	·796	·657	·475	·239	·934	·541	3·037	·389	·555	·480
·56	4·837	4·703	4·527	4·297	4·001	3·619	3·127	2·495	1·682	0·632
·57	·879	·749	·578	·356	·068	·696	·218	·602	·809	·784
·58	·920	·795	·630	·414	·134	·773	·308	·708	·935	·937
·59	·961	·841	·681	·472	·201	·850	·398	·814	2·062	1·089
·60	5·003	·887	·733	·531	·268	·927	·488	·921	·189	·242
·61	5·044	4·932	4·784	4·589	4·335	4·005	3·578	3·027	2·315	1·394
·62	·085	·978	·836	·647	·401	·082	·668	·133	·442	·546
·63	·127	5·024	·887	·706	·468	·159	·758	·240	·569	·699
·64	·168	·070	·939	·764	·535	·236	·849	·346	·695	·851
·65	·209	·116	·990	·823	·602	·313	·939	·452	·822	2·004
·66	5·251	5·162	5·042	4·881	4·669	4·391	4·029	3·559	2·949	2·156
·67	·292	·208	·093	·939	·735	·468	·119	·665	3·075	·308
·68	·333	·254	·145	·998	·802	·545	·209	·771	·202	·461
·69	·375	·300	·196	5·056	·869	·622	·299	·878	·329	·613
·70	·416	·346	·248	·114	·936	·700	·390	·984	·455	·766
·71	5·457	5·392	5·299	5·173	5·003	4·777	4·480	4·090	3·582	2·918
·72	·499	·437	·351	·231	·069	·854	·570	·197	·709	3·070
·73	·540	·483	·402	·289	·136	·931	·660	·303	·835	·223
·74	·581	·529	·454	·348	·203	5·008	·750	·409	·962	·375
·75	·623	·575	·505	·406	·270	·086	·840	·516	4·089	·528
·76	5·664	5·621	5·557	5·464	5·336	5·163	4·930	4·622	4·215	3·680
·77	·705	·667	·608	·523	·403	·240	5·021	·728	·342	·832
·78	·747	·713	·660	·581	·470	·317	·111	·835	·469	·985
·79	·788	·759	·711	·639	·537	·394	·201	·941	·595	4·137
·80	·829	·805	·763	·698	·604	·472	·291	5·047	·722	·290
·81	5·870	5·851	5·814	5·756	5·670	5·549	5·381	5·154	4·849	4·442
·82	·912	·896	·866	·815	·737	·626	·471	·260	·975	·594
·83	·953	·942	·917	·873	·804	·703	·561	·366	5·102	·747
·84	·994	·988	·969	·931	·871	·780	·652	·473	·229	·899
·85	6·036	6·034	6·020	·990	·938	·858	·742	·579	·355	5·052
·86	6·077	6·080	6·072	6·048	6·004	5·935	5·832	5·685	5·482	5·204
·87	·118	·126	·123	·106	·071	6·012	·922	·792	·609	·356
·88	·160	·172	·175	·165	·138	·089	6·012	·898	·735	·509
·89	·201	·218	·226	·223	·205	·166	·102	6·004	·862	·661
·90	·242	·264	·278	·281	·272	·244	·192	·111	·988	·814
·91	6·284	6·310	6·329	6·340	6·338	6·321	6·283	6·217	6·115	5·966
·92	·325	·355	·381	·398	·405	·398	·373	·323	·242	6·118
·93	·366	·401	·432	·456	·472	·475	·463	·430	·368	·271
·94	·408	·447	·484	·515	·539	·553	·553	·536	·495	·423
·95	·449	·493	·535	·573	·605	·630	·643	·642	·622	·576
·96	6·490	6·539	6·587	6·631	6·672	6·707	6·733	6·749	6·748	6·728
·97	·532	·585	·638	·690	·739	·784	·824	·855	·875	·880
·98	·573	·631	·690	·748	·806	·861	·914	·961	7·002	7·033
·99	·614	·677	·741	·807	·873	·939	7·004	7·068	·128	·185
1·00	·656	·723	·793	·865	·939	7·016	·094	·174	·255	·338

TABLE VII (*cont.*)—Working probits

$$(Y = 7{\cdot}0 - 7{\cdot}9 \; ; \; p = 0{\cdot}60 - 1{\cdot}00)$$

Response rate, p	Expected probit, Y									
	7·0	7·1	7·2	7·3	7·4	7·5	7·6	7·7	7·8	7·9
·60	0·013									
·61	0·198									
·62	·383									
·63	·568									
·64	·753									
·65	·939									
·66	1·124									
·67	·309	0·003								
·68	·494	·231								
·69	·680	·458								
·70	·865	·685								
·71	2·050	0·913								
·72	·235	1·140								
·73	·420	·307								
·74	·606	·595	0·263							
·75	·791	·822	·545							
·76	2·976	2·050	0·827							
·77	3·161	·277	1·108							
·78	·347	·504	·390							
·79	·532	·732	·672	0·265						
·80	·717	·939	·954	·618						
·81	3·902	3·186	2·236	0·971						
·82	4·087	·414	·518	1·324						
·83	·273	·641	·800	·677	0·175					
·84	·458	·868	3·082	2·030	·621					
·85	·043	4·096	·364	·383	1·068					
·86	4·828	4·323	3·615	2·736	1·514					
·87	5·014	·551	·927	3·089	·961	0·438				
·88	·199	·778	4·209	·442	2·408	1·008				
·89	·384	5·005	·491	·795	·854	·579				
·90	·569	·233	·773	4·148	3·301	2·149	0·581			
·91	5·754	5·460	5·055	4·501	3·747	2·720	1·317			
·92	·940	·687	·337	·854	4·194	3·290	2·054	0·356		
·93	6·125	·915	·619	5·207	·640	·861	·790	1·316		
·94	·310	6·142	·901	·560	5·087	4·431	3·526	2·275	0·542	
·95	·495	·369	6·182	·914	·533	5·002	4·262	3·235	1·806	
·96	6·681	6·597	6·464	6·267	5·980	5·572	4·998	4·194	3·069	1·493
·97	·866	·824	·746	·620	6·426	6·143	5·735	5·154	4·333	3·173
·98	7·051	7·051	7·028	·973	·873	·713	6·471	6·114	5·596	4·853
·99	·236	·279	·310	7·326	7·319	7·284	7·207	7·073	6·859	6·533
1·00	·421	·506	·592	·679	·766	·854	·943	8·033	8·123	8·213

TABLE VIII—The logit transformation

Response rate	0·00	0·01	0·02	0·03	0·04	0·05	0·06	0·07	0·08	0·09
0·00	—	2·70	3·05	3·26	3·41	3·53	3·62	3·71	3·78	3·84
0·10	3·90	3·95	4·00	4·05	4·09	4·13	4·17	4·21	4·24	4·27
0·20	4·31	4·34	4·37	4·40	4·42	4·45	4·48	4·50	4·53	4·55
0·30	4·58	4·60	4·62	4·65	4·67	4·69	4·71	4·73	4·76	4·78
0·40	4·80	4·82	4·84	4·86	4·88	4·90	4·92	4·94	4·96	4·98
0·50	5·00	5·02	5·04	5·06	5·08	5·10	5·12	5·14	5·16	5·18
0·60	5·20	5·22	5·24	5·27	5·29	5·31	5·33	5·35	5·38	5·40
0·70	5·42	5·45	5·47	5·50	5·52	5·55	5·58	5·60	5·63	5·66
0·80	5·69	5·73	5·76	5·79	5·83	5·87	5·91	5·95	6·00	6·05
0·90	6·10	6·16	6·22	6·29	6·38	6·47	6·59	6·74	6·95	7·30

Response rate	0·000	0·001	0·002	0·003	0·004	0·005	0·006	0·007	0·008	0·009
0·97	6·74	6·76	6·77	6·79	6·81	6·83	6·85	6·87	6·90	6·92
0·98	6·95	6·97	7·00	7·03	7·06	7·09	7·13	7·16	7·21	7·25
0·99	7·30	7·35	7·41	7·48	7·55	7·65	7·76	7·90	8·11	8·45

TABLE IX—Minimum and maximum working logits, range, and weighting coefficient

Minimum working logit Expected logit Y	Y_0	Range A	Maximum working logit Y_1	Expected logit Y	Weighting coefficient w
1·1	0·5998	1,221·3	9·4002	8·9	·00164
1·2	0·6997	1,000·1	9·3003	8·8	·00200
1·3	0·7997	819·0	9·2003	8·7	·00244
1·4	0·8996	670·7	9·1004	8·6	·00298
1·5	0·9995	549·3	9·0005	8·5	·00364
1·6	1·0994	449·92	8·9006	8·4	·00445
1·7	1·1993	368·55	8·8007	8·3	·00543
1·8	1·2992	301·92	8·7008	8·2	·00662
1·9	1·3990	247·38	8·6010	8·1	·00808
2·0	1·4988	202·72	8·5012	8·0	·00987
2·1	1·5985	166·15	8·4015	7·9	·01204
2·2	1·6982	136·22	8·3018	7·8	·01468
2·3	1·7977	111·71	8·2023	7·7	·01790
2·4	1·8972	91·64	8·1028	7·6	·02182
2·5	1·9966	75·21	8·0034	7·5	·02659
2·6	2·0959	61·759	7·9041	7·4	·03238
2·7	2·1950	50·747	7·8050	7·3	·03941
2·8	2·2939	41·732	7·7061	7·2	·04793
2·9	2·3925	34·351	7·6075	7·1	·05822
3·0	2·4908	28·308	7·5092	7·0	·07065
3·1	2·5888	23·362	7·4112	6·0	·08561
3·2	2·6863	19·313	7·3137	6·8	·10356
3·3	2·7833	15·999	7·2167	6·7	·12501
3·4	2·8796	13·287	7·1204	6·6	·15053
3·5	2·9751	11·068	7·0249	6·5	·18071
3·6	3·0696	9·2527	6·9304	6·4	·21615
3·7	3·1629	7·7690	6·8371	6·3	·25743
3·8	3·2546	6·5569	6·7454	6·2	·30502
3·9	3·3446	5·5679	6·6554	6·1	·35920
4·0	3·4323	4·7622	6·5677	6·0	·41997
4·1	3·5174	4·1075	6·4826	5·9	·48692
4·2	3·5991	3·5775	6·4009	5·8	·55906
4·3	3·6767	3·1509	6·3233	5·7	·63474
4·4	3·7494	2·8107	6·2506	5·6	·71158
4·5	3·8161	2·5431	6·1839	5·5	·78645
4·6	3·8753	2·3374	6·1247	5·4	·85564
4·7	3·9256	2·1855	6·0744	5·3	·91514
4·8	3·9648	2·0811	6·0352	5·2	·96104
4·9	3·9906	2·0201	6·0094	5·1	·99007
5·0	4·0000	2·0000	6·0000	5·0	1·00000
5·1	3·9893	2·0201	6·0107	4·9	·99007
5·2	3·9541	2·0811	6·0459	4·8	·96104
5·3	3·8889	2·1855	6·1111	4·7	·91514
5·4	3·7873	2·3374	6·2127	4·6	·85564
5·5	3·6408	2·5431	6·3592	4·5	·78645
5·6	3·4399	2·8107	6·5601	4·4	·71158
5·7	3·1724	3·1509	6·8276	4·3	·63474
5·8	2·8234	3·5775	7·1766	4·2	·55906
5·9	2·3751	4·1075	7·6249	4·1	·48692
6·0	1·8055	4·7622	8·1945	4·0	·41997
6·1	1·0875	5·5679	8·9125	3·9	·35920
6·2	0·1885	6·5569	9·8115	3·8	·30502
6·3	− 0·9319	7·7690	10·9319	3·7	·25743
6·4	− 2·3223	9·2527	12·3223	3·6	·21615
6·5	− 4·0428	11·0677	14·0428	3·5	·18071

TABLE X—Working logits

Y	Empirical response rate										
	0·00	0·05	0·10	0·15	0·20	0·25	0·30	0·35	0·40	0·45	0·50
2·0	1·50										
2·1	1·60	9·91									
2·2	1·70	8·51									
2·3	1·80	7·38									
2·4	1·90	6·48									
2·5	2·00	5·76	9·52								
2·6	2·10	5·18	8·27								
2·7	2·20	4·73	7·27	9·81							
2·8	2·29	4·38	6·47	8·55							
2·9	2·39	4·11	5·83	7·55	9·26						
3·0	2·49	3·91	5·32	6·74	8·15	9·57					
3·2	2·69	3·65	4·62	5·58	6·55	7·51	8·48	9·45			
3·4	2·88	3·54	4·21	4·87	5·54	6·20	6·87	7·53	8·19	8·86	9·52
3·6	3·07	3·53	3·99	4·46	4·92	5·38	5·85	6·31	6·77	7·23	7·70
3·8	3·25	3·58	3·91	4·24	4·57	4·89	5·22	5·55	5·88	6·21	6·53
4·0	3·43	3·67	3·91	4·15	4·38	4·62	4·86	5·10	5·34	5·58	5·81
4·2	3·60	3·78	3·96	4·14	4·31	4·49	4·67	4·85	5·03	5·21	5·39
4·4	3·75	3·89	4·03	4·17	4·31	4·45	4·59	4·73	4·87	5·01	5·15
4·6	3·88	3·99	4·11	4·23	4·34	4·46	4·58	4·69	4·81	4·93	5·04
4·8	3·96	4·07	4·17	4·28	4·38	4·49	4·59	4·69	4·80	4·90	5·01
5·0	4·00	4·10	4·20	4·30	4·40	4·50	4·60	4·70	4·80	4·90	5·00
5·2	3·95	4·06	4·16	4·27	4·37	4·47	4·58	4·68	4·79	4·89	4·99
5·4	3·79	3·90	4·02	4·14	4·25	4·37	4·49	4·61	4·72	4·84	4·96
5·6	3·44	3·58	3·72	3·86	4·00	4·14	4·28	4·42	4·56	4·70	4·85
5·8	2·82	3·00	3·18	3·36	3·54	3·72	3·90	4·08	4·25	4·43	4·61
6·0	1·81	2·04	2·28	2·52	2·76	3·00	3·23	3·47	3·71	3·95	4·19
6·2	0·19	0·52	0·84	1·17	1·50	1·83	2·16	2·48	2·81	3·14	3·47
6·4							0·45	0·92	1·38	1·84	2·30
6·6											0·48

TABLE X (cont.)—Working logits

Y	0·50	0·55	0·60	0·65	0·70	0·75	0·80	0·85	0·90	0·95	1·00
					Empirical response rate						
3·4	9·52										
3·6	7·70	8·16	8·62	9·08	9·55						
3·8	6·53	6·86	7·19	7·52	7·84	8·17	8·50	8·83	9·16	9·48	9·81
4·0	5·81	6·05	6·29	6·53	6·77	7·00	7·24	7·48	7·72	7·96	8·19
4·2	5·39	5·57	5·75	5·92	6·10	6·28	6·46	6·64	6·82	7·00	7·18
4·4	5·15	5·30	5·44	5·58	5·72	5·86	6·00	6·14	6·28	6·42	6·56
4·6	5·04	5·16	5·28	5·39	5·51	5·63	5·75	5·86	5·98	6·10	6·21
4·8	5·01	5·11	5·21	5·32	5·42	5·53	5·63	5·73	5·84	5·94	6·05
5·0	5·00	5·10	5·20	5·30	5·40	5·50	5·60	5·70	5·80	5·90	6·00
5·2	4·99	5·10	5·20	5·31	5·41	5·51	5·62	5·72	5·83	5·93	6·04
5·4	4·96	5·07	5·19	5·31	5·42	5·54	5·66	5·77	5·89	6·01	6·12
5·6	4·85	4·99	5·13	5·27	5·41	5·55	5·69	5·83	5·97	6·11	6·25
5·8	4·61	4·79	4·97	5·15	5·33	5·51	5·69	5·86	6·04	6·22	6·40
6·0	4·19	4·42	4·66	4·90	5·14	5·38	5·62	5·85	6·09	6·33	6·57
6·2	3·47	3·79	4·12	4·45	4·78	5·11	5·43	5·76	6·09	6·42	6·75
6·4	2·30	2·77	3·23	3·69	4·15	4·62	5·08	5·54	6·01	6·47	6·93
6·6	0·48	1·14	1·81	2·47	3·13	3·80	4·46	5·13	5·79	6·46	7·12
6·8				0·55	1·52	2·49	3·45	4·42	5·38	6·35	7·31
7·0						0·43	1·85	3·26	4·68	6·09	7·51
7·1							0·74	2·45	4·17	5·89	7·61
7·2								1·45	3·53	5·62	7·71
7·3								0·19	2·73	5·27	7·80
7·4									1·73	4·82	7·90
7·5									0·48	4·24	8·00
7·6										3·52	8·10
7·7										2·62	8·20
7·8										1·49	8·30
7·9										0·09	8·40
8·0											8·50

TABLE XI—The angle transformation

[Fisher & Yates, 1963, Table XII]

Response rate	0·00	0·01	0·02	0·03	0·04	0·05	0·06	0·07	0·08	0·09
0·00	0	5·7	8·1	10·0	11·5	12·9	14·2	15·3	16·4	17·5
0·10	18·4	19·4	20·3	21·1	22·0	22·8	23·6	24·4	25·1	25·8
0·20	26·6	27·3	28·0	28·7	29·3	30·0	30·7	31·3	31·9	32·6
0·30	33·2	33·8	34·4	35·1	35·7	36·3	36·9	37·5	38·1	38·6
0·40	39·2	39·8	40·4	41·0	41·6	42·1	42·7	43·3	43·9	44·4
0·50	45·0	45·6	46·1	46·7	47·3	47·9	48·4	49·0	49·6	50·2
0·60	50·8	51·4	51·9	52·5	53·1	53·7	54·3	54·9	55·6	56·2
0·70	56·8	57·4	58·1	58·7	59·3	60·0	60·7	61·3	62·0	62·7
0·80	63·4	64·2	64·9	65·6	66·4	67·2	68·0	68·9	69·7	70·6
0·90	71·6	72·5	73·6	74·7	75·8	77·1	78·5	80·0	81·9	84·3

Response rate	0·000	0·001	0·002	0·003	0·004	0·005	0·006	0·007	0·008	0·009
0·97	80·0	80·2	80·4	80·5	80·7	80·9	81·1	81·3	81·5	81·7
0·98	81·9	82·1	82·3	82·5	82·7	83·0	83·2	83·5	83·7	84·0
0·99	84·3	84·6	84·9	85·2	85·6	85·9	86·4	86·9	87·4	88·2

TABLE XII—Minimum and maximum working angles and range

| Minimum working angle | | Range | Maximum working angle | |
Expected angle Y	Y_0	A	Y_1	Expected angle Y
1	0·5	1,641·7	89·5	89
2	1·0	821·4	89·0	88
3	1·5	548·1	88·5	87
4	2·0	411·7	88·0	86
5	2·5	330·0	87·5	85
6	3·0	275·6	87·0	84
7	3·5	236·8	86 5	83
8	4·0	207·9	86·0	82
9	4·5	185·4	85·5	81
10	4·9	167·5	85 1	80
11	5·4	152·9	84·6	79
12	5·9	140·9	84 1	78
13	6·4	130·7	83 6	77
14	6·9	122·0	83·1	76
15	7 3	114·6	82·7	75
16	7·8	108·1	82 2	74
17	8·2	102·5	81·8	73
18	8·7	97·5	81·3	72
19	9·1	93·1	80·9	71
20	9·6	89·1	80·4	70
21	10·0	85 6	80·0	69
22	10·4	82·5	79·6	68
23	10·8	79·7	79·2	67
24	11 2	77 1	78·8	66
25	11 6	74·8	78 4	65
26	12·0	72·7	78 0	64
27	12·4	70·8	77·6	63
28	12·8	69·1	77·2	62
29	13·1	67·6	76·9	61
30	13 5	66·2	76·5	60
31	13·8	64·9	76·2	59
32	14·1	63·7	75·9	58
33	14 4	62·7	75·6	57
34	14 7	61·8	75·3	56
35	14·9	61·0	75·1 ˙	55
36	15 2	60·2	74·8	54
37	15 4	59·6	74·6	53
38	15 6	59·0	74·4	52
39	15·8	58·6	74·2	51
40	16·0	58·3	74·0	50

TABLE XII *(cont.)*—**Minimum and maximum working angles and range**

Minimum working angle		Range	Maximum working angle	
Expected angle Y	Y_0	A	Y_1	Expected angle Y
41	16·1	57·9	73·9	49
42	16·2	57·6	73·8	48
43	16·3	57·4	73·7	47
44	16·3	57·3	73·7	46
45	16·4	57·3	73·6	45
46	16·4	57·3	73·6	44
47	16·3	57·4	73·7	43
48	16·2	57·6	73·8	42
49	16·0	57·9	74·0	41
50	15·7	58·3	74·3	40
51	15·6	58·6	74·4	39
52	15·4	59·0	74·6	38
53	15·0	59·6	75·0	37
54	14·6	60·2	75·4	36
55	14·1	61·0	75·9	35
56	13·5	61·8	76·5	34
57	12·9	62·7	77·1	33
58	12·2	63·7	77·8	32
59	11·3	64·9	78·7	31
60	10·3	66·2	79·7	30
61	9·3	67·6	80·7	29
62	8·1	69·1	81·9	28
63	6·8	70·8	83·2	27
64	5·3	72·7	84·7	26
65	3·6	74·8	86·4	25

TABLE XIII—Working angles

Y	\multicolumn{11}{c}{Empirical response rate}

Y	0·00	0·05	0·10	0·15	0·20	0·25	0·30	0·35	0·40	0·45	0·50
1	0·5	82·6									
2	1·0	42·1	83·1								
3	1·5	28·9	56·3	83·7							
4	2·0	22·6	43·2	63·8	84·3						
5	2·5	19·0	35·5	52·0	68·5	85·0					
6	3·0	16·8	30·5	44·3	58·1	71·9	85·7				
7	3·5	15·3	27·2	39·0	50·9	62·7	74·5	86·4			
8	4·0	14·4	24·8	35·2	45·5	55·9	66·3	76·7	87·1		
9	4·5	13·7	23·0	32·3	41·5	50·8	60·1	69·4	78·6	87·9	
10	5·0	13·3	21·7	30·1	38·5	46·8	55·2	63·6	72·0	80·3	88·7
12	5·9	13·0	20·0	27·0	34·1	41·1	48·2	55·2	62·3	69·3	76·3
14	6·9	13·0	19·1	25·2	31·3	37·4	43·5	49·6	55·7	61·8	67·9
16	7·8	13·2	18·6	24·0	29·4	34·8	40·2	45·6	51·0	56·4	61·8
18	8·7	13·6	18·4	23·3	28·2	33·1	37·9	42·8	47·7	52·6	57·4
20	9·6	14·0	18·5	22·9	27·4	31·9	36·3	40·8	45·2	49·7	54·1
22	10·4	14·6	18·7	22·8	26·9	31·0	35·2	39·3	43·4	47·5	51·7
24	11·2	15·1	19·0	22·8	26·7	30·5	34·4	38·2	42·1	45·9	49·8
26	12·0	15·7	19·3	22·9	26·6	30·2	33·8	37·5	41·1	44·7	48·4
28	12·8	16·2	19·7	23·1	26·6	30·0	33·5	37·0	40·4	43·9	47·3
30	13·5	16·8	20·1	23·4	26·7	30·0	33·3	36·6	39·9	43·2	46·5
32	14·1	17·3	20·5	23·7	26·8	30·0	33·2	36·4	39·6	42·8	46·0
34	14·7	17·8	20·9	24·0	27·0	30·1	33·2	36·3	39·4	42·5	45·6
36	15·2	18·2	21·2	24·2	27·2	30·2	33·3	36·3	39·3	42·3	45·3
38	15·6	18·6	21·5	24·5	27·4	30·4	33·3	36·3	39·2	42·2	45·1
40	16·0	18·9	21·8	24·7	27·6	30·5	33·4	36·3	39·2	42·1	45·0
42	16·2	19·1	22·0	24·9	27·7	30·6	33·5	36·4	39·3	42·1	45·0
44	16·3	19·2	22·1	24·9	27·8	30·7	33·5	36·4	39·3	42·1	45·0
46	16·3	19·2	22·1	24·9	27·8	30·7	33·5	36·4	39·3	42·1	45·0
48	16·2	19·1	21·9	24·8	27·7	39·6	33·5	36·3	39·2	42·1	45·0
50	15·9	18·8	21·7	24·6	27·5	30·4	33·3	36·2	39·1	42·0	45·0
52	15·3	18·3	21·2	24·2	27·1	30·1	33·0	36·0	39·0	41·9	44·9
54	14·6	17·6	20·6	23·6	26·6	29·6	32·6	35·7	38·7	41·7	44·7
56	13·5	16·6	19·7	22·8	25·9	29·0	32·1	35·2	38·2	41·3	44·4
58	12·2	15·3	18·5	21·7	24·9	28·1	31·3	34·5	37·6	40·8	44·0
60	10·4	13·7	17·0	20·3	23·6	26·9	30·2	33·5	36·8	40·2	43·5
62	8·1	11·6	15·0	18·5	21·9	25·4	28·9	32·3	35·8	39·2	42·7
64	5·3	8·9	12·5	16·2	19·8	23·4	27·1	30·7	34·3	38·0	41·6
66	1·6	5·5	9·4	13·2	17·1	20·9	24·8	28·6	32·5	36·3	40·2
68		1·2	5·3	9·5	13·6	17·7	21·8	26·0	30·1	34·2	38·3
70			0·2	4·7	9·1	13·6	18·0	22·5	26·9	31·4	35·9
72					3·3	8·2	13·1	17·9	22·8	27·7	32·6
74						1·1	6·5	11·9	17·3	22·7	28·2
76								3·8	9·9	16·0	22·1
78										6·6	13·7
80											1·3

TABLE XIII (*cont.*)—Working angles

Y	Empirical response rate										
	0·50	0·55	0·60	0·65	0·70	0·75	0·80	0·85	0·90	0·95	1·00
10	88·7										
12	76·3	83·4									
14	67·9	74·0	80·1	86·2							
16	61·8	67·3	72·7	78·1	83·5	88·9					
18	57·4	62·3	67·2	72·1	76·9	81·8	86·7				
20	54·1	58·6	63·1	67·5	72·0	76·4	80·9	85·3	89·8		
22	51·7	55·8	59·9	64·0	68·2	72·3	76·4	80·5	84·7	88·8	
24	49·8	53·7	57·5	61·4	65·2	69·1	72·9	76·8	80·6	84·5	88·4
26	48·4	52·0	55·7	59·3	62·9	66·6	70·2	73·8	77·5	81·1	84·7
28	47·3	50·8	54·2	57·7	61·1	64·6	68·1	71·5	75·0	78·4	81·9
30	46·5	49·8	53·2	56·5	59·8	63·1	66·4	69·7	73·0	76·3	79·6
32	46·0	49·2	52·4	55·5	58·7	61·9	65·1	68·3	71·5	74·7	77·8
34	45·6	48·7	51·8	54·8	57·9	61·0	64·1	67·2	70·3	73·4	76·5
36	45·3	48·3	51·3	54·3	57·4	60·4	63·4	66·4	69·4	72·4	75·4
38	45·1	48·1	51·0	54·0	57·0	59·9	62·9	65·8	68·8	71·7	74·7
40	45·0	48·0	50·9	53·8	56·7	59·6	62·5	65·4	68·3	71·2	74·1
42	45·0	47·9	50·8	53·7	56·5	59·4	62·3	65·2	68·1	70·9	73·8
44	45·0	47·9	50·7	53·6	56·5	59·3	62·2	65·1	67·9	70·8	73·7
46	45·0	47·9	50·7	53·6	56·5	59·3	62·2	65·1	67·9	70·8	73·7
48	45·0	47·9	50·7	53·6	56·5	59·4	62·3	65·1	68·0	70·9	73·8
50	45·0	47·9	50·8	53·7	56·6	59·5	62·4	65·3	68·2	71·1	74·0
52	44·9	47·8	50·8	53·7	56·7	59·6	62·6	65·5	68·5	71·4	74·4
54	44·7	47·7	50·7	53·7	56·7	59·7	62·8	65·8	68·8	71·8	74·8
56	44·4	47·5	50·6	53·7	56·8	59·9	63·0	66·0	69·1	72·2	75·3
58	44·0	47·2	50·4	53·6	56·8	60·0	63·2	66·3	69·5	72·7	75·9
60	43·5	46·8	50·1	53·4	56·7	60·0	63·3	66·6	69·9	73·2	76·5
62	42·7	46·1	49·6	53·0	56·5	60·0	63·4	66·9	70·3	73·8	77·2
64	41·6	45·3	48·9	52·5	56·2	59·8	63·4	67·1	70·7	74·3	78·0
66	40·2	44·1	47·9	51·8	55·6	59·5	63·3	67·2	71·0	74·9	78·8
68	38·3	42·5	46·6	50·7	54·8	59·0	63·1	67·2	71·3	75·4	79·6
70	35·9	40·3	44·8	49·2	53·7	58·1	62·6	67·1	71·5	76·0	80·4
72	32·6	37·4	42·3	47·2	52·1	56·9	61·8	66·7	71·6	76·4	81·3
74	28·2	33·6	39·0	44·4	49·8	55·2	60·6	66·0	71·4	76·8	82·2
76	22·1	28·2	34·3	40·4	46·5	52·6	58·7	64·8	70·9	77·0	83·1
78	13·7	20·7	27·7	34·8	41·8	48·9	55·9	63·0	70·0	77·0	84·1
80	1·3	9·7	18·0	26·4	34·8	43·2	51·5	59·9	68·3	76·7	85·0
81		2·1	11·4	20·6	29·9	39·2	48·5	57·7	67·0	76·3	85·5
82			2·9	13·3	23·7	34·1	44·5	54·8	65·2	75·6	86·0
83				3·6	15·5	27·3	39·1	51·0	62·8	74·7	86·5
84					4·3	18·1	31·9	45·7	59·5	73·2	87·0
85						5·0	21·5	38·0	54·5	71·0	87·5
86							5·7	26·2	46·8	67·4	88·0
87								6·3	33·7	61·1	88·5
88									6·9	47·9	89·0
89										7·4	89·5

TABLE XIV—Transformation of angles to probits

Angle	0	1	2	3	4	5	6	7	8	9
0	—	1·57	1·97	2·22	2·41	2·57	2·71	2·83	2·93	3·03
10	3·12	3·21	3·29	3·36	3·43	3·50	3·57	3·63	3·69	3·75
20	3·81	3·87	3·92	3·98	4·03	4·08	4·13	4·18	4·23	4·28
30	4·33	4·37	4·42	4·47	4·51	4·56	4·60	4·65	4·69	4·74
40	4·78	4·82	4·87	4·91	4·96	5·00	5·04	5·09	5·13	5·18
50	5·22	5·26	5·31	5·35	5·40	5·44	5·49	5·53	5·58	5·63
60	5·67	5·72	5·77	5·82	5·87	5·92	5·97	6·02	6·08	6·13
70	6·19	6·25	6·31	6·37	6·43	6·50	6·57	6·64	6·71	6·79
80	6·88	6·97	7·07	7·17	7·29	7·43	7·59	7·78	8·03	8·43

TABLE XV—Transformation of angles to logits

Angle	0	1	2	3	4	5	6	7	8	9
0	—	0·95	1·65	2·05	2·34	2·56	2·75	2·90	3·04	3·16
10	3·26	3·36	3·45	3·53	3·61	3·68	3·75	3·81	3·88	3·93
20	3·99	4·04	4·09	4·14	4·19	4·24	4·28	4·33	4·37	4·41
30	4·45	4·49	4·53	4·57	4·61	4·64	4·68	4·72	4·75	4·79
40	4.82	4·86	4·90	4·93	4·97	5·00	5·03	5·07	5·10	5·14
50	5·18	5·21	5·25	5·28	5·32	5·36	5·39	5·43	5·47	5·51
60	5.55	5.59	5.63	5·67	5·72	5·76	5·81	5·86	5·91	5·96
70	6·01	6·07	6·12	6·19	6·25	6·32	6·39	6·47	6·55	6·64
80	6·74	6·84	6·96	7·10	7·25	7·44	7·66	7·95	8·35	9·05

TABLE XVI—The loglog transformation

Pro-portion sterile	·000	·001	·002	·003	·004	·005	·006	·007	·008	·009
·00	—	1·93	1·83	1·76	1·71	1·67	1·63	1·60	1·57	1·55
	·00	·01	·02	·03	·04	·05	·06	·07	·08	·09
·0	—	1·53	1·36	1·25	1·17	1·10	1·03	0·98	0·93	0·88
·1	0·83	0·79	0·75	0·71	0·68	0·64	0·61	0·57	0·54	0·51
·2	0·48	0·45	0·41	0·39	0·36	0·33	0·30	0·27	0·24	0·21
·3	0·19	0·16	0·13	0·10	0·08	0·05	0·02	−0·01	−0·03	−0·06
·4	−0·09	−0·11	−0·14	−0·17	−0·20	−0·23	−0·25	−0·28	−0·31	−0·34
·5	−0·37	−0·40	−0·42	−0·45	−0·48	−0·51	−0·55	−0·58	−0·61	−0·64
·6	−0·67	−0·70	−0·74	−0·77	−0·81	−0·84	−0·88	−0·92	−0·95	−0·99
·7	−1·03	−1·07	−1·11	−1·16	−1·20	−1·25	−1·29	−1·34	−1·39	−1·45
·8	−1·50	−1·56	−1·62	−1·68	−1·75	−1·82	−1·89	−1·97	−2·06	−2·15
·9	−2·25	−2·36	−2·48	−2·62	−2·78	−2·97	−3·20	−3·49	−3·90	−4·60
	·000	·001	·002	·003	·004	·005	·006	·007	·008	·009
·97	−3·49	−3·53	−3·56	−3·60	−3·64	−3·68	−3·72	−3·76	−3·81	−3·85
·98	−3·90	−3·95	−4·01	−4·07	−4·13	−4·19	−4·26	−4·34	−4·42	−4·50
·99	−4·60	−4·71	−4·82	−4·96	−5·11	−5·30	−5·52	−5·81	−6·21	−6·91

TABLE XVII—Minimum and maximum working loglog deviates, range, and weighting coefficient

Expected loglog Y	Minimum working deviate η_0	Range A	Maximum working deviate η_1	Weighting ceofficient w
2·5	− 0·0821	16,034·	—	0·00076
2·4	− 0·0907	5,559·0	—	0·00198
2·3	− 0·1003	2,152·1	—	0·00463
2·2	− 0·1108	920·59	—	0·00980
2·1	− 0·1225	431·03	—	0·01895
2·0	− 0·1353	219·00	—	0·03376
1·9	− 0·1496	119·81	—	0·05587
1·8	− 0·1653	70·080	69·915	0·08653
1·7	− 0·1827	43·552	43·369	0·12622
1·6	− 0·2019	28·589	28·387	0·17448
1·5	− 0·2231	19·721	19·498	0·22985
1·4	− 0·2466	14·228	13·981	0·29005
1·3	− 0·2725	10·689	10·417	0·35223
1·2	− 0·3012	8·3321	8·0309	0·41342
1·1	− 0·3329	6·7138	6·3809	0·47080
1·0	− 0·3679	5·5750	5·2071	0·52204
0·9	− 0·4066	4·7163	4·3097	0·57071
0·8	− 0·4493	4·1601	3·7108	0·59975
0·7	− 0·4966	3·7201	3·2235	0·62471
0·6	− 0·5488	3·3944	2·8456	0·64034
0·5	− 0·6065	3·1541	2·5476	0·64716
0·4	− 0·6703	2·9797	2·3094	0·64598
0·3	− 0·7408	2·8572	2·1164	0·63780
0·2	− 0·8187	2·7771	1·9584	0·62369
0·1	− 0·9048	2·7323	1·8275	0·60473
0·0	− 1·0000	2·7183	1·7183	0·58198
− 0·1	− 1·1052	2·7315	1·6263	0·55638
− 0·2	− 1·2214	2·7697	1·5483	0·52880
− 0·3	− 1·3499	2·8316	1·4817	0·49999
− 0·4	− 1·4918	2·9163	1·4245	0·47057
− 0·5	− 1·6487	3·0238	1·3751	0·44107
− 0·6	− 1·8221	3·1544	1·3323	0·41192
− 0·7	− 2·0138	3·3088	1·2950	0·38345
− 0·8	− 2·2255	3·4880	1·2625	0·35592
− 0·9	− 2·4596	3·6935	1·2339	0·32951
− 1·0	− 2·7183	3·9270	1·2087	0·30435
− 1·1	− 3·0042	4·1907	1·1865	0·28054
− 1·2	− 3·3201	4·4870	1·1669	0·25811
− 1·3	− 3·6693	4·8188	1·1495	0·23708
− 1·4	− 4·0552	5·1893	1·1341	0·21744
− 1·5	− 4·4817	5·6020	1·1203	0·19916

TABLE XVII (*cont.*)—**Minimum and maximum working loglog deviates, range, and weighting coefficient**

Expected loglog Y	Minimum working deviate η_0	Range A	Maximum working deviate η_1	Weighting coefficient w
− 1·6	− 4·9530	6·0611	1·1081	0·18220
− 1·7	− 5·4739	6·5711	1·0972	0·16650
− 1·8	− 6·0496	7·1370	1·0874	0·15201
− 1·9	− 6·6859	7·7646	1·0787	0·13866
− 2·0	− 7·3891	8·4599	1·0708	0·12638
− 2·1	− 8·1662	9·2300	1·0638	0·11511
− 2·2	− 9·0250	10·083	1·0575	0·10478
− 2·3	− 9·9742	11·026	1·0518	0·09532
− 2·4	− 11·023	12·070	1·0468	0·08667
− 2·5	− 12·182	13·224	1·0422	0·07876
− 2·6	− 13·464	14·502	1·0381	0·07155
− 2·7	− 14·880	15·914	1·0344	0·06497
− 2·8	− 16·445	17·476	1·0310	0·05898
− 2·9	− 18·174	19·202	1·0280	0·05352
− 3·0	− 20·086	21·111	1·0253	0·04856
− 3·1	− 22·198	23·221	1·0229	0·04404
− 3·2	− 24·533	25·554	1·0207	0·03994
− 3·3	− 27·113	28·132	1·0187	0·03621
− 3·4	− 29·964	30·981	1·0169	0·03282
− 3·5	− 33·115	34·130	1·0153	0·02974
− 3·6	− 36·598	37·612	1·0138	0·02695
− 3·7	− 40·447	41·459	1·0125	0·02442
− 3·8	− 44·701	45·712	1·0113	0·02212
− 3·9	− 49·402	50·412	1·0102	0·02004
− 4·0	− 54·598	55·607	1·0092	0·01815
− 4·1	− 60·340	61·348	1·0083	0·01644
− 4·2	− 66·686	67·694	1·0075	0·01488
− 4·3	− 73·700	74·707	1·0068	0·01348
− 4·4	− 81·451	82·457	1·0062	0·01220
− 4·5	− 90·017	91·023	1·0056	0·01105
− 4·6	− 99·484	100·49	1·0050	0·01000
− 4·7	—	110·95	1·0046	0·00905
− 4·8	—	122·51	1·0041	0·00820
− 4·9	—	135·29	1·0037	0·00742
− 5·0	—	149·41	1·0034	0·00672
− 5·1	—	165·02	1·0031	0·00608
− 5·2	—	182·27	1·0028	0·00550
− 5·3	—	201·34	1·0025	0·00498
− 5·4	—	222·41	1·0023	0·00451
− 5·5	—	245·69	1·0020	0·00408
− 5·6	—	271·43	1·0018	0·00369
− 5·7	—	299·87	1·0017	0·00334
− 5·8	—	331·30	1·0015	0·00302
− 5·9	—	366·04	1·0014	0·00274
− 6·0	—	404·43	1·0012	0·00248

TABLE XVII (*cont.*)—**Minimum and maximum working loglog deviates, range, and weighting coefficient**

Expected loglog Y	Minimum working deviates η_0	Range A	Maximum working deviate η_1	Weighting coefficient w
− 6·1	—	446·86	1·0011	0·00224
− 6·2	—	493·75	1·0010	0·00203
− 6·3	—	545·57	1·0009	0·00183
− 6·4	—	602·85	1·0008	0·00166
− 6·5	—	666·14	1·0008	0·00150
− 6·6	—	736·10	1·0007	0·00136
− 6·7	—	813·41	1·0006	0·00123
− 6·8	—	898·85	1·0006	0·00111
− 6·9	—	993·28	1·0005	0·00101
− 7·0	—	1,097·6	1·0005	0·00091
− 7·1	—	1,213·0	1·0004	0·00082
− 7·2	—	1,340·0	1·0004	0·00075
− 7·3	—	1,481·3	1·0003	0·00068
− 7·4	—	1,637·0	1·0003	0·00061
− 7·5	—	1,809·0	1·0003	0·00055
− 7·6	—	1,999·2	1·0003	0·00050
− 7·7	—	2,209·3	1·0002	0·00045
− 7·8	—	2,441·6	1·0002	0·00041
− 7·9	—	2,698·3	1·0002	0·00037
− 8·0	—	2,982·0	1·0002	0·00034
− 8·1	—	3,295·5	1·0002	0·00030
− 8·2	—	3,641·9	1·0001	0·00027
− 8·3	—	4,024·9	1·0001	0·00025
− 8·4	—	4,448·1	1·0001	0·00022
− 8·5	—	4,915·8	1·0001	0·00020
− 8·6	—	5,432·7	1·0001	0·00018
− 8·7	—	6,003·9	1·0001	0·00017
− 8·8	—	6,635·2	1·0001	0·00015
− 8·9	—	7,333·0	1·0001	0·00014
− 9·0	—	8,104·1	1·0001	0·00012

TABLE XVIII—Distribution of range of transition in dilution series
[Table of probability that range exceeds a stated value, abridged from Stevens (1958)]

| Dilution ratio (a) | 2 | 2 | 4 | 4 | 4 | 4 |
Plates per dilution (n)	1	2	1	2	3	4
Range of transition						
1	·500	·930	·158	·717	·890	·955
2	·500	·820	·158	·373	·511	·682
3	·317	·625	·045	·123	·209	·294
4	·183	·415	·012	·034	·060	·088
5	·099	·246	·003	·009	·015	·023
6	·052	·135	·001	·002	·004	·006
7	·026	·071	—	·001	·001	·001
8	·013	·037	—	—	—	—
9	·007	·019	—	—	—	—
10	·003	·009	—	—	—	—
11	·002	·005	—	—	—	—
12	·001	·002	—	—	—	—
13	—	·001	—	—	—	—
14	—	·001	—	—	—	—

| Dilution ratio (a) | 10 | 10 | 10 | 10 | 10 | 10 | 10 |
Plates per dilution (n)	1	2	3	4	5	6	8
Range of transition							
1	·041	·525	·731	·838	·899	·936	·973
2	·041	·114	·193	·271	·340	·404	·512
3	·004	·013	·023	·035	·047	·060	·087
4	—	·001	·002	·004	·005	·006	·009
5	—	—	—	—	—	·001	·001

INDEX OF AUTHORS

INDEX OF SUBJECTS